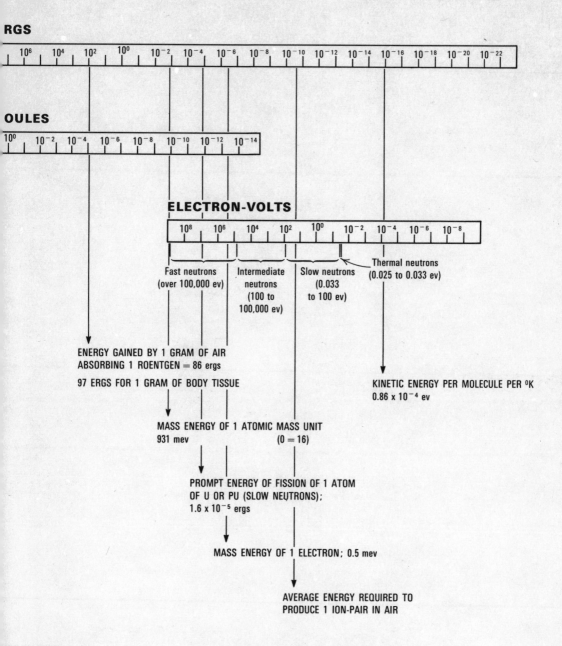

THE ENERGY LEVEL OF THINGS

rom J. R. Williams, *Missiles and Rockets,* October 3, 1960

ENGINEERING
THERMODYNAMICS

ENGINEERING THERMODYNAMICS

WILLIAM C. REYNOLDS

Department of Mechanical Engineering
Stanford University

HENRY C. PERKINS

Department of Aerospace and Mechanical Engineering
University of Arizona

New York San Francisco St. Louis **McGRAW-HILL BOOK COMPANY**
Düsseldorf London Mexico Panama Sydney Toronto

This book was set in Monotype Modern 8A, printed on permanent paper, and bound by The Maple Press Company. The designer was Ronald Q. Lewton; the drawings were done by David A. Strassman and Joseph Clark. The editors were B. J. Clark and Michael A. Ungersma. Charles A. Goehring supervised production.

ENGINEERING THERMODYNAMICS

Printed in the United States of America.

Library of Congress catalog card number: 74-95824

890 MAMM 7987654

52045

PREFACE

This text was developed as an alternative version of the senior author's book, *Thermodynamics*. The primary spirit of these two books is the same; microscopic arguments are used to provide insight into the basic macroscopic postulates. Indeed, the fundamental developments of the first seven chapters are fully identical in the two books. Beyond this the texts begin to differ. The parent text treats a broad range of applications in engineering, physical chemistry, and includes introductory chapters in statistical thermodynamics, kinetic theory, and irreversible thermodynamics. In contrast, this book concentrates along the lines of more traditional engineering courses. The applications possess a stronger engineering flavor, and introductory chapters on applied one-dimensional gas dynamics and heat transfer are included. Thus, the parent text best serves a basic course for engineers anticipating graduate study, where these subjects will be covered in depth. On the other hand, this version is better suited for mechanical engineers going into practice upon graduation, or for engineers in other fields desiring an introductory background in some important areas of mechanical engineering.

Throughout the text, the value of a systematic methodology in analyses is emphasized. Such an approach is absolutely essential and should be required in the student's problem assignments. A lack of understanding of the fundamentals of engineering frequently is caused by students consistently starting problems "in the middle." Overly easy homework problems can often be successfully solved in this manner, and we have purposely provided longer and more difficult problems, particularly in the later chapters where several of the thermodynamic principles can be brought to bear in a single analysis. We have found that getting into the analysis of simple thermodynamic systems as soon as possible provides good motivation for further developments in theory. For this reason, energy-balance applications are taken up before the introduction of second-law concepts. This arrangement also provides a period for digestion of state and first-law concepts and helps spread the introduction of new ideas more evenly over the course.

Our objective has been to develop the subject matter in a way that retains the generality and simplicity of purely macroscopic thermodynamics and yet draws upon the student's insight into microscopic matters. To this end the microscopic arguments are used to provide an intuitive basis for macroscopic postulates; the laws of thermodynamics are *not* derived from microscopic postulates. This approach preserves the generality of macroscopic thermodynamics and at the same time places the roots for energy, entropy, and temperature firmly in the microscopic world. Our intention is to clearly establish the tie between the macroscopic and microscopic viewpoints at an early stage and provide the student with a full appreciation of the importance of both views.

This book could not have been written without the continued encouragement and suggestions of faculty colleagues and students at our two institutions. In particular, we both obtained a real appreciation for the methodology of thermodynamic analysis from Professor A. L. London. Professors S. J. Kline, A. Anderson, and Philip Schmidt made many helpful criticisms and suggestions during the development of the parent text. The patience of our wives and families in enduring our discussions of Rankine cycles, choked flow, etc., should also be acknowledged.

WILLIAM C. REYNOLDS

HENRY C. PERKINS

CONTENTS

Preface   v

Chapter One

SOME INTRODUCTORY CONSIDERATIONS   1

    1·1   The nature of thermodynamics   1
    1·2   Concepts, models, and laws   3
    1·3   A fresh look at some familiar concepts   4
    1·4   Mechanical concepts of energy   12
    1·5   Continuum concepts   13
    1·6   The conceptual basis of dimensional systems   15

Chapter Two

ENERGY AND THE FIRST LAW   22

    2·1   Introduction   22
    2·2   Systems   23
    2·3   Energy   24
    2·4   Conservation of energy   27
    2·5   Energy transfer as work   30
    2·6   Evaluation of energy transfer as work   31
    2·7   Some particular work modes   36
    2·8   Work for particular processes   40
    2·9   Energy transfer as heat   42
    2·10 The first law for a control mass   44
    2·11 Examples of control-mass energy balances   45
    2·12 Energy equivalents   51
    2·13 Summary of some important terms   51

Chapter Three

PROPERTIES AND STATE   **57**

3·1   Concepts of property and state   **57**
3·2   Equilibrium and the thermodynamic state   **59**
3·3   Temperature   **61**
3·4   Intensive and extensive state   **65**
3·5   Independent variations of the thermodynamic state   **66**
3·6   The state postulate   **67**

Chapter Four

STATES OF SIMPLE SUBSTANCES   **72**

4·1   The simple substance   **72**
4·2   Equations of state   **73**
4·3   The general nature of a simple compressible substance   **75**
4·4   Using the tabular and graphical equations of state   **78**
4·5   Metastable states in phase transitions   **80**
4·6   An engineering example   **80**
4·7   Some other thermodynamic properties   **82**
4·8   The perfect gas   **86**
4·9   The simple magnetic substance   **90**

Chapter Five

ENERGY ANALYSIS OF THERMODYNAMIC SYSTEMS   **94**

5·1   General methodology   **94**
5·2   Examples of control-mass energy analysis   **96**
5·3   The control-volume transformation   **108**
5·4   Examples of control-volume energy analysis   **112**

Chapter Six

ENTROPY AND THE SECOND LAW   **137**

6·1   The essence of the second law   **137**
6·2   Allowed quantum states   **139**
6·3   Quantum-state probabilities   **141**
6·4   Entropy   **144**
6·5   Approach to equilibrium   **149**
6·6   Summary   **156**

Chapter Seven
SOME CONSEQUENCES OF THE SECOND LAW   162

7·1   Introduction   162
7·2   Entropy as a function of state   163
7·3   The thermodynamic definition of temperature   164
7·4   The thermodynamic definition of pressure   168
7·5   Intensive representations and some extensions   171
7·6   Macroscopic evaluation of entropy   173
7·7   Reversible and irreversible processes   175
7·8   An example of a second-law analysis   178
7·9   Two idealized systems   180
7·10 Entropy change and production for a control mass   184
7·11 Examples of control-mass second-law analysis   187
7·12 Equivalence of the mechanical and thermodynamic
      pressures   188
7·13 Equivalence of the thermodynamic and empirical
      temperatures   190
7·14 Applications of the second law to energy-conversion
      systems   191
7·15 A remark on the thermodynamic temperature   197
7·16 The second law for a control volume   197
7·17 Examples of second-law analysis   199
7·18 A summary of the first and second laws   204

Chapter Eight
THE THERMODYNAMICS OF STATE   210

8·1   Introduction   210
8·2   The Gibbs equation   210
8·3   Equation of state for the perfect gas   212
8·4   Other P-v-T equations for gases   220
8·5   Algebraic equation of state for an incompressible liquid   224
8·6   Differential equations of state   228
8·7   Some important property relations   231
8·8   Thermodynamics of the simple magnetic substance   239
8·9   Algebraic equation of state for the Curie substance   241

Chapter Nine
CHARACTERISTICS OF SOME THERMODYNAMIC SYSTEMS   247

9·1   Analysis of thermodynamic systems   247
9·2   The Carnot cycle   249
9·3   Pattern processes   251

9·4   A particular vapor power system   255
9·5   Modern utilization of the Rankine cycle   260
9·6   Other Rankine cycle modifications   266
9·7   Some thoughts on the working fluid   271
9·8   Other vapor power cycles   272
9·9   Vapor refrigeration systems   273
9·10 Some problems and advantages of all-gas cycles   279
9·11 A particular gas-turbine power system   280
9·12 Some remarks on the steady-flow compression process   283
9·13 The Brayton cycle and its modifications   285
9·14 Other gas power cycles   291
9·15 Air-cycle refrigerator   297
9·16 A simple thrusting system   299
9·17 Other thrusting systems   303
9·18 Direct energy-conversion systems   307
9·19 Concluding remarks   314

Chapter Ten

THERMODYNAMICS OF NONREACTING MIXTURES   328

10·1 Descriptions of mixtures   328
10·2 Mixtures of independent substances   330
10·3 Mixtures of perfect gases   333
10·4 Application to air–water-vapor mixtures   337
10·5 Air conditioning   345

Chapter Eleven

THERMODYNAMICS OF REACTING MIXTURES   355

11·1 Some chemical concepts and terms   355
11·2 Fuel analysis and product composition   357
11·3 Standardized energy and enthalpy   359
11·4 Heats of reaction, heating values   361
11·5 Some illustrative calculations   363
11·6 Absolute entropy and the third law of thermodynamics   369
11·7 A second-law application   371

Chapter Twelve

EQUILIBRIUM   377

12·1 The general approach   377
12·2 Equilibrium   378

12·3 Evaluation of the electrochemical potential   380
12·4 Electrochemical potentials in a mixture of perfect gases   383
12·5 The Gibbs phase rule   385
12·6 Alteration of the saturated-vapor pressure by an inert gas   388
12·7 General conditions for chemical equilibrium of a mixture   390
12·8 Degrees of reaction freedom: The simple reactive mixture   393
12·9 Equations of reaction equilibrium   394
12·10 Reactions in perfect-gas mixtures   395
12·11 Calculation examples   397
12·12 Van't Hoff equation   400
12·13 Application to the fuel cell   401
12·14 Current methods and applications of the thermodynamic
      theory of combustion   403

Chapter Thirteen

AN INTRODUCTION TO COMPRESSIBLE FLOW   407

13·1 The momentum principle   407
13·2 Some momentum-principle applications   412
13·3 Stagnation properties in compressible flow   413
13·4 Mach number, speed of sound, regimes in compressible
      flow   414
13·5 A nozzle design problem   418
13·6 One-dimensional steady isentropic flow   420
13·7 Choking in isentropic flow   425
13·8 Isentropic flow in convergent-divergent passages   426
13·9 Shock waves   428
13·10 Compressibility effects in flows with friction and heat
      transfer   434
13·11 Examples of compressible flow calculations   435

Chapter Fourteen

AN INTRODUCTION TO HEAT TRANSFER   449

14·1 Some basic concepts   449
14·2 The conduction rate equation   451
14·3 Some simple conduction problems   453
14·4 Convection   465
14·5 Convection calculation examples   468

14·6 Fins   474
14·7 Heat exchangers   478
14·8 Radiation   483
14·9 Summary   486

Appendix A

UNIT SYSTEMS AND DIMENSIONAL EQUIVALENTS   495

Appendix B

THERMODYNAMIC PROPERTIES OF SUBSTANCES   505

Appendix C

INFORMATION FOR HEAT TRANSFER ANALYSIS   555

NOMENCLATURE   569

ANSWERS TO SELECTED PROBLEMS   575

Index   579

ENGINEERING
THERMODYNAMICS

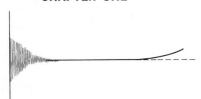

CHAPTER ONE

SOME INTRODUCTORY CONSIDERATIONS

1·1 THE NATURE OF THERMODYNAMICS

Thermodynamics deals with matter and interactions between matter; since every technological system involves matter, thermodynamic analysis is very important in engineering. Examples of thermodynamic analysis are given throughout this text. In particular, the examples of Chaps. Five and Nine show applications to engineering systems, and those of Chaps. Eight and Ten indicate the role of thermodynamics in the study of substances. The student may wish to scan these examples now to get some idea about the direction and scope of the subject.

Thermodynamics centers about the notions of *energy;* the idea that energy is always conserved is both the fundamental starting point and the basis for quantitative analysis. A second concept in thermodynamics is *entropy;* entropy provides a means for determining if a process is possible. Processes which produce entropy are possible, those which destroy entropy are impossible. These ideas of energy and entropy provide the framework of thermodynamics, and a clear understanding of them is therefore crucial. For this reason we shall place heavy emphasis on the development of real understanding of these and related concepts. This development requires exposure to the ideas, a chance to use them operationally, and time for satisfactory digestion. Consequently we shall introduce new concepts gradually and with some repetition, and shall make use of the ideas in practical analysis shortly after their first introduction. The successful student will be one who works hardest on understanding concepts. The engineering calculations that we shall do are intended as vehicles for gaining understanding of the concepts and for developing the ability to carry out such a calculation independently.

What do we need to know about matter in order to carry out an engineering analysis of a system of interest? Matter is composed of particles; any visible piece of matter contains a tremendous number of molecules, atoms, electrons, etc., each of which can have energy in a variety of ways. A *microscopic* description of such a piece would require the enumeration of the state of each particle, an obviously impractical task. In thermodynamics we seek to reduce the bits of information required to adequately describe states of matter from something of the order of 10^{23} to "few." This is accomplished by some sort of *statistical averaging;* we are willing to forego knowledge of microscopic detail in favor of simplicity. Thermodynamics is therefore a *macroscopic* science, which allows us to relate the averaged (macroscopic) properties of matter. Fortunately, the microscopic aspects are not essential in many important technical problems, and we can obtain excellent engineering solutions using the simpler macroscopic ideas.

The ultimate nature of matter is microscopic, of course, and our understanding of macroscopic theories can be considerably enhanced by drawing on microscopic concepts. For instance, it may be hard to visualize an object sitting motionless on a table as having any energy; but the thought of electrons whirling about vibrating nuclei provides a vivid physical picture of that energy and makes it much easier to visualize various means for changing the energy of the object. In this text we shall take optimum advantage of microscopic ideas, using them to provide physical interpretations of macroscopic properties and intuitive bases for macroscopic postulates.

Thermodynamic theory allows us to relate various properties of matter, so that by measuring some of them we can calculate others. Although microscopic ideas are indeed helpful to understanding, thermodynamics does not require the postulation of any particular microscopic models of matter. Other physical theories have been developed which do require specific microscopic models, and from these emerge predictions for the *values* of properties of the substance represented by the model. In statistical mechanics some sort of statistical model of the substance is postulated, and in kinetic theory a dynamic model is employed. These theories, although more specific in their output, are less general than those of thermodynamics. In fact, results from thermodynamics are usually used in association with the microscopic theories. Historically thermodynamics, statistical mechanics, and kinetic theory have developed separately, usually from somewhat different foundations. Our use of microscopic concepts allows us to lay a more common foundation for these three subjects, such that their relation and interdependence can more easily be appreciated. We shall go into some simple microscopic analyses following development of the key thermodynamic ideas.

The knowledge of the behavior of matter obtained from thermodynamics is extremely important in engineering analysis. When carried out in a systematic fashion, such analyses are not very difficult; but we cannot emphasize enough the importance of a systematic methodology, without which easy problems become hard. In parallel with more theoretical thermodynamic developments we shall use the methodology in illustrative engineering examples. Understanding of the basic thermodynamic concepts and principles and the ability to apply them in engineering are the primary objectives of our study.

In this chapter we shall attempt to establish a point of view through discussion of ideas already familiar to the student. The fundamental approach and philosophy adopted in this review of the basic concepts, models, and laws of related branches of physics will be carried over to the new thermodynamic ideas in subsequent chapters.

1·2 CONCEPTS, MODELS, AND LAWS

Concepts form the basis for any science. These are ideas, usually somewhat vague (especially when first encountered), which often defy really adequate definition. The meaning of a new concept can seldom be grasped from reading a one-paragraph discussion. There must be time to become accustomed to the concept, to integrate it with prior knowledge, and to associate it with personal experience. Inability to work with the details of a new subject can often be traced to inadequate understanding of its basic concepts.

The physical world is very complicated, and to include every minute detail in a theoretical analysis would be impracticable. Science has made big steps forward by the use of *models*, which, although always representing some simplifications over reality, reduce the mathematics to a tractable level. The range of validity and utility of the resulting theory is consequently restricted by the idealizations made in formulating the model. Newtonian mechanics is quite adequate for analysis of the great majority of everyday mechanical processes, and inclusion of relativistic effects in such mechanical analysis is an unnecessary complication. However, in many instances such effects are important, and it is the responsibility of the user of any theory to know both its bases and its limitations.

Concepts and models are not enough in themselves for a physical theory. These notions must be expressed in appropriate mathematical terms through basic equations, or *laws*. We choose to look upon a physical law as a contrivance of man that allows him to explain and predict phenomena of nature. Such predictions will be only as accurate and encompassing as the models on which the laws are based, and as new information is gathered and new understanding is developed, man may find it convenient, or perhaps necessary, to alter the basic laws. For example, mechanics is a direct outgrowth of Kepler's astronomical studies and his laws relating to the motion of planets about the sun. Newton generalized these observations and formed new, more basic laws, from which Kepler's rules could be deduced as special consequences. Later Newton's mechanics became merely a special case of Einstein's relativistic mechanics. In general, laws are replaced not because they are incorrect, but because their range of validity is restricted. Such was the case in the early development of thermodynamics, where at one time heat was thought of as something contained within matter. A useful but extremely limited caloric theory of heat, built upon this concept, was discarded more than a century ago; unfortunately, carryover of this misconception inhibits understanding of contemporary thermodynamics.

In many fields of science the concepts are very close to everyday experience, and the difficulties are primarily mathematical in nature. In most of thermodynamics the converse is true; the mathematics is not complicated but the concepts are sometimes difficult to grasp at the beginning, and most of the errors in thermodynamic analysis arise because of lack of clarity in either concepts or methodology. For this reason we shall spend a good deal of time on these matters; they should not be taken lightly, even though it may not be evident why so much attention is paid to apparently small details. To begin the discussion, let us review some concepts that are already familiar, examining them in the manner we shall subsequently employ in thermodynamics.

1·3 A FRESH LOOK AT SOME FAMILIAR CONCEPTS

One of the most important and central concepts in physics is *force*. It took man millenniums to evolve the force concept as a tool for explaining the varied interactions between objects in his environment. He observed that any one of a number of things can cause a given object to assume a certain position or undergo a certain gyration. The perception that in discussing the behavior of the object a particular cause can be replaced by a hypothetical "force" heralded the beginning of mechanics. Today we use this concept almost unconsciously whenever we replace the action of one body upon another by an appropriate force (see Fig. 1·1).

Forces are conceived as those pushes and pulls that tend to make objects move, and an essential part of the concept is that forces are somehow in balance when the object under study is motionless (or when its motion is uniform). It is essential to appreciate that the notion of a balance of forces in the absence of acceleration is an integral part of the force concept; whether or not forces "really exist" is a philosophical question which we need not debate. The fact is that the force concept allows us accurately to predict events in the real world, and this alone justifies its invention.

Forces are conceived as having both magnitude and direction and are treated mathematically as vectors. The vector sum of all forces acting on a body that is not accelerating must be zero.

We imagine that any two bodies in contact will exert forces upon one another. When we analyze the motion of one body, we mentally remove the

FIG. 1·1   *The effect of either the spring or the shaft on body A can be replaced by* F

FIG. 1·2 *The notion that "action equals reaction" is an integral part of the force concept*

other and replace its influence on the first by a force (Fig. 1·2). If we wish instead to study the motion of the second body, the first body would be replaced by a force of exactly the same magnitude but acting in the opposite direction. This "action-reaction" principle was formulated by Newton as his third law, but it is really an integral part of the concept of force.

No conceptual quantity becomes operationally useful until some way for its measurement has been established. One possible way of setting up a scale for force is to select some standard spring and say that the force it exerts is some selected constant times its deflection. This scheme has the distinct disadvantage of making the force scale dependent on the choice of material in the spring, among other factors. Suppose someone else set up a similar scale, based on a different kind of spring; the two scales could be adjusted to agree at one point but could not be expected to agree elsewhere. To each one the other would be nonlinear. It is always more desirable to devise scales of measure that are completely independent of the nature of any substance. In principle it is possible to do this for force, taking advantage of the notion that the resultant force on a stationary body is zero. Imagine selecting any reproducible force, such as that produced by a selected spring compressed some selected amount, and designating this as a unit force. Let this force act on a body in sole opposition to two identical forces selected so as to keep the spring at its standard deflection when the body is motionless (the two identical forces could be obtained from any two identical springs, for example). The two identical forces must each be half the unit force, and either can be used to measure such a force (see Fig. 1·3). This process can be continued, and we can collect a set of springs, each measuring some rational fraction or multiple of the unit force. We can therefore, in principle, measure any unknown force to any desired degree of accuracy. The force scale is unique in that it is independent of the nature of any substance. It will be the same regardless of the material of which the springs are made.

FIG. 1·3 *A unique force scale can be established using symmetry and the concepts of force*

FIG. 1·4 *The force is the same in both reference frames*

An important part of the concept of force is that the magnitude of a force is unchanged by a change in the *reference frame*. Forces are therefore absolute, while the motions they produce are relative (see Fig. 1·4).

The force concept allows us to explain the lack of translational accelerations but is in itself insufficient when rotational accelerations are involved. For example, consider the bar of Fig. 1·5, acted upon by three horizontal coplanar forces. The vector sum of these forces is indeed zero, yet we know from experience that the bar would undergo clockwise rotational acceleration. The additional concept of the *moment* of a force provides the explanation, and that moment is the product of the force times its distance from some reference point. But why should the first power of the distance, and not its square, or its cube, or its logarithm, be involved? We used symmetry arguments in setting up a unique force scale, and they can be used again to deduce an appropriate definition for the moment of a force. The thought processes involved are shown in Fig. 1·6. The symmetry of the coplanar force set of Fig. 1·6a requires that it be a *zero set*, meaning that the forces would produce neither translational nor rotational accelerations if they acted on the bar. Figure 1·6b also shows a zero set, and the sum of these two zero sets (Fig. 1·6c) forms a third *nonsymmetric zero set*. In Fig. 1·6d the ratio of the forces at A and C is the inverse of the ratio of their distance from point O. This argument can be continued, and one can construct an infinite number of zero sets with one force at O, another at C, and the third force at some point A along the bar. In every case the ratio of the force at A to that at C is found to be exactly the inverse of the

FIG. 1·5 *The bar would pivot about 0*

(a) *By symmetry, with this zero set of forces the bar will not pivot*

(b) *By symmetry, this is also a zero set*

(c) *Therefore this is also a zero set*

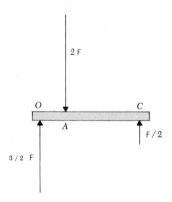

(d) *So this must be a zero set*

FIG. 1·6 *Deducing the law of the lever by symmetry*

ratio of their distances from the potential pivot point O,

$$\frac{\mathsf{F}_A}{\mathsf{F}_C} = \frac{L_C}{L_A} \tag{1·1}$$

which is well known as the *law of the lever* (see Fig. 1·7). An equivalent statement is that the *moments* of the forces F_A and F_C are equal but opposite, where we define the moment of a force F about a point O by

$$M_{\mathsf{F}/O} = \mathsf{F}r$$

where the distance r has the meaning indicated in Fig. 1·8.

The approach to the concept of force presented above is typical of the approach we shall take to other thermodynamics concepts. In particular, recall the development of the unique force scale, which is independent of any arbitrary choice of spring material. It should be possible to define scales for all fundamental properties of matter that are independent of this type of arbitrariness. In a moment we shall see how this can be done for the concepts of mass and

FIG. 1·7   *The law of the lever;*
$F_A/F_C = L_C/L_A$

FIG. 1·8   *The moment of a force*

charge. Temperature is a fundamental property in thermodynamics, and it should be possible to establish a temperature scale that does not depend on arbitrary thermometer materials or markings. One of the important contributions of thermodynamics is a real conceptual basis for temperature, including a temperature scale that is independent of such arbitrary choices. We shall introduce this concept of temperature and the associated means for its measurement in Chap. Seven.

Quantitative prediction of the acceleration of bodies requires the introduction of another familiar concept, *mass*. A body acted on by an unbalanced force does not suddenly increase its speed, but rather accelerates gradually at a rate which is dependent on the magnitude of the force. The *inertial mass*

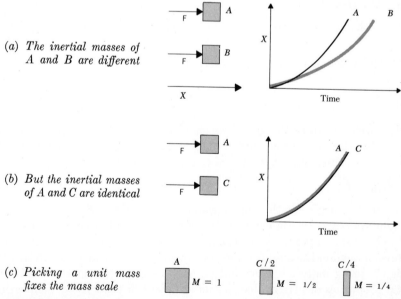

(a) *The inertial masses of A and B are different*

(b) *But the inertial masses of A and C are identical*

(c) *Picking a unit mass fixes the mass scale*

FIG. 1·9   *Devising a unique scale for inertial mass using symmetry arguments* of an object is conceived as a property characteristic of its resistance to velocity change. Any two objects that undergo identical translational accelerations when acted upon by the same force have identical inertial masses (Fig. 1·9).

An idea inherent in the Newtonian concept of inertial mass is that the mass of two objects taken together is the sum of their individual inertial masses; cutting a homogeneous body into two identical parts produces two identical masses, each with half the original mass. The notion of *conservation of mass* is therefore an integral part of the concept of mass. In principle, a unique scale for inertial mass may be constructed using the same sort of arguments used to construct a force scale. The reasoning involved is indicated in Fig. 1·9.

Any object that is dropped will accelerate as it falls, even though the object is not in physical contact with any other body. To explain this behavior man had to conceive *gravitational forces,* which one body, such as the earth, can exert on another, even though they are far apart. This leads to the concept of *gravitational mass,* conceived as that property of matter representative of its distant interactions with other bodies. If the forces exerted by the earth (or any other mass) on any two objects are identical, they must have identical gravitational masses. A unique scale for gravitational mass can be devised using a simple laboratory balance, as shown in Fig. 1·10.

Suppose we use the same object for a unit mass in constructing both the inertial- and gravitational-mass scales. While the inertial and gravitational masses of this object will be identical, there is no reason to expect the scales to be identical. Yet very careful experiments have shown that the two scales are equivalent to within at least one part in 10^{10}, and consequently we consider them as fully identical.†

The terms "mass" and "weight" are frequently confused. By *weight* we mean the gravitational force exerted by the earth on an object near the earth's

† R. H. Dicke, The Eötvös Experiment, *Scientific American,* December, 1961.

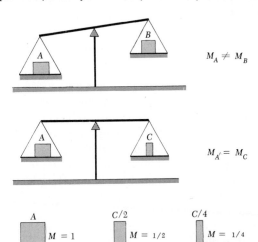

$$M_A \neq M_B$$

$$M_A = M_C$$

FIG. 1·10 *Symmetry can also be used to establish a unique scale of gravitational mass*

A $M = 1$ C/2 $M = 1/2$ C/4 $M = 1/4$

surface. The weight of a body depends on its location, while its mass is conceived as being independent of position. Two exceptions are forced upon us by historical circumstances. The term "atomic weight" has come to be used to denote the ratio of the mass of an atom to $\frac{1}{16}$ the mass of an oxygen atom. The atomic weight is therefore a number without dimensions. "Molecular weight" is used for the sum of the atomic weights of all atoms in a molecule and is also dimensionless.

The *molal mass* is important in chemistry and thermodynamics. A *mole* is defined as an amount of a given substance numerically equal to its molecular weight. For example, a gram mole of helium (molecular weight = 4.003) would have a mass of 4.003 g. The mass of any sample of a given substance is then simply the number of moles present times the molal mass, which is the mass of a single mole of the substance. The molal mass of helium is 4.003 g/gmole.

Consider now a group of N molecules of a substance whose molecular weight and molal mass are m and $\hat{M}$, respectively. If the mass of individual molecules is m, the total mass of the N molecules is

$$M = N\mathsf{m} = Nm\,\frac{\mathsf{m}_0}{16}$$

where m_0 is the mass of an oxygen atom. However, it is also true that

$$\blacktriangleright \qquad M = \mathfrak{N}\hat{M}$$

where $\mathfrak{N}$ denotes the number of moles present. It therefore follows that

$$\frac{\mathfrak{N}}{N}\,\frac{\hat{M}}{m} = \frac{\mathsf{m}_0}{16}$$

Since $\hat{M}$ and m are numerically equal, it follows that *the number of molecules in a mole is the same for every substance,*

$$\blacktriangleright \qquad \frac{N}{\mathfrak{N}} = \mathrm{N}_0 = \text{constant} \tag{1·2}$$

The constant N_0 is called *Avogadro's number;* its value is 6.025×10^{23}/gmole.

A convenient concept in mechanics is the *particle,* an idealized body in which all the mass is imagined to be concentrated at a single point. A particle has no shape and can undergo only translational motions. Experimentally it is found that the product of the acceleration and the mass of an object treated as a particle is proportional to the force acting on it. If we were to set up *arbitrary* scales of mass, force, length, and time, there would be no reason to expect the constant of proportionality to be unity. The equation describing the motion would then be

$$\mathsf{F} = k_N M a \tag{1·3}$$

which is merely *Newton's second law* in a somewhat more general form. There may be some virtue in adjusting the scales of force and mass to make the constant k_N come out to be unity, and we shall discuss this later in the chapter.

The classical model of gravitational attraction is that the attractive force exerted mutually by two particles follows the law

$$\mathbf{F} = k_G \frac{M_1 M_2}{R^2} \tag{1.4}$$

Here M_1 and M_2 are the two masses, R is the distance between them, and k_G is a *universal gravitational constant*. The mechanism by which these forces are exerted is not well understood; perhaps when the concept of gravitation is more fully developed it will be possible to deduce that the inverse square of the distance is appropriate in a more fundamental manner.

The fundamental concept of electromagnetics is that of *charge*. Its invention arose out of the need for an explanation of forces which can exist between physically separated objects, forces which could not be accounted for in terms of gravitation. Charge is conceived as a property of electric particles and can give rise to either attractive or repulsive forces. The concept of charge is intimately tied to the idea that charge is a conserved quantity. Two objects that have been rubbed together will attract one another; we explain this by saying that one object has been positively charged and the other negatively charged (in order to conserve charge). We observe that bodies having charges of equal sign repel one another and that objects with opposite charge attract, and we adopt these conventions as part of the charge concept.

With the concept that electrostatic forces are somehow associated with charge, it becomes possible to tell when two objects have the same charge. This occurs when they each exert the same force on a third charged body. When a charged object is touched to an identical uncharged object, the objects assume identical charges. Symmetry considerations, together with the concept of charge as a conserved quantity, indicate that each object then has half the original charge. The notion that charge is conserved allows us to establish a unique scale of charge which is independent of the nature of any substance (see Fig. 1·11).

Experimentally it is found that the repulsive force between two stationary point charges is proportional to the product of their charges and inversely

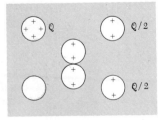

FIG. 1·11 *Establishing a unique charge scale with symmetry arguments*

proportional to the square of the distance between them,

$$\mathsf{F} = k_C \frac{Q_1 Q_2}{R^2} \tag{1.5}$$

This is *Coulomb's law;* the constant k_C depends upon the arbitrary choices of unit forces and charges. It is possible to construct dimensional systems in which k_C comes out to be unity, and we shall discuss this later in the chapter.

Moving charges exert additional forces upon one another. If the charges are not moving too rapidly, the additional forces are given by the *Biot-Savart law.*† The constant of proportionality in this expression similarly depends upon the particular choices of force and charge scales.

1.4 MECHANICAL CONCEPTS OF ENERGY

Consider the equation of motion of a single particle,

$$\mathbf{F} = k_N M \frac{d\mathbf{V}}{dt} \tag{1.6}$$

Multiplying by dt and integrating from t_1 to t_2,

$$\int_{t_1}^{t_2} \mathbf{F} \, dt = k_N M (\mathbf{V}_2 - \mathbf{V}_1) \tag{1.7}$$

It is customary to call the integral the *impulse* and to call the quantity $M\mathbf{V}$ the *momentum.* The basic equation of mechanics therefore tells us that the impulse provided is proportional to the increase in momentum of the particle.

Recognizing that by definition $\mathbf{V} = d\mathbf{X}/dt$, we can multiply Eq. (1.6) by $d\mathbf{X}$ (vector dot product) and integrate between any two points in space, obtaining‡

$$\int_{\mathbf{X}_1}^{\mathbf{X}_2} \mathbf{F} \cdot d\mathbf{X} = k_N \frac{M}{2} (\mathsf{V}_2{}^2 - \mathsf{V}_1{}^2) \tag{1.8}$$

It is customary to call the integral the *work* done on the particle and to refer to the quantity $k_N M \mathsf{V}^2/2$ as the *kinetic energy* of the particle. The basic mechanical law then tells us that the work done by the force on the particle is equal to the increase in its kinetic energy. Note that the expression for kinetic energy is developed by manipulations from a fundamental equation.

In discussing the motion of a particle it is often convenient to conceive a *force field.* For example, the gravitational force on a mass is sometimes expressed in terms of a gravitational field $\mathbf{G}$ as

$$\mathbf{F} = M\mathbf{G}$$

In Eq. (1.8) the energy transferred as work to a particle by the gravitational

---

† See Appendix A, Table A.2.

‡ Here V^2 means $\mathbf{V} \cdot \mathbf{V}$.

force would then be

$$\int_{X_1}^{X_2} M\mathbf{G} \cdot d\mathbf{X} = k_N \frac{M}{2} (\mathsf{V}_2{}^2 - \mathsf{V}_1{}^2)$$

One can show that the gravitational field may alternatively be expressed in terms of a scalar potential ϕ such that†

$$\mathbf{G} = - \operatorname{grad} \phi$$

Force fields having a potential are said to be *conservative*. The integral of Eq. (1·8) may therefore be evaluated and the result expressed as

$$k_N \frac{M}{2} \mathsf{V}_1{}^2 + M\phi_1 = k_N \frac{M}{2} \mathsf{V}_2{}^2 + M\phi_2$$

The term $M\phi$ is called the *potential energy* of the particle. We see that the laws of mechanics require that the energy of such a particle, that is, the sum of the kinetic and potential energies, be *conserved*.‡ Derivation of an expression for the potential energy of a body near the earth's surface is left as an exercise (Prob. 1·20).

The concept of energy as a conserved quantity has been central in science since the late seventeenth century. At first the idea was applied only to a freely falling body; as additional systems were considered, new kinds of energy had to be introduced in order that the conservation aspect be retained. Considerations of charge led to coulomb energy and eventually to the concept of energy in an electromagnetic field. With the modifications of mechanics introduced by relativity theory, came rest-mass energy. Physicists have conceived new particles solely in order to retain the conservation of energy at the nuclear and subnuclear levels. Man has become fond of the conservation-of-energy concept and, being unwilling to discard it, has been forced to visualize new kinds of energy. One wonders if simpler explanations of nature might be obtained by forgetting about the concepts of force and energy and starting over with new concepts. While this may some day happen, the engineer of today must use present-day concepts, models, and laws to devise his systems, and the notions of force, mass, work, and in particular, the conservation of energy, are quite adequate for his purposes.

1·5 CONTINUUM CONCEPTS

The concept of the particle is useful on both the smallest and largest scales, and it is indeed amazing that the motion of planets and electrons can be described in such similar terms. When considering systems of many, many particles, the concept of a *continuum* is often useful. In the continuum view matter is seen as being distributed through space and not, as in the particle

---

† In one-dimensional terms, $\mathbf{G} = -d\phi/dx$.

‡ When only gravitational forces act on the particle.

FIG. 1·12 *Density at a point*

FIG. 1·13 *Density cannot be defined if the spatial variations are too great*

view, localized. Matter exists in "big chunks," having mass, energy, and momentum, as do particles, but also possessing some additional continuum characteristics, such as volume, density, and temperature.

From the continuum standpoint we can speak of properties at a point. For example, consider taking smaller and smaller sized volumes about a point and measuring the ratio mass/volume. This ratio will approach a limit, defined as the *density at the point* (Fig. 1·12),

$$\rho = \lim_{V \to V_\epsilon} \frac{M}{V}$$

If the volume is made too small (smaller than V_ϵ), the ratio will fluctuate in time as the molecular population of the volume changes. The continuum idealization is therefore not useful for volumes which are too small. If the spatial variations in mass/volume are too great, a limit may not exist, and the continuum method would be invalid. Such a case is shown in Fig. 1·13.

Other continuum concepts include *mass-flow rate, electric current,* and *mass flux.* Consider an imaginary plane within a fluid; molecules will continually cross this plane in both directions, but if more cross one way than go the other there will be a net mass flow. Denoting δM_r and δM_l as the amounts of mass which cross to the right and left during the time interval δt, the mass-flow rate to the right is defined as

$$\dot{M} = \lim_{\delta t \to \delta t_\epsilon} \frac{\delta M_r - \delta M_l}{\delta l}$$

where δt_ϵ denotes some very small time interval (see Fig. 1·14). δt_ϵ must be

FIG. 1·14 *A net passage of molecules to the right gives rise to an equivalent mass flow*

FIG. 1·15　*Pressure;* $P = \overline{\mathsf{F}}/A$

sufficiently long that many particles cross the plane in this period; consequently the mass-flow rate loses its usefulness in processes which occur at extremely rapid rates. The terms "mass flux" and "current flux" refer to limiting rates of flow *per unit of area*. Formal definitions of these quantities are left as exercises.

The *pressure* exerted by a fluid on the walls of a container is also a continuum concept (see Fig. 1·15). At the microscopic level we can explain pressure as resulting from impacts of particles on the wall. These impacts result in a force which is macroscopically measurable, and in the continuum view we think of this force as being uniformly distributed over the wall. The pressure is then the limiting *force per unit of area*, which we can evaluate at any point on the wall.

In continuum analyses the manipulations of calculus are employed; for example, the mass of a body can be expressed in terms of the integrated density distribution as

$$M = \int_{\text{vol}} \rho \, dV$$

Thermodynamics is essentially a continuum science, and hence these continuum concepts will be very important throughout our study.

1·6 THE CONCEPTUAL BASIS OF DIMENSIONAL SYSTEMS

There probably never was a student who at one time or another was not confused by the many different systems of units used in various fields of engineering. Such confusion disappears once the *concepts* behind dimensions and unit systems are properly understood. We shall work in various unit systems throughout this text, and it is well that we spend some time clarifying these concepts now.

We have emphasized that it is possible to construct scales of measure for the conceptual quantities and that it is most desirable that these scales be independent of the nature of the materials employed in setting the standards. There is a great deal of choice as to the scales which we arbitrarily select. For example, we normally work in dimensional systems in which arbitrary scales of length and time have been established, and in which velocity has the dimensions of length divided by time. We could alternatively set up a system in which scales for velocity and time were arbitrarily chosen, and then length would have the dimensions of velocity multiplied by time. We could select arbitrary standards for length, velocity, and time; however, in such a system velocity would be proportional, but not necessarily equal, to the rate of change of length with time. The essential idea to grasp is that the quantities for which arbitrary scales of measure are set up can be picked in many ways, and it just happens that the early scientists picked certain sets.

We use the word "dimension" to mean a name given to any measurable quantity. Length, time, mass, area, and velocity are *dimensions*. The *primary quantities* of a particular dimensional system are those for which we decide to set up arbitrary scales of measure. *Secondary quantities* are those whose dimensions are expressed in terms of the dimensions of primary quantities. In the dimensional systems we customarily employ, length and time are primary quantities and velocity and area are secondary quantities.

The primary scales of measure are expressed in terms of *units*. For example, foot, inch, and meter are all different *units* with the common *dimension* of length. Each of the primary scales is based on a carefully chosen standard. In olden times the standards of measure were things like the king's foot, but today we are in the midst of a switch to more available, more highly reproducible standards. The international standard of length used to be the distance between two marks on a platinum-iridium bar, but in 1960 an atomic standard based on the wavelength of the orange-red line in the spectrum of krypton 86 was adopted by international agreement. The meter is now defined as 1,650,763.73 times this wavelength. The present standard of time is the second. Until 1960 it was defined as 1/86,400 of a mean solar day; then the definition was changed to 1/31,556,925.9747 of the tropical year 1900.† Hopefully a more accessible, precisely reproducible atomic standard will be adopted in the not-too-distant future.‡

Length and time are primary quantities in all dimensional systems in common use. In some systems *mass* is also taken as a primary quantity. A standard 1-kg mass of platinum-iridium is kept at the International Bureau of Weights and Measures in France. In other dimensional systems *force* is chosen as a primary quantity; the standard of force can be taken as the weight of the platinum-iridium mass at some prescribed point on earth. Nature has provided an excellent standard of charge in the electron, and we can think of using this as a basis for a charge scale.

The dimensions of secondary quantities are fixed by the equations which relate them to the primary quantities. For example, in the mks system length (meter), mass (kilogram), and time (second) are taken as the primary quantities. Force is a secondary quantity in this dimensional system; the dimensions and

† *National Bureau of Standards Technical News Bulletin*, vol. 44, no. 12, December, 1960.
‡ At the 1964 International Conference on Weights and Measures a definition of a cesium radiation frequency was adopted as a temporary atomic standard.

magnitudes of forces result from the arbitrary selection of unity for the value of the constant k_N in Newton's second law, which then becomes (for a particle)

$$\mathsf{F} = Ma$$

The secondary quantity acceleration has the dimensions of length/time², so force has the dimensions of mass × length/time² and the units of kg-m/sec² in the mks system.

Another common system is the absolute engineering flt system, in which force, length, and time are the primary quantities. Here the dimensions and units of mass result from arbitrarily setting $k_N = 1$. Newton's law then is again $\mathsf{F} = Ma$, but mass has the dimensions of force/(length/time²) and the units of lbf-sec²/ft in this system.

It is important to realize that the constants in physical laws do not just happen to be equal to 1; they are often picked to have this or some other value. Confusion about electrical-unit systems is often a result of failure to understand this point.

A third dimensional system used a great deal in engineering is the fmlt engineering system, in which both force *and* mass plus length and time are chosen as the primary quantities. The scales for force and mass are chosen such that the weight of an object at sea level on earth is numerically equal to its mass. Force and mass are assigned the units of lbf (pound force) and lbm (pound mass), respectively. Newton's law is not $\mathsf{F} = Ma$ in this unit system; instead the constant k_N is considered as having the experimentally determined value of

$$k_N = \frac{1}{32.1739} \text{ lbf-sec}^2/\text{ft-lbm}$$

It is customary to denote the reciprocal of k_N by g_c; in the fmlt engineering system,

▶ $\quad g_c = 32.1739 \text{ ft-lbm/lbf-sec}^2$

This is a *universal constant* which emerges in Newton's law as a result of the arbitrary choices for standards of measure. In this text we shall henceforth write Newton's second law for a particle as

▶ $\quad \mathsf{F} = \frac{1}{g_c} Ma$ $\qquad\qquad\qquad\qquad\qquad\qquad$ (1·9)

The constant g_c has the value unity and is dimensionless in the mks, cgs, and absolute engineering systems. The term g_c should not be confused with the local acceleration of gravity g_g. While g_c and g_g are *numerically* equal in the fmlt engineering system, their dimensions are different. A tabulation of four dimensional systems used in mechanics and physics is presented in Table A·1 of Appendix A.

Electrical-unit systems show even more variance. The absolute electrostatic cgs system is simply an extension of the cgs system in which the dimensions and units of charge are fixed by selecting the constant in Coulomb's law to be 1. In the absolute electromagnetic cgs system the constant in the Biot-Savart law is picked to be 1, and the constant in Coulomb's law then emerges as an experimentally determined value. Most contemporary work is done in the rationalized practical mksc system, in which charge is a primary quantity, and the constants in both Coulomb's and the Biot-Savart laws have odd experimentally determined values. Table A·2 shows these three dimensional systems.

Sometimes the units of secondary quantities, expressed in terms of the primary units, become sufficiently complicated that we find it convenient to give names, or *aliases*, to particular combinations. Some important examples are evident in Tables A·1 and A·2. One can appreciate the desirability of denoting the combination $coul^2\text{-}sec^2\text{-}kg^{-1}\text{-}m^{-2}$ by the simple alias "farad," but the desirability of also calling a centimeter an "abhenry" might be argued.

To illustrate the ideas of dimensional systems, let us set up a system in which only length and time are chosen as primary quantities. Both force and mass will be secondary quantities, and we shall determine their dimensions and units by arbitrarily selecting the constant in Newton's law to be 2 and the constant in the gravitational law to be unity. In our new system these laws would be

$$F = 2Ma$$

$$F = \frac{M_1 M_2}{R^2}$$

Considering two identical mutually gravitating masses and the accelerations they undergo, we equate the above two equations and solve for M, finding

$$M = 2aR^2 \tag{1·10}$$

Mass will therefore have the dimensions of $length^3/time^2$ in this new system. If we adopt the meter and the second as primary standards, mass would have the units m^3/sec^2. We might choose the alias "chunk" for this combination of primary units. The dimensions of force would then be $length^4/time^4$, and we could give the alias "push" to $1\ m^4/sec^4$.

Conversion factors from the mks system to our new system would not be found in standard tables, but we can work out our own conversion factors for this system. Consider two bodies, each having a mass of 1 kg in the mks system, freely gravitating toward one another. Suppose they are 1 m apart. The acceleration which they undergo can be computed first from the mks equations

$$F = Ma$$

$$F = \frac{k_G M^2}{R^2}$$

Then

$$a = \frac{k_G M}{R^2} = \frac{6.67 \times 10^{-11} \text{ m}^3/\text{kg-sec}^2 \times 1 \text{ kg}}{1 \text{ m}^2}$$

$$= 6.67 \times 10^{-11} \text{ m}/\text{sec}^2$$

The mass in the new unit system may now be computed from Eq. $(1 \cdot 10)$ as

$$M = 2(6.67 \times 10^{-11} \text{ m}/\text{sec}^2) \ 1 \text{ m}^2 = 13.34 \times 10^{-11} \text{ m}^3/\text{sec}^2$$

We therefore have the conversion equivalence

$$1 \text{ kg} = 13.34 \times 10^{-11} \text{ m}^3/\text{sec}^2 = 13.34 \times 10^{-11} \text{ chunks}$$

The conversion between newtons and pushes could be obtained in the same way. Appendix A is devoted to further consideration of unit systems.

SELECTED READING

Resnick, R., and D. Halliday, *Physics, Part 1*, chap. 1, chap. 5, John Wiley & Sons, Inc., New York, 1966.

Kestin, J., *A Course in Thermodynamics*, chap. 1, Blaisdell Publishing Co., Inc., Waltham, Mass., 1966.

Zemansky, M. W., and H. C. Van Ness, *Basic Engineering Thermodynamics*, secs. 1.1–1.4, McGraw-Hill Book Company, New York, 1966.

QUESTIONS

$1 \cdot 1$ What are your concepts of length and time?

$1 \cdot 2$ What is the value of g_c on the moon?

$1 \cdot 3$ Why is it not true that $g_g/g_c = 1$ in the engineering system, even though the numerical values of g_g and g_c may be the same?

$1 \cdot 4$ What is the difference between work and power?

$1 \cdot 5$ No one has ever seen an electron. Why do we say that they exist?

$1 \cdot 6$ Consider $\mathsf{F} \, dX$, $d \, (\mathsf{F}X)$, and $X \, d\mathsf{F}$. Which is work, and why? Which can be integrated without knowing how F varies with X?

$1 \cdot 7$ Invent an analogy of the microscopic and macroscopic viewpoints that would be useful in explaining these concepts to a layman.

$1 \cdot 8$ How might you explain the concepts of energy, force, and charge to a high school freshman?

$1 \cdot 9$ How do concepts differ from definitions?

$1 \cdot 10$ Estimate the length of time and amount of paper required to write down the coordinates of every molecule in a mole of gas.

$1 \cdot 11$ At what age did you first hear about energy? At what age did you first understand the concept? Have you ever heard about entropy?

$1 \cdot 12$ Is it wrong, or merely inconvenient, to conceive of the earth as the center of the solar system?

$1 \cdot 13$ What is your mass in lbm? What is your height in statfarads?

1·14 Push very hard on a stone wall. How much work did you do on the wall? Why did you get tired?

1·15 In Newtonian mechanics which of the following are absolute, which are relative, and why? (a) Force, (b) mass, (c) length, (d) time, (e) momentum, (f) energy, (g) work, and (h) velocity.

1·16 Why is it important to make a distinction between lbm and lbf? Can they be canceled in an equation?

1·17 What is a gmole? A lbmole?

1·18 What is a continuum? Under what circumstances might the continuum idealizations be invalid?

PROBLEMS

1·1 Discuss the differences between concepts and definitions. What are the basic concepts of geometry? What are some geometrical definitions?

1·2 In the Middle Ages it was thought that length up was somehow not the same as length horizontally ("after all, things fall down but never fall sideways!"). Discuss how the concepts of these two lengths have changed since that time. Can you draw any parallelisms with the present dual concepts of mass?

1·3 Discuss the possible means for devising fundamental measures of length and time.

1·4 Derive an expression for the electric field strength $\mathbf{E}$ in the vicinity of a point charge Q using Coulomb's law.

1·5 Derive an expression for the gravitational field strength $\mathbf{G}$ in the vicinity of a point mass M using the universal gravitation law.

1·6 Consider an observer in a frame which is accelerating linearly at acceleration a_0. What should he write for Newton's law in his coordinate frame? What would be his energy accounting for the work done by a force on a particle?

1·7 A body having a mass of 1 kg falls from rest from a height of 30 ft. Express its kinetic energy in Btu, ft-lbf, and ev.

1·8 Using the inverse-square gravitational law, calculate the work required to lift a 1000-kg satellite from the earth's surface to an altitude of 100 miles and inject it into orbit at 17,500 mph. How long would a 300-hp engine have to be run to produce this much energy? How many automotive batteries would be required if the orbiting could be done electrically (600 watt-hr is the total available energy from a typical automotive wet cell)? Why is this not the procedure normally used?

1·9 Estimate your kinetic energy while running 10 mph. State the result in ergs, Btu, and ev. Did you do any work on the ground in achieving this speed?

1·10 A 100-megaton hydrogen bomb releases 10^{25} ergs of energy. Compare this to the kinetic energy of an iron asteroid 10 km in diameter approaching the earth at 50,000 m/sec.

1·11 Determine the value of g_c in the engineering unit system from things which you know in the mks system and the conversions from kg to lbm, m to ft, and newtons to lbf.

1·12 Set up a dimension system in which length and time are the only primary quantities. Pick the constants in Newton's law, Coulomb's law, and the universal gravitational law to be unity. Use the meter and the second as the primary standards and determine the equivalence of a 1-kg mass and a 1-coul charge in the new unit system.

1·13 Set up a dimension system in which the mass of the earth is taken as 1 chunk, the diameter of the earth is 1 clearthru, and the period of the earth around the sun is 1 oncearound. Fix the units of force by selecting the gravitational constant to be unity. Obtain a table of conversion factors in the form

1 m = (   ) clearthrus
1 kg = (   ) chunks
1 sec = (   ) oncearounds
1 lbf = (   ) chunk²/clearthru²

Write Newton's second law in this unit system, and determine the value for g_c. Selecting k_C to be unity in Coulomb's law, express the units of charge, and give the conversion factor from coul to charge in the new unit system.

1·14 Set up a dimension system in which time is the only primary quantity. Pick the constants in Newton's second law, Coulomb's law, and the gravitational law to be unity, and in addition, pick the speed of light to be unity (dimensionless). Length will then have the dimensions of time. Use the sec as the unit of time, and determine the equivalents of 1 kg, 1 m, and 1 coul.

1·15 Set up a dimension system in which force and charge are the primary quantities. Pick the constants in Coulomb's law, Newton's law, and the universal gravitational law to be ½, and state the dimensions of length, time, and mass in terms of the primary dimensions. Determine the equivalents of 1 m, 1 kg, and 1 sec in the new unit system, taking the newton and the coulomb as the fundamental units of force and charge.

1·16 Set up a dimension system in which the primary quantities are mass, length, time, and charge. Pick the constant in Coulomb's law to be unity. Find the dimensions of force and of the constant in Newton's law in this system (in terms of M, L, T, and Q). Choosing the kg, m, sec, and coul as the basic units for the primary quantities, calculate the value of the constant in Newton's law for the new dimensional system, and determine the equivalence of 1 newton in the new system. Is this the same as 1 newton in the mksc system?

1·17 Set up a dimension system in which the only primary quantities are length and time. Pick the constants in Newton's law, the gravitational law, and Coulomb's law to be π. State the dimensions of force, mass, and charge (in terms of length and time) in this new system. Taking the unit time as the leap year (1 leap year = 366 days) and the unit of length as the earthrad (1 earthrad = 4000 miles), find the equivalents of 1 kgm, 1 lbf, 1 cal, 1 Btu, 1 coul, and 1 amp in the new system.

1·18 Discuss the point of the previous six problems.

1·19 Discuss the implications of Prob. 1·14; do you think there might be any unknown basic laws relating mass, force, length, time, and charge?

1·20 Show that the potential energy of a body of mass M in a uniform gravitational field, where the free-fall acceleration is g_g, is equal to Mg_g/g_c.

CHAPTER TWO

ENERGY AND THE FIRST LAW

2·1 INTRODUCTION

We are about to lay the foundations for a broad physical theory. While thermodynamics can be developed from purely macroscopic postulates and definitions, without any reference at all to the microscopic, we shall follow a somewhat different approach. Microscopic concepts will be used to develop understanding about the nature of matter and to provide an intuitive basis for the fundamental macroscopic postulates.

Any physical theory is couched in terms of abstract mathematical symbols which in some way are presumed to be associated with physical measurables. Simplicity and economy are two important features of any really successful theory; nothing could be simpler than $F = Ma$, and yet look at the tremendous number of important problems the analyst can solve with this one basic idea. Thermodynamics also seeks simplicity; rather than insisting on knowing what each and every particle in a mole of gas is doing at every instant, we content ourselves with knowledge of certain averages, and in so doing reduce the number of bits of information required to sufficiently describe the gas from something of the order of 10^{23} to "few." Just how many this "few" is depends on what system we are analyzing; we shall give some rules for determining this number later on.

The simplest type of basic "law" is one which states that some physical quantity is conserved. The central concept in thermodynamics is energy, and thermodynamic theory is constructed in such a way that energy is conserved. The conservation of energy is the key equation of the theory, playing much the same role in thermodynamic analysis as does Newton's second law in mechanics. In mechanics one deals with only a few kinds of energy; in electromagnetics and chemistry other kinds of energy appear. Thermodynamics provides the common tie among these various forms of energy and will provide deeper insight into a variety of subjects already studied. This chapter deals with the concept of energy and its conservation in macroscopic systems.

2·2 SYSTEMS

In any scientific or engineering analysis it is very important to identify clearly whatever it is that is under consideration. We shall use the term *system* in a very broad sense to identify the subject of discussion or analysis. The system is something defined by the analyst for his particular problem at hand. A system might be a particular collection of matter, such as the gas in a bottle. Or it might be a region in space, such as the bottle and whatever happens to be in it at the moment. Sometimes we include fields in our definition of the system; for example, the gas in the bottle and the electric field in the bottle might be defined as the system. At other times fields are defined to be "outside" of the system; thus, the gas may be the system, but the fields that occupy the same space are considered "external" to the system. Another situation in which two systems share the same space occurs in analysis of ionized gases; the ions are often treated as one system, and the electrons as another. Interacting systems are often of quite different types; for example, in the study of liquid droplets the liquid interior to the surface is sometimes treated as one system, and the surface molecules as another. A system might be very simple, such as a piece of matter, or very complex, such as a nuclear power generation plant. Matter may flow through a system, such as a jet engine, or the system may be completely devoid of matter, such as the system of radiation in an enclosed volume. The system is whatever we wish to discuss, and we must be very careful each time to describe precisely just what it is that we are talking about. Hence we shall place considerable emphasis on the definition of systems in this text.

When motions are involved, the definition of the system must include a *reference frame* in which the motions will be measured. An *inertial frame* is one in which any free particle moves at constant velocity. The laws of mechanics as normally written apply only in inertial frames, and hence one must be careful in choosing the reference frame if these laws are to be invoked in the analysis.

It is often helpful to indicate the system under consideration by enclosing it with dotted lines in a sketch. Of course, one cannot tell from the sketch whether the system is the *matter* inside the lines or the *space* inside the lines (which may contain different material at different times). In order to differentiate, the term *control mass* is used to indicate a system consisting of specified matter, and the term *control volume* is used to indicate a system specified by space. In working with the properties of materials one usually uses control masses; however, much engineering analysis involves some sort of flow process, and then control volumes are used instead. Often the sketch is not enough to convey the system definition to the reader, in which case a few words of definition are desirable. The student should learn to give adequate system definitions, for much confusion can result when an analyst and his reader are talking about different systems ("Do you mean the space or the matter in it?"). Many examples of system definition can be found in this and later chapters, particularly in Chaps. Five and Nine; inspection of these systems at this time will also give the student some idea of where we are going in our study of thermodynamics.

Having carefully defined the system, everything else is automatically its *environment.* The interactions between a system and its environment are the main interest in thermodynamics. It is frequently convenient to make the conceptual idealization that the system is *isolated* from any interaction with its environment; we say conceptual because isolation requires walls around the system that are impermeable to matter, rigid, nonconducting to electric charge, and so on. All conserved quantities are "trapped" within an isolated system. For example, since no mass can escape, the mass of an isolated system is constant. So is its charge. The notion that a similar restriction applies to energy is central in thermodynamics.

In the rest of this chapter we shall confine our attention to systems consisting of specified matter, that is, to control masses. Energy, but *not* matter, can cross the boundary of such a system; the various mechanisms for this energy transfer are the main topic of this chapter.

2·3 ENERGY

What is energy? In Chap. One we reviewed the mechanics of a particle, and found that integration of the equations of motion leads to a term $MV^2/2g_c$, which is called the kinetic energy of the particle. This term is a function of the velocity and mass of the particle, and can be computed without knowledge of how this velocity was attained. In this sense it is something that belongs to the particle, that is, it is a *property* of the particle.† If the particle collides with another particle, the second particle can be put into motion, that is, its kinetic energy will be increased, and the laws of mechanics tell us that the kinetic energy of the first particle will decrease. It is clear that this particular type of energy, kinetic energy, is somehow associated with the motions of the particle; it is "what makes the particle go." In thermodynamics we want to generalize the concept of energy; all matter, all systems have energy, and energy plays a dominant role in the explanation of interactions between systems.

We can view each piece of matter as being composed of many fundamental particles, each whizzing about in accordance with the laws of mechanics. We know from physics that each particle can have energy in several forms, and it will be helpful to review these forms now. We shall call them "microscopic energy modes" (Fig. 2·1).

Molecules possess energy by virtue of their translation through space. This

† The concept of property will be developed more fully in the next chapters.

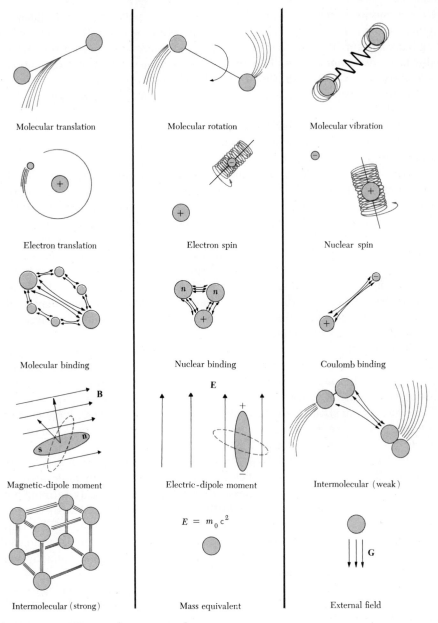

FIG. 2·1 *Microscopic energy modes*

kinetic energy is termed *translational energy*. For polyatomic molecules *rotational kinetic energy* is also important. If the atoms of the molecule are vibrating back and forth about their common center of mass we say that the molecule also has *vibrational energy*. The energy of gas molecules at low temperatures is largely associated with the translational and rotational modes, while at higher temperatures the vibrational modes begin to contribute significantly to the total energy.

Electrons whirling about their nucleus have kinetic energy, the amount of which depends on their orbit. Usually the electrons tend to be in the inner low-energy orbits; atoms with electrons in more distant orbits are said to be in *excited states* and have more energy than normal atoms of that species. It is also necessary to think of electrons as spinning and thereby possessing some *spin energy*. Many of the other fundamental particles also seem to have spin energy.

Molecules are held together by molecular binding forces, including coulomb and gravitational forces. All these forces seem to be conservative, and thus we think of potential energy in association with these intermolecular forces. Forces between the electrons and the nucleus are responsible for keeping the electrons in orbit, and there is potential energy associated with these forces. The nucleus is held together by forces much stronger than molecular binding forces, and consequently the nuclear binding energy is considerably larger than the binding energy of a molecule.

The orbiting electrons constitute tiny electric currents, producing little magnetic dipoles. In the presence of an external magnetic field these dipoles can be twisted, and there is energy associated with these dipole moments. An electrically neutral atom does not have all its charges in the same place, and consequently constitutes an electric-dipole moment, which can have energy in the presence of an external electric field. These dipole-moment energies are important in dielectrics and paramagnetic substances.

Ionized molecules and free electrons have forces exerted on them by external electric and magnetic fields, and consequently can have associated energies. All particles with mass possess potential energy in gravitational fields.

Collections of particles have additional energy associated with the forces between molecules. In liquids and solids these energies are especially important, but in low-density gases the amount of energy due to intermolecular potentials is quite small. Evaporation is a process requiring enough energy to free molecules from these strong bonds.

In relativistic mechanics it becomes necessary to include the energy equivalence of matter; we think of a particle having rest mass M_0 as possessing rest-mass energy $M_0 c^2$. This energy constitutes a large percentage of the energy of a molecule, but in nonnuclear reactions the change in rest mass is so small that changes in rest-mass energy are negligible compared to changes in the other forms of energy.

These various microscopic energy modes are not very much in evidence when we look at a piece of metal on a table, or at gas in a bottle. If we pick up the metal and hurl it away it clearly acquires kinetic energy. It is easy to measure the velocity of the metal piece, and thereby to determine the kinetic energy of the object as a whole. This is called the "bulk" kinetic energy of the piece. It is not really the kinetic energy of all the molecules, because in addition to the easily observed bulk motion the molecules are executing very small-scale motions that also contribute to their kinetic energy. There are other "bulk" energy modes that are easy to measure macroscopically. For example, the metal piece would have a potential energy in a gravitational field, and this energy could be computed from simple macroscopic data. It is usually convenient to separate the "bulk" or macroscopically measurable mechanical energy from the energy of the "hidden microscopic modes." We do this by saying that the total system energy, E, is the sum of the bulk kinetic and potential energies KE and PE, and the *internal energy*, customarily denoted by U. This split of the total energy is expressible as

$$\blacktriangleright \qquad E = KE + PE + U \qquad\qquad (2\cdot1)$$

The internal energy U therefore represents all the energy associated with the microscopic modes, that is, the energy not accounted for in the bulk mechanical energy terms. Since U cannot be measured directly, it must somehow be determined by inference. Evaluation of the internal energy U as a function of the "state" or "condition" of the system is one of the central problems in thermodynamics.

An aspect of the energy concept to which we have already alluded is that the energy of two systems taken together is the sum of their individual energies. Hence, the energy of the whole is the sum of the energy of the parts. This idea is very useful when we want to evaluate the energy of a complex system, for we can evaluate the energy of individual pieces and then add to get the total system energy. In the language of thermodynamics, this additive feature is indicated by saying that energy is *extensive*.

Let us make a remark at this point which indicates the flavor of things to come. Most matter exists in forms with the energy tied up as internal energy. The internal energy is "randomly oriented," that is, "disorganized" (this is what "hides" it from a macroscopic view), and hence is not readily useful. One job of the engineer is to devise means for converting disordered molecular motions into organized motions capable of being used macroscopically. A brief inspection now of the systems described in Chap. Nine will give a preview of some of the ways in which this "unraveling" of internal energy can be accomplished.

2·4 CONSERVATION OF ENERGY

A fundamental aspect of the energy concept is that energy is conserved, that is, the energy of an isolated system is constant. Equations stating this

FIG. 2·2   *The system includes both bodies; it is an isolated system*

"law" provide the basis for quantitative analysis of the changes that take place between interacting systems.

For example, suppose that two moving bodies hit head on, and then come to rest. One of the laws of matter, the momentum principle, says that, since the bodies come to rest, the momenta of the two bodies must have been exactly equal in magnitude and opposite in sign at the moment of collision. What happens to their energy? Two frequently heard *incorrect* statements are

1   The energy was lost.
2   The energy was dissipated into heat.

The first statement is correct only if applied to the organized mechanical energy of motion. As a result of the impact, the bulk kinetic energy of the bodies is "converted" into internal energy. The energy is no longer macroscopically evident as kinetic energy, but the increase in internal energy is clearly evidenced by increase in the temperature of each body. No energy was lost, the energy was just rearranged. The second statement could be made correct by replacing "heat" by "internal energy." As we shall shortly see, heat and internal energy are two quite different things; the energy associated with microscopic motions and forces is internal energy, not heat. The use of the term "dissipation" in the second statement suggests that energy in the form of bulk kinetic energy is somehow more desirable than internal energy. This is indeed true, for the perfect organization of bulk motion makes it fully useful (say to raise a weight), but the random, disorganized microscopic motions reflected by the internal energy make energy in this form less "available" for use in a practical macroscopic device.

The conservation of energy can be expressed algebraically for the two colliding bodies a and b; the *system* we consider consists of the two bodies together (Fig. 2·2), and we consider them over the *time period* from an instant before collision, denoted by 1, to just after collision, when both are at rest. The initial energy of the system is

$$E_1 = E_{a1} + E_{b1} = \frac{1}{2g_c} M_a V_{a1}{}^2 + \frac{1}{2g_c} M_b V_{b1}{}^2 + U_{a1} + U_{b1} \qquad (2\cdot2a)$$

The final energy of the system is

$$E_2 = U_{a2} + U_{b2} \qquad (2\cdot2b)$$

Since the two bodies form an isolated system, the energy of the system must not change, and hence

$$E_1 = E_2 \qquad (2 \cdot 3)$$

$$\underset{\substack{\text{initial} \\ \text{energy}}}{E_1} \quad \underset{\substack{\text{final} \\ \text{energy}}}{E_2}$$

Substituting Eqs. $(2 \cdot 2)$ into Eq. $(2 \cdot 3)$, we can solve for the total increase in internal energy U of the system,

$$U_2 - U_1 = (U_{a2} - U_{a1}) + (U_{b2} - U_{b1}) = \frac{1}{2g_c} (M_a V_{a1}{}^2 + M_b V_{b1}{}^2) \qquad (2 \cdot 4)$$

Knowing the masses and velocities, we could calculate $U_2 - U_1$. However, we do not have enough information to determine the increase in internal energy of each body individually.

The example above illustrates two important things. First, the notion of conservation of energy, as applied to an *isolated system*, says that the energy of the isolated system is constant. Second, the "energy balance" provides a means for determining the *change* in internal energy of a body from *macroscopic* data (in this case the mass and velocities of the bodies). Thus, the very idea that energy is conserved provides a means for inferring changes in the internal energy.

Where does the principle of conservation of energy come from? Can it be proved? These are frequent questions, the answers for which lie in the understanding of the *concept* of energy. We want to be able to predict nature, and so we conceive of energy. In a very real sense, energy is an invention of *man*, not of nature. Rather than being "that which makes things go," perhaps we should view it as something that we use to predict and explain how things go. Whenever conservation of energy is apparently violated, the physicist "discovers" a new form of energy. That is, he *defines* a new form of energy in order to keep the principle of energy conservation unviolated. The thing that makes energy "real" is that it is very useful. It is not very often that man has had to "invent" new energy forms, and hence he can proceed with his scientific and engineering analysis with considerable confidence that his "energy balances" contain the relevant energy terms. Asking for proof of the conservation-of-energy principle is like asking for proof that addition is communitive; the fact that $A + B = B + A$ is an inherent part of the concept of addition. What *is* a relevant question is, "What can I do with addition?" In thermodynamics, the relevant counterpart is "What can I do with the conservation-of-energy principle?" and the answer to this is that practically all scientific and engineering analysis involves energy considerations.

An additional idea is required to make the energy concept quantitative; we must have some *scale* of energy. This is obtained from the notion that the increase in energy of a particle is equal to the *work done* by the force acting on the particle. The work done on the particle is defined as

$$W = \int_1^2 \mathbf{F} \cdot d\mathbf{X} \qquad (2 \cdot 5)$$

where 1 and 2 represent two consecutive times. $\mathbf{F}$ is the force on the particle, taken positive in the direction of positive $\mathbf{X}$, where $\mathbf{X}$ is the particle position. We then put

$$E_2 - E_1 = W = \int_1^2 \mathbf{F} \cdot d\mathbf{X} \tag{2.6}$$

which allows us to compute the change in energy if we know $\mathbf{F}(\mathbf{X})$ (this is exactly the procedure reviewed in Sec. 1·4). The connection between the energy change of a particle and *work* is fundamental in both the Newtonian and relativistic mechanics. Work, then, provides the *fundamental measure* of energy.

To summarize, there are four ideas inherent in the concept of energy:

1   Every system has energy (E).
2   Energy is extensive ($E_{a+b} = E_a + E_b$).
3   The energy of an isolated system is constant.
4   Work provides the fundamental measure of energy.

2·5   ENERGY TRANSFER AS WORK

We come now to considering the mechanisms by which the energy of a nonisolated system can be altered. Since the system and its environment form an isolated system, if the energy of the system increases the energy of the environment must decrease a corresponding amount in order to maintain conservation of energy. We can therefore view the interaction as a process of energy transfer, and *work* is one of the mechanisms for such energy transfer.

Following the definition used in mechanics, the amount of energy transfer *to* a system as work (the "work done *on* the system") associated with some infinitesimal change in the position of matter inside is

$$\blacktriangleright \qquad dW = \mathbf{F} \cdot d\mathbf{X} = \mathsf{F}\, dX \tag{2.7a}$$

Here F is a force exerted by the environment on matter within the system, and dX is the infinitesimal motion of that matter in the direction of F which occurs during the period of observation. $\mathbf{F} \cdot d\mathbf{X}$ is the equivalent vector definition. Both F and X must be macroscopic measurables; they represent the net visible effect of billions of molecules, and not forces or motions of individual molecules.

We emphasize that dX must be motion observed with respect to a chosen coordinate frame. If the frame is attached to the matter, then there is no energy transfer as work in that particular analysis. Also, the force must be exerted by the environment on the matter within the system; forces exerted between matter in different parts of the system may cause internal rearrangements of energy, but lead to no energy transfer across the system boundary. One must therefore focus on the boundary of the system in order to identify and evaluate energy transfer as work.

If the motion extends from point 1 to point 2 in space, then the total amount of energy transfer as work is obtained by summing over all infinitesimal displacements, that is, by integrating Eq. (2·7a). If we represent the total amount of energy transfer as work by W_{12}, then we have

$$\blacktriangleright \qquad W_{12} \equiv \int_1^2 dW = \int_1^2 \mathbf{F} \cdot d\mathbf{X} \qquad\qquad (2\cdot7b)$$

There are important physical differences between the quantities standing behind the symbols d and d. The term dX may be immediately integrated, and the change in X thereby found,

$$\int_{X_1}^{X_2} dX = X_2 - X_1$$

The quantity X is something which exists at each point in space, and the symbols X_1 and X_2 have definite meaning. In contrast, the integral of dW cannot be computed unless we know how the force $\mathbf{F}$ varies with X. The value of the integral of dW between any two points X_1 and X_2 therefore depends on how the force varies with position, that is, on the particular process involved. The work at a given point has absolutely no meaning. Whereas the integral of dX represents the difference in the values of X at two points, the integral of dW depends upon the particular manner in which the system is taken from one configuration to another. The ratio dX/dt would mean the derivative of X with respect to t, or the rate of change of X. In contrast, the ratio $\dot{W} \equiv dW/dt$ would be the *amount* of work done per unit of time, or the *rate of energy transfer as work*. We have adopted this special symbology to emphasize the conceptual physical differences between things that are associated with the conditions of a system and those that are associated with the processes which the system undergoes.

2·6 EVALUATION OF ENERGY TRANSFER AS WORK

In order to carry out a successful system energy analysis one must be able to evaluate the magnitudes of energy transfers as work, that is, the work done on or by the system. Having defined the system, the next step in this evaluation is to define the direction of positive energy transfer. We shall *always* indicate our choice for positive energy transfers by showing the energy transfers on the system sketch. For example, consider the system of Fig. 2·3a. The system is defined by the dotted lines, and is the little cart. The reference coordinate system is attached to the ground, and the force $\mathbf{F}$ is exerted as a push on the back of the cart by a metal rod. Note that we have elected to consider the work done by $\mathbf{F}$ positive if it leads to an energy transfer *into* the system. (If the work was subsequently calculated to be -35 ft-lbf we would then know that the energy transfer actually took place in the direction opposite to our initial assumption.)

Let us analyze the system of Fig. 2·3a. The amount of energy transfer as

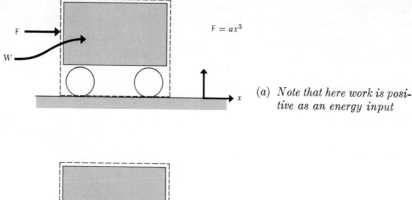

$F = ax^3$

(a) *Note that here work is positive as an energy input*

(b) *The reference frame is fixed on the ground*

FIG. 2·3

work to the cart due to its motion under the influence of **F** is, from the basic definition,

$$W_{12} = \int_1^2 \mathbf{F}\, dx = \int_1^2 ax^3\, dx = \frac{a}{4}\,(x_2{}^4 - x_1{}^4) \tag{2·8}$$

If there were no other energy transfers involved, this work would show up as an increase in the energy stored within the system. We might neglect any changes in the internal energy or in the rotational energy of the wheels, in which case the only significant energy change would be in the bulk translational kinetic energy of the cart as a whole. An energy balance on the cart could then be used to calculate the final cart velocity.

A somewhat more subtle example is provided by the system of Fig. 2·3b. Now we have added a crank to one of the wheels, and we exert a force F_c to the left on the crank handle causing the cart to move to the right. There is also a traction force F_t on the wheels; under ideal rolling conditions, the motion of the material in the wheel at the contact point is vertically up and down, and hence this matter has *no* component of motion in the direction of F_t. Consequently there is no energy transfer as work associated with the force F_t. There is some work associated with F_c, however, and a common mistake is to say that this work is $\int F_c\, dx$, where x is the position of the cart. Recalling the basic definition of work, the proper displacement is that of the matter on which the force acts, which in this case is the handle and not the cart body. If R is the length of the handle, then $R\,d\theta$ is the horizontal displacement of the handle relative to the wheel axis associated with an infinitesimal rotation $d\theta$ (when the crank shaft is in the position shown). Is the work associated with F_c equal to $\mathsf{F}_cR\,d\theta$? No, not for the system as defined, for the displacement $R\,d\theta$ is relative to a reference frame on the cart, while we chose a frame on the ground! The displacement relative to the ground frame is $r\,d\theta - R\,d\theta$, where r is the wheel radius. But this is a displacement to the *right*, while the force F_c acts to the *left*. Hence, the amount of energy transfer as work to the system as defined, relative to the indicated reference frame, is

$$dW = -\mathsf{F}_c(r - R)\,d\theta = \mathsf{F}_c(R - r)\,d\theta \qquad (2\cdot 9a)$$

This example illustrates the need for very careful consideration of just what the system is *before* one begins to evaluate work.

Suppose in the example of Fig. $2\cdot 3b$ we instead choose a reference frame attached to the cart. In this frame the displacement of the handle in the direction of F_c *is* $R\,d\theta$, and hence the amount of energy transfer as work in this frame is

$$dW' = \mathsf{F}_cR\,d\theta \qquad (2\cdot 9b)$$

The product F_cR is defined as the *torque* T on the wheel shaft, and hence dW' could be written as†

$$dW' = T\,d\theta \qquad (2\cdot 9c)$$

Equation $(2\cdot 9c)$ is a special case of the general expression for the work done on a system by a torque. If $\mathbf{T}$ is the torque vector, and $d\boldsymbol{\theta}$ is the vector angular displacement of the matter within the system on which the torque acts, then the amount of energy transfer as work *to* the system relative to a frame attached to the torque axis, is

$$\blacktriangleright \qquad dW = \mathbf{T} \cdot d\boldsymbol{\theta} \qquad (2\cdot 10)$$

Since mechanical systems frequently involve rotating shafts, the expression is rather important.

The forces of Fig. $2\cdot 3$ are examples of *surface forces*. They are exerted on the matter at the surface of the system and the appropriate displacement is the displacement of the matter at the surface. Another type of force is a *body force*, which acts on the material in the system interior. For such forces the appropriate displacement must be that of the matter on which the body force acts. This may or may not be the same as the displacement of a system boundary. For example, consider the system of Fig. $2\cdot 4a$. The system does not include the electric field. The system boundaries are held stationary, but the charged plate within the system moves when the electric field strength is increased. If the charge on the plate is Q, and the electric field strength is $\mathbf{E}$, the force

† Note that the cart would not have any kinetic energy in this reference frame (see Prob. $1\cdot 6$).

FIG. 2·4

(a) *The system includes the material but not the electric field*

(b) *Note that the work terms depend on the system definition*

on the plate is $\mathbf{F} = Q\mathbf{E}$ to the right. The amount of energy transfer as work to the system associated with motion of the plate an infinitesimal amount $d\mathbf{x}$ to the right is then

$$dW = Q(\mathbf{E} \cdot d\mathbf{x}) \qquad\qquad (2\cdot11a)$$

Integrating between two positions x_1 and x_2, the total energy transfer as work for the process 1-2 is

$$W_{12} = \int_1^2 Q\mathbf{E} \cdot d\mathbf{x} \qquad\qquad (2\cdot11b)$$

To complete the integration we would have to know $\mathbf{E}(\mathbf{x})$ during the process. The energy transferred into the system as work would result in an increase in the system energy, and an energy balance would be the central tool for analysis of this system.

In the example of Fig. 2·4a the system was defined to include the plate, the sponge, and the gas, but to exclude the electric field. The energy transfer as work between the plate and the gas was internal to the system, and hence would not appear as an energy transfer term in the energy balance. However, if the system is instead defined as in Fig. 2·4b the energy transfer as work from the gas to the plate must be considered. The energy transfer as work from the environment (that is, the electric field, which is external to the system) is again given by Eqs. (2·11). If the pressure exerted by the gas on the plate is P, and the plate area is A, the force on the plate is PA, and the amount of energy transfer as work at the left-hand boundary of the system is

$$dW' = PA \, dx \qquad\qquad (2\cdot12a)$$

Integrating, the total amount of energy transfer as work from the gas to the plate is

$$W'_{12} = \int_1^2 PA \, dx \qquad\qquad (2\cdot12b)$$

We would have to know how the gas pressure varied with x in order to complete the integration. This example illustrates that the work terms included in an energy analysis depend very much on the choice of the system. A clear system definition is therefore essential to a clear analysis.

Let us think about the microscopic aspects of the work terms discussed above. As the molecules in the metal rod that pushes the cart of Fig. 2·3 move to the right, strong repulsive forces are developed between them and the molecules at the surface of the cart. As a result, the cart molecules are made to move, and the work expression Eq. (2·8) represents the net effect of these billions of individual molecular interactions. The charged particles in the plate of Fig. 2·4a are each acted on by the electric field, and as they move, each receives energy from the electric field. The total energy transfer as work to all the charged particles is what Eq. (2·11) represents. The molecules in the gas in Fig. 2·4 are flying about, and occasionally collide with the plate. When they do they exert forces on the molecules in the plate, and if they move the plate there is a transfer of energy from the gas molecules to the plate molecules. This is the energy transfer as work which we evaluated in Eqs. (2·12).

Correct evaluation of the energy transfer as work is a necessary part in any thermodynamic analysis. The steps in this evaluation are summarized below.

1 Define the system and reference frame.
2 Define the forces acting on the system and the motions of the material on which these forces act.
3 Define the sign of positive energy transfer for each different "work mode" by an arrow on the system sketch.
4 Apply the basic definition of work [Eq. (2·7)] consistently with the above definitions over the time period under examination.
5 Bring in the additional information needed to complete the integrations.

One must be particularly consistent in evaluating work done by a conservative force field in order to avoid "double accounting" in the subsequent energy balance. The potential-energy change is by definition the work done by the conservative force, and hence both the potential energy and the work done by the conservative force must never appear in the same energy analysis. Two alternative approaches are demonstrated in Fig. 2·5. In Fig. 2·5a we account for the work done by the rope force F_H and the body force w, but do not include a potential-energy term in the system energy. In Fig. 2·5b we instead use the potential energy, and include only the work done by the rope force. The net energy input as work, dW, is equal to the increase in energy, dE, in either case.†

† Another approach is to assign the potential energy to the "field." If the field is part of the system, Fig. 2·5b is appropriate. If the system is defined to exclude the field, Fig. 2·5a is proper.

$$d W = F_H \, dX - w \, dX$$
$$dE = d\left(\frac{m\mathsf{V}^2}{2g_c}\right)$$

$$d W = F_H \, dX$$
$$dE = d\left(\frac{m\mathsf{V}^2}{2g_c} + wX\right)$$

(a) *Without potential-energy concept (the system excludes the gravitational field)*

(b) *With potential-energy concept (the system includes the gravitational field)*

FIG. 2·5   *One must be consistent when making an energy analysis where a conservative force is involved. Note $dW = dE$ in either case*

2·7 SOME PARTICULAR WORK MODES

There are a number of work modes that occur frequently in thermodynamic analysis, and they deserve special mention here.

Expansion or compression of a fluid. A great many thermodynamic systems involve fluids (that is, a liquid or a gas), and hence the work associated with expansion or compression of a fluid is very important. The piston-cylinder system of Fig. 2·6a provides an easy way to visualize and compute the amount of energy transfer as work associated with a change in the fluid volume. Denoting the fluid pressure by P, and the piston area by A, the force on the piston is PA, and the amount of energy transfer as work *from* the fluid *to* the piston (see the sign convention of the sketch!) is, for an elemental expansion dx,

$$d W = PA \, dx$$

But since $A \, dx = dV$ is the increase in fluid volume, the amount of energy transfer as work from the fluid may be written as

▶ $d W = P \, dV$ (2·13a)

By considering a fluid volume of *arbitrary* shape it may easily be shown that

FIG. 2·6

(a) *The fluid is expanding*   (b) *The fluid is being compressed* this same expression applies for the energy transfer as work *from* the fluid *to* its environment, and hence Eq. (2·13a) has considerable utility in thermodynamic analysis.

Suppose we consider the compression of a fluid. Now it is easier to consider the work positive if energy is transferred *to* the fluid (Fig. 2·6b). The force which the piston exerts on the fluid at the system boundaries is PA and displacement of the fluid at the piston surface is dx'. Hence, the amount of energy transfer as work *from* the piston *to* the fluid is

$$dW' = PA \, dx'$$

We can again relate this work to the change in fluid volume. Denoting the *increase* in fluid volume by dV (in the conventions of calculus dx always represents an increase in x), we write $dV = -A \, dx'$ (dx' is positive, so dV will be negative). Hence,

$$dW' = -P \, dV \qquad\qquad (2\cdot13b)$$

is the amount of work done *by* the piston *on* the fluid. Comparing the energy-transfer sign conventions of Figs. 2·6a and 2·6b, we see that $dW' = -dW$. Hence Eqs. (2·13a) and (2·13b) are consistent. This will always be the case; for a particular choice of the direction of positive energy transfer as work, the expression for the work will be independent of whether the energy is actually added or removed (dx will be positive in one case and negative in the other).

Extension of a solid. We consider extension of a solid rod as shown in Fig. 2·7. Denoting the normal stress in the x direction by σ_x, the "pulling" force exerted by the holder on the solid is $\sigma_x A$. The amount of energy transfer as work *from* the holder *to* the solid when the solid is stretched is†

$$dW = \sigma_x A \, dx$$

Now, the *strain* ϵ_x in the x direction is defined as the deformation per unit length, so

$$d\epsilon_x = \frac{dx}{L} = \frac{A \, dx}{V}$$

† Note if we replace σ_x by $-P$ (P is a "push," σ_x is a "pull"), and take proper account of the differing directions of positive energy transfer in this and the fluid expansion case, equivalent results are obtained.

FIG. 2·7   *Stretching a thin rod requires work*

and hence the amount of energy transfer as work *to* the solid can be written as†

$$\blacktriangleright \qquad dW = V\sigma_x \, d\epsilon_x \qquad (2\cdot14)$$

In the microscopic view we see individual molecules of the holder pulling on molecules of the solid, thereby straining the crystal bonds in the solid structure. The net macroscopic effect of these microscopic interactions is represented by Eq. $(2\cdot14)$.

Stretching of a liquid surface. Consider a liquid sheet suspended between two plates, as shown in Fig. $2\cdot8$. The molecules near the liquid surface are

FIG. 2·8 *The liquid extends a large distance b into the paper*

attracted more strongly by internal liquid molecules than by the very distant gas molecules, and this gives rise to a macroscopically measurable force in the liquid-gas surface. The *interfacial tension*, σ, is defined as the force *per unit of length* acting normal to a line in the surface. The total interfacial tension force exerted on each plate is therefore $2\sigma b$, where b is the depth of the liquid sheet normal to the plane of the paper. The energy transfer as work *from* the plates *to* the liquid when the plate separation is increased an amount dx is

$$dW = 4\sigma b \frac{dx}{2} = 2\sigma b \, dx$$

Now, the change in surface area is simply $dA = 2b \, dx$, and hence the energy transfer as work *to* the liquid can be written as

$$\blacktriangleright \qquad dW = \sigma \, dA \qquad (2\cdot15)$$

In the microscopic view, work is required to pull individual molecules into the new surface, and Eq. $(2\cdot15)$ represents the macroscopic evaluation of this microscopic effect.

Work due to magnetization and polarization. Microscopic electric dipoles within dielectrics resist turning, and work is therefore done on such substances

---

† Here we considered only one-dimensional deformation. It may be shown that the amount of energy transfer as work per unit volume *to* a solid undergoing arbitrary three-dimensional deformation is

$$dW = \sum_{i=1}^{3} \sum_{j=1}^{3} \sigma_{ij} \, d\epsilon_{ij}$$

where σ_{ij} and ϵ_{ij} are the stress and deformation tensors.

when they are polarized. For a system through which the electric and polarization fields are uniform, it may be shown that the energy transfer as work to the dielectric material† from the electric field when the polarization is infinitesimally increased is

▶ $\qquad dW = \mathbf{E} \cdot d(V\mathbf{P})$ $\qquad\qquad\qquad\qquad\qquad\qquad$ (2·16)

Here $\mathbf{E}$ represents the strength of the electric field within the dielectric, $\mathbf{P}$ the polarization field (electric-dipole moment per unit of volume), and V the system volume.

Similarly, work can be done on magnetic materials when the magnetization is changed, for the microscopic magnetic-dipole moments resist turning. For a system through which the magnetic and magnetization fields are uniform, it may be shown that the energy transfer as work to the material† from the magnetic field when the magnetization is increased an infinitesimal amount is

▶ $\qquad dW = \mu_0\mathbf{H} \cdot d(V\mathbf{M})$ $\qquad\qquad\qquad\qquad\qquad\qquad$ (2·17)

Here $\mathbf{H}$ is the strength of the applied magnetic field, $\mathbf{M}$ is the magnetization vector (magnetic-dipole moment per unit of volume), and μ_0 is a constant (the "permeability" of free-space). Unlike work due to compression or extension, polarization and magnetization do not result in macroscopic motions. However, they do result in alignment of the particles, and this ordered alignment is macroscopically detectable as an increase in the total dipole moment.

TABLE 2·1 SOME PARTICULAR WORK MODES

Mode	dW, energy transfer to substance as work	Restrictions
Fluid compression	$-P\,dV$	P uniform over volume
Solid extension	$V\sigma_x\,d\epsilon_x$	One-dimensional strain only
Liquid surface extension	$\sigma\,dA$	σ uniform over area
Polarization	$\mathbf{E} \cdot d(V\mathbf{P})$	$\mathbf{P}$ and $\mathbf{E}$ uniform through volume
Magnetization	$\mu_0\mathbf{H} \cdot d(V\mathbf{M})$	$\mathbf{H}$ and $\mathbf{M}$ uniform through volume

The expressions for work in the particular cases discussed here are all of the form

$\qquad dW = \mathsf{F}\,dX$

For example, for liquid extension $\mathsf{F} = \sigma$ and $X = A$. They may be scalars (P and V), vectors ($\mathbf{E}$ and $\mathbf{P}$), or tensors (σ_{ij} and ϵ_{ij}). F and dX do not necessarily

† The electric and magnetic fields are excluded from the systems. These expressions are for the rationalized mksc unit system. See, for example, David Halliday and Robert Resnick, *Physics*, combined ed., secs. 27-26 and 33-34, John Wiley & Sons, Inc., New York, 1962.

have the dimensions of force and displacement, but they are frequently called the "generalized force" and "generalized displacement," respectively. These F's and X's are very important in the general thermodynamic theory of materials. The amounts of energy transfer as work for these several modes are summarized in Table 2·1.

2·8 WORK FOR PARTICULAR PROCESSES

The amount of energy transfer as work for a given process can be computed if the variation of F with X during the process is known. For example, consider a system consisting of mass M of a certain gas, which we compress from some state 1 to another state 2. The work done *on* the gas is determined by integrating Eq. (2·13b), and is

$$W_{12} = -\int_1^2 MP\, dv$$

where v is the volume per unit of mass, that is, the *specific volume,*

$$v \equiv V/M$$

We must know how P varies with v during the process in order to complete the integration; Fig. 2·9 demonstrates two different cases.

For example, suppose we idealize that the pressure exerted by the gas is related to the specific volume and temperature by†

$$Pv = RT$$

where R is a constant for the gas. The energy transfer as work to the gas is then

$$W_{12} = -M\int_{v_1}^{v_2} \frac{RT}{v}\, dv$$

† This is valid for an "ideal," or "perfect," gas. The concept of temperature will be developed in the next chapter.

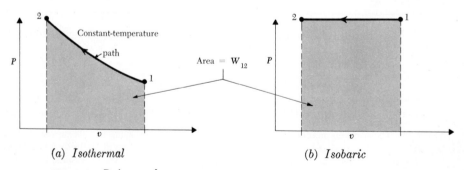

(a) *Isothermal*   (b) *Isobaric*

FIG. 2·9 *Doing work on a gas*

We would have to know how the temperature varies with the specific volume during this process in order to perform the integration. In particular, for an *isothermal* (constant-temperature) *process*

$$W_{12} = - MRT \ln \frac{v_2}{v_1}$$

Another case of interest is the *isobaric* (constant-pressure) *process*, where the energy transfer as work to a unit of mass of the gas is

$$W_{12} = \int_1^2 -P \, dv = P(v_1 - v_2)$$

As a second example, consider the amount of energy transfer as work to a paramagnetic Curie salt,† for which the magnetic field strength and magnetization are related to the temperature by

$$\mathsf{M} = \frac{C\mathsf{H}}{T}$$

Here C is the "Curie constant" of the salt. From Eq. $(2 \cdot 17)$,

$$W_{12} = \int_{\mathsf{M}_1}^{\mathsf{M}_2} \frac{\mu_0 V T}{C} \mathsf{M} \, d\mathsf{M}$$

The manner in which the temperature varies during this process would be an important factor in determining the amount of work done for a given increase in magnetization (see Fig. $2 \cdot 10$). In particular, for an *isothermal* magnetization process

$$W_{12} = \frac{\mu_0 V T}{2C} (\mathsf{M}_2{}^2 - \mathsf{M}_1{}^2)$$

† We assume constant volume.

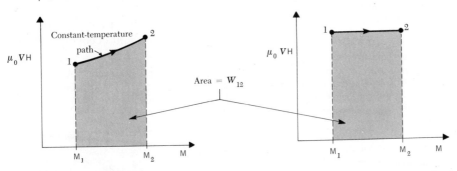

(a) *Isothermal* (b) *Constant external field*

FIG. 2·10 *Doing work on a magnetic substance*

Alternatively, if the substance were magnetized in a constant external field (H constant), the amount of energy transfer to the material as work would be

$$W_{12} = \mu_0 V H(M_2 - M_1)$$

In these examples simple algebraic expressions could be found. In many cases of interest it will be necessary to integrate numerically or graphically to obtain the amount of energy transfer as work for a given process.

2·9 ENERGY TRANSFER AS HEAT

We have discussed several means by which macroscopic work can be done on a system, causing its energy to change. However, it is possible to transfer energy to a system in ways which are not observable as macroscopic work. Consider the system shown in Fig. 2·11. We might picture the atoms in the walls surrounding the system as little vibrating masses. Some will be heading toward the boundary when some are heading away, and as a result, there might be no observable motion. However, the interaction of these atoms with the molecules in the system can result in changes of the energy of individual particles and hence a change in the internal energy of the system. The macroscopically observable work is zero, so we must find some other way to account for the energy change. This second mechanism of energy transfer depicted in Fig. 2·11 is called *energy transfer as heat. Heat* is energy transfer as work on the microscopic scale which fails to be accounted for by macroscopic evaluations of work. In the microscopic view there is no such thing as heat; heat is required in the macroscopic view as a means for accounting for microscopically disorganized energy transfer which, through its disorganization, is "hidden" from direct macroscopic view. Heat is a central *concept* in thermodynamics.

Heat, like work, is energy in the process of being transferred. Heat and work are not "stored" within matter; they are "done on" or "done by" matter. Energy is what is stored, and work and heat are two ways of transferring energy across the boundaries of a system. Once energy has gotten into the system it is impossible to tell whether the energy was transferred in as heat or as work. The term "heat of a substance"† is thus as meaningless as "work of a substance."

The symbol Q is usually employed to represent an amount of energy transfer

† The literature contains some remnants of the caloric theory of heat, in which heat was pictured as a conserved substance. In present thermodynamic theory heat is not conserved and is not a property of matter. Still, some handbooks tabulate "heats of the liquid," "sensible heats," and "latent heats." These terms will be related to modern terminology in subsequent chapters.

FIG. 2·11 *Energy transfer not observable as macroscopic work is called energy transfer as heat.*

as heat; dQ therefore represents an infinitesimal amount of energy transfer as heat. As with work, we shall always indicate the direction of positive energy transfer as heat by an arrow on the system sketch. The value of Q depends on the details of the process, and not on the end conditions of the system. For example, consider the system in Fig. $2 \cdot 12$. The fluid temperature can be changed by transferring energy in as work through the stirrer, or as heat via the flame. In the first case $Q = 0$, and in the second case $Q > 0$. The initial and final system states, and the change in the system internal energy, could be the same in both cases.†

† It is very important to distinguish clearly between the concepts of internal energy and heat, and an account of the experiences of Professor J. Yule will assist in this regard. Professor J. Yule was experimenting with the apparatus of Fig. $2 \cdot 12$, which involved a fluid in a container with a mechanical stirrer. On one Friday afternoon in December, 1843, Professor Yule left the device in his laboratory under the care of his assistant, Dr. B. T. Ewe, who was known for his clever practical jokes. At that time the fluid temperature was 25°C. Upon return to the laboratory the following Monday, Professor Yule found that the fluid temperature was 40°C, indicating a greater internal energy. His student, Cal Orick, immediately presumed that Ewe had heated the device with the bunsen flame during the chilly weekend. "It *must* be so," said Orick, "for see, the temperature has clearly risen!" But Yule, being a properly cautious scientist, was not so sure. He had previously discovered that it was possible to increase the fluid temperature (and the internal energy) by driving the stirrer, a process that clearly fits in the category of *work*. Even after much argument Yule could not convince Orick that they just could not tell whether the clever Ewe had added the extra energy to the fluid as work using the stirrer or as heat using the bunsen flame. Ewe finally confessed to a very neat trick: he had first taken energy *out* of the fluid as heat by placing the device on a block of ice, and then had raised the temperature using the stirrer. Hence, in the actual process carried out by Ewe, there had been a *removal* of energy as heat and an *addition* of energy as work! The *net* effect of this *cooling-work* process had been an *increase* in the *internal energy* (and temperature) of the fluid! After this experience Cal Orick went mad, Professor J. Yule became a fellow of the Royal Society, and Dr. B. T. Ewe became a laboratory instructor at an obscure western university.

Fluid

FIG. 2·12 *The addition of energy either as heat or as work will increase the fluid temperature*

In the next chapter we shall carefully treat a concept closely related to energy transfer as heat, namely *temperature*. We mention it now in the hope of preventing any confusion between the concepts of heat, temperature, and internal energy. If two bodies are brought into contact, and any energy transfer as heat takes place between them, we say that the energy passed from the body at the higher temperature to the one at the lower temperature. The words "hot" and "cold" describe the relative temperatures of the two bodies, respectively. Temperature can be viewed as a driving potential for energy transfer as heat.

If we wish to isolate a system we must prevent all flows of energy to or from the system. A rigid wall will prevent any $P\,dV$ work; a wall impermeable to electric fields will prevent any polarization work. In order to prevent any energy transfer as heat we conceive of an *adiabatic wall*, which cannot transmit any energy as heat. The adiabatic wall is a useful fiction (like the rigid wall). The hollow space in a vacuum flask forms adequate approximation to an adiabatic wall for many laboratory experiments. The term "adiabatic process" is used to denote any process in which no energy transfer as heat occurs across the boundaries of the system under study. The concepts of an adiabatic wall and an adiabatic process are very important in thermodynamics.

2·10 THE FIRST LAW FOR A CONTROL MASS

We are now able to express the conservation of energy notion analytically for an important special kind of system, a control mass. A *control mass* is a system of specified matter; its mass is therefore fixed. As our previous discussion indicates, we can change the energy of a control mass by transfer of energy either as heat or as work, and *these are the only ways*. The control mass and its environment together form an isolated system; their total energy must remain constant. If the energy of one increases, the energy of the other must decrease by precisely the same amount. Work and heat are the sole mechanisms by which such energy transfers take place.

The total energy input to the control mass must account precisely for the increase in the control mass energy; the algebraic statement of this accounting is called the *energy balance*. In terms of the system and symbols of Fig. 2·13,

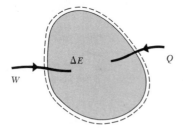

FIG. 2·13 *Show the boundaries and all energy flows on the control-mass diagram. Note the definitions of the directions of positive energy transfer*

the energy balance is

▶ $$W + Q = \underset{\substack{\text{energy} \\ \text{input}}}{\quad} \underset{\substack{\text{increase in} \\ \text{energy storage}}}{\Delta E} \qquad\qquad (2\cdot18a)$$

Here W and Q represent the amounts of energy transfer *to* the control mass as work and heat, respectively, and ΔE is the *increase* in the energy of the control mass,

▶ $$\Delta E \equiv E_{\text{final}} - E_{\text{initial}}$$

(The symbol Δ will *always* be used to mean "final-minus-initial," that is, "the increase in . . . .") Alternatively, we could analyze the control mass over an infinitesimal part of the process, in which case the energy balance would be

▶ $$dW + dQ = \underset{\substack{\text{energy} \\ \text{input}}}{\quad} \underset{\substack{\text{increase in} \\ \text{energy storage}}}{dE} \qquad\qquad (2\cdot18b)$$

Here dW and dQ represent infinitesimal amounts of energy transfer to the control mass, and dE represents the infinitesimal increase in the control-mass energy. (The symbol d always means "an infinitesimal increase in . . ."; the symbol d means "an infinitesimal amount of . . . .")

The first basic principle of thermodynamics is that matter has energy, and energy is conserved; we call this idea the *first law of thermodynamics.* Equations (2·18) are particular forms of the first law of thermodynamics and apply only to a collection of given particles; later we shall extend the mathematical representations of the first law to a wider class of systems. The analysis of a thermodynamic system invariably begins with energy-balance considerations, which are called *first-law analyses;* some simple examples of such analyses follow.

2·11 EXAMPLES OF CONTROL-MASS ENERGY BALANCES

The primary aim of this chapter is the development of the concepts of energy, internal energy, work, and heat. We need more tools before we can begin to do much productive thermodynamic analysis, but some examples at this stage should assist in clarifying the basic ideas. The examples that follow are intended to point up some important ideas from the preceding discussions and to indicate a general approach to analysis of thermodynamic systems. A more complete energy-balance methodology will be given in Chap. Five.

Gas compression. Two lbm of a gas is squeezed in a device from a volume of 14 ft³ to a volume of 9 ft³. During this time the pressure remains constant at 2000 lbf/ft², and it is known from other considerations that the internal energy decreases by 6000 ft-lbf. How much energy was transferred as heat to or from the gas for this process?

We first define the control mass to include only the gas. It is clear from the problem statement that energy will be put into the system as work, and so we

FIG. 2·14 *The control mass and energy flows*

choose the sign of positive work as indicated in Fig. 2·14. It may not be immediately clear which way the energy transfer as heat takes place; let's define Q to be positive as an energy input, and we indicate this on Fig. 2·14. We also assume that the only system energy is its internal energy U. In terms of the system and symbols of Fig. 2·14, the energy balance is then

$$\underset{\substack{\text{energy}\\\text{input}}}{W + Q} = \underset{\substack{\text{increase in}\\\text{energy storage}}}{\Delta U} \tag{2·19}$$

where $\Delta U = U_2 - U_1$ and the subscripts 1 and 2 denote the initial and final states. We know the internal energy change, and can compute Q from the energy balance if we can evaluate W. We have already derived an expression for the work done *on* a gas during compression, namely

$$W = -\int_1^2 P \, dV$$

Since the pressure P is constant, we integrate and have

$$W = P(V_1 - V_2) = 2000 \text{ lbf/ft}^2 \times (14 - 9) \text{ ft}^3 = 10,000 \text{ ft-lbf}$$

Solving Eq. (2·19) for Q,

$$Q = \Delta U - W = -6000 - 10,000 = -16,000 \text{ ft-lbf}$$

The minus number means that we guessed the actual direction of energy transfer as heat incorrectly. The answer is that 16,000 ft-lbf of energy was transferred as heat *from* the gas.

If we had correctly guessed the actual direction of energy transfer as heat, and pointed the Q arrow the other way on Fig. 2·14, the energy balance would read

$$\underset{\substack{\text{energy}\\\text{input}}}{W} = \underset{\substack{\text{energy}\\\text{output}}}{Q} + \underset{\substack{\text{increase in}\\\text{energy storage}}}{\Delta U}$$

and the calculation would lead to

$$Q = W - \Delta U = 16,000 \text{ ft-lbf}$$

Note that the correct problem solution can be obtained with either analysis; the main requirement is self-consistency.

A pneumatic catapult. A light airplane catapult uses high-pressure steam to launch aircraft with the system shown schematically in Fig. 2·15. Initially

FIG. 2·15   *The control mass includes the steam and all moving mechanical parts. We neglect interaction with the air*

the cylinder volume is 10 ft³, and finally it is 35 ft³. The launch velocity is 200 ft/sec, and the combined mass of the piston, linkage, and aircraft is 6000 lbm. The process occurs very rapidly, so there is not much time for energy transfer as heat between the steam and the cylinder walls and hence $Q = 0$ is a good idealization. We wish to determine the change in internal energy of the steam for this process.

We take the control mass shown in Fig. 2·15. It includes the steam, the launch gear, and the aircraft, and we consider it over the launch period. To simplify the analysis we shall neglect the interaction with the air during the launch, and we shall neglect friction. These idealizations permit us to treat the control mass as an isolated system. There is no transfer of either energy or matter across its boundaries. The energy balance is therefore simply

$$\Delta E = 0 \qquad\qquad (2·20)$$
increase in
energy storage

Now, the energy consists of the internal energy U_s of the steam, the internal energy of the mechanical parts, and bulk kinetic energy KE. We assume that the internal energy of the metal does not change during the process, and that the bulk kinetic energy of the steam is negligible. Then, denoting the initial and final conditions by subscripts 1 and 2, respectively, the energy change ΔE is

$$\Delta E = \Delta U_s + \Delta KE_m$$

The increase in the kinetic energy of the mechanical parts

$$\Delta KE_m = \Delta \left(\frac{1}{2} \frac{M}{g_c} \mathsf{V}^2 \right) = \frac{1}{2} \frac{M}{g_c} (\mathsf{V}_2{}^2 - \mathsf{V}_1{}^2)$$

$$= \frac{6000 \text{ lbm}}{2 \times 32.2 \text{ ft-lbm/lbf-sec}^2} [(200)^2 - 0] \text{ ft}^2/\text{sec}^2$$

$$= 3.74 \times 10^6 \text{ ft-lbf}$$

The energy balance, Eq. (2·20), then says

$$\Delta U_s = -\Delta KE_m = -3.74 \times 10^6 \text{ ft-lbf}$$

Hence, the internal energy of the steam *decreases* by 3.74×10^6 ft-lbf during

(a) *The control mass is just*   (b) *The control mass is just the*
the gas   *moving mechanical parts*

FIG. 2·16

the launch. The catapult extracts some of the disorganized molecular kinetic energy and transforms it into organized kinetic energy of the aircraft.

Suppose we wished to calculate the work done by the steam on the piston. We could analyze either of the control masses of Fig. 2·16. If we take the steam as the system, the energy balance is

$$\underset{\substack{\text{energy} \\ \text{input}}}{0} = \underset{\substack{\text{energy} \\ \text{output}}}{W} + \underset{\substack{\text{increase in} \\ \text{energy storage}}}{\Delta U_s}$$

or

$$W = 3.74 \times 10^6 \text{ ft-lbf}$$

If instead we take the launch gear and aircraft as the system, the energy balance is

$$\underset{\substack{\text{energy} \\ \text{input}}}{W} = \underset{\substack{\text{increase in} \\ \text{energy storage}}}{\Delta KE_m} = 3.74 \times 10^6 \text{ ft-lbf}$$

Neglect of interaction with the air in the analysis above may introduce significant error if the steam pressure is not well above atmospheric pressure. The next approximation should include work done by the system in pushing air out of the way as the control mass expands. Calculation of this work would require more detailed knowledge of the geometry of the cylinder system. We see that the analyst must sometimes consider more than one system to complete his calculation. There are often several ways to do the analysis, and all correct ways will give the same answer. It might be noted that the work could not be computed as $\int P \, dV$ because we don't know enough about the steam pressure during the expansion.

The energetics of a dielectric medium. Consider a dielectric in which the dipole moment per unit volume **P** is related to the applied electric field **E** by

$$\mathbf{P} = \epsilon_0(\kappa - 1)\mathbf{E} \tag{2·21}$$

where κ is the "dielectric constant." Derive an expression for the work done by the electric field when the electric field is changed from $\mathbf{E}_1$ to $\mathbf{E}_2$.

The control mass consists of the dielectric, but does not include the external

FIG. 2·17 *The system includes the dielectric but not the electric field*

electric field which occupies the same space. The amount of energy transfer as work from the electric field to the dielectric material is [Eq. (2·16)]

$$W = \int_1^2 \mathbf{E}V \cdot d\mathbf{P} \tag{2·22}$$

where V is the system volume. Using Eq. (2·21),

$$W = \epsilon_0 V(\kappa - 1) \int_1^2 \mathbf{E} \cdot d\mathbf{E} = \tfrac{1}{2}\epsilon_0 V(\kappa - 1)(\mathsf{E}_2{}^2 - \mathsf{E}_1{}^2) \tag{2·23}$$

Now, the energy balance on the control mass is (Fig. 2·17)

$$\underset{\substack{\text{energy} \\ \text{input}}}{Q + W} = \underset{\substack{\text{increase in} \\ \text{energy storage}}}{\Delta U} \tag{2·24}$$

where U is the internal energy of the dielectric. Combining Eqs. (2·23) and (2·24),

$$\Delta U = Q + \tfrac{1}{2}\epsilon_0 V(\kappa - 1)(\mathsf{E}_2{}^2 - \mathsf{E}_1{}^2) \tag{2·25}$$

In particular, for the special case of $Q = 0$, which is called an *adiabatic process*, the increase in the energy of the dielectric is equal to the work done by the electric field, which may be represented as the change in the quantity $\tfrac{1}{2}\epsilon_0 V(\kappa - 1)\mathbf{E}^2$. It is sometimes stated in books on electrostatics that this quantity is the energy of the dielectric. We see that this is the case only if it is assumed that the dielectric always undergoes adiabatic polarization. This is normally an excellent assumption in electronic circuits where the frequencies of polarization are so rapid that there is no time for any significant amount of energy transfer as heat to take place.

A complex power system. A nuclear power station consists of the hardware shown in Fig. 2·18. In the primary circulation loop, liquid NaK (sodium-potassium eutectic) is circulated by a pump through the reactor, which provides the energy source, and then through a boiler in which water flowing in the secondary loop becomes steam. This steam is fed to a turbine, which drives the electrical power generation equipment. In order to close the secondary loop, the steam is condensed and then pumped up to a high pressure. This complicated system is the sort that we shall be able to analyze in detail before very long; a simple analysis of certain aspects is possible now with only the tools at hand.

Suppose the desired turbine shaft power output is 100 Mw, and it is expected

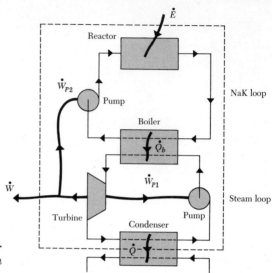

FIG. 2·18 *A nuclear power generation system*

that a system having an energy-conversion efficiency of 33 percent can be built. The energy-conversion efficiency η is the ratio of the power output $\dot{W}$ to the reactor power input $\dot{E}$. A simple energy balance will permit us to determine the required reactor power and the rate at which energy is discarded to the atmosphere via the condenser.

From the definition of the efficiency,

$$\eta = \dot{W}/\dot{E}$$

so

$$\dot{E} = \frac{\dot{W}}{\eta} = \frac{100 \text{ Mw}}{0.33} = 300 \text{ Mw}$$

Now, consider an energy balance on the control mass shown. It includes all the complicated hardware, but does not include the fissionable material. The rate of energy transfer to the control mass from the fission system is $\dot{E}$. The rate of energy transfer from the control mass as heat is $\dot{Q}$, and the rate of energy transfer from the control mass as work is $\dot{W}$. We assume that the system is operating steadily, and consequently as time passes there is no change in the energy stored inside the control mass. The energy balance, made over any time period t, therefore gives

$$\underset{\substack{\text{energy} \\ \text{input}}}{\dot{E}t} = \underset{\substack{\text{energy} \\ \text{output}}}{\dot{W}t + \dot{Q}t}$$

Hence,

$$\dot{Q} = \dot{E} - \dot{W} = 300 - 100 = 200 \text{ Mw}$$

This large energy-rejection rate may seem outlandish; we discard more energy than we use. Yet the efficiency of 33 percent is typical of modern power stations. We shall see why these efficiencies are so low later in our study.

2·12 ENERGY EQUIVALENTS

Magnitudes of energy can be assigned in many ways. Fundamentally the dimensions of energy are force times distance. For example, in the engineering system of units ft-lbf is the basic energy unit. Note that kg-m is not an energy unit, since the kilogram is a unit of mass rather than force. The unit of energy in the rationalized mksc system is the kg-m^2/sec^2, or joule (see Table A·1).

Two important remnants of the caloric theory of heat are the Btu (British thermal unit) and the calorie. At one time these were defined in terms of the amount of energy transfer as heat required to raise a unit of mass of water 1 F° and 1 C°, respectively. Today they are related by definition to the mechanical units as shown below:

1 Btu ≡ 778.16 ft-lbf   Approximately the amount of energy transfer as heat required to increase the temperature of 1 lbm of water 1 F° at "room" conditions.

1 kcal ≡ 4186.05 kg-m^2/sec^2 Approximately the amount of energy
= 1000 cal   transfer as heat required to increase the temperature of 1 kg of water 1 C° at "room" conditions.

An important energy unit in physics is the *electron volt*. This is the amount of energy required to move an electron against a 1-volt potential, and is defined as

1 ev ≡ 1.602 × 10^{-19} joule

In high-energy physics the kev, mev, bev, and gev, respectively 10^3, 10^6, 10^9, 10^{12} ev, are often employed.

The engineer frequently talks in terms of *power*, the rate of energy transfer or expenditure. The watt is an alias for 1 joule/sec (see Table A·1). The horsepower had historic roots not unlike those of the Btu, but today by definition

1 hp ≡ 550 ft-lbf/sec

A compilation of some important conversion factors, including energy and power, is contained in Appendix A.

2·13 SUMMARY OF SOME IMPORTANT TERMS

A number of concepts and definitions have been introduced in this chapter; the key ideas are summarized below.

System   Whatever we define as the thing being studied.

Control mass   A system defined to be a specific piece of matter.

Environment   Everything except the system.

Isolated system   A system which does not interact with its environment.

Internal energy   Energy of matter associated with the randomly oriented motions of the molecules and the forces between them (the energy of the "hidden microscopic modes").

Work   Energy transfer by the action of a macroscopically measurable force on matter within the system ("organized" microscopic work).

Heat   Energy transfer which is not recognized macroscopically as work ("disorganized" microscopic work).

Temperature   A characteristic of matter which serves as a driving potential for energy transfer as heat. Energy is transferred as heat from the body at the greater temperature to the one at the lower temperature.

Hot, cold   Adjectives describing bodies of high and low temperature.

Adiabatic wall   One which prevents energy transfer as heat.

SELECTED READING

Lee, J. F., and F. W. Sears, *Thermodynamics*, secs. 3-1 through 3-10, Addison-Wesley Publishing Co., Inc., Reading, Mass., 1963.

Reif, F., *Fundamentals of Statistical and Thermal Physics*, secs. 2.6–2.11, McGraw-Hill Book Company, New York, 1965.

Resnick, R., and D. Halliday, *Physics, Part 1*, chap. 21, secs. 22-1, 22-6, 22-7, John Wiley & Sons, Inc., New York, 1966.

Van Wylen, G. J., and R. E. Sonntag, *Fundamentals of Classical Thermodynamics*, chap. 4, John Wiley & Sons, Inc., New York, 1965.

Zemansky, M. W., and G. C. Van Ness, *Basic Engineering Thermodynamics*, secs. 3.1–4.8, McGraw-Hill Book Company, New York, 1966.

QUESTIONS

2·1 What concepts were introduced in this chapter? What basic postulates? What definitions?

2·2 A control volume is any defined region in space; under what conditions will a control volume be a control mass? An isolated system?

2·3 How might you explain the concepts of energy, heat, work, and internal energy to a six-year-old?

2·4 "The oven is at 300 degrees of heat." What is wrong with this statement?

2·5 "The heat within a gas is evidenced by the random motion of its molecules." What is wrong with this statement?

2·6 Can energy be transferred to one molecule as work? As heat?

2·7 When two molecules of a gas collide, is there any friction?

2·8 Stir a pail of water. What happens to the energy that you transfer to the water as work?

2·9 If you say that a rock has potential energy in the earth's gravitational field, what must you say about the work done by the weight force when the rock is dropped?

2·10 Explain the difference between heat and internal energy.

2·11 Can you conceive of matter in a zero energy state?

2·12 Under what circumstances is work equal to $F(X_2 - X_1)$?

2·13 A house is receiving energy as heat from resistance heating elements, but the temperature of the house is not changing. What do you think is happening to the energy transferred as heat?

2·14 It is possible to increase the temperature of a substance, such as a gas, without any energy being transferred as heat. Think of an example, define the system, and identify the energy transfers across the boundaries.

PROBLEMS

2·1 Consider the rectangular free-surface water piston-cylinder system shown. The width of the chamber is b (normal to paper), and the atmospheric pressure is P_0. (a) From basic considerations, show that the force exerted by the water on the piston is $F = (P_0 + \gamma h/2)hb$, where γ is the weight density (weight per unit of volume) of water. (b) Calculate the work done by the water on the piston and the work done by the atmosphere on the water when the chamber length is increased slowly from X_1 to X_2. Express in terms of P_0, b, h_1, h_2, X_1, X_2 and γ.

2·2 A hollow steel sphere of mass M and volume V is hung from a cable in a fluid having weight density (weight per unit of volume) γ. Compute the work that an external agent must do on the cable in order to lift the sphere a distance h through the fluid. The motion is very slow, and frictional forces may be neglected. Is there any work done on the fluid in this process? What happens to the energy transferred as work?

2·3 Consider the pulley-belt system shown. The tension force in the top belt is T, and the tension in the lower part may be neglected. The pulleys rotate at angular velocity ω. Which is the driving pulley? The power being transmitted is $T\,D\omega/2$. Define a system, show the forces acting on it and the direction through which they move, and derive this result from the definition of work.

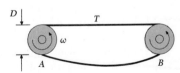

2·4 Repeat the development of Eq. (2·13) for a spherical system where the boundaries move radially.

2·5 Assuming that the atmosphere is locally isothermal, the density variation with pressure is given by

$$\rho = \rho_0 \frac{P}{P_0}$$

where ρ is the density, P the pressure, and the subscript zero denotes the earth's surface. Show that the pressure variation through the isothermal atmosphere is

$$\frac{P}{P_0} = \exp\left(-\frac{\rho_0 g_g z}{g_c P_0}\right)$$

where z is the height above the surface, and g_g is the (constant) acceleration of gravity.

2·6 Using the atmospheric pressure distribution of Prob. 2·5, derive an expression for the work done by the skin of a balloon on the atmosphere in rising slowly to a height h above the surface. Assume that the initial balloon volume is V_0 and that the volume varies inversely with pressure during the ascent. Neglect local variations in pressure around the balloon.

2·7 Using the atmospheric pressure distribution of Prob. 2·5, derive an expression for the work done by the skin of a balloon in rising slowly to a height h above the surface. Assume that the initial balloon volume is V_0, and that the volume varies linearly with height, attaining a value V_1 at h.

2·8 Work Prob. 2·7 assuming that the volume varies exponentially with height.

2·9 Using the atmospheric pressure distribution of Prob. 2·5, derive an expression for the work done by the skin of a balloon on the atmosphere in rising slowly from the earth's surface to a height h. Assume that the balloon is spherical and does not change size. (Some approximations relating to the small size of the balloon may be useful in carrying out necessary integrations.)

2·10 A man on a moving truck lifts a 100-lbm weight 2 ft vertically. If the truck is moving horizontally, how much work did the man do on the weight relative to a man on the opposite side of the earth? How much relative to a pixie on the weight? How much relative to the truck driver? In which reference frame did the man get the most tired?

2·11 A man in an elevator moving upward at a velocity of 10 ft/sec lifts a 50-lbf weight 3 ft off the elevator floor. This all takes 30 sec. How much work did the man do on the weight relative to the elevator operator? How much relative to an observer on the ground floor? How much relative to an observer in an elevator going down at the same speed? Explain why the work is different and what happens to the energy transferred to the weight as work in the three cases. In which reference frame does the man get the most tired?

2·12 A 3-lbm quantity of a substance is made to undergo a process within a piston-cylinder system, starting from an initial volume of 2 ft³ and an initial pressure of 100 lbf/in.² The final volume is 4 ft³. Compute the work done by the substance for the following processes: (*a*) pressure remains constant, (*b*) pressure times volume remains constant, (*c*) pressure is directly proportional to volume, and (*d*) pressure is proportional to the square of the volume.

2·13 Liquid water at 32°F weighs 62.42 lbf/ft³, and ice at the same temperature weighs 57.2 lbf/ft³. Consider a system which is initially an ice cube 1 in. on a side. How much work does this system do on the atmosphere when it melts?

2·14 Six lbm of a substance is compressed in a piston-cylinder system from an initial volume of 4 ft³ to a final volume of 2 ft³. The initial pressure is 100 lbf/in.² Compute the amount of energy transfer as work (ft-lbf and Btu) to the substance if (a) the pressure is constant during compression, and (b) the pressure varies inversely with volume. If the process of case (b) is adiabatic, what is the change in internal energy of the substance?

2·15 Consider the cylinder of liquid suspended between two cones as shown in the sketch. Show that the amount of work done on the cones when the cone separation is increased an infinitesimal amount can be written as

$$dW = \sigma(dA - \cos \theta \, dA_w)$$

where σ is the interfacial tension between the liquid and the gas, A is the liquid-gas interfacial area, A_w is the "wetted area," and θ is the contact angle. *Hint:* What is the liquid pressure?

2·16 Most dielectrics are such that the polarization is related to the electric field by $\mathbf{P} = (\kappa - 1)\epsilon_0 \mathbf{E}$, where κ is the dielectric constant, and ϵ_0 is a physical constant (Table A·2). The dielectric constant is typically a function of temperature. (a) Derive an expression for the work done on a dielectric when it is polarized at constant temperature. (b) The dielectric constant of acetone as a function of temperature is given in the table. Compute the work done (joules) on 1 cm³ of acetone when the electric field $\mathbf{E}$ is increased from zero to 10^4 volt/m while the temperature varies from 0 to 50°C, if the temperature varies linearly with $\mathbf{E}$ during this process. *Hint:* Don't be afraid of graphical integration.

T, °C	κ
-80	31.0
20	21.4
50	18.7

2·17 Five lbm of a material is heated at constant volume from a state where its internal energy is 40 Btu/lbm to a state where its internal energy is 60 Btu/lbm. Compute the amount of energy transfer as heat for this process (Btu).

2·18 A substance expands from $V_1 = 1$ ft³ to $V_2 = 6$ ft³ in a constant pressure process at 100 lbf/in.² The initial and final internal energies are $U_1 = 40$ Btu and $U_2 = 20$ Btu, respectively. Find the direction and magnitude of the energy transfer as heat for this process (Btu).

2·19 A sample of gas (not ideal) is made to undergo an expansion process during which its pressure and volume are related as shown in the table below. The energy of the gas at the start and finish of the process are measured and found to be 5 Btu and 3.2 Btu, respectively. Determine the amounts of energy transferred as heat and work during this process. Express in Btu's.

V, ft^3	P, lbf/in.^{2}
1	40
2	27
3	21
4	18

2·20 A 200-lbm chunk of lead falls from a height of 30 ft and smashes into a rigid concrete floor. Calculate the increase in the internal energy ΔU (Btu's), assuming that no energy is transferred as heat from the lead.

2·21 An ideal gas ($Pv = RT$) is heated at constant volume until its temperature is doubled and then cooled at constant pressure until it is returned to its initial temperature. Derive an expression for the work done on the gas. It is a peculiarity of an ideal gas that its internal energy is a function only of temperature. What is the net energy transfer as heat for the process described?

2·22 A paramagnetic salt obeying Curie's law ($\mathbf{M} = C\mathbf{H}/T$) is made to undergo a process at constant $\mathbf{M}$ in which the applied field $\mathbf{H}$ is doubled (and the temperature doubled), followed by a magnetization process during which the applied field is held constant. This process returns the salt to its initial temperature. Derive an expression for the energy transfer as work for this process in terms of the initial values of $\mathbf{H}$ and $\mathbf{M}$. It may be shown that the internal energy U of such a salt is a function only of temperature. What is the net energy transfer as heat for the process described?

2·23 A paramagnetic salt obeying Curie's law ($\mathbf{M} = C\mathbf{H}/T$) is made to undergo a process at constant temperature T during which its magnetization $\mathbf{M}$ is doubled. This is followed by a heating process in which its temperature is doubled while the applied magnetic field $\mathbf{H}$ is held fixed. It may be shown that the internal energy of such a "Curie substance" depends only on temperature. Derive expressions for the total amounts of energy transfer as heat and work to the substance for the two-step process; express the results in terms of the initial values of T, $\mathbf{H}$, and $\mathbf{M}$, and the initial and final values of the internal energy U.

2·24 Assuming that the internal energy of iron is $0.1T$ Btu per lbm, where T is the iron temperature, estimate the maximum increase in temperature of the iron asteroid of Prob. 1·10 when it crashes to earth.

CHAPTER THREE

PROPERTIES
AND STATE

3·1 CONCEPTS OF PROPERTY AND STATE

Any engineering system is made up of various amounts and kinds of matter. Description of such a system and prediction of its performance characteristics requires knowledge of the properties of the various materials and the ability to predict changes in their states. Thus, understanding of the concepts of state and property are essential to any engineer; these are the goals of this chapter.

A *property* is any characteristic or attribute which can in principle be quantitatively evaluated. Volume, mass, energy, temperature, pressure, magnetization, polarization, and color are all properties of matter. Both single particles and systems of many particles which we treat as continua have the properties mass and energy, but only a continuum has the properties volume, pressure, and temperature.

Properties are things that matter "has." *Work and heat are not properties,* for they are things that are "done" on a system in order to produce changes in the properties. Energy transfer as work or heat will be evidenced by changes in properties, but the amounts of energy transfer depend on the manner in which a given change takes place. For example, consider the problem of compressing a gas from one condition where the pressure is P_1 and the volume is V_1 to some other state P_2, V_2. This can be accomplished in an infinite variety of ways, two of which are shown in Fig. 3·1. The amount of work done on the gas in these two cases is obviously different, yet the changes in properties are identical. The integral $\int dW = \int P \, dV$ between two states depends on the path of integration $P(V)$; in contrast, the integral of any property, such as $\int dV$ or $\int dP$, depends only on the initial and final properties.

The *state* of something is its condition, as described by a list of the values of its properties. For example, the position coordinates and velocity components can completely describe the state of a single particle. On the other hand, in some instances it is sufficient merely to know the mass and energy of the particle, and its state is therefore satisfactorily described by fewer properties. The complete description of a system of many particles, such as 1 cm³ of a gas,

57

FIG. 3·1 *Note that the amount of energy transfer as work depends on the process path, and hence the work done is not a property of the end states.*

would require specification of the position coordinates and velocity components for each particle within the boundaries. The list of these properties would be very long—indeed, so long that it probably could never be written down, certainly not before some of the properties had changed. More economical descriptions of state are certainly desirable; we must find some way to reduce the number of relevant properties from something of the order of 10^{23} to "few." We might settle for knowing merely the volume of the system and the energy of each particle; still, this list would also be very long. A less complete way to describe the system would be to give merely its energy and volume, but these may fluctuate rapidly in time as the particles within the system interact with the particles outside the boundary (see Fig. 3·2). We might hope that the *average* properties would be sufficiently informative to allow adequate solution to our engineering problems; indeed, we normally work with properties representing the average of some feature of all the particles comprising the system. These averages are called *macroscopic properties*.

We can further reduce the list of relevant properties by noting that not all macroscopic properties are relevant in a particular analysis. For example, the color of a jet airplane is certainly not relevant in an analysis of its lift-drag characteristics. On the other hand, the color may be relevant in an analysis of its sales potential. It is helpful to group properties into classes that are relevant in different kinds of analysis. We do this by thinking about different subclasses of state. For example, the lift-drag characteristics of the airplane would be a property of its geometry, that is, of its *geometric state*. Its speed and altitude would be properties of its *kinetic state*, and the temperature and humidity in the cabin would be properties of its *thermodynamic state*. The color would be a

FIG. 3·2 *The average properties are used in thermodynamics*

TABLE 3·1 SOME DIFFERENT SUBCLASSES OF STATE

State	Properties
Geometric	Length, width, breadth, moment of inertia, volume, etc.
Kinematic	Position, speed, acceleration, etc.
Hydrodynamic	Pressure, shearing stress, strain rate, etc.
Electromagnetic	Electric field strength, magnetic-dipole moment, charge, etc.
Chemical	Chemical composition, free charge, energy, entropy, etc.
Esthetic	Smell, color, eye-catchingness, etc.
Thermodynamic	Energy, temperature, volume, pressure, stress, magnetic-dipole moment, entropy, etc.
Quantum-mechanical	Momentum and energy of each particle, total volume, etc.

property of its *esthetic state*. Some different subclasses of state are listed in Table 3·1.

In thermodynamics the central theme is energy and energy transfer. The properties of interest are therefore those that are involved with energy in some way. These we call *thermodynamic properties*. For example, the amount of energy transfer as work *to* a fluid when it is compressed is $dW = -P\,dV$, where P is the pressure and V is the volume. The *pressure* is therefore clearly a thermodynamic property. This equation holds regardless of how the volume changes, that is, irrespective of the *shape* of the fluid. The shape is therefore irrelevant in the thermodynamic analysis of fluids; the length, width, and depth of a fluid piece are properties of its *geometric* state, but are *irrelevant* to its thermodynamic state. But the *volume* is relevant to the energy transfer as work and hence volume is a thermodynamic property. We shall enlarge on the concepts of the thermodynamic state and thermodynamic properties in the next section.

In order to complete a thermodynamic analysis it may be necessary to consider other kinds of state. For example, a consideration of the geometric state might allow one to calculate the volume needed in the thermodynamic analysis. Consideration of the kinematic state of an accelerating gas stream may be necessary in order to calculate the gas temperature. A thermodynamic analysis therefore often involves a companion geometrical, dynamical, electrodynamic, or chemical analysis.

3·2 EQUILIBRIUM AND THE THERMODYNAMIC STATE

The state of a system is determined by the molecules within the system boundaries. These molecules undergo continual changes in their individual

FIG. 3·3 *The pressures of A and B must be equal for mechanical equilibrium*

states as they interact with one another. If we isolate a system and allow its molecules to freely interact with one another, the state of the system will undergo visible macroscopic change. But after some time the changes that can be detected with macroscopic instruments will cease; the microscopic activity continues, but somehow the macroscopic state has "reached equilibrium." The macroscopic measurables have definite constant values. Just what equilibrium is, and how it can be identified, we shall now discuss.

Consider the system of Fig. 3·3. The cylinder contains a floating piston, with different amounts of two different gases A and B on opposite sides. Suppose the piston is locked in a certain position, and the pressures of the two gases are unequal. If we unlock the piston the unbalance of pressure will accelerate the piston in one direction. We would say that the two gas systems A and B were not in *mechanical equilibrium* with one another. If, on the other hand, the two pressures were identical, then the piston would not move upon release; A and B would be in mechanical equilibrium with one another. We see that *pressure* is a property that two systems have in common when they are in *mechanical equilibrium*. This, in fact, is the *thermodynamic concept of pressure*.

Suppose now we lock the piston, and allow the two gases to interact across the piston. Any energy transfer that takes place must be as heat, for locking the piston prevents energy transfer as work. When energy transfer as heat is possible, but none occurs, we say that the systems A and B are in *thermal equilibrium*, and that they have the same *temperature*. Temperature is the property that two systems have in common when they are in thermal equilibrium; this is the *thermodynamic concept of temperature*.

There are other kinds of equilibrium, three of which deserve brief comment. Two systems are said to be in *electrostatic equilibrium* if there is no tendency for a net charge flow between them when they are brought into contact. The electrostatic potential is a property that two systems have in common when they are in electrostatic equilibrium. Two phases of a substance (for example, solid and liquid) are said to be in *phase equilibrium* if there is no tendency for phase transformation (for example, melting) when they are brought into contact. A mixture of gases is said to be in *chemical equilibrium* if there is no tendency for a net reaction to take place when they are allowed to interact.

The term *thermodynamic equilibrium* is used to indicate a condition of equilibrium with respect to *all* possible macroscopic changes in a system where the molecules are free to interact with one another in any way. There is no macroscopic energy, matter, or charge flow within a system in thermodynamic equilibrium, though the molecules are free to produce such flows. In order to test a piece of matter to see if it is in thermodynamic equilibrium, we imagine isolating the matter and watching for macroscopically observable changes. If none occur, the matter was in thermodynamic equilibrium at the moment of isolation. We emphasize that the molecules must be free to move about in order to rearrange the energy, mass, or charge when we make this test.

When we treat a complex system not in equilibrium, the usual procedure is to mentally dissect the system into small pieces which we can treat *individually* as being in thermodynamic equilibrium. For example, in studying the gas flow in a rocket nozzle we might treat each small piece of fluid as being in thermodynamic equilibrium, and then consider the changes in its state as it interacts with the other fluid pieces. The electrons and ions in a plasma are often treated as separate systems, each in thermodynamic equilibrium, but not in equilibrium with each other. The analysis of the interaction between these two systems allows one to predict the approach to equilibrium for the entire plasma. By dissecting the systems in this manner their states can be evaluated by giving the equilibrium properties of each part. The equilibrium properties are therefore of paramount importance in thermodynamic theory and thermodynamic analysis.

Those macroscopic properties that can in principle be measured as functions of the thermodynamic equilibrium state and that are in some way relevant to energy are called *thermodynamic properties*. Any conglomerate feature of all the molecules, such as their total energy, is a thermodynamic property. Any property defined in terms of other thermodynamic properties must be a thermodynamic property. The *thermodynamic state* is the condition of the matter as described by all the thermodynamic properties. The thermodynamic properties are all fixed when the thermodynamic state is fixed. But they are not all independently variable, and hence the thermodynamic state can be "fixed" by giving values for just a few thermodynamic properties. We shall shortly develop a rule for telling how many properties must be known to fix the thermodynamic state. In later chapters we shall use thermodynamic theory to discover equations relating various thermodynamic properties.

3·3 TEMPERATURE

One of the important properties is temperature. What is temperature? A primitive view is that temperature is the reading on a mercury-in-glass thermometer. But who put the markings there, and what do they really mean? What was so special about the mercury-glass combination? These are deeply probing questions, questions which seek some more fundamental idea of the *concept* of temperature.

The housewife thinks of temperature as how hot she must set the oven to cook the roast. The computer engineer thinks of temperature as how cool he must keep the transistors to make them work reliably. The plasma physicist views temperature as a measure of the kinetic energy of the molecules or electrons. And the astronomer views temperature as a measure of the radiant energy emission from stars. These rather diverging concepts of temperature have one thing in common: they all relate to energy or energy transfer, and hence clearly mark temperature as a *thermodynamic* property.

Another common element in these remarks about temperature is that they each suggest that matter is somehow more energetic at a high temperature than at a low temperature. When two systems not in thermal equilibrium are brought into contact, energy transfer as heat will take place between them from the "hotter" one to the "cooler." We say that the hotter system has a greater temperature; the temperature then provides a means for telling in which direction the energy transfer as heat occurs when the systems come into contact. In the absence of other energy flows, there will be no energy transfer as heat between two systems at the same temperature.

Now, if two systems are in thermal equilibrium, then they must have the same temperature. If each is in equilibrium with a third, then all three have the same temperature, and hence any two or all three are in thermal equilibrium. This notion is sometimes called the *zeroth law of thermodynamics*. It is actually an implicit part of the concept of temperature.

It is important to make a clear distinction in one's mind between the concepts of heat, temperature, and internal energy, and hence we now review these again. Internal energy is the energy possessed by molecules that is "hidden" from direct macroscopic view by the disorganized character of the microscopic state. That energy may or may not have been put into the matter through transfer of energy as heat. Heat is energy transfer that is not accounted for in macroscopic evaluation of energy transfer as work; heat is microscopic work that is hidden from direct macroscopic view by the disorganized nature of the energy transfer process. Temperature is a property of matter; if the temperature of one body is greater than the temperature of a second, then any energy transfer as heat will take place from the first body to the second. The internal energy of a substance will depend in part, but not exclusively, on the temperature. Hence the temperature is *not* in general a complete measure of the internal energy. As we shall see, temperature can only be defined when a body is in equilibrium; the body has energy regardless of whether it is in equilibrium or not. A body doesn't "have" any heat; it may have received some energy as heat, but now that energy appears as internal energy, and one cannot tell from the body's state whether that energy entered the body as heat or as work. Internal energy and temperatures are *properties* of matter; heat is not a property. Temperature and internal energy are also inherently different kinds of properties. The temperature of a small piece of a large body is the same as the temperature of the body as a whole; the energy of the small piece is but a small fraction of the energy of the entire body.

To make the temperature concept operational, we need some sort of temperature *scale*. The uniformly spaced markings on a mercury-in-glass thermometer provide one such scale over a limited range. If instead a uniformly marked alcohol-in-glass thermometer is used, the two temperature scales can be made to agree at two points, but not in between. It seems odd that if temperature is such a fundamental concept its scales should be subject to the whims of a thermometer maker. It would be much more desirable if some scale of temperature could be established which is independent of the choice of thermometers. This can indeed be done; means can be devised for measuring the *ratio* of two temperatures without reference to any thermometric material. A conceptually unique scale for temperature can thereby be established in a manner similar to the way we outlined in Chap. One for establishing unique scales for force, mass, and charge. Being able to measure ratios, one is free to select the value for *one* point on the temperature scale, and the measured ratios then give all other temperatures.

In order to develop the thermodynamic definition and scales for temperature we need to understand both the first and second laws of thermodynamics, and we are not yet ready to make these developments. Consequently we shall for the moment work with an empirical temperature scale, that based on the gas thermometer. This scale appears to be identical with the thermodynamic temperature scale, and so we can consider the perfect-gas thermometer as a device for measuring thermodynamic temperature. In Chap. Seven we shall develop the thermodynamic definition of temperature and show the equivalence with the empirical perfect-gas temperature scale.

The empirical gas temperature is based on the observation that the temperature of a gas confined at constant volume is a monotone-increasing function of the gas pressure. The scale is established by arbitrarily selecting a value for the temperature of a mixture of water, water vapor, and ice in thermal equilibrium. Such a mixture can exist at only one temperature (called the *triple point*) and the temperature of this mixture provides an excellent easily reproducible standard.

The thermometer consists of a glass bulb into which various amounts of gas can be placed. The pressure may be measured in several ways, but the volume change so introduced must be zero. Suppose we wish to determine a particular temperature, say, the boiling point of water at 1 atm pressure. A given amount of gas is placed in the bulb, which is then immersed in the triple-point mixture. The thermometer is allowed to reach thermal equilibrium with the mixture, and the gas pressure is then measured. We denote this pressure by P_s. The thermometer is then inserted into the boiling water and the procedure is repeated; the new pressure we call P_m. The ratio P_m/P_s might be taken to be the ratio of the two temperatures T_m/T_s; however, if this is done one obtains different temperature scales depending on the amount of gas in the thermometer. The procedure followed in precision thermometry is to repeat the above measurements with less and less gas in the bulb and to plot the ratio P_m/P_s versus P_s, extrapolating to zero pressure, as shown in Fig. 3·4. The surprising result is that many gases seem to yield the same limiting ratio,

FIG. 3·4 *Readings from a constant-volume gas thermometer*

which is therefore, in a limited way, independent of the nature of the substance chosen. The temperature scale is then set by putting

$$\frac{T_m}{T_s} = \lim_{P_s \to 0} \frac{P_m}{P_s}.$$

By an international agreement made in 1954, the temperature at the H_2O triple point is set at 273.16°K (*degrees Kelvin*). The number may seem quite arbitrary, but with this particular choice the newer *one-point scale* corresponds closely with earlier temperature scales defined on the basis of assumed linear behavior between two arbitrarily selected points. It is important to emphasize that the scales of force, mass, length, time, charge, and temperature are all one-point scales, which are set by selecting values and units for only *one* easily reproducible situation.

It is convenient to distinguish between *levels* of temperature and temperature *intervals*. Sometimes actual temperatures are specified in terms of degrees Kelvin, or °K, and temperature intervals or differences are given in terms of Kelvin degrees, or K°.

The thermodynamic temperature scale, to which the Kelvin scale is equivalent, is called an *absolute temperature scale;* its zero would always occur at the same condition, regardless of what value we happened to choose for the triple-point temperature. A second absolute temperature scale in use is the Rankine scale, defined by setting

$$1 \text{ K}° = \tfrac{9}{5} \text{ R}°$$

This makes the H_2O triple-point temperature correspond to 491.69°R.

Associated with the Kelvin and Rankine scales are the Celsius (formerly centigrade) and Fahrenheit *relative temperature scales*. The Celsius scale is such that 1 C° = 1 K°, but it has its zero point shifted to 273.15°K; this makes 0°K correspond to −273.15°C. Similarly, 1 F° = 1 R°, but 0°F corresponds to 459.67°R. These four temperature scales are compared in Fig. 3·5.

It should be pointed out that the empirical gas scale can be used only at temperatures above the boiling point of the gas and below the melting point of the container. Outside this range other empirical temperatures must be used. The thermodynamic definition of temperature given in Chap. Seven is a continuous definition of temperature valid over all ranges and therefore provides an essential link between the several empirical measures of temperature.

FIG. 3·5 *The °R and °K scales are "absolute" temperature scales*

3·4 INTENSIVE AND EXTENSIVE STATE

It is convenient to distinguish between two types of properties. Suppose we have two pieces of the same substance in equilibrium with one another. If we bring them together, and consider them as one system, the energy and volume of the new system will be the *sum* of the energies and volumes of the two parts. But the temperature and pressure of the new system will be the same as the temperature and pressure of each part. Those properties that depend on the *size* or *extent* of the system are called *extensive* properties; volume, mass, energy, surface area, and electric-dipole moment are all extensive properties. Extensive properties have values regardless of whether the system is in equilibrium state or not. In contrast, those properties that are independent of the size of the system are called *intensive* properties; temperature, pressure, and electric field intensity are intensive properties. As a rule these properties only have meaning for systems in equilibrium states.

It is customary to define some additional intensive properties associated with the extensive properties. For example, the volume per unit mass is called the *specific volume*,

$$v \equiv \frac{V}{M}$$

and the internal energy per unit mass is called the *specific internal energy*,

$$u \equiv \frac{U}{M}$$

Thus, the specific volume and specific internal energy of a system made up of two identical pieces are the same as those of each piece.

The intensive properties are useful because they can be tabulated or graphed without reference to the amount of material under study. The charts and tables in Appendix B are examples.

A great deal is known about a system when the intensive properties are specified. In fact, its thermodynamic state is completely known apart from a single measure of size (say the mass). The state of the system as specified by the intensive thermodynamic properties is called the *intensive thermodynamic state*. The addition of a size measure (mass) completes the description of the *extensive thermodynamic state*.

3·5 INDEPENDENT VARIATIONS OF THE THERMODYNAMIC STATE

The thermodynamic properties of a substance are not independently variable, for various relationships exist between the intensive thermodynamic properties. For example, the pressure, temperature, and specific volume of a gas are frequently idealized to be related by

$$Pv = RT$$

where R is a constant for the gas. Only two of P, v, and T can be independently varied. In this section we shall develop a rule for determining the number of independently variable thermodynamic properties for any substance.

Thermodynamics deals with energy, and the thermodynamic properties are those which in some way are related to energy. The number of ways in which we can independently vary the energy of a given substance tells us the number of independent thermodynamic properties.

Let's first consider the various ways in which we can transfer energy as work to the substance under study. If the substance is compressible we can increase its energy through $-P\,dV$ work. If it is magnetic we can increase its energy through magnetization work $\mu_0 \mathbf{H} \cdot d(\mathbf{M}V)$. For a particular substance we consider all the relevant work modes shown in Table 2·1; there will be at least one independently variable property for each mode (volume, magnetic moment, and so on). In addition, we can hold these properties fixed and vary the energy through transfer of energy as heat (which varies the temperature). This gives us one more free variable. The count is in fact complete; for each of the independent ways of varying the energy of a given substance there is one independently variable thermodynamic property. We shall formalize this idea following some additional arguments in its behalf.

Let us first consider the nature of the work modes. As we noted in Chap. Two, each is of the form $\mathbf{F}\,dX$, where $\mathbf{F}$ is some sort of "generalized force" and dX is a "generalized displacement." If $\mathbf{F}$ is independent of the direction and rate of change of the process, then the amount of energy transfer to the system when X is increased by dX will be exactly the same as the amount of energy transfer from the system when X is decreased by this same amount. This means that *the work mode is reversible;* the amount of energy added in a forward process can be removed by the reverse process. It is clear that any work mode for which $\mathbf{F}$ is a *property* of the thermodynamic state of the substance will be reversible in this sense. Each of the work modes listed in Table 2·1 is of this category. If, on the other hand, $\mathbf{F}$ depends on the direction or rate of the process, and not just on the thermodynamic state, the process can exhibit hysteresis, and hence is irreversible. Viscous work on a fluid falls into this category; in contrast, $-P \, dV$ work for the same fluid can be reversible. The concept of reversible work developed here will suffice for the moment. In Chap. Seven we shall give a somewhat deeper meaning to reversible processes.

Let us now consider a piece of fluid, and see how we might change its thermodynamic state. We take a certain mass of a given fluid, so the composition of the system is fixed. Now, we can clearly change the state by compressing the fluid, thereby changing both the volume and energy. We can simultaneously cool the fluid in order to keep its energy fixed; this gives us a change of state at fixed energy, where the volume is the adjustable variable. We can also hold the volume fixed and adjust the energy independently through energy transfer as heat. So, the volume and energy are clearly two independently variable properties. Can we hold the volume and energy fixed, and vary other thermodynamic properties? We might think of trying to vary the pressure, but this is impossible if we keep the volume and energy fixed. Squeezing the fluid would indeed raise the pressure, but would change the volume; heating would also raise the pressure, but would change the energy. Suppose we stir the fluid; this will increase the pressure, but it will also increase the energy. In fact, the same change of state could alternatively be produced through energy transfer as heat. We might try other irreversible work modes, but we always see that the effects of the irreversible work modes can be accomplished by a combination of reversible work and energy transfer as heat. We are inescapably led to the conclusion that there is but one freely variable property for each *reversible* work mode; this free variable is the generalized displacement X. But we can also hold all the X's fixed and vary the energy through energy transfer as heat. Thus, if there are n relevant reversible work modes for a given substance, there are only $n + 1$ independently variable thermodynamic properties.

We can view the set of properties $(X_1, X_2, \ldots, X_n, E)$ to be the independently variable set. However, we can give up control over one of these and thereby obtain the freedom to vary some other property. For example, we can vary the pressure and volume of a fluid system independently if we do not simultaneously insist on control over the energy simply by heating the substance at the desired volume until the desired pressure is achieved.

3·6 THE STATE POSTULATE

We formalize the ideas discussed above in the *state postulate:*

The number of independently variable thermodynamic properties for a specified system is equal to the number of relevant reversible work modes plus one.

There are several ideas implicit in the words used. "Specified system" implies a specified amount of some specified matter; "thermodynamic properties" implies that we refer to those characteristics relevant to energy and to *thermodynamic equilibrium states.* The reference "relevant reversible work modes" means that we count only important work modes for the system in question and do not count irreversible work modes. The "plus one" is for the independent control of energy through heating or irreversible work.

Note that the rule gives the number of independent properties but does *not* say that *any* $n + 1$ properties are independent. The n X's and the energy always constitute an independent set, however.

The postulate as stated above deals with any amount of a specified substance. It is often convenient to work with a unit mass of the substance, and a form of the state postulate relating to intensive thermodynamic properties is therefore useful. Imagine that the system consists of a unit mass of the substance. The state postulate then can be interpreted as a rule for the number of independent thermodynamic properties of a unit mass, that is, for the number of independent *intensive* thermodynamic properties of the substance:

The number of independent intensive thermodynamic properties of a specified substance is equal to the number of reversible work modes plus one.

Again we interpret the implications of the wording; "specified substance" implies the percentages of each kind of molecule; "thermodynamic properties" implies those properties of the substance relevant to energy and to *thermodynamic equilibrium states*. Again only the relevant reversible work modes are to be counted. The rule gives the number of independent intensive thermodynamic properties, but does *not* imply that *any* set of $n + 1$ intensive properties will always be independently variable. For example, the internal energy and temperature of an "ideal gas" are not independently variable, as we shall see.

To illustrate the use of the state postulate, consider a substance for which the only important reversible work mode is compression or expansion ($P \, dv$ work). The rule says that there will be two independently variable intensive thermodynamic properties for such a substance; specification of the values for any two independent intensive thermodynamic properties will fix the values of all other intensive thermodynamic properties. For example, specification of the specific volume v and the specific internal energy u fixes the intensive thermodynamic state completely; temperature, pressure, and all other intensive thermodynamic properties for that substance are unique functions of u and v,

$$T = T(u, v) \qquad P = P(u, v)$$

Figures B·1 in Appendix B give examples of these relationships for water in graphical form. If we set $u = 1400$ Btu/lbm and $v = 0.3$ ft³/lbm, then we read from this graph that P is 3000 psia and T is 1200°F. Figures B·1 to B·11 are all examples of substances of this type; the student should familiarize himself with these "graphical equations of state" that we shall be using continually in engineering analysis.

As a second example, suppose we consider a substance for which the relevant reversible work modes are volume change ($P \, dv$ work) and electrostatic polarization [$\mathbf{E} \cdot d(v\mathbf{P})$ work]. Such a substance would have three independent intensive thermodynamic properties; the specific volume v, dipole moment per unit volume $\mathbf{P}$, and specific internal energy u are an independent set. The values for all other intensive thermodynamic properties are dependent on the values of these three properties. Thus,

$$P = P(u, v, \mathbf{P}) \qquad T = T(u, v, \mathbf{P}) \qquad \mathbf{E} = \mathbf{E}(u, v, \mathbf{P})$$

The relationships between the properties are called *equations of state*. Examples of such "equations" in graphical and tabular form constitute Appendix B. For certain idealized substances the equations of state are algebraic (such as $Pv = RT$). Today a modern engineering center will have the equation of state information stored within the memory of a digital computer as tables or fitted equations for use when needed in engineering analysis. The next chapter is devoted to discussion of the equations of state for a very special but extremely important class of substances.

SELECTED READING

Kestin, J., *A Course in Thermodynamics*, chap. 2, Blaisdell Publishing Co., Inc., Waltham, Mass., 1966.

Lee, J. F., and F. W. Sears, *Thermodynamics*, secs. 1-1 through 1-2, Addison-Wesley Publishing Co., Inc., Reading, Mass., 1963.

Van Wylen, G. J., and R. E. Sonntag, *Fundamentals of Classical Thermodynamics*, secs. 2.1–3.1, John Wiley & Sons, Inc., New York, 1965.

Zemansky, M. W., and H. C. Van Ness, *Basic Engineering Thermodynamics*, secs. 1.5–2.2, McGraw-Hill Book Company, New York, 1966.

QUESTIONS

3·1 What concepts were introduced in this chapter? What basic postulates? What definitions?

3·2 Give an example of a property which is relevant to the thermodynamic state, and one which is irrelevant.

3·3 Why is heat not a property?

3·4 In handbooks we sometimes find something called the "heat of the liquid" tabulated as a function of temperature and pressure. Is it possible to tabulate heat as a function of state?

3·5 Give an example of a system which is not in equilibrium and an example of one which is in a thermodynamic state.

3·6 "Heat and energy bear the same relation to matter as rain and water bear to a reservoir." Explain this analogy.

3·7 How would you explain the concepts of property and state to your grandmother?

3·8 Why is the differential quantity dW not the differential of a property?

3·9 Can changes of state occur within a system without energy transfer across the boundaries?

3·10 Can the thermodynamic state of a substance be changed without any energy transfer?

3·11 What is a reversible work mode?

3·12 Can you visualize a substance for which shear work would be reversible?

3·13 Devise means for independently varying the pressure and volume of a gas; can the pressure and volume be treated as independent properties?

3·14 What is the difference between intensive and extensive properties?

3·15 Invent a test which will allow you to discover whether a property is intensive or extensive.

PROBLEMS

3·1 The simplest equations of state are obtained when only one work mode is considered important, that is, where there are only two independent intensive properties. Give a set of independent intensive thermodynamic properties for each of the following "simple substances":
   (a) "Simple compressible substance," $P\,dV$ work only
   (b) "Simple magnetic substance," magnetization only
   (c) "Simple dielectric substance," polarization only
   (d) "Simple surface," surface extension only
   (e) "Simple elastic substance," one-dimensional pure strain only

3·2 For most substances the internal energy can be varied by varying the temperature and density, but for some special substances the internal energy is a function only of temperature. When work is done in an isothermal process on a substance whose internal energy is dependent only on the temperature, how much energy is transferred as heat, and in what direction?

3·3 Consider the "generalized forces and displacements" for a liquid-vapor-solid capillary system, as derived in Prob. 2·15. Assuming the liquid is incompressible, list a set of independent extensive properties for the system. What must you add if the liquid is compressible? Is the contact angle an intensive or extensive property?

3·4 A system initially consists of 3 lbm of a substance having specific internal energy u of 20 Btu/lbm and 6 lbm of the same substance having an internal energy of 30 Btu/lbm. 150 Btu of energy is transferred as heat to this system, and it is allowed to come to equilibrium. What will be the specific internal energy of the substance in the final equilibrium state?

3·5 Consider a simple substance for which the temperature may be expressed functionally in terms of energy and volume or, alternatively, in terms of energy and pressure: $T = T(u, v)$ or $T = T(u, P)$. Differentiate these two expressions using the chain rule of calculus; use a subscript on the partial derivatives to indicate which variables are kept constant [for example, $(\partial T/\partial u)_P$ for the partial derivative of T with respect to u, with the pressure held constant].

3·6 In a study of the properties of a liquid a 2-lbm sample was heated at constant volume from 400 to 450°F. This required an energy input as heat of 11.2 watt-hr. Calculate the difference in specific internal energy (Btu/lbm) between the initial and final states.

3·7 In a study of the properties of a gas a 3-lbm sample was heated at constant volume from 1100 to 1140°F. This required an energy input as heat of 35.0 Btu. Calculate the difference in specific internal energy between the initial and final states.

3·8 In a study of the properties of a liquid, a 2-lbm sample of liquid was heated at a constant pressure of 1 atm from 200 to 250°F. The density of the liquid is 38 lbm/ft³ and 36 lbm/ft³ at the initial and final states, respectively. An energy input as heat of 42 Btu was required. Determine the difference in the specific internal energies between the initial and final states.

3·9 In order to determine the properties of a dense gas at high pressures, 10 lbm of the gas was heated at 4000 psia from 700 to 740°F. The gas volumes were 0.287 ft³ and 0.328 ft³ in the initial and final states, respectively, and the required energy transfer as heat to the gas was 537 Btu. Determine the difference in the specific internal energy between the initial and final states.

3·10 In order to determine the properties of a gas, 0.1 lbm was heated in a 2-ft³ container. The amounts of energy input as heat required to achieve temperatures above the initial temperature $T_1 = 500°R$ value were as follows:

T_2, °R	Q_{12}, Btu
600	1.71
700	3.44
800	5.18
900	6.94
1000	8.72
1100	10.54
1200	12.39

Calculate the internal energy of the gas and plot as a function of T for this v.

3·11 The pressure may be thought of as a function of the temperature and specific volume for the perfect gas $(Pv = RT)$. Prepare a three-dimensional sketch of this equation of state; project lines of constant temperature onto a P-v plane and sketch the resulting two-dimensional "map." How many "coordinates" are necessary for a "fix" on the state?

3·12 Make a table of all the intensive and extensive properties of matter that you know. List some means of measurement for as many as you can.

3·13 A substance for which the only reversible work mode is $-P\,dV$ is made to undergo first an adiabatic expansion process, then a constant-pressure compression process, and finally a constant-volume pressurization process which returns the substance to its initial state. What is the total change in internal energy for this "cycle"? Is there a net transfer of energy to or from the substance as work for this cycle? Is there any net energy transfer as heat? If so, is it to or from the substance?

3·14 In some presentations of thermodynamics a basic starting point is the hypothesis that for any control mass

$$\oint dW = \oint dQ$$

The integrals are to be taken around a cycle which returns the control mass to its initial state. If dW is interpreted as positive if work is done by the control mass, what must be the interpretation of dQ in the above equation? Derive this equation invoking the first law and the state postulate.

CHAPTER FOUR

STATES OF SIMPLE SUBSTANCES

4·1 THE SIMPLE SUBSTANCE

The simplest descriptions of matter are obtained for substances idealized as having only one relevant reversible work mode. We call such a substance a *simple substance*. The state postulate tells us that the number of independently variable intensive thermodynamic properties of such a simple substance is only *two*.

The term *simple compressible substance* is applied to any substance for which the only important reversible work mode is volume change ($P\,dv$ work). The theory of simple compressible substances is quite well developed, and considerable data have been accumulated relating the thermodynamic properties of many such substances. No substance is truly simple, but we find that satisfactory engineering analyses can usually be made by treating the substances involved as simple compressible substances.

The simplest descriptions of magnetic substances are obtained when magnetization is considered to be the only significant reversible work mode. Since most magnetic materials are solids, the work of volume change is usually small, and the idealization that a material is a *simple magnetic substance* is often quite valid. Similarly, we can speak of the *simple dielectric substance* as one for which the only important reversible work mode is electric polarization.

Pairs of independent intensive thermodynamic properties for these three simple substances are as follows:

Simple compressible substance, $P\,dv$ work only: (u, v) or (u, P)
Simple magnetic substance, magnetization only: $(u, \mathbf{M})$ or $(u, \mathbf{H})$
Simple dielectric substance, polarization only: $(u, \mathbf{P})$ or $(u, \mathbf{E})$

Thermodynamics concentrates most heavily on the simple compressible substance, which is often called merely a "simple substance."† We shall examine this and other types of simple substances in this chapter.

† In some texts the term "simple system" is used instead.

4·2 EQUATIONS OF STATE

From the state postulate we know that the temperature and pressure of a simple compressible substance can be expressed functionally as

$$T = T(u, v)$$
$$P = P(u, v)$$

These relations imply that we could completely fix the intensive thermodynamic state of a simple compressible substance by specification of any two independently variable intensive thermodynamic properties. As we shall see in a moment, temperature and pressure are not always independently variable. However, temperature and specific volume are always independent properties for a simple compressible substance, and we can alternatively think of the pressure and specific internal energy as being functions of these properties,

$$P = P(T, v)$$
$$u = u(T, v)$$

In certain special cases these equations can be expressed in explicit algebraic form, but in general it is easier to represent them graphically or by tables.† The equations, in algebraic, graphical, or tabular form, which relate the intensive thermodynamic properties of any substance are termed the *equations of state* of the substance.

A simple compressible substance can exist in different forms. In the gaseous form the molecules are far apart and move about freely, continually finding that they have new neighbors. Very little of the energy is associated with intermolecular forces. In the liquid form the molecules are much more densely packed but are still free to move about. A considerable amount of energy must be added to a liquid to break the strong force bonds which keep the liquid dense (compared to a gas). In solid forms the molecules are restrained to definite positions in the crystal lattice, and consequently always have the same neighbors. Melting of a solid is accomplished by adding enough energy to free individual molecules from one another. There may be different structures in the crystal lattice, and hence different forms of the solid.

Some equilibrium states involve the presence of more than one form. For example, solid and liquid forms of water coexist in thermodynamic equilibrium at approximately 0°C. At a certain pressure and temperature near 0°C three forms of water can coexist in thermodynamic equilibrium. Such coexisting forms are called *phases*, and the group of phases is called a *multiphase mixture*.

The properties of each phase of a mixture can be treated separately, and the properties of the mixture then determined by appropriate combination. For example, the energy of the mixture is the sum of the energies of all phases.

---

† Property tabulations are now available for many substances in forms suitable for use in a digital computer.

However, the temperature and pressure of the mixture are the same as the common temperature and pressure of each phase. In graphical representations it is equally convenient to treat the mixture properties directly; the fractions by mass of each phase then become relevant intensive thermodynamic properties.

In engineering we continually use equation-of-state information provided in textbooks, Bureau of Standards brochures, the International Critical Tables, and various engineering, physics, and chemistry handbooks. There are three primary means by which these charts, tables, and equations are developed. First, laboratory measurements provide the main source of numerical values. Second, equations relating various properties can be developed by application of thermodynamic theory (Chap. Eight); these play a very important role in checking laboratory data, in interpolation, extrapolation, and even in evaluation of other thermodynamic properties (such as the entropy). A third way that equations of state are obtained is through application of quantum-statistical thermodynamics (as in Fig. B·12). By postulation of an appropriate microscopic model of the substance, application of certain quantum-mechanical fundamentals allows one to predict the equations of state. These must of course be checked against laboratory data, and must be consistent with the equations obtained from thermodynamic theory. The quantum-statistical thermodynamic method is perhaps the most fundamental but is also the most sophisticated. In fact, only the simplest of molecules can be treated by routine applications of this theory. Hence the large body of equation-of-state information presently available is based primarily on laboratory data and thermodynamic theory, and these are the tools we shall emphasize in the main portion of this text.

Laboratory measurement of temperature, pressure, and specific volume are relatively straightforward. Measurement of the specific internal energy requires that the substance be put through some process where the amounts of energy transfer can be measured accurately. The energy transfer as work can be calculated from its basic definition, for example, $dW = -P\,dV$. The energy transfer as heat can be supplied from a device that takes in energy as measurable work and rejects all this energy to the substance as heat. Such a device might consist of an electric generator with a resistive load. Knowing these energy transfers, the change in internal energy for the test specimen can be determined. Execution of a large number of such experiments allows one to map out the specific internal energy as a function of the thermodynamic state (say as a function of the specific volume and temperature), *relative* to the energy at some arbitrarily chosen *datum state*. The value of the energy at the datum state is normally chosen as zero. Since energy-balance analyses always involve energy changes, and not absolute values of energy, the use of an arbitrary datum suffices as long as the substance is not involved in any chemical reactions with other substances. When reactions are involved, one must be careful to tie the energies of the various substances together properly in order to have a proper energy accounting for the chemical reaction. We shall discuss how this is done in Chap. Eleven.

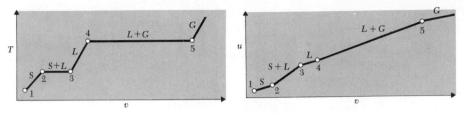

FIG. 4·1   *History of a constant-pressure heating experiment*

4·3 THE GENERAL NATURE OF A SIMPLE COMPRESSIBLE SUBSTANCE

Let us now imagine performing an experiment on a sample of some simple compressible substance. Suppose we carry out a heating process in a piston-cylinder system in a manner that keeps the pressure constant. At each step in the process we add a small amount of energy as heat, allow the substance to expand (thereby doing work) to keep the pressure constant, and then after waiting for equilibrium to be established we record the values for temperature, pressure, and volume. The energy balance then allows us to calculate the incremental change in internal energy between the first and second thermodynamic states. By this experiment we can map out the thermodynamic properties at states having this certain pressure, and these could become part of a basic tabulation of the type given in Appendix B.

A typical outcome of such an experiment is shown in Fig. 4·1. If we start with a solid at state 1, adding energy would raise the temperature to state 2, where the solid would begin to melt. For a given pressure there is one certain temperature at which solid and liquid phases exist in thermodynamic equilibrium. Further energy addition at this pressure results only in more melting,

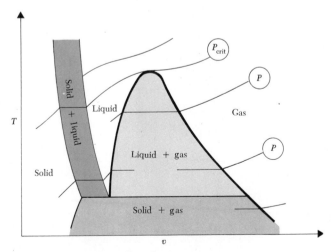

FIG. 4·2   *A typical T-v diagram*

FIG. 4·3 *P-v-T surface for a substance which expands upon melting*

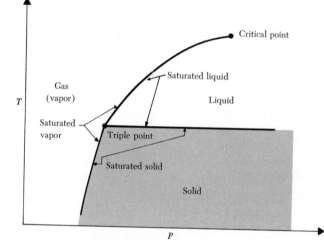

FIG. 4·4 *A typical T-P diagram*

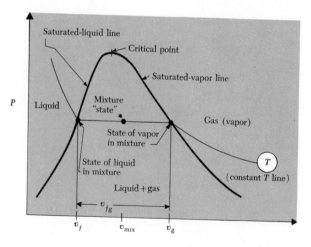

FIG. 4·5 *The vapor dome on a P-v plane*

with the intensive thermodynamic states of the solid and liquid remaining constant. This melting would continue until only liquid remains (mixture state 3); for most substances this would be a state of larger mixture, specific volume. A further increase in energy would result in increasing the temperature, until at state 4 the liquid would begin to evaporate. From state 4 to state 5 liquid and gas phases would exist together at a constant temperature and pressure, and the volume might undergo a tremendous increase. At state 5 the liquid would finally be completely evaporated, and further additions of energy would cause the temperature of the gas (vapor) to increase. Eventually, at very high temperatures, the molecules would become ionized and we would call the ion-electron mixture a *plasma*. In plasma states the electric and magnetic work modes might be important, and idealization that the substance is a simple substance might no longer be realistic.

Repeating the experiment with different starting states, a whole series of "constant-pressure lines" could be traced out (Fig. 4·2). At pressures below a certain "critical pressure" we would always encounter a region of coexisting liquid and gas phases; but at greater pressures there would cease to be a well-defined "boiling point," and the transition from the liquid form to the gas form would be continuous rather than abrupt.

Figure 4·2 constitutes part of the graphical equation of state for a simple compressible substance. We see clearly that the pressure is a unique function of the temperature and volume. Moreover, the temperature of a multiphase mixture is fixed solely by the pressure. In other words, *in the mixed-phase regions temperature and pressure cannot be specified independently*.

Graphing the functional relation $P = P(T, v)$ would require a three-dimensional map, and the projections of Fig. 4·2 are more convenient for quantitative work. However, it is instructive to examine a qualitative three-dimensional P-v-T surface, and one is shown in Fig. 4·3. The equation of state $P = P(T, v)$ is represented by a surface standing in the P-v-T space. Figure 4·2 represents a view of this surface from above, and the lines of constant pressure are obtained by taking horizontal sections through the surface.

States at which a phase change begins or ends are called *saturation states*. The highest pressure and temperature at which distinct liquid and gas phases can coexist define the *critical point*. The dome-shaped region in Figs. 4·2 and 4·5 bounded by the saturated-liquid line and the saturated-vapor line is referred to as the *vapor dome*. In thermodynamic systems the engineer is primarily concerned with liquid, vapor (gas),† and the liquid-vapor mixed-phase region. The area to the right of the vapor dome is commonly called the *superheated-vapor region*. To the left of the saturated-liquid line the substance is said to be in a *subcooled-liquid state*. States at pressures greater than the critical pressure are commonly called *supercritical states*. Note that the three-phase line appears as a point when the surface is viewed in a T-P plane (Fig. 4·4). This point is called the *triple point*.

† We shall use the terms "vapor" and "gas" interchangeably.

FIG. 4·6 *P-v-T surface for a substance which contracts upon melting*

FIG. 4·7 *A typical u-T-P surface*

It is common practice to denote states on the saturated-liquid line by the subscript *f* and states on the saturated-vapor line by the subscript *g*. The difference between the saturated-vapor and saturated-liquid properties is frequently denoted by the subscript *fg*. For example,

$$v_{fg} \equiv v_g - v_f$$
$$u_{fg} \equiv u_g - u_f$$

Figures 4·1 to 4·3 represent the behavior of a substance that expands upon melting, and most substances are of this nature. However, one of the most important substances, water,† contracts upon melting. A three-dimensional *P-v-T* relationship for such a substance is shown in Fig. 4·6. A typical *u-T-P* surface would appear as shown in Fig. 4·7. Simple compressible substances differ markedly in their thermodynamic characteristics, as is illustrated by the variations in the critical-point properties shown in Table B·8, Appendix B.

4·4 USING THE TABULAR AND GRAPHICAL EQUATIONS OF STATE

Measurements of *P*, *v*, *T*, *u*, and other thermodynamic properties have been obtained for many substances, and graphical or tabular equations of state are now available for use in engineering analysis. Tables B·1, B·3, B·4, and B·5 are typical examples of *saturation tables*. Such tables give the properties of the individual liquid and gas (vapor) phases of a liquid-gas mixture. Tables of the properties of gaseous forms (for example, Table B·2) are called *superheat tables*. Note that the saturation tables have a *single* entry point; knowledge of the temperature, or alternatively the pressure, suffices to fix the state of each

† We use the term "water" to mean H_2O in any of its forms.

phase of the mixture. The mixture state is fixed when a second property of the mixture, say its specific volume, is fixed. In contrast, the superheat tables have *two* entry points; knowledge of both T and P fixes the intensive state of the vapor completely.

Graphical representations of the equation of state are particularly convenient, because most of the pertinent information can be put on a single page. Such a representation for H_2O is shown in Fig. B·1. Here the internal energy u and volume v are used as the independent coordinates, and the thermodynamic state is completely specified by fixing the values of these two properties. Note that the state can be fixed by specifying values for any two independent properties. For example, water at a pressure of 100 psia and density of 0.2 lbm/ft³ (corresponding to $v = 5.0$ ft³/lbm) will be in the gaseous phase at a temperature of 405°F and will have a specific internal energy of 1139 Btu/lbm. The u-v plot of Fig. B·1 is included here primarily for purposes of illustration. Thermodynamic data are usually presented on other "planes," using as coordinates properties that we have yet to define, but we can make use of the charts even before we know the meaning of all the properties. For example, using Fig. B·5, we find the volume of saturated O_2 vapor at 100°K as slightly under 3000 ml/gmole, and the saturation pressure as about 2.5 atm. On Fig. B·6, we read the specific volume of CO_2 vapor at 0°F and 100 psia as about 1.2 ft³/lbm.

The properties of a liquid-vapor mixture can be read directly from the graphical equations. Alternatively, the mixture properties can be computed from the properties of the individual phases as tabulated in the saturation tables if we know the relative amounts of the two phases present in the mixture. It is convenient to introduce an additional property, the *quality*, defined as the fraction of the total mass which is saturated *vapor*. The symbol x is commonly used for this mixture property; $1 - x$ is then the fraction of the mass that is saturated liquid. Then, if M is the total mass, the volume and internal energy are

$$V = (1 - x)Mv_f + xMv_g$$
$$U = (1 - x)Mu_f + xMu_g$$

The specific volume and specific internal energy of a simple compressible substance in the mixed-phase region are then

$\blacktriangleright$ $\quad\quad v = (1 - x)v_f + xv_g$ · $\hspace{4cm}$ (4·1)

$\blacktriangleright$ $\quad\quad u = (1 - x)u_f + xu_g$ $\hspace{4.2cm}$ (4·2)

The pressure and temperature of the mixture are, of course, the same as the pressure and temperature of the saturated liquid and vapor. For example, consider 2.5 lbm of H_2O at 100 psia in a two-phase state, with a quality of 0.6. The liquid and vapor masses are

$$M_f = (1 - 0.6) \times 2.5 = 1 \text{ lbm}$$
$$M_g = 0.6 \times 2.5 = 1.5 \text{ lbm}$$

We find values for v_f, v_g, u_f, and u_g in Table B·1b. The volume occupied by the mixture is then

$$V = Mv = 2.5 \times [(1 - 0.6) \times 0.0177 + 0.6 \times 4.43] = 6.66 \text{ ft}^3$$

The internal energy of the mixture is

$$U = Mu = 2.5 \times [(1 - 0.6) \times 298 + 0.6 \times 1105] = 1950 \text{ Btu}$$

The temperature of the mixture is 327.8°F, or 787.5°R.

4·5 METASTABLE STATES IN PHASE TRANSITIONS

It is important to realize that the phase transitions discussed above are not always observed at precisely the points indicated in the tables. Suppose we expand the volume available to a liquid-vapor mixture. The pressure within the liquid might actually be significantly reduced below the saturation pressure before any vapor is formed, for vapor can only be formed at a "nucleus," such as a small vapor bubble. Rough walls normally contain many such nuclei, but with a smooth glass container one can virtually eliminate all nuclei, and hence prevent the formation of new vapor within the liquid. Water in a clean beaker can be heated several degrees above 212°F without noticeable boiling. The insertion of a roughened glass rod, which provides nucleation sites, gives rise to immediate vapor formation from these sites. The state of the "superheated liquid" in this demonstration is not given in any of the tables of thermodynamic properties, for the superheated liquid is not in an equilibrium state. A small disturbance (the insertion of the rod) initiates a dramatic change in state (vaporization). A similar effect is observed when water is cooled in a clean beaker at 1 atm. With care, the water can be cooled well below 32°F without solidification. A tap on the beaker then triggers a sudden crystallization throughout the liquid. The "supercooled liquid" is likewise not in an equilibrium state. A related phenomenon occurs during condensation; the vapor requires some small liquid droplets to act as nuclei for the condensation process. This has considerable importance in steam turbine nozzles, where the vapor is usually expanded to somewhat below the saturation pressure before condensation actually occurs.

Analysis of these *metastable equilibrium states* is beyond our present scope. Most engineering problems can be adequately treated by assuming that the phase transitions occur exactly at the saturation conditions, and this is the approach that we shall take.

4·6 AN ENGINEERING EXAMPLE

The tabular and graphical equations of state are used in conjunction with the energy balance in analysis of engineering systems. The energy balance provides quantitative information relating the change in internal energy to the energy transfers for the process, and the equations of state relate the energy to other thermodynamic properties whose values may be of interest in the particular system. For example, suppose we wish to compute the amount of energy which must be transferred as heat to 5 lbm of H_2O initially at 200°F and 2 psia pressure in order to increase the temperature to 1200°F if the heating occurs at constant volume.

We begin the solution by defining a control mass consisting of the 5 lbm of water. As shown in Fig. 4·8a, energy inflow as heat will be considered positive, and there is no work involved. The only energy possessed by the system is its internal energy U, so the energy balance, made over the time for the state change to take place, is

$$\underset{\substack{\text{energy} \\ \text{input}}}{Q} = \underset{\substack{\text{increase in} \\ \text{energy storage}}}{\Delta U}$$

Here

$$\Delta U = M(u_2 - u_1)$$

where u_1 and u_2 represent the internal energy in the initial and final states.

At this point it becomes necessary to make the idealization that the substance is in a state of thermodynamic equilibrium at the start of the process and in another such state at the end of the process. The equation of state for water, treated as a simple compressible substance, can then be employed (see Appendix B). For the initial state, from Fig. B·1 we find

$$P_1 = 2 \text{ psia} \qquad u_1 = 1080 \text{ Btu/lbm}$$
$$T_1 = 200°F \qquad v_1 = 198 \text{ ft}^3/\text{lbm}$$

The final state is fixed with the aid of a *process representation*, Fig. 4·8b. Such a diagram shows the reader how the problem is solved as well as helping the analyst in his solution. Then, reading from Fig. B·1, we find that the final

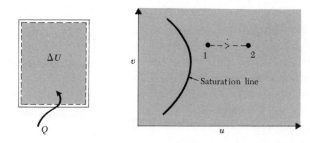

FIG. 4·8

(a) *The control mass* (b) *The process representation*

state is

$$v_2 = 198 \text{ ft}^3/\text{lbm} \qquad P_2 = 5 \text{ psia}$$
$$T_2 = 1200°\text{F} \qquad u_2 = 1440 \text{ Btu/lbm}$$

Substituting into the energy balance, we find

$$Q = 5 \text{ lbm} \times (1440 - 1080) \text{ Btu/lbm} = 1800 \text{ Btu}$$

In Chap. Five we shall see many other examples illustrating the use of equations of state in engineering analysis.

4·7 SOME OTHER THERMODYNAMIC PROPERTIES

Quite frequently other thermodynamic properties will be defined in terms of P, v, T, and u, and we shall now discuss some of these. In single-phase regions, where pressure and temperature are independent, we can think of the volume as being a function of pressure and temperature,

$$v = v(T, P)$$

The difference in specific volume between any two states separated by infinitesimal differences dT and dP can be obtained by expanding the function $v(T, P)$ in a Taylor's series about the point (T, P),

$$v(T + dT, P + dP) = v(T, P) + \left(\frac{\partial v}{\partial T}\right)_P dT + \left(\frac{\partial v}{\partial P}\right)_T dP + \cdots$$

The partial derivatives are to be evaluated at the point (T, P), and the subscripts on the partial derivatives indicate which other variable is held constant during the differentiation. The *difference* between the specific volumes of the two states is then (to first order)

$$dv = v(T + dT, P + dP) - v(T, P)$$

or,†

$$dv = \left(\frac{\partial v}{\partial T}\right)_P dT + \left(\frac{\partial v}{\partial P}\right)_T dP \qquad (4·3)$$

The derivative $(\partial v/\partial T)_P$ represents the slope of a line of constant pressure on a v-T plane. A similar interpretation can be given to the second derivative (Fig. 4·9). These derivatives are themselves intensive thermodynamic properties, since they have definite values at any fixed thermodynamic state. The first represents the sensitivity of the specific volume to changes in temperature at constant pressure, and the second is a measure of the change in specific volume associated with a change in pressure at constant temperature. Two

† Alternatively, this result can be obtained directly from the chain rule of the calculus of a function of two variables.

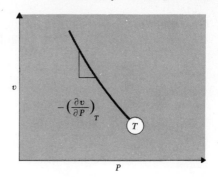

FIG. 4·9 *The slopes are intensive thermodynamic properties*

thermodynamic properties related to these derivatives are the *isobaric* (constant-pressure) *compressibility*,

$$\blacktriangleright \qquad \beta \equiv \frac{1}{v}\left(\frac{\partial v}{\partial T}\right)_P \qquad\qquad (4\cdot4)$$

and the *isothermal* (constant-temperature) *compressibility*,

$$\blacktriangleright \qquad \kappa \equiv -\frac{1}{v}\left(\frac{\partial v}{\partial P}\right)_T \qquad\qquad (4\cdot5)$$

These compressibility factors are frequently tabulated functions of state. The "coefficient of linear expansion" used in elementary strength-of-materials texts is $\frac{1}{3}\beta$. "Young's modulus of elasticity" is proportional to κ.

In terms of β and κ, Eq. (Eq. 4·3) becomes

$$dv = \beta v\, dT - \kappa v\, dP \qquad\qquad (4\cdot6)$$

This represents a differential equation relating specific volume to temperature and pressure on the equation-of-state surface. Its usefulness arises from the fact that β and κ are sometimes slowly varying functions of T and P. Equation (4·6) can be written as

$$\int_{v_0}^{v} \frac{dv}{v} = \int_{T_0}^{T} \beta\, dT - \int_{P_0}^{P} \kappa\, dP$$

If β and κ are constants, we can integrate from some state (T_0, P_0), where the specific volume is v_0, to any other state (T, P), obtaining

$$\ln \frac{v}{v_0} = \beta(T - T_0) - \kappa(P - P_0)$$

This is often an adequate approximation over limited pressure and temperature ranges.

It should be apparent that the calculus of functions of two variables is of considerable utility in the thermodynamics of simple substances. In particular, consider three functions x, y, and z, any two of which may be selected as the independent pair. Then, from calculus, it follows that†

$$\blacktriangleright \quad \left(\frac{\partial x}{\partial y}\right)_z = \frac{1}{(\partial y/\partial x)_z} \tag{4.7}$$

$$\blacktriangleright \quad \left(\frac{\partial x}{\partial y}\right)_z \left(\frac{\partial y}{\partial z}\right)_x \left(\frac{\partial z}{\partial x}\right)_y = -1 \tag{4.8}$$

To use these mathematical properties of functions, we for example note that, in regions of P-v-T space where P and T are independent, $v = v(P, T)$, so

$$\left(\frac{\partial P}{\partial T}\right)_v \left(\frac{\partial T}{\partial v}\right)_P \left(\frac{\partial v}{\partial P}\right)_T = -1$$

or

$$\left(\frac{\partial P}{\partial T}\right)_v = -\frac{(\partial v/\partial T)_P}{(\partial v/\partial P)_T} = \frac{\beta}{\kappa} \tag{4.9}$$

Hence, knowledge of the isobaric compressibility β and the isothermal compressibility κ would allow us to determine from Eq. (4·9) how the pressure changes with temperature for a constant-volume heating process. We shall make considerable use of the calculus of functions of several variables, and the student is urged to review this material now if necessary.

There are several properties related to the internal energy that are important. Suppose we view the specific internal energy u as being fixed by specification of T and v,

$$u = u(T, v)$$

The difference in energy between any two states separated by infinitesimal temperature and specific-volume differences dT and dv is then

$$du = \left(\frac{\partial u}{\partial T}\right)_v dT + \left(\frac{\partial u}{\partial v}\right)_T dv \tag{4.10}$$

† Consider $x = x(y, z)$ and $y = y(x, z)$. Then, from the chain rule,

$$dx = \left(\frac{\partial x}{\partial y}\right)_z dy + \left(\frac{\partial x}{\partial z}\right)_y dz$$

$$dy = \left(\frac{\partial y}{\partial x}\right)_z dx + \left(\frac{\partial y}{\partial z}\right)_x dz$$

Eliminating dy from these two equations,

$$\left[1 - \left(\frac{\partial x}{\partial y}\right)_z \left(\frac{\partial y}{\partial x}\right)_z\right] dx = \left[\left(\frac{\partial x}{\partial y}\right)_z \left(\frac{\partial y}{\partial z}\right)_x + \left(\frac{\partial x}{\partial z}\right)_y\right] dz$$

But the changes dx and dz are independent. Letting $dz = 0$, Eq. (4·7) follows. Letting $dx = 0$ and using Eq. (4·7), Eq. (4·8) is obtained.

The derivative $(\partial u/\partial T)_v$ represents the slope of a line of constant v on a u-T thermodynamic plane. The derivative is also a function of state, that is, a thermodynamic property, and is called the *specific heat at constant volume*,†

$$\blacktriangleright \qquad c_v \equiv \left(\frac{\partial u}{\partial T}\right)_v \qquad\qquad (4\cdot11)$$

Another thermodynamic property which we shall find to be of particular importance is the *enthalpy h* defined by‡

$$\blacktriangleright \qquad h \equiv u + Pv \qquad\qquad (4\cdot12)$$

We leave as an exercise the proof that the enthalpy of a liquid-vapor mixture is

$$\blacktriangleright \qquad h = (1 - x)h_f + xh_g \qquad\qquad (4\cdot13)$$

The enthalpy of a simple substance is obviously only a function of the thermodynamic state. For states where T and P are independent (single-phase states), we may put

$$h = h(T, P)$$

Then, taking the differential,

$$dh = \left(\frac{\partial h}{\partial T}\right)_P dT + \left(\frac{\partial h}{\partial P}\right)_T dP \qquad\qquad (4\cdot14)$$

The derivative $(\partial h/\partial T)_P$ is called the *specific heat at constant pressure*,§

$$\blacktriangleright \qquad c_P \equiv \left(\frac{\partial h}{\partial T}\right)_P \qquad\qquad (4\cdot15)$$

† The name given to c_v is somewhat unfortunate in that only for very special conditions is the derivative $(\partial u/\partial T)_v$ related to energy transfer as heat. If a process is carried out slowly at constant volume no work will be done, and any energy increase will be due solely to energy transfer as heat. For such a process c_v does represent the energy increase per unit of temperature rise (per unit of mass), and consequently historically was called the "specific heat at constant volume." We feel that c_v should be thought of in terms of its definition as a certain partial derivative, and not as being related to energy transfer as heat in the special constant-volume process.

‡ The product of pressure and specific volume has the units of energy per unit of mass, as does u. However, it is customary to give u values in Btu/lbm and measure pressure and volume in mechanical units (lbf and ft). One must be careful to make the two parts of the enthalpy dimensionally equivalent in any numerical computations. Enthalpy is sometimes called the "heat content," another term with more historical than physical significance.

§ c_P is sometimes called the "heat capacity at constant pressure." As with c_v, it is best to think of c_P as a partial derivative. Only in very special processes (constant pressure) is c_P related to energy transfer as heat, yet it is a useful thermodynamic function in many other situations. In engineering units the dimensions of c_P and c_v are usually written as Btu/lbm-°R. However, it would be better to write them as Btu/lbm-R°.

The derivatives c_P and c_v constitute two of the most important thermodynamic derivative functions, and values have been experimentally determined as functions of the thermodynamic state for a tremendous number of simple compressible substances.

4·8 THE PERFECT GAS

Under appropriate conditions, the equations of state for the vapor of any substance can be approximated by the algebraic equations of state for an "ideal" or "perfect" gas. The defining equation for the perfect gas is

▶ $$Pv = RT \tag{4·16}$$

Here R is a constant for a particular gas, and is related to the *universal gas constant* ℜ and the molal mass $\hat{M}$ by

▶ $$R = \frac{\Re}{\hat{M}} \tag{4·17}$$

where†

$$\Re = 1545 \text{ ft-lbf/lbmole-}°\text{R}$$

Note that T is the *absolute* temperature, °K or °R.

The value of R can be determined by plotting Pv/T as a function of state. In any region where this value is constant the perfect-gas approximation is adequate. Figure 8·10 shows the value of the *compressibility factor* $Z \equiv Pv/RT$ as a function of the ratio of the temperature and pressure to their values at the critical point; where the ratio Z is near unity the perfect-gas approximation is valid. Note that the perfect-gas model is best at pressures low compared to the critical pressure or at temperatures high compared to the critical temperature. We shall discuss the perfect-gas model in more detail in Chap. Eight, and here state only a few of its important features, which will be useful in the next chapter. Of particular importance are the algebraic equations of state, which are very useful in obtaining closed-form analytical solutions in engineering analysis.

One of the important features of a perfect gas is that its internal energy depends only upon its temperature. In Chap. Eight we will show that this must be the case for any gas obeying Eq. (4·16). This feature is also shown nicely in Figs. B·1 and B·4, where the isotherms are seen to coincide with lines of constant u in the vapor range at pressures well below the critical pressure. This type of inspection of the graphical equations of state for different substances provides an easy way to determine if the perfect-gas approximation will be valid in the range of interest. Since the Pv product for a perfect gas also depends only upon temperature, the enthalpy $h = u + Pv$ is also a function only of

† See also Table A·4.

temperature. Figures B·2, B·7, and B·8 likewise show that the isotherms correspond with lines of constant h for gases at low pressures. The region of perfect-gas behavior can be found by this type of examination. For example, in Fig. B·6 we see that the h and T lines for CO_2 do *not* coincide, indicating that it would not be reasonable to treat CO_2 as a perfect gas in the region covered. However, at higher temperatures CO_2 can be idealized as a perfect gas, provided that the pressure is not too great.

Since u depends only on T for a perfect gas, it follows from Eqs. (4·10) and (4·11) that

$$du = c_v(T) \, dT \tag{4·18}$$

Note that c_v depends only upon T for a perfect gas. Since h depends only on T for a perfect gas, it likewise follows from Eqs. (4·14) and (4·15) that

$$dh = c_P(T) \, dT \tag{4·19}$$

We also have

$$dh = du + d(Pv) = c_v \, dT + R \, dT$$

and hence, *for a perfect gas,*

$$c_P = c_v + R \tag{4·20}$$

We emphasize that in general u and h depend on the density as well as temperature; the perfect gas is a very special gas.

Figure B·17 shows the values of c_P, c_v, and $k = c_P/c_v$ for several gases. Note the specific heats do not depend very much on pressure; the $P = 0$ limit represents perfect gas behavior. Note that the low-pressure specific heats are slowly varying functions of temperature, increasing slightly with increasing temperature. At low temperatures the main contribution to the energy of a gas is provided by molecular translation. At higher temperatures there is more and more energy associated with molecular vibration and rotation, and this causes the slight increase in specific heats. Quantum-statistical thermodynamics can be used to evaluate c_p and c_v; cf. Reynolds, *Thermodynamics*, 2d ed., McGraw-Hill.

Since the specific heats are nearly constant over fairly wide ranges in temperature, it is often useful to treat them as constants, which allows us to integrate Eqs. (4·18) and (4·19) in closed form. Replacing c_v and c_P by their averages over the range of temperature in question, we integrate and find

$$u_1 - u_0 = c_v \cdot (T_1 - T_0) \tag{4·21}$$
$$h_1 - h_0 = c_P \cdot (T_1 - T_0) \tag{4·22}$$

These equations are very useful in calculating internal energy or enthalpy differences. It must be remembered that they hold only for a *perfect gas with constant specific heats;* it is the responsibility of the analyst to establish that this approximation is sufficiently good for the problem at hand. Appreciable errors can result if the gas involved departs significantly from this idealized behavior.

Table B·6 gives the values of R and nominal values for c_v, c_P, and k for several gases. If one needs to consider the variation of the specific heats with temperature, then the integrations must be performed numerically, using the measured functions $c_v(T)$ and $c_P(T)$. This has been done for several gases. Table B·9 gives the values for $h(T)$ and $u(T)$ for air, treated as a perfect gas with variable specific heats. An arbitrary temperature datum point was used for the lower limit of the u integration. Table B·13 gives additional data for the enthalpy *per mole* for several gases. The arbitrary datum for this tabulation is different than that for the other graphs and tables in Appendix B, and hence one should use either this data or other data, *but not both*, in any particular analysis. The other entries in these tables will be explained later in the text.

To illustrate the use of the perfect-gas equation of state in an engineering problem, suppose we consider the process of slow compression of air in a piston-cylinder system. Since the process is slow, there is adequate time for equalization of the gas and cylinder-wall temperatures through energy transfer as heat. We therefore assume that the process is one of constant temperature, and wish to calculate the amount of energy transfer as heat from the gas to the cylinder walls. The system diagram and process representation are shown in Fig. 4·10.

With some experience in thermodynamic analysis, the student will learn that this type of problem can be handled with reasonable accuracy by treating the air as a perfect gas with constant specific heats. The critical temperature for air is about 132°K, and the critical pressure is about 37 atmospheres. Thus, for room temperatures (300°K) and above the ratio $T^* = T/T_{\text{crit}}$ exceeds 2.2, and for pressures up to 10 atm the ratio $P^* = P/P_{\text{crit}}$ is less than 0.27. Figure 8·9 then indicates that the compressibility factor $Z \equiv Pv/RT$ is very close to unity in this range, and the perfect-gas model is therefore quite adequate for many purposes. Figure B·8 shows that the enthalpy and temperature lines nearly coincide over this range, which again suggests that the perfect-gas model might be adequate. Figure B·17 indicates that the specific heat of air will not vary much

FIG. 4·10

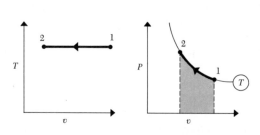

(a) *The control mass*   (b) *The process representation*

over a wide range of temperatures, so let's carry out the analysis treating air as a perfect gas with constant specific heats.

An energy balance on the control mass gives

$$\underset{\substack{\text{energy} \\ \text{input}}}{W} = \underset{\substack{\text{energy} \\ \text{output}}}{Q} + \underset{\substack{\text{increase in} \\ \text{energy storage}}}{\Delta U}$$

where W and Q are the energy transfer as work and heat as defined in Fig. $4 \cdot 10a$. Since the initial and final temperatures are identical, the initial and final internal energies of the gas (treated as a perfect gas) are identical, and hence $\Delta U = 0$ (*we again remark that this is a feature peculiar to the perfect gas*). We can use the energy balance to calculate Q if W can be evaluated. Assuming that the P-v-T relationship during the process is the same as those for equilibrium states (this will be a good approximation if the process is slow such that at any instant the gas is nearly in thermodynamic equilibrium), the work done on the gas for the isothermal process is

$$W = \int_1^2 - P \, dV = -M \int_1^2 P \, dv = -MRT \int_1^2 \frac{1}{v} \, dv$$

$$= MRT \ln \frac{v_1}{v_2} = MRT \ln \frac{V_1}{V_2}$$

So, if we have 4 lbm of air for which $R = 0.0686$ Btu/lbm-°R (Table B·6), T is 20°F (480°R), and $V_1/V_2 = 2$,

$$W = 4 \times 0.0686 \times 480 \times \ln (2) = 91 \text{ Btu}$$

Then, from the energy balance, since $\Delta u = 0$,

$$Q = 0 + W = 91 \text{ Btu}$$

This example forms a good point for the student to focus sharply on the differences between internal energy, heat, and temperature.

As a second example, let's solve the problem of Sec. $4 \cdot 6$ using the perfect-gas approximation. The energy balance is the same (Fig. $4 \cdot 8$), namely

$$Q = M(u_2 - u_1)$$

This time we treat the H_2O vapor as a perfect gas, with (Table B·6) $c_v = 0.336$ Btu/lbm-°R. Then, using Eq. ($4 \cdot 21$),

$$u_2 - u_1 = c_v(T_2 - T_1) = 0.336 \times (1660 - 660) = 336 \text{ Btu/lbm}$$

and

$$Q = 5 \times 336 = 1680 \text{ Btu}$$

Note that this result is in error by approximately 7 percent in comparison to the exact value previously determined as 1800 Btu. Now, the final pressure is calculated from Eq. (4·16), which gives

$$\frac{P_2}{P_1} = \frac{T_2}{T_1}$$

Hence,

$$P_2 = {}^{1660}\!/_{660} \times 2 = 5.03 \text{ psia}$$

If we did not have access to the exact property tabulations for water vapor, we might estimate the specific volume using Eq. (4·16). For H_2O, $R = 85.58$ ft-lbf/lbm-°R (Table B·6). Then, at state 1,

$$v_1 = \frac{RT_1}{P_1} = 85.58 \times \frac{(200 + 460)}{2 \times 144} = 196 \text{ ft}^3/\text{lbm}$$

which is within about 1 percent of the tabulated value.

We can check the applicability of the perfect-gas approximation by computing the value of $Z \equiv Pv/RT$ at states 1 and 2. Using the state data collected in Sec. 4·6,

$$Z_1 = \frac{P_1 v_1}{RT_1} = \frac{2 \times 144 \times 198}{85.58 \times (200 + 460)} = 1.01$$

$$Z_2 = \frac{P_2 v_2}{RT_2} = \frac{5 \times 144 \times 198}{85.58 \times (1200 + 460)} = 1.003$$

Note that both values are very close to unity. Since both states have the same density, the state of higher temperature (2) should more closely resemble the perfect gas, and this is indeed the case. The main error in the simplified analysis is not the assumption that $Pv = RT$, but the idealization that c_v is constant over the wide range of temperatures involved.

4·9 THE SIMPLE MAGNETIC SUBSTANCE

While magnetic solids are indeed compressible, the work associated with magnetization usually is much more important than the work of compression, and it is often reasonable to idealize that such a substance is a *simple magnetic substance*. The temperature and magnetization (magnetic-dipole moment) may be taken as an independent set of intensive thermodynamic properties, and the internal energy may be expressed as

$$u = u(T, \mathbf{M})$$

A *specific heat at constant magnetization* can be defined as

$$c_{\mathbf{M}} \equiv \left(\frac{\partial u}{\partial T}\right)_{\mathbf{M}} \tag{4·23}$$

Using the manipulations of calculus, we can develop the analog of Eq. (4·9),

$$\left(\frac{\partial \mathbf{H}}{\partial T}\right)_{\mathbf{M}} = -\frac{(\partial \mathbf{M}/\partial T)_{\mathbf{H}}}{(\partial \mathbf{M}/\partial \mathbf{H})_T} \tag{4·24}$$

A graphical equation of state for one common paramagnetic salt is shown in Fig. B·12.

SELECTED READING

Jones, J. B., and G. A. Hawkins, *Engineering Thermodynamics*, chaps. 3 and 5, John Wiley & Sons, Inc., New York, 1960.

Keenan, J. H., and F. G. Keys, *Thermodynamic Properties of Steam*, introduction, John Wiley & Sons, Inc., New York, 1936.

Lee, J. F., and F. W. Sears, *Thermodynamics*, chap. 2, Addison-Wesley Publishing Co., Inc., Reading, Mass., 1963.

Van Wylen, G. J., and R. E. Sonntag, *Fundamentals of Classical Thermodynamics*, chap. 3, secs. 5.11 and 5.13, John Wiley & Sons, Inc., New York, 1965.

Zemansky, M. W., and H. C. Van Ness, *Basic Engineering Thermodynamics*, chap. 5, secs. 11.1–11.10, McGraw-Hill Book Company, New York, 1966.

QUESTIONS

4·1 What is state? What is a property? How many independent intensive thermodynamic properties does a simple substance have?

4·2 What is a phase? What is the vapor dome? What is a superheated vapor? What is a supercritical state? What is a saturated liquid?

4·3 What happens when a saturated liquid is heated at constant pressure? What happens when it is cooled at constant pressure?

4·4 What happens when a saturated liquid is heated at constant volume?

4·5 What do you think happens when a saturated vapor is compressed adiabatically? What happens when it is expanded adiabatically?

4·6 What are the definitions of h, c_v, and c_P?

4·7 Lead blocks sink in liquid lead; does lead expand or contract upon melting?

4·8 Why do the liquid and vapor in a mixture of the same substance have the same temperature and pressure? Would two gases in a mixture each exert the same pressure?

4·9 What is your estimate of the pressure of the freon-12 (liquid and vapor) in the pipes of a refrigerator that has been idle for several days (see Fig. B·7)?

4·10 If ice is thrown into a hot pressure cooker and the mixture is allowed to cool on the stove, will it end up at the triple point?

4·11 Give a molecular explanation of evaporation and one of sublimation.

4·12 What thermodynamic-property data can you find in your chemistry or engineering handbook?

4·13 Why are saturation states simpler to tabulate than superheated-vapor or subcooled-liquid states?

4·14 Why do we arbitrarily select the energy of a substance to be zero at some point? How must this point be described (pressure, temperature, or both)?

4·15 Why is it not true that $\rho = (1 - x)\rho_f + x\rho_g$, where ρ is the mass density $(\rho = 1/v)$?

4·16 How can we tell if a gas behaves like a perfect gas?

PROBLEMS

4·1 What are the enthalpy and internal energy of a mixture of mercury of 0.40 quality at 1000°F? What are the volume fractions of the liquid and vapor in the mixture (see Table B·3)?

4·2 Calculate the values of ρ, u, and h for a liquid-vapor H_2O mixture of 0.2 quality at 1 atm (Table B·1b).

4·3 Calculate the values of v, u, and h for a liquid-vapor H_2O mixture of 0.2 quality at 600°F (Table B·1a).

4·4 Calculate the value of h_{fg} for nitrogen at 1 atm using the data of Fig. B·4.

4·5 Calculate the value of u_{fg} for CO_2 at 100 psia using the data of Fig. B·6.

4·6 Look up the enthalpy of saturated methyl-chloride vapor at 100°F in the *Handbook of Chemistry and Physics*.

4·7 Liquid oxygen in a rocket-propellant tank is at a pressure somewhere near 1 atm. From Fig. B·5 estimate the temperature of the lox-vapor mixture.

4·8 Compare the volume changes undergone by 1 lbm of water upon evaporation at 1 atm pressure, at 500°F, and at the critical point.

4·9 In order to illustrate the nature of the critical point, one can place CO_2 in a quartz vial, and seal the device. Assuming that $v_{crit} = 0.04$ ft³/lbm, and that the device is filled at "room temperature" (60°F), and using Fig. B·6, find: (a) the pressure in the vial at room temperature; (b) the proper percent liquid mass to assure passage through the critical point upon heating; (c) the percent liquid *volume* associated with part (b). (Calculate v_f from x, v_{mix}, and v_g.)

4·10 Using the data of Appendix B, estimate β, κ, h, c_v, and c_P for H_2O at 1000°F and 100 psia.

4·11 Using the data of Table B·7, estimate the density of copper, in lbm/in.³, at 100°F and 5 atm pressure.

4·12 Taking the internal energy of copper to be zero at 50°K and 1 atm pressure, prepare a curve showing the internal energy as a function of temperature at 1 atm, using the data of Table B·7. Give u in Btu/lbm and T in °F.

4·13 Calculate the approximate value of c_v for the liquid studied in Prob. 3·6.

4·14 Calculate the approximate value of c_v for the gas studied in Prob. 3·7.

4·15 Calculate the value of c_P for the liquid material in Prob. 3·8.

4·16 Calculate the approximate value of c_P for the gas studied in Prob. 3·9.

4·17 Calculate the value of c_v for the gas studied in Prob. 3·10 and plot as a function of temperature at that specific volume.

4·18 Using Fig. B·12 as a guide, sketch a three-dimensional **M-H-**T surface for a paramagnetic salt.

4·19 Sketch u-T and v-T diagrams for H_2O, showing lines of constant pressure. Include the liquid, vapor, and mixed-phase regions.

4·20 Verify that Eq. (4·9) holds for a perfect gas by differentiation and substitution.

4·21 Estimate the temperature to which water at the bottom of a 500-ft-deep lake would have to be heated before it would begin to boil.

4·22 Plot the ratio Pv/T versus T for H_2O along a line of 1 atm pressure and show the conditions under which the perfect-gas approximation is reasonable. Taking $\hat{M}$ to be 18.016 lbm/lbmole, evaluate the universal-gas constant and compare with the accepted value.

4·23 A Curie substance is any magnetic substance obeying the simple equation of state $M = CH/T$, where C is the Curie constant. Plot M versus H for iron-ammonium alum (Fig. B·12) along a line of $T = 1°K$, find the region in which Curie's law is obeyed, and determine the value of the Curie constant.

4·24 What are the values of the specific heat at constant volume and the specific heat at constant pressure of H_2O of 0.30 quality at 100 psia?

4·25 Determine the value of c_M for iron-ammonium alum (Fig. B·12) at $1°K$ in a weak external field. Express the result in Btu/lbm-°R and compare with the corresponding specific heat of saturated H_2O vapor at 1 atm pressure.

4·26 What are the values of $(\partial v/\partial T)_P$, $(\partial P/\partial v)_T$, $(\partial v/\partial P)_T$, and $(\partial T/\partial P)_v$ for a perfect gas?

4·27 For a Curie substance M, H, and T are related by $M = CH/T$, where C is a constant. Evaluate $(\partial H/\partial T)_M$, $(\partial M/\partial H)_T$, $(\partial T/\partial H)_M$, and $(\partial T/\partial M)_H$. Express the meaning of each term in words.

4·28 Consider a dielectric substance for which $P = (\kappa - 1)\epsilon_0 E$, where κ is the dielectric "constant" and ϵ_0 is a physical constant (Table A·2). κ normally depends upon temperature. Assuming $\kappa = \kappa_0[1 + a(T - T_0)]$, evaluate $(\partial P/\partial T)_E$, $(\partial P/\partial E)_T$, $(\partial E/\partial T)_P$, and $(\partial E/\partial P)_T$. Express the meaning of each in words.

4·29 Compute the density of gaseous H_2O at each of the following states using the perfect-gas model, and compare with the actual values given in Table B·2.
1 psia, 200°F   1 atm, 800°F   3000 psia, 700°F

4·30 Compute the density of gaseous CO_2 at each of the following states using the perfect-gas model, and compare with the actual values given in Fig. B·6.
10 psia, 20°F   150 psia, 60°F   1500 psia, 140°F

CHAPTER FIVE

ENERGY ANALYSIS OF THERMODYNAMIC SYSTEMS

5·1 GENERAL METHODOLOGY

The conservation-of-energy statement and equations of state permit solution of a number of interesting and important technical problems. Additional concepts and tools are needed for complete thermodynamic analysis, but we shall begin to apply the ideas of the first law and state at this point in order to indicate the manner in which thermodynamics is used in engineering.

First-law analysis is essentially an accounting procedure, in which we take account of energy transfers to and from a system and of changes of energy inside the system. There are two main types of accounting procedures. In *control-mass analysis* we write the conservation-of-energy equation for a specified piece of matter, while in *control-volume analysis* we work instead with specified regions in space.† The latter being somewhat more difficult, we shall begin by illustrating energy analysis for a control mass.

An accounting procedure must be carried out over a set accounting period, and an essential step in control-mass analysis is specification of the *time base*. This might be a given period of time, or the time required for something to happen, or we might specify that our accounting be done on an *instantaneous-rate* basis. Some specification is necessary.

The accounting will be carried out with symbols used to represent energy transfers to and from the control mass, and some sort of sign convention must always be set up for the energy flows. The important thing in first-law analysis is to recognize all the energy transfers and changes that take place and to relate these in a proper mathematical manner. The sign convention chosen for W and

---

† The terms "system," or "closed system," and "open system" are used by many texts instead of "control mass" and "control volume."

Q is not particularly important, provided that both the person doing the analysis and the one reading it understand what it is. We shall adopt the policy of selecting whatever convention seems appropriate for the analysis at hand and indicate the directions of *positive* energy flows by arrows on the system sketch. This scheme has the additional advantage that the energy flows to be considered are all identified, and where and how the energy crosses the boundary is quite clear. There should always be a one-to-one correspondence between the energy flows shown on the system sketch and those that appear in the energy balance.

In working with energy changes we shall follow the conventions of calculus, in which dx and Δx always represent *increases* in the value of x. ΔE will always represent an *increase* in the energy stored within the control mass.

Having made the energy balance, the next step is to bring in enough other information to permit reduction of the problem to one equation in one unknown. This information might be in the form of equations of state, information about the nature of the process, or other information obtained by applying the principle of conservation of mass, Newton's law, or other fundamental principles to the system.

In any analysis various approximations, or *idealizations*, must be made to reduce the problem to a manageable size. These idealizations must be clearly understood by both the analyst and the reader of his analysis, and hence we prefer to list these specifically at the start of the analysis. Sometimes idealizations are implicitly indicated on the system sketch; for example, the absence of an energy transfer term Q would imply that we idealize that energy transfer as heat is negligible during the time period over which the energy balance will be made. Such idealizations should be specifically listed to assure their communication to the reader.

We cannot emphasize enough the importance of a good system sketch, complete with all the relevant energy-transfer terms. A good sketch can be of great value to the analyst in getting his thinking straight about the process, in helping him be consistent throughout the analysis, and also in helping him see what steps must be taken to complete the analysis.

An equally important working diagram is the *process representation*. This is one or more diagrams showing what happens to matter within the system on suitable thermodynamic planes. In most analyses one must find some way to fix the states of the matter at the start or finish of the process, and the process representation is of great value in helping the analyst feel his way through a complex problem. Hence, one should always try to draw the process representation *before* carrying out the analysis in order to orient his thinking properly and efficiently.

In summary, the general methodology for energy-balance analysis is as follows:

1   Define the system carefully and completely, indicating its boundaries on a sketch (control mass or control volume?).

2   List the relevant idealizations.

3   Indicate the flows of energy to be considered in the energy balance, and set up their sign convention on the system sketch.

4   Indicate the time basis for the energy balance.

5   Sketch the process representation.

6   Write the energy balance in terms of the symbols shown on the system sketch; there should be a one-to-one correspondence between the terms in the equation and those on the sketch.

7   Bring in equations of state or other information as necessary to allow solution of the problem.

We shall now illustrate this methodology for the control mass by example. The analyses which follow were selected to illustrate different aspects of first-law analysis from the control-mass viewpoint. Different kinds of idealizations are introduced in the various developments, the use of graphical and tabular equations of state are demonstrated, and some important definitions and general consequences are given. Every one of the examples should be studied carefully, even though they may appear to be extremely simple and straightforward (as indeed they are, if a systematic methodology is followed).

5·2 EXAMPLES OF CONTROL-MASS ENERGY ANALYSIS

Evaporation at constant pressure. Three lbm of H_2O, in a piston-cylinder system, is initially in the saturated-liquid state at 100 psia. Energy is added slowly to the water as heat, and the piston moves in such a way that the pressure remains constant. How much work is done by the water, and how much energy must be transferred as heat in order to bring the water to the saturated-vapor state? See Fig. 5·1.

We could select the water or the water plus the piston as the control mass. Since we are interested in energy transfers to the water, and the piston is merely a means for maintaining the constant pressure, we take only the water as our

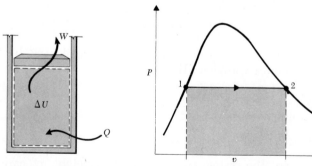

FIG. 5·1

(a) *The control mass*

(b) *The process representation*

control mass. The change of state is depicted by the process representation, which is nicely shown on a P-v plane.

In order to solve the problem we idealize that the changes in the gravitational potential energy of the water are negligible in comparison with the changes in the internal energy. We idealize further that the presence of the gravitational field does not significantly alter the behavior of the water molecules, so that the relationships between the thermodynamic properties are the same as if the water were truly a simple compressible substance. In short, we idealize that the water behaves like a simple compressible substance and is in equilibrium states at the start and end of the process.

Employing these idealizations, the energy balance, made over the period for the process to occur, is

$$\underset{\substack{\text{energy} \\ \text{input}}}{Q} = \underset{\substack{\text{energy} \\ \text{output}}}{W} + \underset{\substack{\text{increase in} \\ \text{energy storage}}}{\Delta U}$$

where

$$\Delta U = M(u_2 - u_1)$$

Fixing the initial and final states from Table B·1, at the initial state (saturated liquid at 100 psia)

$P_1 = 100$ psia $\qquad\qquad T_1 = 327.81°F$
$u_1 = 298.08$ Btu/lbm $\qquad v_1 = 0.01774$ ft^3/lbm

and at the final state (saturated vapor at 100 psia)

$P_2 = 100$ psia $\qquad\qquad T_2 = 327.81°F$
$u_2 = 1105.2$ Btu/lbm $\qquad v_2 = 4.432$ ft^3/lbm

Note that the volume occupied by the water increases tremendously.

We could now compute the net energy added to the water, but as yet we cannot tell how much is added as heat and how much is taken away as work. The fact that the pressure remains constant during the process allows us to compute the work very simply. The work done by the water is

$$W = \int_1^2 dW = \int_1^2 P\, dV = M \int_1^2 P\, dv$$

Since the pressure is constant,

$$W = MP(v_2 - v_1)$$

The work done is therefore

$$W = 3 \text{ lbm} \times 100 \text{ lbf/in.}^2 \times 144 \text{ in.}^2/\text{ft}^2 \times (4.432 - 0.017) \text{ ft}^3/\text{lbm}$$

$$= 191{,}000 \text{ ft-lbf} \times \frac{1 \text{ Btu}}{778 \text{ ft-lbf}} = 245 \text{ Btu}$$

We can finally calculate the energy added as heat:

$$Q = 245 \text{ Btu} + 3 \text{ lbm} \times (1105.2 - 298.08) \text{ Btu/lbm} = 2665 \text{ Btu}$$

The energy transfer as heat could have been calculated directly if we had noticed that it is expressible as

$$Q = M[P(v_2 - v_1) + (u_2 - u_1)] = M(h_2 - h_1)$$

Note that the energy transfer as heat (per unit of mass) to a simple compressible substance during a constant pressure process is equal to the increase in its enthalpy.

Values for h_1 and h_2 could have been obtained from Table B·1.

The energy transfer as heat required to evaporate a unit of mass of a simple compressible substance at *constant pressure* is therefore simply $h_g - h_f = h_{fg}$ and is sometimes called the *enthalpy of evaporation*† of that substance. Note that it depends on pressure and vanishes at the critical point.

A dry-ice cooler. One lbm of dry ice (CO_2) at 1 atm pressure is placed on top of a piece of meat in a cooler. The dry ice sublimes at constant pressure as a result of energy transfer as heat from the warmer meat. What is the temperature of the CO_2, and how much energy is transferred as heat from the meat? See Fig. 5·2.

For the control mass we pick the CO_2, including the solid and vapor. The boundary of this control mass moves as the solid sublimes, and so there will be energy transfer as work, in this case from the expanding CO_2 to the environment. We assume no energy transfer as heat from the CO_2 to the surrounding air and neglect mixing of the CO_2 with the air. The energy balance is then

$$\underset{\substack{\text{energy} \\ \text{input}}}{Q} = \underset{\substack{\text{energy} \\ \text{output}}}{W} + \underset{\substack{\text{increase in} \\ \text{energy storage}}}{\Delta U}$$

† The term "latent heat of vaporization" is also used.

FIG. 5·2

(a) *The control mass*   (b) *The process representation*

where

$$\Delta U = M(u_2 - u_1)$$

As in the previous example, the work done by the expanding CO_2 is related to the pressure (constant by assumption) and the volume change,

$$W = MP(v_2 - v_1)$$

Solving for the energy transfer as heat to the CO_2 and expressing it in terms of the change in the enthalpy property,

$$Q = M[(u_2 - u_1) + P(v_2 - v_1)]$$
$$= M[(u_2 + P_2 v_2) - (u_1 + P_1 v_1)] = M(h_2 - h_1)$$

The equation of state for CO_2 is given on a *temperature-entropy plane* in Fig. B·6. The entropy is an important thermodynamic property which we shall discuss in the next chapters. For the time being we can use the equation of state as given in Fig. B·6 without worrying about this property. The initial state is saturated solid at 1 atm, and from Fig. B·6 we read the enthalpy of this state as 31 Btu/lbm. The final state, 2, is saturated vapor at 1 atm, for which we read the enthalpy as 276 Btu/lbm. The positions of these states on the temperature-entropy diagram are indicated on the process representation in Fig. 5·2b.

From Fig. B·6 we also read the saturation temperature corresponding to 15 psia as −108°F. The energy transferred as heat from the meat to the CO_2 is then

$$Q = 1 \text{ lbm} \times (276 - 31) \text{ Btu/lbm} = 245 \text{ Btu}$$

The difference h_{sg} is called the *enthalpy of sublimation*† and represents the energy which must be added as heat to completely sublime a unit of mass of a substance at constant pressure.

Thermal magnetization. One cm^3 of the paramagnetic substance iron-ammonium alum is magnetized in a constant external field H of 5000 gauss by cooling. The initial temperature is 1°K and the final temperature is 0.5°K; how much energy must be transferred as heat from the alum? See Fig. 5·3.

† Sublimation is the transformation of a solid directly into a gas at constant pressure. The term "latent heat of sublimation" is sometimes used for $h_{sg} = h_g - h_s$.

FIG. 5·3

(a) *The control mass*   (b) *The process representation*

This problem is complicated by the fact that the thermodynamic-property data (Fig. B·12) are given in absolute magnetostatic units, while the expressions for work of magnetization given in Chap. Two are in the rationalized mksc system. The required unit conversions will be good practice.

The energy terms considered to be important are shown on the control-mass diagram; the energy balance, made over the time for the process to occur, is

$$\underset{\substack{\text{energy} \\ \text{input}}}{W} = \underset{\substack{\text{energy} \\ \text{output}}}{Q} + \underset{\substack{\text{increase in} \\ \text{energy storage}}}{\Delta U}$$

where

$$\Delta U = M(u_2 - u_1)$$

From the graphical equation of state we obtain the initial and final internal energies (assuming that the initial and final states are states of thermodynamic equilibrium),

$$u_1 = 1.56 \times 10^4 \text{ ergs/g} \qquad u_2 = 1.39 \times 10^4 \text{ ergs/g}$$

Idealizing the alum as a simple magnetic substance, the work done on the alum by the external field is [see Eq. (2·17)]

$$W = \int_1^2 dW = \int_1^2 V\mu_0 \mathsf{H} \, d\mathsf{M}$$

The work calculation is made particularly simple by the fact that the applied field is held constant. For constant H the work becomes

$$W = \mu_0 V \mathsf{H}(\mathsf{M}_2 - \mathsf{M}_1)$$

From Fig. B·12 we read the initial and final magnetizations as

$$\mathsf{M}_1 = 62 \text{ gauss} \qquad \mathsf{M}_2 = 84 \text{ gauss}$$

We choose to convert everything to the rationalized mksc unit system. From Appendix A we find the dimensional equivalents

1 gauss of H = 79.6 coul/sec-m of H
1 gauss of M = 1000 coul/sec-m of M

Then, in the rationalized mksc system we have

$$\mathsf{H} = 40 \times 10^4 \text{ coul/sec-m}$$
$$\mathsf{M}_1 = 62 \times 10^3 \text{ coul/sec-m}$$
$$\mathsf{M}_2 = 84 \times 10^3 \text{ coul/sec-m}$$
$$\mu_0 = 1.256 \times 10^{-6} \text{ kg-m/coul}^2$$

The energy transfer as work to the alum is therefore

$$W = (0.01 \text{ m})^3 \times 1.256 \times 10^{-6} \text{ kg-m/coul}^2 \times 40 \times 10^4 \text{ coul/sec-m}$$
$$\times (84 - 62) \times 10^3 \text{ coul/sec-m}$$
$$= 0.0109 \text{ kg-m}^2/\text{sec}^2 = 0.0109 \text{ joule}$$

The density of the alum is (Fig. B·12) 1.71 g/cm³. The internal-energy increase is therefore

$$M(u_2 - u_1) = 1.71 \text{ g} \times (1.39 \times 10^4 - 1.56 \times 10^4)(\text{g-cm}^2/\text{sec})/\text{g}$$
$$= -0.3 \times 10^4 \text{ erg} = -0.0003 \text{ joule}$$

So the energy which must be transferred from the alum as heat is

$$Q = 0.0109 - (-0.0003) \text{ joule} = 0.0112 \text{ joule}$$

This energy is transferred to some environment at a temperature *lower* than 0.5°K.

Thermal mixing at constant pressure. Two lbm of saturated-liquid mercury at 1 psia is mixed with 4 lbm of 1400°F mercury vapor at 1 psia. The mixing vessel is such that the pressure remains constant during this process, and no energy transfer as heat occurs between the vessel and the mercury. Determine the equilibrium state reached by this mixture.

In the previous examples the control mass was in a state of equilibrium at the start of the process, so the calculation of the initial energy was quite straightforward. In this example we shall see how to make the corresponding evaluation for a system that is not in equilibrium.

Since the amount of liquid might change during the process, we cannot take only the liquid or only the vapor as the control mass. Instead we take the entire 6 lbm of mercury. By assumption, no energy transfer as heat occurs, but we do expect the volume to change, resulting in an energy transfer as work. The only energy stored within the control mass is the internal energy of the mercury; the energy balance, made over the time for the process to take place, is therefore (Fig. 5.4)

$$\underset{\substack{\text{energy} \\ \text{input}}}{W} = \underset{\substack{\text{increase in} \\ \text{energy storage}}}{\Delta U}$$

FIG. 5·4

(a) *The control mass*

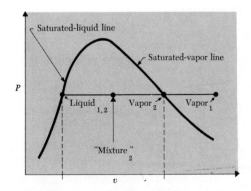

(b) *The process representation*

where

$$\Delta U = U_2 - U_1$$

The work calculation is again made easy by the fact that the pressure is constant. When the piston moves in an amount dx, the energy transfer as work from the environment to the control mass is

$$dW = PA\ dx = -P\ dV$$

Integrating,

$$W = \int_1^2 -P\ dV = P(V_1 - V_2)$$

Combining with the energy balance,

$$U_2 + PV_2 = U_1 + PV_1 \tag{5.1}$$

To evaluate the initial terms we assume that the liquid is in an equilibrium state and the vapor is in an equilibrium state, even though they are not in equilibrium with one another. The graphical and tabular equations of state, Fig. B·10 and Table B·3, may then be employed for each phase. Since the available equation-of-state information is in terms of the enthalpy property, we express the right-hand side of Eq. (5·1) as

$$U_1 + PV_1 = M_{l_1}u_{l_1} + M_{v_1}u_{v_1} + P(M_{l_1}v_{l_1} + M_{v_1}v_{v_1})$$
$$= M_{l_1}h_{l_1} + M_{v_1}h_{v_1}$$

Now, from the tables, the initial liquid enthalpy is (saturated liquid at 1 psia, Table B·3)

$$h_{l_1} = 13.96\ \text{Btu/lbm}$$
$$T_1 = 457.7°\text{F}$$

The initial vapor enthalpy is found from Fig. B·10 as

$$h_{v_1} = 164\ \text{Btu/lbm}$$

Substituting the numbers,

$$U_1 + PV_1 = 2 \times 13.96 + 4 \times 164 = 684\ \text{Btu}$$

The final state is a state of equilibrium, for which

$$U_2 + PV_2 = M(u + Pv)_2 = Mh_2$$

The enthalpy in the final state is therefore

$$h_2 = \frac{684\ \text{Btu}}{6\ \text{lbm}} = 114\ \text{Btu/lbm}$$

The final pressure and enthalpy may be used to fix the final state. Upon inspection of Fig. B·10 we see that the final state is a mixture of saturated liquid and vapor at 1 psia and that the "moisture" $(1 - x)$ is about 21 percent (0.79 quality). Alternatively, we could use the information in Table B·3:

$$114 = (1 - x_2) \times 13.96 + x_2 \times 140.7$$
$$x_2 = 0.79$$

A pneumatic lift. Air is used in a pneumatic lift (Fig. 5·5). The air is initially contained in a 10 ft³ steel tank at 80°F and 100 psia. When lifting is required, the valve is opened and air is bled out into the cylinder. The cylinder is initially filled with air at 1 atm, 60°F, has a cross-sectional area of 1 ft², and a lifting height of 3 ft. Its initial volume is 0.5 ft³. When the pressure in the cylinder reaches 50 psia the load begins to move upward, maintaining this cylinder pressure until the piston has traveled 3 ft. The load then stops, but air continues to flow into the cylinder. Eventually the pressures in the tank and cylinder are equal, and through energy transfer as heat all the air attains a temperature of 60°F. Calculate the final air pressure and the amount of energy transfer as heat from the tank walls to the air.

In making the energy balance we consider the time period from the start to the end, where the air is in equilibrium throughout the system, and the load is at its highest point. We take the air as the control mass, and consider the energy flows indicated in Fig. 5·5. The energy balance is

$$\underset{\substack{\text{energy} \\ \text{input}}}{Q} = \underset{\substack{\text{energy} \\ \text{output}}}{W} + \underset{\substack{\text{increase in} \\ \text{energy storage}}}{\Delta U}$$

In order to calculate Q we must first evaluate ΔU and W. The work computation is facilitated by consideration of the process representation. Work will be done by the control mass on the piston only when the piston is moving, and during this period the cylinder pressure is assumed to remain at 50 psia. During this period the force exerted by the gas on the piston is $144 \times 50 = 7200$ lbf, and the piston moves a distance of 3 ft. Hence

$$W = 7200 \times 3 = 21{,}600 \text{ ft-lbf}/(778 \text{ ft-lbf/Btu})$$
$$= 27.8 \text{ Btu}$$

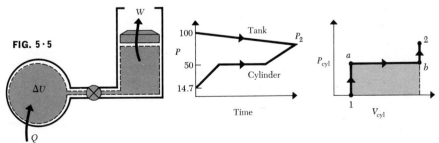

FIG. 5·5

(a) *The control mass*   (b) *The process representation*

Idealizing that the air behaves as a perfect gas, we have enough information to establish the initial and final air states completely. From Table B·6, we obtain the following constants for air:

$$c_v = 0.171 \text{ Btu/lbm-}°\text{R} \qquad R = 53.3 \text{ ft-lbf/lbm-}°\text{R}$$

Initial state

Tank air   80°F(=540°R), 100 psia
     Using Eq. (4·16),

$$\rho = \frac{1}{v} = \frac{P}{RT} = \frac{100 \times 144}{53.3 \times 540} = 0.498 \text{ lbm/ft}^3$$

Hence

$$M_t = 10 \times 0.498 = 4.98 \text{ lbm}$$

Using Eq. (4·21), with $T_0 = 0°\text{F} = 460°\text{R}$,

$$u_t = 0.171 \times (540 - 460) = 13.7 \text{ Btu/lbm}$$

Hence

$$U_t = Mu = 4.98 \times 13.7 = 68.1 \text{ Btu}$$

Cylinder air   60°F (= 520°R), 14.7 psia

$$\rho = \frac{P}{RT} = \frac{14.7 \times 144}{53.3 \times 520} = 0.0764 \text{ lbm/ft}^3$$
$$M_c = 0.5 \times 0.0764 = 0.038 \text{ lbm}$$
$$u_c = 0.171 \times (520 - 460) = 10.3 \text{ Btu/lbm}$$
$$U_c = 0.038 \times 10.3 = 0.39 \text{ Btu}$$

So, the total mass and energy in the initial configuration are

$$M = 4.98 + 0.038 = 5.02 \text{ lbm}$$
$$U_1 = 68.1 + 0.39 = 68.5 \text{ Btu}$$

Final state   All air at 60°F (520°R)
     The total final volume is

$$V = 10.00 + 0.5 + 3.0 = 13.5 \text{ ft}^3$$

Hence the final density is

$$\rho_2 = \frac{M}{V} = \frac{5.02}{13.5} = 0.372 \text{ lbm/ft}^3$$

The final pressure is, from Eq. (4·16),

$$P_2 = \rho_2 R T_2 = 0.372 \times 53.3 \times 520 = 10,400 \text{ lbf/ft}^2$$
$$= 71.7 \text{ psia}$$

The final specific internal energy is [Eq. $(4 \cdot 21)$]

$u_2 = 0.171 \times (520 - 460) = 10.3 \text{ Btu/lbm}$

So

$U_2 = Mu_2 = 5.02 \times 10.3 = 52.0 \text{ Btu}$

We now calculate the internal energy increase as

$\Delta U = U_2 - U_1 = 52.0 - 68.5 = -16.5 \text{ Btu}$

(The minus sign indicates that the internal energy actually decreases.) Substituting for W and ΔU in the energy balance,

$Q = 27.8 + (-16.5) = 11.3 \text{ Btu}$

The student should particularly note the manner in which we used the process representations to orient our thinking and to guide the analysis.

A steady-flow system. The previous examples of control-mass analysis have dealt exclusively with nonflow systems, for which the control-mass method is ideal. Flow systems are of great interest in engineering, and the control-volume view is better suited to analysis of such systems. In a moment we are going to work out a proper energy equation for a control volume, and subsequently we shall consider all flow problems from the control-volume point of view. However, flow problems may be worked by the control-mass method, though this is somewhat awkward. In the interests of motivating the control-volume transformation and clarifying the physics involved, we shall now do a particular flow-system analysis by the *control-mass* method.

Consider a rather general "black-box" device, where fluid flows in one end and out the other. Energy is transferred as heat to the box, and power is transmitted into the device through a rotating shaft. We define the control mass to be the box and all its contents, and the fluid in the inlet and discharge pipes from section 1 through section 2 at time t. This control mass is indicated in Fig. $5 \cdot 6$.

The analysis will be made over an infinitesimal time interval dt. During this period the control mass will move, and its position at time $t + dt$ is indicated in Fig. $5 \cdot 6$. We shall assume that the inlet and discharge flows are *one-dimensional,* meaning that the velocities and thermodynamic properties are constant across the inlet and exit pipes. We also idealize this as a *steady-flow steady-state* situation, meaning that the velocities and thermodynamic properties *at each point in space* are unchanging in time.†

Let's illustrate the approach to be used in the energy analysis in a simpler analysis of the mass conservation. Applying the conservation-of-mass principle

† The state of a piece of fluid passing through the device does change; and the states of the fluid at various positions within the device may be different.

Control-mass boundary at time t

Control-mass boundary at time $t + dt$

dQ

V_1

A

dW_1

dE

$V_1\, dt$

1

C

2

dW_2

B

V_2

$V_2\, dt$

2

dW_{shaft}

FIG. 5·6 *The control mass*

to the control mass, we obtain

$$dM = 0$$

where M is the mass of the control mass. This mass can be represented in terms of the spatial distribution of matter, that is, in terms of the mass in regions A, B, and C of Fig. 5·6. Using the steady-flow steady-state condition,

$$M(t) = M_A + M_C$$
$$M(t + dt) = M_B + M_C$$
$$dM = M(t + dt) - M(t) = M_B - M_A$$

The volumes of A and B are $(AV)_1\, dt$ and $(AV)_2\, dt$, where V_1 and V_2 are the velocities at sections 1 and 2. Hence the *mass balance* becomes

$$dM = (\rho AV)_2\, dt - (\rho AV)_1\, dt = 0$$

The term $(\rho AV)_1\, dt$ represents the amount of mass dM which crosses section 1 in the time interval dt. The *rate of mass flow* $\dot{M}$ is defined as†

$$\blacktriangleright \qquad \dot{M} \equiv \frac{dM}{dt} = (\rho AV) \tag{5·2}$$

Note that V is the velocity *normal* to the flow area A. The mass balance can now be interpreted as appling to the *space C* (the *control volume*),

$$\dot{M}_1 = \dot{M}_2$$

mass-
inflow
rate

mass-
outflow
rate

This merely states that the rate of mass inflow *to the control volume* must equal the rate of mass outflow *from the control volume* under steady-flow steady-state conditions, which is obviously the proper control-volume mass balance. How-

† Note that $\dot{M} \neq dM/dt$. See the Nomenclature at the back of the book.

ever, the proper energy equation is not as obvious, and we must derive it carefully.

An energy balance on the control mass, made over the time period dt, yields

$$\underbrace{dW_1 + dW_{\text{shaft}} + dQ}_{\text{energy input}} = \underbrace{dW_2}_{\substack{\text{energy}\\\text{output}}} + \underbrace{dE}_{\substack{\text{increase in}\\\text{energy storage}}}$$

The work terms dW_1 and dW_2 represent energy transfers to and from the control mass due to normal motion of its boundaries in the pipes near sections 1 and 2. To evaluate these terms we assume that the pressure exerted by the fluid on the duct walls is the same as that exerted by the fluid immediately outside the control mass on the fluid just inside the boundary. In other words, the pressure *within the fluid* is presumed to be the same in all directions. Denoting the fluid pressures at sections 1 and 2 by P_1 and P_2 and assuming that these pressures act uniformly over the flow cross sections at those points, we have

$$dW_1 = (PA)_1 \mathsf{V}_1 \, dt$$
$$dW_2 = (PA)_2 \mathsf{V}_2 \, dt$$

The change in the energy of the control mass can be represented in terms of the energies of regions A, B, and C of Fig. 5·6. Using the steady-flow steady-state idealization, we obtain

$$E(t) = E_A + E_C$$
$$E(t + dt) = E_C + E_B$$
$$dE = E(t + dt) - E(t) = E_B - E_A$$

We denote the energy per unit of mass of fluid at 1 and 2 by e_1 and e_2. This represents the internal energy, plus kinetic energy due to motion, plus potential energy due to conservative force fields,

$$e = u + PE + KE$$

Then, the increase in energy within the control mass is

$$dE = e_2\rho_2(A_2\mathsf{V}_2 \, dt) - e_1\rho_1(A_1\mathsf{V}_1 \, dt)$$

and the energy balance becomes

$$(PA\mathsf{V})_1 \, dt - (PA\mathsf{V})_2 \, dt + dW_{\text{shaft}} + dQ = (eA\rho\mathsf{V})_2 \, dt - (eA\rho\mathsf{V})_1 \, dt$$

The *rates* of energy transfer as work and heat are defined as

$$\blacktriangleright \qquad \dot{W}_{\text{shaft}} \equiv \frac{dW_{\text{shaft}}}{dt} \qquad \dot{Q} \equiv \frac{dQ}{dt} \tag{5·3}$$

Dividing by dt and introducing the mass-flow rate $\dot{M} = A\rho\mathsf{V}$, the energy balance may be written as

$$\underbrace{[\dot{M}(e + Pv)]_1 + \dot{W}_{\text{shaft}} + \dot{Q}}_{\text{energy-input rate}} = \underbrace{[\dot{M}(e + Pv)]_2}_{\text{energy-output rate}}$$

Note that the terms in this equation can be interpreted as applying to the *space C* (the *control volume*).

After a while the mass of fluid that we took for our control mass will have passed out of the device, and we are not really concerned about it subsequently. Of greater interest are the properties of and energy transfers to the device and whatever fluid happens to be in it at any given moment. The energy equation above relates the properties at sections 1 and 2 to the rates of energy transfer as heat and work to the device, and consequently is just what we need. Suppose we knew the temperature and pressure at states 1 and 2 and could thereby fix the thermodynamic states of the fluid. If, in addition, we could in some way determine the mass-flow rate and knew the rate of energy transfer as heat, the energy balance could be used to calculate the shaft-power output. This is a typical use for a first-law equation.

As we indicated, the control-mass point of view could be used to handle all flow problems. The analysis would always involve motion of the boundaries in the inlet and exit ducts and a representation of the energy of the control mass in terms of the distribution of energy through space. We might as well do a reasonably general analysis of this type once and then use it whenever it is applicable in flow-system analysis. This brings us now to the control-volume transformation.

5·3 THE CONTROL-VOLUME TRANSFORMATION

A *control volume* is any defined region in space. This region may be moving through space, and its shape and volume may be changing. However, most often we deal with control volumes that are of fixed shape and size and are fixed in the reference frame, so we shall consider this special case first.

Consider a control volume whose boundaries are fixed in space and stationary. Matter flows across the boundaries of this control volume, as indicated in Fig. 5·7. Following our previous analysis, we assume that the flow streams are one-dimensional at points where mass crosses the control-volume boundary.

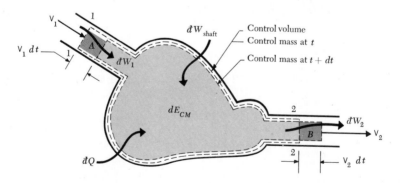

FIG. 5·7 *A control volume*

We again assume that the pressure exerted by the fluid on the duct walls is the same as the force per unit of area on an imaginary cut across the duct. This will be a good idealization, except in some cases where viscous shear is important, but there the one-dimensional idealization would be invalid anyway. We allow energy transfer as heat across the boundary of the control volume, but we must be careful in handling such energy transfer at points where mass enters the control volume, and to avoid confusion we shall assume that no energy is transferred as heat at the inlet and exit stations. We also presume that we can choose the control-volume boundaries such that we can neglect work arising from tangential shearing motions of the boundary, except for energy transfer as work through rotating shafts. Thus a number of important restrictions have been made, all of which can be removed by proper extension of the analysis. It is important to realize that our resulting control-volume energy equation will not be fully general, though it will be sufficiently general for most of our purposes.

To develop the proper control-volume energy-conservation expression, we shall consider two infinitesimally differing instants in time, t and $t + dt$, and apply the conservation-of-energy principle to the particular control mass whose boundaries at time t happen to correspond exactly to those of the control volume. Work will be done on the control mass by the rotating shaft and also by the normal motion of the control-mass boundary at the two points where matter flows into and out of the control volume. An energy balance on the control mass, made over the time period dt, gives

$$\underbrace{(PA)_1 \mathsf{V}_1\, dt + dW_{\text{shaft}} + dQ}_{\text{energy input}} = \underbrace{(PA)_2 \mathsf{V}_2\, dt}_{\substack{\text{energy} \\ \text{output}}} + \underbrace{dE_{CM}}_{\substack{\text{increase in} \\ \text{energy storage}}}$$

We want to express all terms in this energy balance in terms of properties of the control *volume* rather than the control mass. The energy contained within the control mass at time t is identical with the energy within the control volume at that instant. At time $t + dt$ the energy of the control mass is equal to the energy of the matter within the control-volume boundaries at $t + dt$, plus the energy of the matter within the shaded portion B, minus the energy of the matter within the shaded portion A. We therefore put

$$
\begin{aligned}
dE_{CM} &= E_{CM}(t + dt) - E_{CM}(t) \\
&= E_{CV}(t + dt) + (A_2 \mathsf{V}_2\, dt)\rho_2 e_2 - (A_1 \mathsf{V}_1\, dt)\rho_1 e_1 - E_{CV}(t) \\
&= dE_{CV} + (A\rho\mathsf{V}e)_2\, dt - (A\rho\mathsf{V}e)_1\, dt
\end{aligned}
$$

Here we have used e to represent the total energy of the matter per unit of mass. The terms dW_{shaft} and dQ represent energy transfers across the common boundaries, that is, across the control-volume boundary, which occur during the time interval dt. Substituting for dE_{CM} and regrouping terms,

$$dW_{\text{shaft}} + dQ + (A\rho\mathsf{V})_1 \left(e + \frac{P}{\rho}\right)_1 dt = (A\rho\mathsf{V})_2 \left(e + \frac{P}{\rho}\right)_2 dt + dE_{CV}$$

The term $A\rho V\,dt$ represents infinitesimal mass transfer across the control-volume boundaries, which we denote by dM. Then

$$\blacktriangleright \qquad \underbrace{dW_{\text{shaft}} + dQ + [(e+Pv)\,dM]_{\text{in}}}_{\text{energy input}} = \underbrace{[(e+Pv)\,dM]_{\text{out}}}_{\text{energy output}} + \underbrace{dE_{CV}}_{\substack{\text{increase in}\\ \text{energy storage}}}$$

$$(5\cdot4)$$

This can be viewed as a conservation-of-energy equation *for the control volume,* expressed for a definite period of time. Alternatively, we could divide by dt and express the energy balance on a *rate basis* as

$$\blacktriangleright \qquad \underbrace{\dot{W}_{\text{shaft}} + \dot{Q} + [\dot{M}(e+Pv)]_{\text{in}}}_{\text{energy-input rate}} = \underbrace{[\dot{M}(e+Pv)]_{\text{out}}}_{\substack{\text{energy-output}\\ \text{rate}}} + \underbrace{\left(\frac{dE}{dt}\right)_{CV}}_{\substack{\text{energy-storage}\\ \text{rate}}}$$

$$(5\cdot5)$$

We see that the conservation-of-energy idea can be retained for the control volume, provided that we adopt a slightly modified picture of energy. When matter flows into a control volume, energy is *convected* in by the matter, and in addition, energy is transferred to the control volume as work. The amount of energy transfer as work associated with a unit of mass is Pv. In a sense, entering matter does work on the matter already within the control volume by "pushing it out of the way." The Pv product, when used in this context, is sometimes called *flow work.* It does not represent any energy contained by the fluid.

Note that the energy of matter is still designated by e. Only when matter crosses the boundaries of a control volume will the additional contribution of the Pv product occur in the energy-balance equation. Furthermore, care must be taken to distinguish between the $P\,dv$ work done by a control mass in expanding and the Pv work done by a unit of mass in flowing into a control volume (which may be of fixed size). Note that e, P, and v appearing in the flow terms are to be evaluated at the point where the matter crosses the boundary.

The energy per unit of mass of substance crossing the boundary is composed of internal energy, bulk potential energy, and bulk kinetic energy. We can therefore write

$$e + Pv = KE + PE + u + Pv$$

The appearance of the combination $h \equiv u + Pv$ suggests further utility for tabulations of the enthalpy property.

The kinetic energy of a unit of mass is simply $V^2/2g_c$. The potential energy of a unit of mass in a uniform gravitational field may be shown to equal $(g_g/g_c)z$, where g_g is the local acceleration of gravity (ft/sec²), g_c is the constant in Newton's law (32.17 ft-lbm/lbf-sec²), and z is the height above some arbitrarily selected datum. The electrostatic potential energy of a unit of mass is simply $Q\mathcal{E}$, where Q is the charge per unit of mass and $\mathcal{E}$ is the local value of the electrostatic potential above the (arbitrary) ground state. Hence,

$$e + Pv = h + \frac{V^2}{2g_c} + \frac{g_g}{g_c} z + Q\mathcal{E} + \cdots$$

For a control volume with matter flowing across the boundaries in several places, and with boundaries which may themselves be moving, the conservation-of-energy statement on the time-interval basis leads to

$$\blacktriangleright \quad \underset{\substack{\text{in} \\ \text{energy-input}}}{\sum} (e + Pv) \, dM + dW + dQ = \underset{\substack{\text{out} \\ \text{energy-output}}}{\sum} (e + Pv) \, dM + \underset{\substack{\text{energy-storage}}}{dE_{CV}} \qquad (5 \cdot 6)$$

and on the rate basis to

$$\blacktriangleright \quad \underset{\substack{\text{in} \\ \text{energy-input rate}}}{\sum} (e + Pv)\dot{M} + \dot{W} + \dot{Q} = \underset{\substack{\text{out} \\ \text{energy-output} \\ \text{rate}}}{\sum} (e + Pv)\dot{M} + \underset{\substack{\text{energy-storage} \\ \text{rate}}}{\left(\frac{dE}{dt}\right)_{CV}} \qquad (5 \cdot 7)$$

Here $\dot{W}$ is to be understood as being the sum of shaft-power *input* and power *input* due to normal motion of the control-volume boundaries. $\dot{Q}$ represents the sum of all heat-transfer rates *to* the control volume. If the control-volume boundaries move, $\dot{M}$ must be calculated in terms of the velocity of the fluid *relative and normal to the control surface*.

It is sometimes necessary to replace the sums by integrals, and we then obtain

$$\blacktriangleright \quad -\underset{\substack{CS \\ \text{net energy-input rate}}}{\int} (e + Pv)\rho \mathbf{V}_{\text{rel}} \cdot d\mathbf{A} + \dot{W} + \dot{Q} = \underset{\substack{\text{energy-storage} \\ \text{rate}}}{\frac{d}{dt} \int_{CV} \rho e \, dV} \qquad (5 \cdot 8)$$

The area integration is to be extended over the control surface CS, and $d\mathbf{A}$ represents an *outward* normal vector. The volume integration is extended over the entire control volume. Note that e appears in the energy-storage term, while $e + Pv$ appears in the energy-convection term. $\mathbf{V}_{\text{rel}}$ represents the *outward* velocity *relative to the boundary*, while the *absolute* velocity $\mathbf{V}$ must be used to compute the kinetic energy.

Two important idealizations frequently made in control-volume analysis are (1) that the flow is steady, so that no mass is accumulating within the control volume, and (2) that the state of the matter at each point in space is steady, that is, unchanging in time. This implies that the energy stored within the control volume is unchanging and thereby eliminates the term in the energy equation involving changes in the energy storage. It is therefore not necessary to know the details of what is going on within the control volume. This is very important, because it allows us to analyze intricate systems by examining only the transfers of energy across the control-volume boundary.

The methodology introduced for the control mass may readily be applied in setting up the control-volume energy balance. We shall now illustrate the methodology by examples. In each case it will be necessary to make idealizations in order to render the problem tractable. Such idealizations are usually based on experience, but engineering analysis is both a science and an art and can be learned only by imitation and practice. Thus, careful study of the examples will provide the student's first bit of experience and something to imitate. One can often verify the validity of an idealization by making appropriate estimates and should make every attempt to do so whenever a particular assumption is questionable. The examples serve to bring out many important features of systematic control-volume energy analysis and are typical of the simpler types of problems in engineering thermodynamics.

5·4   EXAMPLES OF CONTROL-VOLUME ENERGY ANALYSIS

Flow through a nozzle. Steam enters the nozzle of a steam turbine with a velocity of 10 ft/sec at a pressure of 500 psia and a temperature of 1000°F. At the nozzle discharge the pressure and temperature are measured and found to be 300°F and 1 atm. What is the discharge velocity? See Fig. 5·8.

FIG. 5·8

(a) *The control volume*   (b) *The process representation*

In any such nozzle frictional effects between the fluid and the walls might be important, but by choosing the boundaries as indicated in Fig. 5·8a these effects become internal. Then, idealizing the flow as steady and assuming that the state at each point in the control volume is invariant in time (steady state), we do not need to know what is going on within the control volume. We also idealize that the control volume is adiabatic, so that no energy transfer as heat takes place across the control-volume boundaries (this is a reasonable simplifying idealization for most nozzles). This does not mean that no energy transfer as heat takes place within the control volume, but any such transfer would not be involved in a steady-flow steady-state analysis.

The conservation-of-mass principle implies that the flow rate is the same at sections 1 and 2. In applying this principle we assume that the flow is one-dimensional at 1 and 2, which means that the properties are uniform across the sections. The energy per unit of mass is taken as

$$e = u + \frac{V^2}{2g_c}$$

In evaluating u as a function of the temperature and pressure we shall assume that the motion in no way alters the thermodynamic equations of state. In microscopic terms, even though the fluid is accelerating, the molecules behave locally as if there were no bulk motion. Satisfactory results are obtained with this idealization, and this experimental support is sufficient justification for its use. We shall also neglect any differences in the potential energy of position of the entering and emergent flows.

The internal process is quite complicated. However, only the states of the fluid at 1 and 2 need to be known, and we can indicate our ignorance of the intermediate states by showing the process as a dotted line (Fig. $5 \cdot 8b$).

Several important simplifying idealizations have been made, and it is a good idea to begin any analysis by listing these:

Steady flow steady state
Adiabatic control volume
One-dimensional flow at 1 and 2 (but not necessarily internally!)
Equation of state the same as for a simple compressible substance
Changes in the potential energy of position negligible

With these idealizations, application of the conservation-of-energy principle to the control volume gives, on a rate basis,

$$\dot{M}\left(u + Pv + \frac{V^2}{2g_c}\right)_1 - \dot{M}\left(u + Pv + \frac{V^2}{2g_c}\right)_2 = 0$$

$$\underbrace{\qquad\qquad\qquad}_{\text{energy-inflow rate}} \quad \underbrace{\qquad\qquad\qquad}_{\text{energy-outflow rate}} \quad \underbrace{\quad}_{\substack{\text{energy-}\\\text{storage}\\\text{rate}}}$$

Solving for the discharge kinetic energy per unit of mass,

$$\frac{V_2{}^2}{2g_c} = \frac{V_1{}^2}{2g_c} + [(u + Pv)_1 - (u + Pv)_2]$$

The intensive thermodynamic states are fixed by the temperature and pressure measurements (see Fig. $B \cdot 1$):

$T_1 = 1000°F$ $\qquad\qquad$ $T_2 = 300°F$
$P_1 = 500$ psia $\qquad\quad$ $P_2 = 14.7$ psia
$u_1 = 1360$ Btu/lbm $\quad$ $u_2 = 1110$ Btu/lbm
$v_1 = 1.7$ ft³/lbm $\qquad$ $v_2 = 31$ ft³/lbm

Hence

$h_1 = (u_1 + P_1 v_1) = 1520$ Btu/lbm
$h_2 = (u_2 + P_2 v_2) = 1193$ Btu/lbm

Then

$$\frac{V_1{}^2}{2g_c} = \frac{10^2}{2 \times 32.2} \; (\text{ft}^2/\text{sec}^2)/(\text{ft-lbm/lbf-sec}^2)$$

$$= 1.55 \; \text{ft-lbf/lbm} = 2 \times 10^{-3} \; \text{Btu/lbm}$$

$$\frac{V_2{}^2}{2g_c} = 2 \times 10^{-3} + 1520 - 1193 = 327 \; \text{Btu/lbm} = 254{,}000 \; \text{ft-lbf/lbm}$$

$$V_2 = \sqrt{2 \times 32.2 \; \text{ft-lbm/lbf-sec}^2 \times 254{,}000 \; \text{ft-lbf/lbm}} = 4100 \; \text{ft/sec}$$

Note that the enthalpies could have been more conveniently found in Table B·2 or on Fig. B·2. Note also that the inlet kinetic energy is very small and could have been neglected.

A mercury turbine. Mercury enters the turbine of a high-temperature auxiliary power system at 1200°F and 30 psia and emerges as a mixture of liquid and vapor of 0.95 quality at 1 psia. What must the flow rate be if the power output is to be 10 kw? See Fig. 5·9.

A typical turbine consists of (1) a nozzle, which accelerates the flow, converting internal energy and flow work to kinetic energy; (2) a rotor, which slows down the fluid, extracting energy from the fluid as work; and (3) a diffuser, which slows the fluid down again, with a resulting rise in pressure. The internal workings of such a device are quite complicated. However, by judicious selection of the control-volume boundaries and the idealizations of steady flow and steady state, one need worry only about the conditions at the points where the flow crosses the boundaries. This is a great advantage of the control-volume approach to steady-flow steady-state problems.

We take the boundary as shown above and make the following idealizations:

Steady flow steady state
Adiabatic control volume
One-dimensional flow at 1 and 2
Kinetic and potential energy negligible at 1 and 2 (but certainly not inside!)
Mercury in thermodynamic equilibrium at 1 and 2

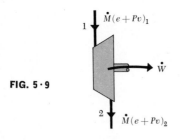

FIG. 5·9

(a) *The control volume*

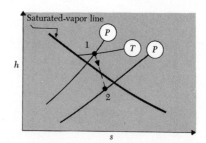

(b) *The process representation*

Under these idealizations, application of the conservation-of-energy principle to the control volume gives

$$\dot{M}(u + Pv)_1 - [\dot{M}(u + Pv)_2 + \dot{W}_{shaft}] = 0$$

energy-in-   energy-outflow rate   energy-
flow rate   storage
                                                            rate

The shaft-energy output per unit of mass is then

$$W_{shaft} = \frac{\dot{W}_{shaft}}{\dot{M}} = h_1 - h_2$$

The enthalpies may be found directly on Fig. B·10, and we then have

$$W_{shaft} = (159 - 134) \text{ Btu/lbm} = 25 \text{ Btu/lbm}$$

The power requirement of 10 kw is equivalent to 34,130 Btu/hr, so the required mass-flow rate is

$$\dot{M} = 34{,}130/25 = 1360 \text{ lbm/hr} = 0.378 \text{ lbm/sec}$$

If the mercury is moving at 100 ft/sec (typical for the inlet of a small mercury turbine), the required flow area can be computed from the relation $\dot{M} = A\rho V$, provided the inlet density is known. The density does not appear on Fig. B·10. However, we can make an estimate of the density by assuming that the vapor behaves like a perfect gas, for which

$$\frac{\rho}{\rho_0} = \frac{P/T}{P_0/T_0}$$

The zero denotes any selected reference state, which we take to be saturated vapor at 20 psia. Then, using the data in Table B·3, we estimate the density at 1 as

$$\rho_1 = \frac{1 \text{ lbm}}{3.09 \text{ ft}^3} \frac{30/(1200 + 460)}{20/(706 + 460)} = 0.34 \text{ lbm/ft}^3$$

At 100 ft/sec the inlet-flow area would be

$$A = \frac{0.378}{0.34 \times 100} = 0.0111 \text{ ft}^2 = 1.6 \text{ in.}^2$$

We can evaluate the validity of our idealization that the kinetic-energy changes are negligible by some typical numbers. Suppose the discharge velocity is 200 ft/sec, with the inlet velocity as 100 ft/sec. The difference in the inflow and outflow kinetic energies, per unit of mass, would then be

$$\frac{V_2^2 - V_1^2}{2g_c} = \frac{200^2 - 100^2}{2 \times 32.2} = 465 \text{ ft-lbf/lbm} = 0.6 \text{ Btu/lbm}$$

This represents an error of about 2 percent when compared to the enthalpy difference of 25 Btu/lbm, and our idealization was therefore quite reasonable for first analysis. The analyst is frequently in a position to make such quantitative estimates of the inaccuracies introduced by his simplifying assumptions and should do so whenever he can.

It is indeed interesting that the size of the system did not enter the thermodynamic calculation, nor did the particular internal configuration of the device. This is typical of thermodynamic energy analysis, in which important system parameters can be set without the need for detailed knowledge of the design.

Liquefaction of oxygen. Oxygen enters a turboexpander at 200°K and 60 atm. The expander discharges into a separator, from which saturated liquid and saturated vapor at 1 atm emerge as separate streams. The system is heavily insulated. The turboexpander shaft-power output is 1700 watts, and the total oxygen-flow rate is 15 g/sec. What percentage of liquefaction is achieved, and what is the net liquid-oxygen-production rate? See Fig. 5·10.

The idealizations are as follows:

> Steady flow steady state
> Adiabatic control volume
> One-dimensional flow at 1, 4, and 3
> Potential and kinetic energies at 1, 4, and 3 negligible
> Thermodynamic equilibrium states at 1, 4, and 3

With these idealizations, an energy balance on the control volume gives, on a rate basis,

$$\underset{\substack{\text{energy-inflow}\\\text{rate}}}{\dot{M}_1(u + Pv)_1} - \underset{\text{energy-outflow rate}}{[\dot{M}_4(u + Pv)_4 + \dot{M}_3(u + Pv)_3 + \dot{W}]} = \underset{\substack{\text{energy-}\\\text{storage}\\\text{rate}}}{0}$$

A mass balance will also be required; for the control volume,

$$\underset{\substack{\text{mass-inflow}\\\text{rate}}}{\dot{M}_1} - \underset{\substack{\text{mass-outflow}\\\text{rate}}}{(\dot{M}_4 + \dot{M}_3)} = \underset{\substack{\text{mass-storage}\\\text{rate}}}{0}$$

FIG. 5·10

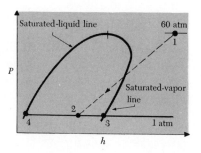

(a) *The control volume*

(b) *The process representation*

The problem will be solved if we can establish the relative flow rates. We put $f = \dot{M}_3/\dot{M}_1$ and the energy balance becomes an equation for f,

$$h_1 - [(1-f)h_4 + fh_3] - \frac{\dot{W}}{\dot{M}_1} = 0$$

The enthalpies are evaluated with the aid of Fig. B·5, and we find (using $\hat{M} = 32.00$ g/gmole)

$$h_1 = \frac{2320}{32.00} = 72.4 \text{ cal/g}$$

$$h_4 = \frac{160}{32.00} = 5.0 \text{ cal/g} \qquad \text{(saturated liquid)}$$

$$h_3 = \frac{1780}{32.00} = 55.7 \text{ cal/g} \qquad \text{(saturated vapor)}$$

The shaft-work output per unit of mass is

$$\frac{\dot{W}}{\dot{M}_1} = \frac{1700 \text{ joule/sec}}{15 \text{ g/sec}} = 1.13 \times 10^2 \text{ joule/g} \times \frac{1 \text{ cal}}{4.18 \text{ joule}} = 27.2 \text{ cal/g}$$

Solving for f and substituting the numbers,

$$f = \frac{27.2 + 5.0 - 72.4}{5.0 - 55.7} = 0.79$$

The system therefore achieves 21 percent liquefaction and delivers saturated liquid oxygen at 1 atm at the rate of 3.1 g/sec.

Do not be led to believe that liquid oxygen can be made "for nothing" in a process from which useful electrical power is obtained. Energy is required to separate oxygen from air, to compress it to 60 atm, and to run the refrigerator which precools it to 200°K. Only a portion of this would be recovered from the turboexpander.

CO₂ evaporator. Three hundred lbm/hr of CO_2 (liquid) will enter a heat exchanger as a saturated liquid at 100 psia and emerge at 75 psia and 20°F. This evaporation and superheating process is to be accomplished by passing dry air through the other side of the exchanger. The air will enter at 70°F, slightly above atmospheric pressure, and must emerge at 50°F at atmospheric pressure. Specify the air-flow rate required and the heat-transfer rate within the exchanger. See Fig. 5·11.

We make the following idealizations:

Steady flow steady state
Adiabatic control volume (energy transfer as heat occurring inside, and neglecting energy transfer as heat across the boundaries indicated)
One-dimensional flow at 1, 2, 3, and 4

Kinetic and potential energy changes negligible

Equilibrium states at 1, 2, 3, and 4 with properties related by thermo-dynamic equations of state

With these idealizations, the energy balance, on a rate basis, is

$$\underbrace{\dot{M}_1 h_1 + \dot{M}_3 h_3}_{\substack{\text{energy-inflow}\\ \text{rate}}} - \underbrace{(\dot{M}_2 h_2 + \dot{M}_4 h_4)}_{\substack{\text{energy-outflow}\\ \text{rate}}} = \underbrace{0}_{\substack{\text{energy-}\\ \text{storage}\\ \text{rate}}}$$

By conservation of mass, $\dot{M}_1 = \dot{M}_2$ and $\dot{M}_3 = \dot{M}_4$.

The enthalpies are found from the given states using Figs. B·6 and B·8:

$h_3 = 137$ Btu/lbm   (saturated liquid at 100 psia, $-55°$F)
$h_4 = 299$ Btu/lbm
$h_1 = 5.5$ cal/g   (21.5°C, ≈ 1 atm)
$h_2 = 2.5$ cal/g   (10°C, 1 atm)

The enthalpy differences are then

$h_4 - h_3 = 299 - 137 = 162$ Btu/lbm
$h_1 - h_2 = 5.5 - 2.5 = 3.0$ cal/g $= 5.4$ Btu/lbm

The required air-flow rate is therefore

$$\dot{M}_{\text{air}} = \frac{162}{5.4} \times 300 \text{ lbm/hr} = 9000 \text{ lbm/hr}$$

To determine the heat-transfer rate within the exchanger, a second energy balance is required. Either side of the exchanger may be used. Having the

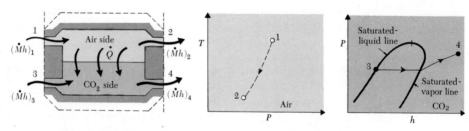

(a) The first control volume   (b) The process representation

(c) The second control volume

FIG. 5·11

most accurate enthalpy-difference information for the CO_2, we select this side (Fig. $5 \cdot 11c$) and idealize as follows:

Steady flow steady state
One-dimensional flows at 3 and 4
Kinetic and potential energy changes negligible
Thermodynamic equilibrium at 3 and 4

The energy balance, on a rate basis, is

$$\underset{\substack{\text{energy-input}\\\text{rate}}}{\dot{Q} + \dot{M}_{CO_2}h_3} = \underset{\substack{\text{energy-output}\\\text{rate}}}{\dot{M}_{CO_2}h_4}$$

Substituting the numbers,

$$\dot{Q} = \dot{M}_{CO_2}(h_4 - h_3) = 300 \times 162 = 48{,}600 \text{ Btu/hr}$$

Determination of the physical dimensions of a heat exchanger which could transfer energy from one stream to the other at this rate over the temperature differences involved is a problem for the heat-transfer analyst and requires more than thermodynamics.

A thermoelectric generator. A thermoelectric generator consists of a series of semiconductor elements, heated on one side and cooled on the other. Electric-current flow is produced as a result of energy transfer as heat. A schematic diagram of a typical device is shown in Fig. $5 \cdot 12$. In a particular experiment the current was measured to be 0.5 amp and the electrostatic potential at 3 was 0.8 volt above that at 4. Energy transfer as heat to the hot side of the generator was taking place at a rate of 5.5 watts. Determine the rate of energy transfer as heat from the cold side and the energy-conversion efficiency.

We shall treat this problem by the control-volume method, since mass (electrons) flows across the indicated control surface. The electrons flowing possess electrostatic potential energy and kinetic energy. In addition, the electrons within the "electron gas" passing through the conductors execute randomly oriented motions, giving the "gas" internal energy in exactly the same

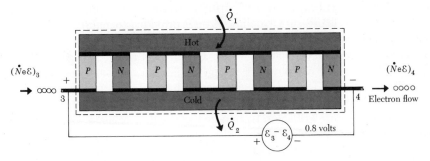

FIG. 5·12   *A thermoelectric generator*

way that molecules of a gas give it internal energy. Moreover, the electron gas will have a pressure and a specific volume, so it will have an enthalpy. The randomly oriented motions of the electrons within the gas are responsible in part for "noise" in electronic circuits. We shall assume that there is no noise in this system, or in other words, that the internal energy of the electron gas is insignificant compared to the electrostatic potential energy. The kinetic energy is also negligible, since electrons in metallic conductors move at very slow "drift velocities." Therefore only the electrostatic potential energy of the electrons will be considered. Idealizations are as follows:

Steady flow steady state
One-dimensional flows
Only electron potential energy important

Denoting the number of electrons crossing the boundary per unit of time by $\dot{N}$ and the charge of an electron by e, an energy balance, made on a rate basis, gives

$$\underset{\substack{\text{energy-inflow}\\\text{rate}}}{[(\dot{N}e\mathcal{E})_3 + \dot{Q}_1]} - \underset{\substack{\text{energy-outflow}\\\text{rate}}}{[(\dot{N}e\mathcal{E})_4 + \dot{Q}_2]} = \underset{\substack{\text{energy-}\\\text{storage}\\\text{rate}}}{0}$$

In terms of the current $i = -\dot{N}e$,

$$i(\mathcal{E}_4 - \mathcal{E}_3) + \dot{Q}_1 - \dot{Q}_2 = 0$$

Solving for $\dot{Q}_2$ and substituting the numbers,

$$\dot{Q}_2 = 5.5 \text{ watts} + 0.5 \text{ amp} \times (-0.8 \text{ volt}) \times 1 \text{ watt/volt-amp} = 5.1 \text{ watts}$$

The term $i(\mathcal{E}_3 - \mathcal{E}_4)$ represents the useful power output of the device; it is equal to 0.4 watt. The *energy-conversion efficiency* is then

$$\eta = \frac{i(\mathcal{E}_3 - \mathcal{E}_4)}{\dot{Q}_1} = \frac{0.4}{5.5} = 0.073$$

This low efficiency is typical of such solid-state direct-energy converters.

An arc heater. Air is to be heated to 8000°K in a steady-flow electric-arc device. The air will enter at 10^{-2} atm at atmospheric temperature and will emerge at the same pressure. Cooling water is provided to maintain low electrode temperatures, and it is estimated that half the electrical-energy input will be transferred as heat to the cooling water. The air-flow rate is to be 10,000 lbm/hr. Specify the required arc power. See Fig. 5·13.

The air will be ionized but electrically neutral. We assume that thermodynamic equilibrium has been obtained by the time that the air emerges. The electric-current flow will again be handled as the flow of mass with electrostatic potential energy. We idealize that the internal energy of the flowing electron "gas" is small compared to its bulk potential energy. Electrons move through solids at very low "drift velocities," so the kinetic energy of the electrons at the

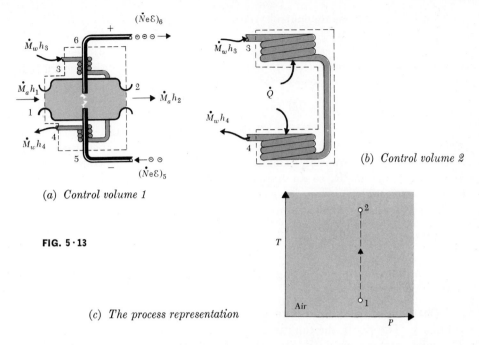

(a) *Control volume 1*

(b) *Control volume 2*

FIG. 5·13

(c) *The process representation*

points at which we draw the control-volume boundaries will be neglected. (It should be noted that the kinetic energy of the electrons striking the anode will be extremely high and could not be neglected were we to make our boundary cut through the air immediately adjacent to the anode.) We make the following idealizations:

Steady flow steady state
One-dimensional flows
Kinetic energy of air and water negligible
Only electrostatic potential energy of electrons important
Control volume 1 adiabatic
Air in thermodynamic equilibrium at 1 and 2
Water in thermodynamic equilibrium at 3 and 4

We again denote the number of electrons flowing per unit of time as $\dot{N}$ and their charge as $\mathbf{e}$. The energy balance, made on a rate basis on control volume 1, gives

$$\underbrace{(\dot{N}\mathcal{E}_5 + \dot{M}_a h_1 + \dot{M}_w h_3)}_{\text{energy-inflow rate}} - \underbrace{(\dot{N}\mathcal{E}_6 + \dot{M}_a h_2 + \dot{M}_w h_4)}_{\text{energy-outflow rate}} = \underbrace{0}_{\substack{\text{energy-}\\\text{storage}\\\text{rate}}}$$

In terms of the current $i = -\dot{N}\mathbf{e}$,

$$i(\mathcal{E}_6 - \mathcal{E}_5) = \dot{M}_a(h_2 - h_1) + \dot{M}_w(h_4 - h_3)$$

The first term should be recognized as the electrical-power input.

An energy balance on control volume 2 leads to

$$\dot{Q} = \dot{M}_w(h_4 - h_3)$$

Using the design estimate that $\dot{Q} = i(\mathcal{E}_6 - \mathcal{E}_5)/2$, we combine the energy balances and obtain

$$\text{Power} = i(\mathcal{E}_6 - \mathcal{E}_5) = 2\dot{M}_a(h_2 - h_1)$$

The enthalpy at state 2 is obtained from the equation of state, Fig. B·9, as 19,000 Btu/lbm. This value is relative to the enthalpy at absolute zero of a gas obeying the equation of state $h = c_P T$ at low temperatures. For air $c_P \approx 0.24$ Btu/lbm-°R, so an estimate of the enthalpy at state 1 might be $0.24 \times 500 = 120$ Btu/lbm. This is negligible in comparison to the enthalpy of the highly energetic air at state 2. Our power calculation then yields

$$\text{Power} = 2 \times 10,000 \text{ lbm/hr} \times (19,000 - 120) \text{ Btu/lbm}$$
$$= 38 \times 10^7 \text{ Btu/hr} = 1.11 \times 10^5 \text{ kw} = 111 \text{ Mw}$$

The total power output of a large central power station would be required to power this arcjet heater!

Charging of a high-pressure tank. A gas is pumped into a tank having volume V. The gas in the tank is initially at pressure P_0 and temperature T_0. The inlet temperature is T_1, and the inflow rate $\dot{M}_1$ is constant. Using the perfect-gas equation of state, derive an expression for the temperature in the tank as a function of time, assuming that the gas inside is perfectly mixed and in a state of thermodynamic equilibrium and that no energy transfer as heat takes place from the tank to the gas. See Fig. 5·14.

Our idealizations are as follows:

The gas may be treated as a perfect gas with constant specific heats
Steady inflow (but not steady state!)
Uniform state inside the tank (perfect internal mixing)
Adiabatic control volume
Equilibrium state within tank at every instant, equilibrium state at 1
Kinetic energy of inflow gas negligible
Inlet state steady (but not the internal state!) and one-dimensional flow at the inlet

FIG. 5·14

(a) *The control volume*   (b) *The process representation*

The energy balance, made over the time interval from the start of filling (time zero) to some later time t, is

$$\underbrace{\dot{M}_1(u_1 + P_1v_1)t}_{\text{energy inflow}} - \underbrace{0}_{\substack{\text{energy}\\\text{outflow}}} = \underbrace{\Delta U}_{\substack{\text{increase}\\\text{in energy}\\\text{storage}}}$$

Then,

$$\Delta U = Mu - M_0u_0$$

A mass balance on the control volume is also needed. Over the same time period,

$$\underbrace{\dot{M}_1t}_{\text{mass inflow}} - \underbrace{0}_{\substack{\text{mass}\\\text{outflow}}} = \underbrace{M - M_0}_{\substack{\text{increase in}\\\text{mass storage}}}$$

Solving for M and substituting into the energy balance,

$$\dot{M}_1h_1t = (M_0 + \dot{M}_1t)u - M_0u_0 \tag{5.9}$$

Note that the enthalpy property is involved in the energy-inflow term, while only the internal energy is involved in the energy-storage term.

The Pv product does not represent energy of matter; it is simply an extra term in the energy balance necessitated by our taking the control-volume rather than control-mass point of view.

We next bring in the equation of state. With the datum at $0°$ R in Eqs. (4·21) and (4·22), we introduce these into Eq. (5·9), obtaining

$$\dot{M}_1c_PT_1t = (M_0 + \dot{M}_1t)c_vT - M_0c_vT_0$$

The temperature T of the gas in the tank can be computed from this equation as a function of time. It is interesting that for very large t the temperature will approach the value

$$T_{\text{lim}} = \frac{c_P}{c_v}T_1 = kT_1$$

Since the ratio k is greater than unity, the limiting internal temperature will be somewhat greater than the temperature of the incoming gas.

A hydroelectric power plant. Suppose we wish to assess the capabilities of a foreign hydroelectric power plant, and have acquired the following field data.

Estimated water flow, 40 ft^3/sec
River inlet 1 atm, 40°F
Discharged at 1 atm, 40.5°F, 800 ft below the intake

We know from experience that the energy transfer as heat to such a power plant is negligible. The enthalpy of water is given approximately by

$$h_2 - h_1 = c_v(T_2 - T_1) + \frac{1}{\rho}(P_2 - P_1)$$

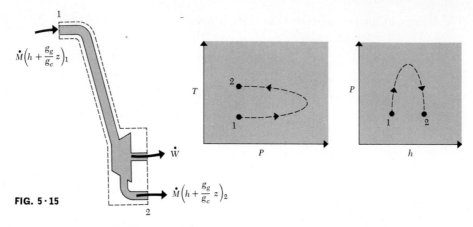

(a) *The control volume*   (b) *The process representation*

FIG. 5·15

where $c_v = 1$ Btu/lbm-°R and $\rho = 62.4$ lbm/ft³. We also estimate that the inlet and discharge ducts have the same flow area, so that the kinetic energy of the water entering the plant is essentially the same as that leaving. With this information, what is our estimate of the power output? See Fig. 5·15.

We make the following idealizations:

Change in kinetic energy of flow streams is negligible
Steady flow steady state
Adiabatic control volume

Note there is no assumption about friction or turbulence or "losses" within the control volume; these are all internal effects, and need not be considered explicitly in a steady-flow, steady-state analysis. They are implicitly considered through their effect on state 2. We would have to make some such assumption if we wanted to *predict* state 2. The energy balance, on a rate basis, is

$$\underbrace{\dot{M}\left(h_1 + \frac{g_g}{g_c}z_1\right)}_{\text{energy-input rate}} = \underbrace{\dot{W} + \dot{M}\left(h_2 + \frac{g_g}{g_c}z_2\right)}_{\text{energy-output rate}}$$

If we take the discharge state 2 as the elevation datum, then $z_2 = 0$ and $z_1 = 800$ ft. The various terms in the energy balance are then

$$\frac{g_g}{g_c}z_1 = \frac{32.2 \text{ ft/sec}^2}{32.2 \text{ ft-lbm/lbf-sec}^2} \times 800 \text{ ft} = 800 \text{ ft-lbf/lbm} = 1.02 \text{ Btu/lbm}$$

$$h_2 - h_1 = c_v(T_2 - T_1) + \frac{1}{\rho}(P_2 - P_1) = 1 \times (40.5 - 40) = 0.5 \text{ Btu/lbm}$$

Hence,

$$\frac{\dot{W}}{\dot{M}} = \frac{g_g}{g_c}z_1 - (h_2 - h_1) = 1.02 - 0.5 = 0.52 \text{ Btu/lbm}$$

Then,

$$\dot{W} = 0.52 \times 62.4 \times 40 = 1298 \text{ Btu/sec} = 1370 \text{ kw} = 1.37 \text{ Mw}$$

A heat pump. The heat pump shows promise of becoming a common household heating system; a simple heat pump consists of the components shown in Fig. 5·16. In an experiment with freon-12 as the working fluid, the following measurements were recorded:

$P_2 = P_3 = 140$ psia
$P_4 = P_1 = 10$ psia
$T_2 = 260°\text{F}$
$T_1 = -20°\text{F}$
Saturated liquid at 3
$\dot{W} = 10$ kw

Determine the condenser and evaporator rates of energy transfer as heat and the flow rate of the freon-12.

In this experiment no pressure drop through the heat exchangers was measurable. This is frequently true, and a good idealization is that the process undergone by a fluid in passing through a heat exchanger is one of *constant pressure*. We begin our analysis of this rather complicated problem by a process representation (Fig. 5·16b) to orient our thinking. The reason for the positioning of state 4 will be evident momentarily.

We have enough information to establish the condenser heat-transfer rate per unit of mass. For control volume 1 we idealize

Steady flow steady state
Kinetic and potential energies negligible
Equilibrium states at 2 and 3
One-dimensional flows at 2 and 3

FIG. 5·16   (a) *The heat pump*   (b) *The process representation*

The energy balance for $CV1$, made on a rate basis, gives

$$\underset{\substack{\text{energy-input} \\ \text{rate}}}{\dot{M}h_2} = \underset{\substack{\text{energy-output} \\ \text{rate}}}{\dot{M}h_3 + \dot{Q}_C}$$

Then, using Fig. B·7,

$$\frac{\dot{Q}_C}{\dot{M}} = h_2 - h_3 = 115 - 31 = 84 \text{ Btu/lbm}$$

We next analyze the valve (control volume 2), with the idealizations

Steady flow steady state
Kinetic and potential energies negligible
Adiabatic control volume
Equilibrium states at 3 and 4
One-dimensional flows at 3 and 4

The energy balance for $CV2$, on a rate basis, then is simply

$$\underset{\substack{\text{energy-input} \\ \text{rate}}}{\dot{M}h_3} = \underset{\substack{\text{energy-output} \\ \text{rate}}}{\dot{M}h_4}$$

or

$$h_3 = h_4 = 31 \text{ Btu/lbm}$$

Note that the energy balance here tells us something about the end states of a process; with these idealizations the enthalpy of the fluid emerging from a valve will be the same as the enthalpy of the entering fluid (though the enthalpy of the fluid within the valve may be quite different).

An energy balance (rate basis) on control volume 3, with idealizations as for control volume 1, yields

$$\underset{\substack{\text{energy-input} \\ \text{rate}}}{\dot{Q}_E + \dot{M}h_4} = \underset{\substack{\text{energy-output} \\ \text{rate}}}{\dot{M}h_1}$$

So the amount of energy transferred as heat to each lbm of freon-12 passing through the evaporator is

$$\frac{\dot{Q}_E}{\dot{M}} = h_1 - h_4 = 76 - 31 = 45 \text{ Btu/lbm}$$

Now for control volume 4 (the compressor) we idealize

Steady flow steady state
Kinetic and potential energies negligible
Adiabatic control volume
Equilibrium states at 1 and 2
One-dimensional flows at 1 and 2

The energy balance for $CV4$, on a rate basis, then gives

$$\underset{\substack{\text{energy-input} \\ \text{rate}}}{\dot{W} + \dot{M}h_1} = \underset{\substack{\text{energy-output} \\ \text{rate}}}{\dot{M}h_2}$$

So the compressor work per lbm of fluid which it handles is

$$\frac{\dot{W}}{\dot{M}} = h_2 - h_1 = 115 - 76 = 39 \text{ Btu/lbm}$$

We can check our calculations by an overall energy balance (control volume 5), made on a rate basis, assuming steady flow steady state:

$$\underset{\substack{\text{energy-input} \\ \text{rate}}}{\dot{W} + \dot{Q}_E} = \underset{\substack{\text{energy-output} \\ \text{rate}}}{\dot{Q}_C}$$

$$\dot{M}(39 + 45 - 84) = 0$$

The *coefficient of performance (cop) of a heat pump* is defined as

$$\text{cop} \equiv \frac{\text{rate of energy transfer to house}}{\text{compressor shaft power}}$$

For our system

$$\text{cop} = \frac{\dot{Q}_C}{\dot{W}} = \frac{\dot{M} \ (84 \text{ Btu/lbm})}{\dot{M} \ (39 \text{ Btu/lbm})} = 2.15$$

Note that the rate of energy transfer into the house is more than twice the electrical power which must be paid for to obtain this heating rate. Note also that the cop could be evaluated without reference to the amount of flow or the total energy-transfer rates. We now compute these from the measured shaft power:

$$\dot{M} = \frac{10 \text{ kw} \times 3413 \text{ Btu/kw-hr}}{39 \text{ Btu/lbm}}$$

$$= 870 \text{ lbm/hr}$$

The rates of energy transfer as heat are therefore

$$\dot{Q}_E = 870 \times 45 = 39{,}100 \text{ Btu/hr}$$
$$\dot{Q}_C = 870 \times 84 = 73{,}000 \text{ Btu/hr}$$

The figure 39,100 Btu/hr is comparable with that of a small commercial freezer. The energy pumped into the house (73,000 Btu/hr) is comparable to that provided by a household furnace.

Heat pumps and refrigerators are sometimes rated in terms of their "tonnage." One ton of refrigeration is defined as 12,000 Btu/hr and is roughly the rate of energy transfer as heat required to freeze 1 ton of ice in a day. Considered as a heat pump, this unit would have a rating of $73,000/12,000 \approx 6$ "tons."

SELECTED READING

Jones, J. B., and G. A. Hawkins, *Engineering Thermodynamics*, secs. 2.7–2.13, John Wiley & Sons, Inc., New York, 1960.

Mooney, D. A., *Introduction to Thermodynamics and Heat Transfer*, chap. 6, Prentice-Hall, Inc., Englewood Cliffs, N.J., 1955.

Van Wylen, G. J., and R. E. Sonntag, *Fundamentals of Classical Thermodynamics*, secs. 5.4–5.10, John Wiley & Sons, Inc., New York, 1965.

QUESTIONS

5·1 What is the difference between a control mass and a control volume?

5·2 How would you distinguish between positive and negative energy transfers?

5·3 Why, in calculus, does dx represent an increase in x? What is the meaning of Δx?

5·4 In the first control-mass example, why was it necessary to idealize that states 1 and 2 were states of thermodynamic equilibrium, and where was this idealization actually used? Why was it not necessary to make a similar idealization about intermediate states?

5·5 What is a process representation?

5·6 In the first control-mass example, why was it necessary to idealize that the alteration in molecular behavior introduced by the gravitational field is negligible, and where was this idealization actually used? What change in the center of mass of the H_2O would produce a change in the potential energy of position equal in magnitude to the change in the internal energy for the process? What is the difference between the idealization that the bulk potential-energy change for the process is negligible and the idealization that the gravitational field does not alter the molecular behavior?

5·7 Why is the enthalpy change equal to the energy transfer as heat to a unit of mass undergoing a constant-pressure process, but not for other processes?

5·8 What is the "latent heat of vaporization" as related to thermodynamic properties?

5·9 Why do the conversion factors between gauss and coul/sec-m differ for **H** and **M**?

5·10 Explain the last statement of the thermal-magnetization example.

5·11 What was assumed about the state of the paramagnetic material *during* the thermal-magnetization process?

5·12 Why does the term Pv appear in the control-volume energy balance and not in that for the control mass?

5·13 Explain why Pv is not energy stored in matter.

5·14 What is the difference between Pv and $P\,dv$, and when do terms of these types appear in energy-conservation equations?

5·15 Why is the enthalpy a useful property to have tabulated?

5·16 Derive the continuity equation $\dot{M} = A\rho\mathbf{V}$.

5·17 Why is the control-volume transformation useful?

5·18 What is steady state? What is steady flow? Why do these idealizations greatly simplify control-volume analysis?

5·19 What is a one-dimensional flow?

5·20 In the first control-volume example, why was it necessary to idealize that the bulk motion does not alter the molecular behavior as seen by an observer riding with the fluid, and where was this idealization actually used?

5·21 What is a rate basis for an energy balance?

5·22 In the nozzle example, the energy stored in the fluid changes as it passes through the control volume. Why, then, is the term marked "energy-storage rate" equal to zero?

5·23 In the turbine example, why is it not necessary to know the state of the fluid inside the turbine?

5·24 Do the idealizations for the oxygen-liquefaction example rule out the possibility of any energy transfer as heat taking place to the fluid inside the control volume?

5·25 Why is the control volume of Fig. 5·11a idealized as adiabatic, while that of Fig. 5·11c is not?

5·26 At what speed do electrons move in a copper wire (see your physics book)?

5·27 Why do we handle electron-flow problems by the control-volume method?

5·28 In the tank-charging example, why is the idealization made that the gas in the tank is in equilibrium at every instant, and where is it used?

5·29 Explain the statement immediately following Eq. (5·9).

5·30 What can you say about the house and outdoor temperatures in the heat-pump example?

5·31 Outline a good energy-analysis methodology.

5·32 Why does it pay to be judicious in selecting a control volume or control mass? Is there sometimes more than one choice?

PROBLEMS

5·1 Two lbm of copper at 300°K are cooled to 250°K at 1 atm. How much energy is transferred as heat, and how much work is done on the copper (Table B·7)?

5·2 How much energy transfer as heat is required to completely evaporate 1 lbm of nitrogen for a constant-temperature process, with $T = 161.09$°R (Fig. B·4)?

5·3 Nitrogen in a 1-ft³ container is heated from the saturated-vapor state at 50 psia to 300°R. How much energy transfer as heat is involved (Fig. B·4)?

5·4 Three lbm of nitrogen is heated at constant pressure from the saturated-liquid state at 100 psia to a temperature of 400°R. How much energy transfer as heat is required? How much work is done by the nitrogen, if any, and on what (Fig. B·4)?

5·5 One lbm of freon-12 is heated in a constant-volume container from the critical point to 700°F. How much energy is transferred as heat to the freon, and from where (Fig. B·7)?

5·6 Iron-ammonium alum is magnetized at 1°K by increasing the external field **H** slowly from zero to 10,000 gauss. How much energy is transferred as heat for this process, and in which direction? How much work is done on the alum, and by what (Fig. B·12)?

5·7 One lbm of copper and 0.5 lbm of saturated H_2O vapor at 1 atm pressure are initially in equilibrium. The water is then heated at constant pressure and held at 400°F until equilibrium between the copper and the water is again obtained. How much energy transfer as heat takes place between the water and its vessel, and how much between the water and the copper (Figs. B·1–B·3, Table B·7)?

5·8 One lbm of CO_2 is expanded adiabatically in a piston-cylinder system from 400 psia and 100°F to the saturated-vapor state at 100 psia. How much work is done by the CO_2 and on what (Fig. B·6)?

5·9 One lbm of O_2 is compressed adiabatically in a piston-cylinder system from the saturated-vapor state at 36.6 psia to a pressure of 17.5 atm and a temperature of 175°K. How much work is done on the O_2 and by what (Fig. B·5)?

5·10 One-half lbm of CO_2 is heated in a 0.5-ft³ vessel from 0 to 200°F. Determine the initial and final states, and the amount of energy transfer as heat to the CO_2.

5·11 One-half lbm of CO_2 is heated at constant pressure from the saturated-vapor state at 100 psia to 200°F. Determine the amounts of energy transfer as heat and work involved in this process.

5·12 An adiabatic piston-cylinder system contains a 1000-watt immersion heater and 2 lbm of H_2O initially at 14.7 psia and 96 percent quality. The heater is operated for 7 minutes, during which the pressure is held constant. Find the final volume of the system.

5·13 A simple engine uses a perfect gas as the working fluid in a piston-cylinder system. The gas is first heated at constant pressure from state 1 to state 2, then cooled at constant volume to state 3 where $T_3 = T_1$, and then cooled at constant temperature, thereby returning to state 1. Derive expressions for the amounts of energy transfer as work and heat (per lbm of gas) for each process in terms of the temperatures and pressures at each state and the constants of the gas. Suppose $T_1 = 500°R$, $P_1 = 20$ psia, $T_2 = 1000°R$, and $k \equiv c_P/c_v = 1.4$. Calculate the cycle efficiency (*net* work output/energy *input* as heat).

5·14 A simple engine uses a perfect gas as the working fluid in a piston-cylinder system. The gas is first heated at constant volume from state 1 to state 2, then heated at constant temperature to state 3 where $P_3 = P_1$, and then cooled at constant pressure, returning to state 1. Derive expressions for the amounts of energy transfer as heat and work (per lbm of gas) for each process in terms of the temperatures and pressures at each state and the constants of the gas. Assuming $T_1 = 500°R$, $P_1 = 20$ psia, $T_2 = 1000°R$, and $k \equiv c_P/c_v = 1.4$, calculate the cycle efficiency (*net* work output/energy *input* as heat).

5·15 When the engine of Prob. 5·13 is reversed it becomes a refrigeration device. Calculate the amount of energy transfer as heat from the cold space for this cycle (per lbm of gas), and the cycle cop (energy transfer as heat from cold space/net work input).

5·16 Do Prob. 5·15 for the engine cycle of Prob. 5·14.

5·17 A low-temperature refrigeration cycle uses iron-ammonium alum (Fig. B·12) as the working substance. The alum is first heated at constant $\mathbf{H} = 3000$ gauss from state 1 where $\mathbf{M}_1 = 90$ gauss to state 2, where $\mathbf{M}_2 = 70$ gauss. It is then heated at constant $\mathbf{M}$ until $\mathbf{H} = 10,000$ gauss at state 3, and then cooled at constant $\mathbf{H}$ to state 4 where $\mathbf{M}_4 = \mathbf{M}_1$. A final cooling process at constant $\mathbf{M}$ returns the alum to state 1. Calculate the amounts of energy transfer as heat for the four processes (erg/g), and the cycle cop (energy transfer as heat from cold space/net energy input as work).

5·18 An engine operating on the reverse cycle to that described in Prob. 5·17 is proposed for use in a deep space probe which can have no part at greater than 2°K. Calculate the net work output per g of alum, the cycle efficiency (net work output/energy input as heat), and the required amount of alum for 1 watt of power if the cycle can be repeated every 22 seconds.

5·19 Consider the piston-cylinder-spring system shown below.

Piston area 1 in.²
Vacuum in spring chamber
Spring force $F = ka$, $k = 300$ lbf/in.

The cylinder initially contains CO_2 at 80°F, and a is initially 2 in. The cylinder walls are then slowly cooled, and the piston moves to the left until $a = \frac{1}{2}$ in. Calculate the energy transfer as heat from the gas for this process.

5·20 Twenty lbm/min of mercury vapor enters a condenser at 800°F, 0.5 psia. The mercury emerges as a saturated liquid at 0.4 psia. Calculate the rate of energy transfer as heat from the mercury side of the condenser (Fig. B·10, Table B·3).

5·21 Oxygen passes through an adiabatic steady-flow compressor at the rate of 1000 lbm/hr, entering as a saturated vapor at 36.6 psia and emerging at 17.5 atm and 175°K. Determine the shaft work per unit of mass of O_2 (compare Prob. 5·9) and the required motor hp.

5·22 Five hundred lbm/min of CO_2 passes through an adiabatic steady-flow turbine, entering at 400 psia and 100°F and emerging as a saturated vapor at 100 psia. What is the shaft-work output per lbm of CO_2 (compare Prob. 5·8), and what is the power (kw) delivered by the turbine?

5·23 Ten lbm/min of mercury enters a small turbine at 30 psia and 1400°F and emerges at 2 psia and 800°F. What is the shaft-power output if the "heat losses" (energy transfer as heat from the turbine casing) are negligible? What is the shaft-power output if the "heat losses" amount to 20 percent of the power output for the adiabatic device (Fig. B·10)?

5·24 Steam flows through a small steam turbine at the rate of 10,000 lbm/hr, entering at 600°F and 200 psia and emerging at 2 psia with 4 percent moisture. The flow enters at 250 ft/sec at a point 6 ft above the discharge and leaves at 140 ft/sec. Compute the shaft-power output, assuming that the device is adiabatic but considering kinetic and potential energies. How much error would be made were these secondary terms neglected? What are the diameters of the inlet and discharge pipes (Fig. B·2, Tables B·1, B·2)?

5·25 If the state at the discharge of the nozzle in the turbine of Prob. 5·24 is 8 percent moisture and 10 psia, what is the velocity at this point?

5·26 Air enters an adiabatic nozzle at 3 atm pressure and 100°F and emerges at 1 atm and 30°F. The inlet velocity is negligible, and the nozzle is adiabatic. What is the discharge velocity (Fig. B·8)?

5·27 The collecting panels of a solar boiler receive energy as heat at the rate of approximately 300 Btu/hr per square foot of collecting surface during the day. How many square feet of collector would be required for a small desert power plant producing 10 kw of electrical power if the electric power output is 8 percent of the collected solar energy? (This is a typical energy-conversion efficiency for such a system.)

5·28 Oxygen flows at the rate of 100 lbm/sec through a line to a large booster rocket. The lox enters the line as a saturated liquid at 2 atm, and the pressure drop is negligible. Specify the maximum permitted heat-transfer rate ("heat leak in") to the lox if a maximum of 0.5 percent vapor can be tolerated at the booster end of the line (Fig. B·5).

5·29 The throttling calorimeter is a device for measuring the state of a liquid-vapor mixture. The procedure is to bleed off a little of the mixture, throttle it through a valve, and make the measurements shown. Explain why P_1 and T_1 do not fix the state of the "wet" mixture, and how P_2 and T_2 measurements allow one to determine state 1. How much throttling is necessary for this scheme to work? Compute the quality at state 1 for the measurements below, assuming the fluid is water (Tables B·1 and B·2).

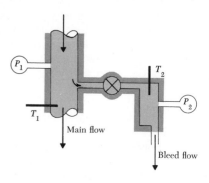

$P_1 = 100$ psia $P_2 = 5$ psia
$T_1 = 327.81°F$ $T_2 = 200°F$

5·30 A valve in an insulated liquid-oxygen fuel line causes a pressure drop of 3 psia. The inlet state is saturated liquid at 2 atm. What is the discharge quality, and how much is the temperature reduced (Fig. B·5)?

5·31 Mercury emerges from the nuclear boiler of a space power system at 500 psia and 0.95 quality and is "flashed" by passing through a flow restriction (valve) into the superheat region to a pressure of 50 psia. What is the temperature of the mercury in this superheated state (Fig. B·10, Table B·3)?

5·32 Determine the air-flow rate that could be used in the air-CO_2-exchanger example if the CO_2 states and the inlet air state are as given but the air emerges as cold as possible.

5·33 A mixture of CO_2 containing 20 percent solid by mass, 20 percent liquid, and 60 percent vapor enters a pipe and emerges all vapor at the inlet pressure and 0°F. The flow rate is 4 lbm/sec. What is the rate at which energy is transferred as heat to the pipe?

5·34 Work the nozzle example using the control-mass approach.

5·35 Work the mercury-turbine example using the control-mass approach.

5·36 Work the tank-charging example using the control-mass approach.

5·37 Ten lbm/min of saturated-liquid mercury at 415°F and 2 lbm/min of mercury vapor at 700°F and 1 psia enter an adiabatic mixing device; the mercury emerges mixed in a single stream at 0.3 psia. What is the temperature of the emergent stream, and (if it is a mixture) what is its quality (Fig. B·10)?

5·38 Oxygen is used in a low-temperature refrigerator. The hardware is similar to that of the heat-pump example. The condenser pressure is 20 atm and the O_2 is evaporated at 2 atm. Liquid emerges from the condenser in the saturated state and vapor from the evaporator at a temperature of 100°K. The compressor outlet temperature is 225°K. Determine the coefficient of performance of this refrigerator, where

cop = (rate of energy removal from cold space)/(compressor power input)

What is the required oxygen-flow rate for a total cooling rate $\dot{Q}_E$ of 10,000 Btu/hr?

5·39 A small solar engine for desert water pumping uses steam as the working fluid. The hardware is shown in the figure. Water enters the pump as a saturated liquid at 120°F and is pumped up to 30 psia by a small centrifugal pump. The boiler evaporates the water at 30 psia, and saturated vapor at this pressure enters the small turbine. The steam leaves the turbine with 6 percent moisture at 120°F and

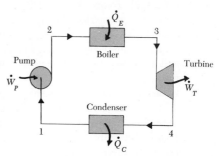

is subsequently condensed. The flow rate is 300 lbm/hr, and the pump is driven by a ½-hp motor operating at full load. Making suitable idealizations, determine the power output of this plant (net hp), the energy-conversion efficiency (net shaft-work output/energy transfer to fluid in boiler), and estimate the number of square feet of solar collectors that would be required, assuming that the collectors can pick up 250 Btu/hr per square foot of exposed surface.

5·40 A proposed nuclear power system for space use employs mercury as the working fluid, using hardware similar to that in Prob. 5·39 above, except that a nuclear reactor replaces the sun as the energy source. The mercury enters the pump as a saturated liquid at 800°F, is compressed, and is then evaporated at 400 psia and superheated to 1400°F in the reactor-boiler. The turbine discharge is at 800°F with 3 percent moisture; pressure drops through the reactor and condenser may be neglected for this thermodynamic analysis. The power required to operate the pump will be 2 percent of the turbine-shaft power. Determine the energy-conversion efficiency for this system (net shaft power/reactor-power input), and the mercury-flow rate and reactor power required for 10 kw of net electrical power, assuming a 95-percent-efficient electrical generator will be employed (Fig. B·10, Table B·3).

5·41 Consider an electrical resistor through which flows a steady current i. The resistor is cooled in order to maintain a steady state. From thermodynamic considerations, show that the rate at which energy must be transferred from the resistor as heat is $\dot{Q} = i \,\Delta \mathcal{E}$, where $\Delta \mathcal{E}$ is the voltage drop across the resistor. What are the restrictions on this result imposed by the idealizations?

5·42 In a linear accelerator electrons are accelerated until their kinetic energy is 10 Mev per electron. If the beam is accidentally diverted it will strike the ⅛-in.-thick copper walls of the cavities and can cause serious damage. Assuming that a beam carrying 10^{18} (electrons/sec)/cm² moving at right angles to the wall strikes the wall and all electrons are stopped, what cooling rate (Btu/hr-ft²) must be provided to prevent a rise in the temperature of the wall? The electrostatic potential energy of the electrons at the point of impact is negligible compared to their kinetic energy.

5·43 Freon-12 will be used as the propellant for a small portable jet
rocket for maneuvering parts
during the assembly of a space
station. The device will consist of
a small spherical tank containing
saturated freon-12 at 80°F, a
valve, and a nozzle. The user will

attach the jet to the package, open the valve momentarily, and let some gas
escape through the nozzle. Energy transfer as heat from the walls to the freon-12
will keep the pressure constant in the cylinder during a short burst, and the
flow through the nozzle may be considered steady. The valve will throttle the
freon-12 to 20 psia, and the nozzle discharge state will be 2 psia and −80°F.
The thrusting force is approximately given by $F = \dot{M}V/g_c$, where $\dot{M}$ is the
mass-flow rate and V the exit velocity. Use requirements call for a thrust of
10 lbf. Determine the specific impulse of this device, $SI = F/\dot{M}$, in lbf/(lbm/sec).
By comparison, a good chemical rocket has an SI of the order of 250 lbf/(lbm/
sec). Specify the size of tank required to hold enough freon-12 for 1000 sec
of operation, assuming that the heat-transfer rate is sufficient to keep the pressure constant for short-duration bursts. Compute the total amount of energy
which must be transferred from the walls to the freon-12 during this 1000 sec
of operation in order to maintain the pressure (Fig. B·7, Table B·5). This requires a careful energy analysis.

5·44 A small power system proposed for use in the arctic has the hardware of Prob. 5·39
and uses CO_2 as the working fluid. However, a supercritical cycle is employed;
condensation occurs underground at −60°F, and saturated CO_2 liquid leaves
the condenser at this temperature. The pump raises the pressure to 1600 psia,
and the liquid emerges from the pump at −40°F. A solar collector is used to
heat the CO_2 to 160°F, and the pressure drop through the "supercritical boiler"
is 200 psia. The CO_2, at 1400 psia and 160°F, then enters the turbine and
emerges at −40°F and 0.90 quality. Find the energy-conversion efficiency (net
shaft-energy output/solar-energy input) for this system. Specify the pump
power, turbine power, and solar-energy-collection rate required for a 10-kw
plant, assuming that the electric generator has an efficiency of 92 percent. Make
appropriate idealizations to allow solutions (Fig. B·6).

5·45 The hardware for a proposed SNAP system for generation of electrical power for
space vehicles is shown on the facing page.
     The boiler is a nuclear reactor in which the working fluid is heated by pas-
sage over the nuclear fuel elements. $\dot{Q}_B$ represents the rate of energy transfer as
heat from the rods to the fluid, and is equal to the reactor power. The condenser
is a heat exchanger in which energy transferred as heat from the fluid is radiated
away to space at the rate $\dot{Q}_C$. Pressure drop through the boiler, condenser, ducting
are negligible, and the pump, valve, turbine, and ducting are adiabatic devices.
     Mercury is proposed as the working fluid. The mercury will leave the con-
denser as a saturated liquid at 30 psia. The pump will raise the pressure to 400
psia, where evaporation will occur. The mercury will leave the reactor at 95 percent quality (at 400 psia). The valve provides pressure drop for load control.

The manufacturer of the electromagnetic pump says he can provide a pump that will do the job for a work input of about 0.5 Btu/lbm of mercury pumped. The turbine manufacturer feels he can build a turbine with an "isentropic efficiency" of 60 percent for the range of flows probably involved. The isentropic efficiency is

$$\eta_s = \frac{h_4 - h_5}{h_4 - h_{5s}}$$

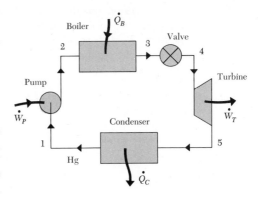

where h_4 and h_5 are the enthalpies entering and leaving the actual turbine, and h_{5s} is the enthalpy at a hypothetical reference state fixed by the inlet entropy (s) and outlet pressure.

(a) Suppose the component manufacturers can indeed deliver as they promise. Determine the component energy flows per lbm of mercury assuming that the valve is wide open so that $P_3 = P_4$. Determine the *net* work output per unit of mass and the overall system efficiency (efficiency of conversion of the reactor power to mechanical shaft power). Then, specify the required mass flow rate if the net shaft power is to be 10 kw. Calculate the pump power, reactor power, turbine power, and condenser cooling rate (kw) for this flow; discuss briefly the distribution of the input reactor energy.

(b) Suppose the velocity of the stream at section 5 is limited to a maximum of 100 ft/sec. Calculate the required duct diameter at this point.

(c) Suppose the valve is partially closed such that the turbine inlet pressure is reduced to 100 psia, while the same evaporating and condensing pressures, and flow, are maintained. Determine the net power output in this configuration, the condenser cooling rate, and the overall system efficiency.

5·46 A geothermal power plant in California uses steam produced underground by natural sources. Steam enters the adiabatic turbine at 362°F and 80 psia, and emerges at 2 psia with 8 percent moisture (92 percent quality). It is then condensed at 2 psia, and then pumped back up to atmospheric pressure. The plant produces 12.5 Mw of electric power. Assuming an electric generator efficiency of 0.95, and neglecting the pump power, determine the steam flow rate and the condenser heat-transfer rate. Why do you think the system has the condenser? Why does it need the pump?

5·47 It is desired to reduce the pressure of cesium vapor from 50 psia at 2400°R to 1.9 psia. Suggest a means for doing this in a steady-flow device without any energy transfer as heat or shaft work to or from the system. For your device, what is the exit temperature at 1.9 psia?

5·48 You are required to determine the state of a mixture of liquid and vapor mercury used in a power plant for a space application. Only P and T measurements can be made. Design a system to fix the mixture state. The system must be reliable, inexpensive, and simple.

5·49 Freon-12 vapor flows at 10 ft/sec at 300 psia and 360°F. It is desired to accelerate the flow to 500 ft/sec at a pressure of 200 psia in a steady-flow device. What hardware is required and what is the exit temperature?

5·50 Consider the steady, one-dimensional, adiabatic, frictionless flow of an ideal gas in a passage of variable area. Suppose that the gas emerges from a chamber at temperature T_0 with negligible kinetic energy, and is accelerated to velocity V in a passage of appropriate design. At this point it now has temperature T, sound speed a, and Mach number $M \equiv \mathsf{V}/a$. For the ideal gas, $a^2 = g_c kRT$. Show that

$$\frac{T_0}{T} = 1 + \frac{k-1}{2} M^2$$

CHAPTER SIX

ENTROPY AND THE SECOND LAW

6·1 THE ESSENCE OF THE SECOND LAW

The central idea of all science is that nature behaves in a manner which in principle is predictable. The concepts of energy and its conservation are used in order to make these predictions quantitative. We have seen how energy-balance analysis is used to predict the change in state of a system due to transfers of energy as heat and work or by spontaneous internal changes. Experience indicates that it is sometimes ideally possible to reverse the directions of energy transfer as heat and work, and thereby reverse the change of state. The energy analyses of the forward and backward processes differ only in the change of sign for each term; that is, the energy analysis is insensitive to the direction of time. But we also know from experience that, while certain spontaneous changes of state can occur in isolated systems, the reverse changes are never observed. Oxygen and hydrogen readily react to form water; but who has ever seen water spontaneously separate into its two basic elements? By itself, first-law analysis cannot reveal the possibility or impossibility of a process; it cannot point the direction of time. The ability to rule out impossible processes is clearly essential to any complete predictive theory of nature. The *second law of thermodynamics* provides the necessary structure for this second type of analysis.

Every system is considered to have a property called its *entropy*. Entropy, like energy, is a *conceptual* property. Part of the concept of entropy is that it is an *extensive* property; the entropy of a system is the sum of the entropies of all its parts. This extensive feature makes it easy to evaluate the entropy of a complex system by hypothetically dissecting it into simpler parts. Another aspect of entropy is the idea that the entropy of an *isolated* system can *never decrease*. This *postulate* is the second law of thermodynamics; it permits entropy to serve as a "signpost of time." Any process that would increase the entropy of an isolated system is possible; any process that would decrease the entropy of an isolated system is impossible; any process that would keep the entropy of an isolated system constant is possible in either the forward or backward direction.

For example, with these second-law ideas we shall be able to predict what chemical reactions can and cannot occur. If we compute the entropy of H_2 and O_2, then the entropy of a system containing 2 moles of H_2 and 1 mole of O_2 can be computed using the extensive feature of entropy. We imagine the H_2 and O_2 reacting in an isolated system, and compute the entropy of the resulting 2 moles of H_2O. It is larger than the sum of the entropies of the 2 moles of H_2 and 1 mole of O_2, and hence the reaction does not violate the second law. However, the reverse reaction would lead to a *decrease* in entropy within the isolated system; this violates the second law, and hence the *reverse* reaction is *impossible*.

As with energy, the understanding of entropy can be greatly enhanced by consideration of the microscopic nature of matter. An analogy will be helpful in grasping the microscopic concepts underlying the second law. Suppose we have a large tray containing a large number of "educated jumping beans," half red and half white. Imagine that we have taught the beans to jump in pairs, thereby trading places, and we set up the tray initially with the white beans on one side and red on the other. An observer viewing the tray from a great distance could not see individual beans; he would say, "That object is white on one side and red on the other." Now we let the beans start jumping; soon our observer might comment, "The red stuff is diffusing through the white; and the system is becoming pink." After a while the tray would appear to our observer a uniform pinkish hue, and he would think that all changes had stopped. From our closer proximity we would see continual change, with the red and white beans relatively evenly distributed. Occasionally we would see momentary concentrations of one color in various spots, but these would disappear quickly and would not be noticed by the sluggish eye of our distant observer. We could repeat this experiment many times; each time the observer would note that the red diffused through the white, and after a while an equilibrium condition was reached. If he noticed this reproducibility, he might attempt to construct a mathematical theory that would explain the diffusion and perhaps even predict its rate. Even in his ignorance of the beans, he might make a rather good theory. But certainly consideration of the beans would allow a better and more understandable theory.

We might permit our observer to experiment on the tray. He could enlarge it, distort it, shake it, but we would allow him to have no permanent control over the behavior of *individual* beans. They would remain free to act as they pleased, jumping randomly from spot to spot. Learning of the existence of the beans, our observer might try to make a statistical theory by postulating that, left to themselves, the bean arrangement tends to become more and more random. As a consequence he would be uncertain about the instantaneous arrangement of the beans, and as time went on any uncertainty he had would surely increase. To make these ideas quantitative he would need some *numerical measure* of the "randomness" or of his "uncertainty" about the detailed bean arrangement when the tray is viewed from afar. When the tray looked half white and half red the beans were relatively well organized and our observer could be relatively certain as to the bean arrangement. As time passed and the tray became pink, the bean arrangements would be more disorganized, and our distant observer would be much less certain about the instantaneous detailed state. The bean randomness or disorder, and his uncertainty, would have increased, and his theory could be based on the postulate that the value of the randomness-uncertainty measure could never decrease.

This analogy has many points of contact with the notions of entropy and the second law of thermodynamics. We can replace the beans by atoms of argon and helium, the tray by an isolating wall, and the observer by ourselves. The same sort of diffusion process would be observed. The quantitative measure of the microscopic randomness, of our uncertainty as to the exact microscopic state when we know only the macroscopic state, is the entropy; we find we can explain the directions of all processes observed in nature with theory developed from the postulate that the microscopic randomness of an *isolated* system, that is, the *entropy* of an isolated system, can never decrease.

In order to use this postulate in an analysis we must be able to evaluate quantitatively the entropy of systems. In statistical thermodynamics the entropy is defined in terms of "probabilities" of the microscopic states. The entropy can then be computed from this definition if the probabilities can be found. In macroscopic thermodynamics the basic concepts of what entropy is and does are employed in order to learn how to evaluate entropy. The microscopic interpretations of entropy are more easily grasped, and consequently we have chosen to start with statistical concepts and definition of entropy. This development is the main theme of this chapter. While the microscopic ideas greatly assist understanding, most practical analysis does not require consideration of the microscopic view. In fact, the entropy can be evaluated from macroscopic laboratory data without any explicit consideration of microscopic states. We shall see how this is done in Chap. Seven. Our combined microscopic-macroscopic approach is designed to help the student understand the concepts and strengthen his ability to work successfully with practical second-law analysis. The objective of this chapter is therefore understanding of the statistical meaning of entropy and the plausibility of the second law. We emphasize that the ability to work quantitatively with the statistical ideas is *not* required now.

6·2 ALLOWED QUANTUM STATES

What are the possible microscopic states of a system? A key idea that we take from quantum mechanics is that the states which atoms, molecules, and entire systems have are *discretely quantized*. For example, a photon associated with radiation of a particular frequency ν can have but one energy. This is given by the Einstein-Planck equation,

$$\epsilon = h\nu \qquad\qquad\qquad (6\cdot 1)$$

The constant h is *Planck's constant*, 6.625×10^{-34} joule-sec. The energy traveling with radiation is therefore said to be *quantized*.

Electrons having a given energy can be used to bombard a sample of a gas, and the emitted radiation can be examined in a spectroscope. At low bombardment energies no radiation is emitted, but when a certain threshold is reached light suddenly appears. With mercury, for example, when the energy of the electrons passes 4.86 ev a bright line at 2537 Å suddenly appears in the spectroscope. The interpretation given this line is that it is produced by the decay of atoms of mercury from an "excited state" to the normal or "ground state." Electrons with energies greater than 4.86 ev are required to produce this excitation, which we view as an increase in the energy of electrons orbiting the nucleus as a result of interactions with the bombarding electrons. The excited state appears to be a definite repeatable level above the ground state. The energy jump between the two states of the atom is calculated assuming that energy is conserved in the decay and that the energy of the emitted radiation is equal to the decrease in the energy of the atom. It is further assumed that a single photon is emitted per decay. The energy-level difference is then given by the Einstein-Planck equation as

$$\epsilon_1 - \epsilon_0 = h\nu$$

When this calculation is made using the measured wavelength of 2537 Å, the energy-level difference is found to be 4.86 ev.

The single line remains as the energy of the impinging electrons is increased, until at about 7 ev a new line appears at 1849 Å, corresponding to an energy change from 6.67 ev to the ground state. At 8.4 ev new lines appear, corresponding to transitions from 7.8 ev to the ground state and to the other excited states. Lines continue to appear, until at 10.4 ev the impinging electrons possess sufficient energy to remove an electron from orbit, ionizing the mercury atom. It appears that the ejected electrons can have any energy, so that the ionized atom can accept any parcel of energy greater than the "ionization potential" of 10.4 ev.

At low temperatures practically all the atoms of mercury exist in the ground state, and bombardment by electrons or other particles is necessary to produce excited states. However, at higher temperatures collisions between the rapidly translating mercury atoms can have the same effect, and as the temperature increases, the excitations and decays become more and more frequent. High temperatures, electron collisions, and every other way of producing emission of light from gas atoms are all means of promoting the atoms to excited states. The skilled spectroscopist can examine the spectrum of a substance and from it enumerate the "allowed quantum states" of its atoms or molecules. The

FIG. 6·1   *Electronic quantum states for a hydrogen atom*

electronic quantum states determined in this manner for the simplest atom, hydrogen, are shown in Fig. 6·1.

The quantum theory of matter and energy seemingly meets every test man has been able to devise. By postulating that any particle or system of particles constrained in some manner (such as being required to orbit a nucleus, being in a magnetic field, or being in a box of specified size) can exist only in certain *allowed quantum states*, we obtain amazingly complete and precise descriptions of all natural phenomena. The allowed states are determined by the nature of the particles and the circumstances in which they find themselves; an equation, known as the *Schrödinger equation*, has been postulated as the basis for calculation of the allowed quantum states. For the present we need only the idea that the allowed states of a system are quantized, and it is not necessary to be able to evaluate these states.

It is important to appreciate that quantization refers to very detailed *microscopic* descriptions of state. At any instant a piece of matter must be in one of its allowed quantum states. Macroscopic instruments, which average over time, will reflect averages over the sequence of quantum states; hence macroscopic descriptions of state are very much less detailed. For example, a microscopic description of state might require values for the energy and position of *each particle*, while macroscopic descriptions might involve only the total energy, volume, the temperature, pressure, and of course the entropy.

6·3 QUANTUM-STATE PROBABILITIES

Systems of many interacting molecules undergo continual change in their quantum state. Macroscopic instruments are unable to follow these rapid changes, and hence tend to average over a long sequence of quantum states. Since we have essentially no control over individual molecules, it is really quite impossible for us to force the system to be in a particular quantum state at the start of an experiment; hence if we repeat the experiment a number of times a different initial quantum state will be involved in each repetition. Consequently a different sequence of quantum states will be traced out in each experiment. A large set of such repetitions (real or hypothetical) is called an *ensemble* of experiments.

Traces of the quantum-state numbers (no one has ever measured these in a real experiment) might look something like those in Fig. 6·2. The sequences

(a) *There is little difference between experiments in this ensemble*

FIG. 6·2 *Quantum-state sequences; each trace represents a different experiment*

(b) *There is much more variation between experiments in this ensemble*

of Fig. 6·2a are nearly identical; at each time a narrow band of quantum states is found. In contrast, the sequences of Fig. 6·2b are much more random; at each instant there is a wide variation in quantum states between experiments. Consequently, a guess about the instantaneous quantum state in a particular experiment might be quite close for sequence (a), but may be way off for sequence (b). A *quantitative* measure of the *likelihood* of a particular quantum state existing at some time would be useful. The *quantum-state probability* $p_i(t)$ provides this measure. $p_i(t)$ is defined as the fraction of the ensemble of experiments in which quantum state i would be realized at time t. If the realized quantum states (those which actually occur) are few, the p_i will be high. If the realized quantum states are many, the p_i will be low. If in every experiment the same quantum state exists at time t, the probability of that quantum state will be unity and the probability of all other quantum states will be zero. The set of all the p_i's is called the *distribution;* it reflects the relative likelihood of particular quantum states. Since the sum of the probabilities of all the allowed quantum states must be unity,

$$\sum_i p_i = 1$$

Suppose we allow a system to reach equilibrium with its environment. Thereafter there are no macroscopic changes, though the microscopic state is undergoing continual change. In equilibrium there is nothing special about any point in time, and consequently the p_i's must be independent of time. The resulting distribution is called the *equilibrium distribution*. In equilibrium p_i can be taken as the fraction of *time* that a single system spends in the ith allowed quantum state. The time-fraction definition of probability is valid only in equilibrium; for nonequilibrium the ensemble-fraction definition must be used.

The system properties used in macroscopic analysis are averages over the continuous sequence of microscopic states. Since in equilibrium the p_i represent the fraction of time spent in each state, if we know any property G_i of each quantum state we can calculate the average G as

$$\langle G \rangle \equiv \sum_i p_i G_i \qquad (6 \cdot 2)$$

Thus, for example, if ϵ_i is the energy of the ith quantum state, the average energy is

$$\langle E \rangle = \sum_i p_i \epsilon_i \qquad (6 \cdot 3)$$

This type of average is also used for systems that are not in equilibrium, that is, where the p_i depend upon time. The average can then be interpreted as an average over an ensemble (real or hypothetical) of experiments; the ensemble average reflects the "expected" value of a property in any particular experiment, and hence ensemble averages are sometimes called "expectation values."

The probabilities indicate the "randomness" of the equilibrium quantum states. For example, suppose we have a system that can exist in one of three quantum states. If the equilibrium distribution is

(a) $p_1 = 1$ $p_2 = 0$ $p_3 = 0$

we know that the system is always in quantum state 1; the randomness is zero. If asked to guess the instantaneous quantum state, we could say "one" with absolute certainty. Suppose that the equilibrium distribution is

(b) $p_1 = 0.8$ $p_2 = 0.2$ $p_3 = 0$

This says that 80 percent of the time the system is in quantum state 1, and 20 percent of the time it is in quantum state 2. Asked to guess the instantaneous state we would again say "one," and in the long run we would be correct 80 percent of the time. This distribution shows more randomness than case (a) above. Our uncertainty as macroscopic observers about the instantaneous microscopic state is certainly greater in (b) than in (a). If the equilibrium distribution is

(c) $p_1 = 0.8$ $p_2 = 0.1$ $p_3 = 0.1$
or (d) $p_1 = 0.1$ $p_2 = 0.8$ $p_3 = 0.1$

the quantum-state sequence will show even more variation or randomness, and we shall be even more uncertain about the instantaneous quantum state. However, the same uncertainty will apply to both (c) and (d). The most randomness is indicated by the distribution

(e) $p_1 = p_2 = p_3 = \frac{1}{3}$

Here each allowed quantum state is equally likely, and we can only guess the instantaneous state with 33 percent chance of being correct. Note that the "broader" the distribution is the more uncertain we must be about the instantaneous quantum state.

We have seen that the distribution conveys a qualitative impression of the randomness of the sequence of quantum states, that is, of our uncertainty as to the instantaneous microscopic state. A list of all the p_i would convey a very good picture of the randomness and uncertainty. This list would be far too long to be usable; it would be much more convenient if we could use a *single number* to measure the amount of randomness and uncertainty reflected by the entire list of p_i. The *entropy* provides this measure.

6·4 ENTROPY

Since the entire set of p_i reflect the quantum-state randomness, it would seem appropriate to look for some function of all the p_i that would serve as a single measure of randomness. We shall call this randomness measure the *entropy*, and denote it by S.

For operational convenience we shall define S such that it is *extensive*. That is, the entropy of system C, composed of parts A and B, must be given by

$$S_C = S_A + S_B \tag{6·4}$$

The randomness measure should also give greater values of S when the system is more random; that is, it should agree with the qualitative ideas about randomness. We are now going to use these ideas to discover an appropriate definition of S in terms of the probability distribution.

Now, we ask what function of the p_i might be useful as a single numerical measure of the randomness? The product of the probabilities $p_1 \times p_2 \cdots \times p_n$ won't do, because it will be zero when *any* one of the p_i is zero. The sum of the p_i won't do either because it always has the value unity. The *average* probability is sometimes used in statistics as a measure of randomness, so let's see if it will work. The average probability is [see Eq. (6·2)]

$$\langle p \rangle = \sum_i p_i p_i = \sum_i p_i{}^2$$

When $\langle p \rangle$ is high only a few quantum states are realized, and there is little randomness. When it is low many quantum states are realized and there is much randomness and uncertainty. Hence the average probability does seem to fit the qualitative requirements of a randomness measure. Is it extensive? To investigate this we first make use of Eq. (6·4). Suppose there are n allowed states for system A and m allowed states for system B. If the allowed states in each part are independent of those in the other, the quantum state for the combined system C can be described by specifying the quantum states of A and B; we denote these by i and j, respectively, and suppose that they are numbered such that $i = 1, 2, \ldots, n, j = 1, 2, \ldots, m$. The allowed states for C can then be denoted by the number pair i, j. For example, C-state 2,6 is the state where part A is in its state $i = 2$ and part B is in its state $j = 6$. There are $n \cdot m$ allowed states for C, corresponding to the $n \cdot m$ points in Fig. 6·3.

The probability of each C state can be computed from the individual probabilities for A and B states. If p_i is the probability of A-state i, and p_j the probability of B-state j, then

$$p_{ij} = p_i \cdot p_j \tag{6·5}$$

is the probability of the C-state i, j. This follows from a basic part of the concept of probability, namely, that probabilities are such that the joint probability of two independent events (the realization of A-state i and the realization of B-state j) is the *product* of their individual probabilities.†

Now, the average probabilities of A and B are

$$\langle p \rangle_A = \sum_{i=1}^{n} p_i^2 \qquad \langle p \rangle_B = \sum_{j=1}^{m} p_j^2$$

and the average probability of C is

$$\langle p \rangle_C = \sum_{i=1}^{n} \sum_{j=1}^{m} p_{ij}^2 = \sum_{i=1}^{n} \sum_{j=1}^{m} (p_i p_j)^2$$

Rearranging the sums,

$$\langle p \rangle_C = \sum_{i=1}^{n} \left[p_i^2 \left(\sum_{j=1}^{m} p_j^2 \right) \right] = \sum_{i=1}^{n} p_i^2 \langle p_B \rangle = \langle p_A \rangle \langle p_B \rangle$$

† For example, if there is only an 0.2 chance that A-state 2 will exist, and only an 0.3 chance that B-state 6 will exist, then there is only an 0.06 chance of them both existing at the same time, that is, C-state 2,6 has a probability of 0.06.

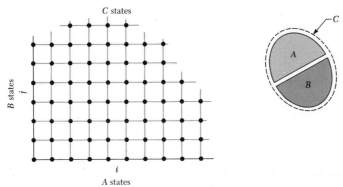

FIG. 6·3   *The allowed states of C are determined from all possible combinations of allowed states of A and B. Each point represents a C state*

Noting that

$$\langle p \rangle_C \neq \langle p \rangle_A + \langle p \rangle_B$$

we conclude that the average probability is *not* extensive; as yet we have not found an appropriate definition for entropy.

Let's be more systematic and ask, "What function of the probability *does* have an average which is extensive?" This leads us to look for a definition of entropy S in the form

$$S = \langle f \rangle = \sum_i p_i f(p_i) \qquad (6 \cdot 6)$$

The function $f(p_i)$ remains to be found. Then

$$S_A = \sum_{i=1}^{n} p_i f(p_i) \qquad S_B = \sum_{j=1}^{m} p_j f(p_j)$$

$$S_C = \sum_{i=1}^{n} \sum_{j=1}^{m} p_{ij} f(p_{ij}) = \sum_{i=1}^{n} \sum_{j=1}^{m} p_i \cdot p_j f(p_i \cdot p_j)$$

Applying Eq. (6·4),

$$\sum_{i=1}^{n} \sum_{j=1}^{m} p_i p_j f(p_i \cdot p_j) = \sum_{i=1}^{n} p_i f(p_i) + \sum_{j=1}^{m} p_j f(p_j) \qquad (6 \cdot 7)$$

f must be such that this is true regardless of the values of the p_i and p_j. A function that will work is $f(\ ) = \ln (\ )$. With this choice, the left-hand side of Eq. (6·7) becomes (recall that $\ln (a \cdot b) = \ln a + \ln b$)

$$\sum_{i=1}^{n} \sum_{j=1}^{m} p_i p_j \ln p_i + \sum_{i=1}^{n} \sum_{j=1}^{m} p_i p_j \ln p_j$$

Rearranging the sums, this becomes

$$\sum_{i=1}^{n} \left[p_i \ln p_i \left(\sum_{j=1}^{m} p_j \right) \right] + \sum_{j=1}^{m} \left[p_j \ln p_j \left(\sum_{i=1}^{n} p_i \right) \right]$$

since

$$\sum_{i=1}^{n} p_i = 1 \qquad \sum_{j=1}^{m} p_j = 1$$

the left-hand side of Eq. (6·7) may be expressed as

$$\sum_{i=1}^{n} p_i \ln p_i + \sum_{j=1}^{m} p_j \ln p_j$$

Hence Eq. (6·7) is precisely satisfied for *any* p_i, p_j, n, and m with this choice for f. It may be shown that† the most general $f(p_i)$ whose average is an extensive property is $f = C \ln p_i$, where C is an arbitrary constant; since p_i is less than unity, we choose the constant to be negative to make the entropy positive. Our definition of entropy, the extensive randomness-uncertainty measure, is therefore

$$\blacktriangleright \qquad S \equiv -k \sum_i p_i \ln p_i \qquad\qquad (6\cdot8)$$

The constant k is chosen as the *Boltzmann* constant,

$$k = 1.380 \times 10^{-23} \text{ joule/°K}$$

This choice makes the thermodynamic temperature (defined in Chap. Seven) the same as the empirical temperature used in previous chapters.

We must now become convinced that the entropy has the proper qualitative features of a randomness or uncertainty measure. Arguments in support of this contention will now be given.

† To show this, consider the special case where $p_i = 1/n$ and $p_j = 1/m$. Then Eq. (6·7) becomes

$$\sum_{i=1}^{n} \sum_{j=1}^{m} \frac{1}{n} \frac{1}{m} f\left(\frac{1}{n}\frac{1}{m}\right) = \sum_{i=1}^{n} \frac{1}{n} f\left(\frac{1}{n}\right) + \sum_{j=1}^{m} \frac{1}{m} f\left(\frac{1}{m}\right)$$

Carrying out the sums

$$f\left(\frac{1}{n}\cdot\frac{1}{m}\right) = f\left(\frac{1}{n}\right) + f\left(\frac{1}{m}\right)$$

The function $f(\ )$ must therefore satisfy the *functional equation*

$$f(xy) = f(x) + f(y)$$

Functional equations are usually solved by obtaining a differential equation which the function must satisfy. To do this, we differentiate the functional equation with respect to x, obtaining

$$y \frac{df(xy)}{d(xy)} = \frac{df(x)}{dx}$$

Differentiating this with respect to y,

$$\frac{df(xy)}{d(xy)} + (xy) \frac{d^2f(xy)}{d(xy)^2} = 0$$

Letting $z = xy$, this is

$$z \frac{d^2f}{dz^2} + \frac{df}{dz} = 0$$

The general solution of this linear second-order differential equation is

$$f(z) = C_1 + C_2 \ln(z)$$

The functional equation will not be satisfied unless $C_1 = 0$. Hence, the most general solution to the functional equation is indeed $f(z) = C \ln(z)$.

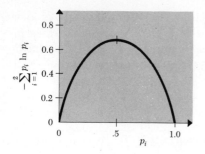

FIG. 6·4 *Note that S is greatest when there is the most randomness*

Since the uniform probability distribution reflects the greatest randomness, no system with n allowed states should ever have a greater entropy than when each state is equally likely ($p_i = 1/n$). Indeed, the maximum value of S occurs for this case. We can see this easily for $n = 2$. Then

$$S = -k(p_1 \ln p_1 + p_2 \ln p_2)$$

Since

$$p_1 + p_2 = 1$$

p_1 and p_2 cannot both be varied independently. Figure 6·4 shows the variations of S with p_1. Note that S is indeed maximum where $p_1 = p_2 = \frac{1}{2}$. One may indeed show that for any n the uniform distribution has the greatest entropy.

Next, consider that class of distributions where each quantum state is equally likely. Suppose there are Ω equally likely quantum states, so $p_i = 1/\Omega$,

$$S = -k \sum_{i=1}^{\Omega} \frac{1}{\Omega} \ln \frac{1}{\Omega} = -k\Omega \left(\frac{1}{\Omega} \ln \frac{1}{\Omega} \right) = -k \ln \frac{1}{\Omega}$$
$$= k \ln \Omega \tag{6·9}$$

Hence, the larger the number of possible states, the greater is the entropy. This would seem to be a proper qualitative feature of a randomness-uncertainty measure.

Consider the probability distributions (a), (b), (c), and (d) used as examples in Sec. 6·3. These distributions, and their entropies, are

(a) $p_1 = 1$ $p_2 = 0$ $p_3 = 0$
$\quad\quad S = -k(1 \ln 1 + 0 \ln 0 + 0 \ln 0) = 0$
(b) $p_1 = 0.8$ $p_2 = 0.2$ $p_3 = 0$
$\quad\quad S = -k[0.8 \ln 0.8 + 0.2 \ln 0.2 + 0 \ln 0] = 0.5002k$
(c) $p_1 = 0.8$ $p_2 = 0.1$ $p_3 = 0.1$
(d) $p_1 = 0.1$ $p_2 = 0.8$ $p_3 = 0.1$
$\quad\quad S = -k[0.8 \ln 0.8 + 0.1 \ln 0.1 + 0.1 \ln 0.1] = 0.6390k$
(e) $p_1 = p_2 = p_3 = \frac{1}{3}$
$\quad\quad S = -k[\frac{1}{3} \ln \frac{1}{3} + \frac{1}{3} \ln \frac{1}{3} + \frac{1}{3} \ln \frac{1}{3}] = k \ln 3 = 1.099k$

Distribution (*a*) reflects no randomness or uncertainty. Distribution (*b*) suggests we know for sure that state 3 is never realized; the higher entropy of distributions (*c*) and (*d*) suggests slightly greater randomness and uncertainty about the state than distribution (*b*). Note that distributions (*c*) and (*d*) have the same entropy. Distribution (*e*), which reflects the greatest randomness and uncertainty, yields the greatest entropy. These all seem to be proper qualitative aspects of a randomness-uncertainty measure; Eq. (6·8) seems to be a plausible definition of entropy.

To summarize, we define the entropy, or microscopic randomness-uncertainty measure, as

$$\blacktriangleright \qquad S \equiv -k \sum_i p_i \ln p_i \qquad\qquad (6\cdot 8)$$

The p_i are the probabilities of individual system quantum states. If all quantum states are equally likely, and there are Ω such equally probable states, it happens that

$$\blacktriangleright \qquad S = k \ln \Omega \qquad\qquad (6\cdot 9)$$

This expression is sometimes taken as the basic definition of entropy. It should be noted that Eq. (6·9), the *Boltzmann* definition of entropy, is appropriate only if each quantum state is equally likely. This is the case for some statistical models of matter, and Eq. (6·9) is widely used in elementary texts on statistical thermodynamics. We shall also make some use of it in subsequent chapters. Equation (6·8), the *Gibbs* definition of entropy, is more general, and hence is preferable as the fundamental definition. The Gibbs definition applies equally well for both equilibrium and nonequilibrium; the Boltzmann definition is only applicable to isolated systems in equilibrium.†

6·5 APPROACH TO EQUILIBRIUM

We have shown that the entropy as defined by Eq. (6·8) is extensive, and has its greatest value when the system quantum state is most random, that is, when we are most uncertain about the instantaneous quantum state. As time passes, we expect the disorder, randomness, and uncertainty, that is, the entropy, of an *isolated* system to increase, and to approach a constant as the isolated

---

† For an excellent discussion of the virtues of Eq. (6·8), see R. C. Tolman, *The Principles of Statistical Mechanics*, p. 562, Oxford University Press, London, 1938. See also L. D. Landau and E. M. Lifshitz, *Statistical Physics*, p. 25, Pergamon Press, New York, 1958; J. H. Keenan and G. N. Hatsopoulos, *Principles of General Thermodynamics*, p. 606, John Wiley & Sons, Inc., New York, 1965; F. Reif, *Fundamentals of Statistical and Thermal Physics*, p. 219, McGraw-Hill Book Company, New York, 1965; M. Tribus, *Thermostatics and Thermodynamics*, p. 84, D. Van Nostrand Company, Inc., Princeton, N.J., 1961.

system approaches equilibrium. The *second law of thermodynamics* is the *postulate* that:

> *The entropy of an isolated system can never decrease.*

In terms of the microscopic notions we have discussed, this seems very plausible. It also works; a vast superstructure of theory has been built upon this postulate, and this theory has never failed to meet the test of a laboratory experiment.

The experiments cited above usually employ macroscopic means to evaluate the entropy, and not the fundamental definition Eq. (6·8). A direct test of the increase in entropy as defined by Eq. (6·8) is difficult to perform in the laboratory, but easy to perform on a computer. We shall now describe such an experiment on an interesting, but nonphysical, system.

Consider a system of 10 particles, each of which can exist in one of 5 states. We denote the particles by A, B, C, . . . , J, and the particle states by their energies 0, 1, 2, 3, and 4. Suppose the system is isolated and has total energy 30. We shall first examine the allowed states of the system. There are many possible system states, some of which are shown in Fig. 6·5. Any state in which the total energy is 30 is possible. All possible combinations were considered with the help of a high-speed computer, and it was found that there are 72,403 possible quantum states. We could not hope to list these here; however, they can be collected into groups of states where the states in each group have the same number of particles in each particle state. For example, quantum states 2 and 3 of Fig. 6·5 would fall in the same group (22). There are only 23 different groups and these are given in Table 6·1.

We can assign probabilities p_i to the 72,403 quantum states. The distribution that maximizes the entropy has each $p_i = 1/72{,}403$, and this is the equilibrium distribution that should be approached in any experiment. Corresponding to any set of $72{,}403 p_i$ is a set of 23 *group* probabilities p_k, each of which is simply the sum of the p_i in that group. Thus, for example, for the equilibrium distribution the probability that the system is in *one* of the 90 states of group 22 is 90/72,403, while the probability that it is in one of the 12,600 states of group 1 is much higher, namely 12,600/72,403. The group probabilities corresponding to the equilibrium distribution are shown in Table 6·1.

Now, suppose the system is in some state in a particular group. We consider changes in state resulting from 2-particle interactions. For example, sup-

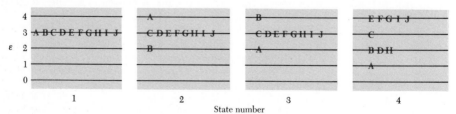

FIG. 6·5 *Some of the allowed states; note each state has a total energy of 30*

TABLE 6·1 THE ALLOWED STATES†

Group k	Number of particles with each energy					Number of quantum states	Equilibrium group probability p_k
	$\varepsilon = 0$	1	2	3	4		
1	0	1	2	3	4	12,600	0.1740
2	0	2	1	2	5	7,560	0.1044
3	1	0	2	2	5	7,560	0.1044
4	1	0	1	4	4	6,300	0.0870
5	0	1	1	5	3	5,040	0.0696
6	0	1	3	1	5	5,040	0.0696
7	1	1	0	3	5	5,040	0.0696
8	1	1	1	1	6	5,040	0.0696
9	0	0	3	4	3	4,200	0.0580
10	0	0	4	2	4	3,150	0.0435
11	0	2	0	4	4	3,150	0.0435
12	0	0	2	6	2	1,260	0.0174
13	0	2	2	0	6	1,260	0.0174
14	2	0	0	2	6	1,260	0.0174
15	1	0	0	6	3	840	0.0116
16	1	0	3	0	6	840	0.0116
17	0	3	0	1	6	840	0.0116
18	0	1	0	7	2	360	0.0050
19	1	2	0	0	7	360	0.0050
20	2	0	1	0	7	360	0.0050
21	0	0	5	0	5	252	0.0035
22	0	0	1	8	1	90	0.0012
23	0	0	0	10	0	1	0.0_414

† Total number of quantum states = 72,403.

pose the system is in quantum state 1 (state-group 23) of Fig. 6·5. Two particles come together, interact, and may or may not change the system state.
There are 45 possible particle pairs for this interaction, and we assume that
each pair is equally likely to interact. For each pair there are two interactions
that take the system to state 22, and one that leaves the system in state 23.
We assume that, for a given particle pair, the possible transitions are equally
likely. Hence, the probability that a given pair-interaction will take the system
to state 22 is $\frac{2}{3}$, while the probability that a pair interaction will leave the
system in state 23 is $\frac{1}{3}$. The transitions from the other state groups are more
complicated, but can be computed according to the transition model (equal
probability for pair selection, equal probability for the possible transitions for
a given pair). Analysis of all pair-interactions permits us to develop a table of

TABLE 6-2   TRANSITION PROBABILITIES

Initial group	Final group										
	1	2	3	4	5	6	7	8	9	10	11
1	0.7052	0.0667	0.0267	0.0222	0.0593	0.0444	0.0089	0	0.0444	0.0133	0.0089
2	0.1111	0.7244	0.0148	0	0	0.0178	0.0222	0.0356	0	0	0.0370
3	0.0444	0.0148	0.7452	0.0741	0	0.0222	0.0089	0.0444	0	0.0222	0
4	0.0444	0	0.0889	0.7319	0.0356	0	0.0444	0	0.0178	0	0.0074
5	0.1482	0	0	0.0444	0.6630	0	0	0	0.0222	0	0.0556
6	0.1111	0.0267	0.0333	0	0	0.7000	0	0.0267	0	0.0556	0
7	0.0222	0.0333	0.0133	0.0556	0	0	0.7600	0.0444	0	0	0.0444
8	0	0.0533	0.0667	0	0	0.0267	0.0444	0.7548	0	0	0
9	0.1333	0	0	0.0267	0.0267	0	0	0	0.6578	0.0889	0
10	0.0533	0	0.0533	0	0	0.0889	0	0	0.1185	0.6711	0
11	0.0356	0.0889	0	0.0148	0.0889	0	0.0711	0	0	0	0.7007
12	0	0	0	0	0.1333	0	0	0	0.2222	0	0
13	0	0.0889	0	0	0	0.1333	0	0.0444	0	0	0
14	0	0	0.0533	0	0	0	0.1067	0.0444	0	0	0
15	0	0	0	0.2222	0.0667	0	0	0	0	0	0
16	0	0	0.1333	0	0	0.0533	0	0.0267	0	0	0
17	0	0.2000	0	0	0.3111	0	0	0.0444	0	0	0
18	0	0	0	0	0	0	0	0	0	0	0
19	0	0	0	0	0	0	0	0.1556	0	0	0
20	0	0	0	0	0	0	0	0.1244	0	0	0
21	0	0	0	0	0	0.0889	0	0	0	0	0
22	0	0	0	0	0	0	0	0	0	0.1852	0
23	0	0	0	0	0	0	0	0	0	0	0

	Final group											
Initial group	12	13	14	15	16	17	18	19	20	21	22	23
1	0	0	0	0	0	0	0	0	0	0	0	0
2	0	0.0148	0	0	0	0.0222	0	0	0	0	0	0
3	0	0	0.0089	0.0296	0.0148	0	0	0	0	0	0	0
4	0	0	0	0.0111	0	0	0	0	0	0	0	0
5	0.0333	0.0333	0	0	0.0089	0	0	0	0	0	0	0
6	0	0	0.0267	0	0	0	0.0222	0	0	0.0044	0	0
7	0	0	0.0111	0	0	0	0	0	0	0	0	0
8	0.0667	0.0111	0	0	0.0044	0.0074	0	0	0	0	0	0
9	0	0	0	0	0	0	0	0.0111	0.0089	0	0	0
10	0	0	0	0	0	0	0	0	0	0.0148	0	0
11	0	0	0	0	0	0	0	0	0	0	0	0
12	0.5970	0	0	0.0089	0.0148	0.0089	0.0089	0.0089	0	0	0.0296	0
13	0	0.7007	0	0	0	0	0	0	0.0148	0	0	0
14	0	0	0.7807	0	0	0	0	0	0	0	0	0
15	0.0133	0	0	0.6711	0	0	0	0	0	0	0	0
16	0	0.0222	0	0	0.7111	0	0	0	0	0.0267	0	0
17	0	0.0133	0	0	0	0.7156	0.0267	0.0267	0.0267	0	0.0222	0
18	0.0311	0	0	0.0622	0	0.0622	0.5733	0	0	0	0	0
19	0	0.0311	0	0	0	0	0	0.7363	0.0148	0	0	0
20	0	0	0.0519	0	0.0622	0	0	0.0148	0.7467	0	0	0
21	0	0	0	0	0.0889	0	0.0889	0	0	0.6370	0	0
22	0.4148	0	0	0	0	0	0	0	0	0	0.4889	0.0074
23	0	0	0	0	0	0	0	0	0	0	0.6667	0.3333

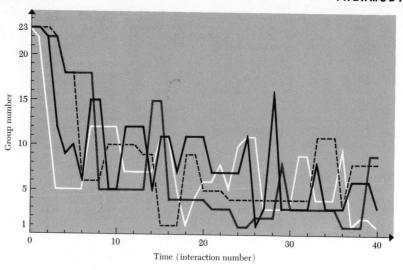

FIG. 6·6 *Four members of the ensemble of experiments*

"transition probabilities" for passage from one quantum state group to another. The results are shown in Table 6·2.†

In the computer experiments we started the system out in state 23, and then followed a long series of interactions chosen randomly in accordance with the transition probabilities of Table 6·2. The experiment was repeated 10,000 times, with a different group history being traced each time. The fraction of the experiments in which each group occurred at time t was used to calculate the group probabilities $p_k(t)$ at each time. The entropy at each time was calculated for the group distribution p_k. The results are shown in Figs. 6·6–6·8. Since the energy of the system was fixed, these results correspond to experiments in an isolated system.

Figure 6·6 shows four members of the ensemble of 10,000 experiments. Each time unit corresponds to one interaction. Note that there is initially no randomness, with all systems in group 23. After the first interaction some remain in group 23 (one third) and some have moved to group 22 (two thirds). At this time there is a slightly greater randomness. The randomness rapidly increases,

---

† The number of possible particle pairs from a particular pair of energy levels, divided by the total number of particle pairs, gives the "particle selection probabilities" for interaction of two particles from those particular energy levels. Then, all possible movements of two particles from those energy levels must be counted to find the "movement probabilities" for particles chosen from particular levels. The product of the particle selection and movement probabilities gives the probability of transition from one group to another by a particular particle selection-movement combination. Summing over all possible selection-movement combinations that take the system from one quantum state group to another, the total probability of passing from the first to the second group is obtained. Table 6.2 was calculated in this manner.

and before long there are some systems in each state at each time. After many interactions the equilibrium condition is reached, and the quantum-group sequence for any particular experiment becomes quite random.

Figure 6·7 shows the evolution of some of the $p_k(t)$. Note that p_{23} drops rapidly, while p_{22} and p_{12} first increase and then relax toward their equilibrium values. Note that after the first interaction p_{22} was up to 0.6666, and p_{23} had dropped to 0.3333. This is indeed in accordance with the transition probabilities.

FIG. 6·7 *Some of the $p_k(t)$ for the ensemble of 10,000 experiments*

FIG. 6·8 *Group-distribution entropy for the ensemble of 10,000 experiments*

Figure 6·8 shows the group-distribution entropy as a function of time. If our postulate about the natural tendency for the microscopic randomness of an isolated system to increase is correct, the group-distribution entropy should increase. Indeed, the entropy did increase as time went on, and finally approached the equilibrium value computed from the p_k of Table 6·1.

Another interesting calculation can be made using the table of transition probabilities. Since the probability of a transition sequence is the product of the individual step transition probabilities, the transition

23 22 12 9 1

has the probability

$0.6667 \times 0.4148 \times 0.2222 \times 0.1333 = 0.82 \times 10^{-2}$

On the other hand, the reverse transition,

1 9 12 22 23

has the probability

$0.0444 \times 0.0667 \times 0.0296 \times 0.0074 = 0.67 \times 10^{-6}$

We see that there is a tremendous probability that the system will move toward and persist in the quantum-state groups having high equilibrium probabilities. Once a system has moved from group 23 to group 1 there is only a very slight chance it will ever return to group 23. This overwhelming likelihood of particular tendencies is exhibited even more dramatically by systems of very many particles. The probability is extremely small that a system of 10^{20} particles will move from a quantum state having a broad distribution of particle energies to a quantum state where all particles have the same energy. Such an event would probably not occur even once in the lifetime of the observer, and is far too rare to be useful in an engineering system.

6·6 SUMMARY

The major points we wish to get across in this chapter are the basic microscopic concepts of entropy and the plausibility of the second law.

Entropy is an *extensive property* of matter. The statistical definition of entropy is

$$\blacktriangleright \qquad S \equiv -\mathsf{k} \sum_i p_i \ln p_i \qquad\qquad (6\cdot8)$$

where p_i is the "probability" of the ith allowed quantum state. The constant k is chosen as the Boltzmann constant, $\mathsf{k} = 1.380 \times 10^{-23}$ joule/°K, to make the thermodynamic temperature scale (Chap. Seven) correspond to the empirical temperature.

Entropy is defined in terms of the p_i because the set of p_i reflect the microscopic randomness and the resulting uncertainty about the microscopic state when given only macroscopic data. The entropy is a *single number* which measures this randomness and uncertainty. The logarithm appears because $\ln p_i$ is the *only* function of p_i whose average is an extensive property.

The entropy of two systems considered as one is the sum of their individual entropies, provided that the allowed quantum states of each system are independent from those of the other.

The *second law of thermodynamics* is the postulate that:

The entropy of an isolated system can never decrease.

Expressed algebraically, the second law is

$$
\left. \begin{array}{l} \blacktriangleright \quad dS \geq 0 \\[1.5em] \blacktriangleright \quad \Delta S \geq 0 \end{array} \right\} \text{ for an isolated system}
$$

or

The second law says that we can never know more about the microscopic details of an isolated system than we know at the moment of isolation. Future measurement might reveal more information, but getting this information would require termination of the isolation. As long as the system remains isolated, our uncertainty as to microscopic detail can never decrease.†

Evaluation of entropy of different substances by Eq. (6·8) is an objective

---

† It is sometimes said that entropy is a measure of microscopic "disorder." Disorder, like beauty, is in the eye of the beholder. Any system that looks random because we are uncertain about the details would look "disordered." Interpreted in this way, the "disorder" concept of entropy is valid.

Sometimes the entropy concept is tied to ideas of the "availability" of energy. The spontaneous changes that take place in an isolated system approaching equilibrium tend to make the distribution of internal energy more random, and hence make it more difficult to extract energy as work (useful "organized" energy transfer). Hence it is sometimes said that the entropy is a measure of the "unavailability of internal energy." An analogy will be helpful in tying this concept of entropy to the uncertainty concepts discussed previously. Suppose you stand facing a baseball pitcher who throws balls at you one at a time. You can see where the balls are headed, and consequently can catch each one, thereby extracting all of its kinetic energy. Since you know precisely where each ball is headed, you can move your glove around and thereby "capture" all of the energy of each ball. Now, turn around, and attempt to catch the balls without being able to see them. With luck you may catch some, and extract all of their kinetic energy. But you will miss many more; without the full knowledge of their trajectories you cannot extract all of their energy as useful work. The greater your uncertainty as to their trajectories, the more "unavailable" is their energy. So it is with the energy associated with the microscopic structure of matter; if the entropy is large, your uncertainty as to the precise microscopic state (given only macroscopic data) is large, and consequently you cannot fully harness the energy of the hidden microscopic modes. Thus, in a very real sense the entropy is indeed a measure of the "unavailability of internal energy."

of statistical thermodynamics. More often the entropy is evaluated by purely macroscopic means, to be discussed in the next chapter.

SELECTED READING

Fast, J. D., *Entropy*, introduction, McGraw-Hill Book Company, New York, 1963.

Goldman, S., *Information Theory*, sec. 1.8, Prentice-Hall, Inc., Englewood Cliffs, N.J., 1953.

Reif, F., *Fundamentals of Statistical and Thermal Physics*, secs. 3.1–3.4, 6.1–6.6, McGraw-Hill Book Company, New York, 1965.

———, *Statistical Physics*, Berkeley Physics Course, vol. 5, secs. 1.1–1.4, 2.1, 2.2, 2.4, McGraw-Hill Book Company, New York, 1967.

Sonntag, R. E., and G. J. Van Wylen, *Fundamentals of Statistical Thermodynamics*, sec. 4.3, John Wiley & Sons, Inc., New York, 1966.

Zemansky, M. W., and H. C. Van Ness, *Basic Engineering Thermodynamics*, sec. 15.6, McGraw-Hill Book Company, New York, 1966.

QUESTIONS

6·1 Why do we need a "second law" of thermodynamics?

6·2 What is the fundamental conceptual property underlying the second law?

6·3 Does the first law rule out the possibility of water spontaneously becoming hydrogen and oxygen in an isolated container?

6·4 How do allowed quantum states differ from macroscopic states?

6·5 What is the "probability" of a quantum state?

6·6 What role does the concept of quantization play in the development of the entropy?

6·7 What is an ensemble-average property?

6·8 What is entropy?

6·9 Is entropy an intensive or extensive property?

6·10 Why is the logarithm involved in the definition of entropy?

6·11 Can the entropy of a system ever decrease?

6·12 What do concepts of uncertainty have to do with thermodynamics?

6·13 How would you explain entropy to your mother?

6·14 Look up entropy in a nontechnical dictionary. Can you reconcile this definition with your concept of entropy?

6·15 When did you first learn about energy? When did you first begin to really understand the concept of energy? Do you understand the concept of entropy?

PROBLEMS

6·1 Consider the following sets of quantum-state probabilities for a system with five allowed states.

(*a*) 0, 0.1, 0.2, 0.3, 0.4

(*b*) 0.2, 0.2, 0.2, 0.2, 0.2

(c) 0.5, 0.5, 0, 0, 0

(d) 0.3, 0.2, 0.3, 0.2, 0

(e) 0.3, 0.3, 0.1, 0.1, 0.3

(f) 1, 0, 0, 0, 0

(g) 0.1, 0.2, 0.4, 0.3, 0

One of these is not proper as a probability set. Which one, and why not? Assuming that the others represent the distributions at six consecutive moments in an ensemble of experiments on an isolated system, which was the initial distribution and which was the final? Rank the others properly between the initial and final distributions.

6·2 Consider a rectangular box containing N molecules. Suppose that each molecule can be on either side of the box with equal probability. What is the probability that all N molecules are on one side? Compute this number for $N = 1, 2, 20$, and 10^{20}.

6·3 Set up a system of 20 molecules as described in Prob. 6·2, using any suitable markers for the molecules. Place them all initially on the left side of the box. Flip a coin and move one particle to right or left (if possible), depending on whether the coin shows heads or tails, respectively. Record the system state during a sequence of such flips. Discuss the outcome of this experiment. What would be the meaning of entropy here, and how would it be calculated?

6·4 Write a digital computer program to perform 10,000 experiments of the type described in Prob. 6·3. Use a random-number generator instead of the coin. Record the number of molecules on each side after each toss, and compute the entropy evolution over the first 100 tosses.

6·5 Repeat the experiment of Prob. 6·3, this time starting the system with 10 molecules on each side. Record the number on the left after each flip. Continue until all molecules are on one side; if you become worn out before then, compute the fraction of the time that such a state would be observed over a very long run of experiments. Does the second law say that such a state could never happen?

6·6 Consider a system of four atoms (A, B, C, and D) that can exist with nuclear spin "up" or "down" (u or d). List all the possible spin states of this system. Group them according to the number of atoms with spin up. Assuming that each spin state is equally likely, determine the probability of each spin-state group. Calculate the entropy of the group probability distribution (take $k = 1$ for simplicity) and compare to $\ln \Omega$, where Ω is the total number of system spin states, and to $\ln \Omega_g$, where Ω_g is the number of spin-state groups. Why do these three "entropies" differ? (In which description do you know most about the system?)

6·7 Consider a system of three indistinguishable molecules, each of which can have energy 0, 1, 2, 3, or 4. Find all system states having a total energy of 6 (one is shown in the figure). Assuming that each system state is equally likely, calculate the probability p_k that energy level k is occupied by at least one particle. Why do these probabilities not add up to unity? Suppose we define a property, g, as the sum of the squares of the energies of the three molecules. What is the ensemble-average g?

6·8 Suppose that in the system of Prob. 6·7 two-particle interactions take the system to other states (or leave the system in the same state) with equal probability for all possible transitions from a given initial state. Make up a table of transition probabilities similar to Table 6·2. If the system is started in the state shown in Prob. 6·7, what is the probability of being in each state after 1, 2, 3, and 4 interactions? Compute the entropies (with k = 1) of the probabilities after 0, 1, 2, 3, and 4 interactions for an ensemble of such experiments, and compare with the "equilibrium" entropy.

6·9 Write a digital computer program to repeat the experiment of Prob. 6·8 1000 times, carrying each experiment through 10 interactions. Use a random-number generator and the transition probability table to find the state sequence in each experiment. Plot the experimentally determined evolution of the probability distribution and the entropy history; compare with the analytical predictions of Prob. 6·8.

6·10 Suppose you have a coin on a table, heads up. Imagine an experiment in which you roll a die and turn the coin over if the die shows a 1 but leave the coin as it stands if 2 to 6 is rolled. What is the probability of turning the coin over on the first roll? On the second roll? What is the probability that the coin will be tails up after the second roll of the die? Compute the probability distribution for the two coin states (H or T) after each of the first 10 rolls of the die. Calculate the entropy of the distribution that would be obtained after each of the first 10 tosses (take k = 1 for simplicity). What distribution is obtained after a large number of tosses, and what is its entropy?

6·11 Perform 100 of the experiments as described in Prob. 6·10 (stop after three rolls) and compare the experimental evolution of the distribution to that predicted theoretically.

6·12 Write a digital computer program to carry out an ensemble of 10,000 experiments as described in Prob. 6·10. Use a random-number routine instead of the die. Compare the experimentally determined evolution of the distribution and entropy to that predicted theoretically.

6·13 Calculate the entropy of a gmole of gas assuming that there are as many system quantum states as there are particles, and that each state is equally likely.

6·14 Repeat Prob. 6·13 assuming there are 10^{20} times as many system quantum states as particles.

6·15 The entropy of 1 gmole of O_2 at 600°R and 1 atm is 49.7 cal/°K. Assuming each quantum state is equally likely, calculate the number of system quantum states for 1 gmole and the ratio of this number to the number of molecules.

6·16 Repeat Prob. 6·15 at 5000°R and 1 atm where the entropy of 1 gmole of O_2 is 67.2 cal/°K. What happens to the number of allowed states as the temperature of O_2 increases?

6·17 The entropy of 1 g of H_2O changes by 1.445 cal/°K when it is evaporated at 1 atm. Assuming that in either the saturated liquid or saturated vapor states the allowed quantum states have equal probability, calculate the ratio of the number of allowed states in the vapor state to that for the liquid.

6·18 How much does the entropy of 1 lbm of mercury change when it is condensed at 415°F? Why does this not violate the second law?

6·19 A two-compartment tank contains saturated water vapor at 100 psia on one side and water vapor at the same temperature but at 1 psia in the other compartment. Each compartment has a volume of 1 ft³. A valve connecting the two compartments is opened, and the water is allowed to come to equilibrium adiabatically.

Calculate the entropy change for this isolated system, using the equation-of-state information in Appendix B (Table B·1 will be especially helpful). Give a microscopic explanation of why the entropy increases.

6·20 A two-compartment tank contains saturated water vapor at 100 psia on one side and water vapor at 100 psia and 1000°F on the other side. Each volume is 1 ft³. Energy is transferred as heat through the dividing wall, and the system is allowed to reach equilibrium in an isolated manner. Compute the final steam states in the two compartments and determine the change in entropy for this isolated system.

CHAPTER SEVEN

SOME CONSEQUENCES OF THE SECOND LAW

7·1 INTRODUCTION

In the last chapter we developed the concepts and definition of entropy and the second law of thermodynamics. It is indeed very helpful to view entropy as a measure of the randomness in, or uncertainty about, the microscopic state of a system. But it is equally clear that the calculation of entropy from its statistical definition [Eq. (6·8)] is rather involved and requires physical input about the microscopic nature of the system. Such calculations fall in the domain of statistical thermodynamics. Before getting involved in such calculations, we should see what we can find out about entropy from purely *macroscopic* considerations. This is the central theme of the present chapter. We shall see that it is possible to relate differences in entropy between two thermodynamic states to other macroscopically measurable properties. This allows us to determine the entropy of a substance as a function of state (relative to an arbitrary datum). The entropy per unit of mass can then be tabulated, graphed, or stored in a computer with the other thermodynamic properties for use in engineering calculations. Our first objective in this chapter is the development of the framework required for the macroscopic evaluation of entropy.

In the initial discussion we shall develop the thermodynamic definition of temperature mentioned in earlier chapters, and a thermodynamic definition of pressure. We shall see that these are equivalent to the empirical temperature and mechanical pressure used earlier. The thermodynamic temperature scale is independent of any arbitrary choice of thermometric substance, and hence the thermodynamic definition of temperature places the temperature concept on really firm ground.

Once we have established the macroscopic basis for entropy evaluation we shall turn to discussion of the role played by entropy and the second law in engineering analysis. We shall see that the postulate that the entropy of an isolated system will never decrease provides a very powerful tool for practical analysis.

7·2 ENTROPY AS A FUNCTION OF STATE

The statistical definition of entropy [Eq. (6·8)] is in terms of the probability of allowed quantum states and is valid in both equilibrium and nonequilibrium situations. Of most interest is the entropy of matter in equilibrium states, where the equilibrium probability distribution is attained. The equilibrium entropy is a thermodynamic property of the substance, and from the state postulate we know that it is a function of only a few macroscopic properties. For example, the equilibrium entropy of a given amount of a simple compressible substance is some function of the energy and volume,

$$S = S(U, V) \tag{7·1}$$

If in addition the substance can be electrically polarized, the equilibrium entropy will also depend on the total dipole moment,

$$S = S(U, V, \mathbf{P}V)$$

Our goal here is to find some *macroscopic* means to determine these functions, thereby eliminating the need to compute entropy from Eq. (6·8).

The entropy is an extensive property, which means that the entropy of a system composed of two parts is the sum of the entropies of the individual parts,

$$S_{A+B} = S_A + S_B \tag{7·2}$$

Recall from Chap. Six that this holds only if the allowed quantum states of parts A and B are independent. Equation (7·2) is useful when we want to compute the entropy of a complex system. For example, the entropy of a two-phase mixture (say liquid water and ice) is computed as the sum of the individual entropies of the two phases,

$$S_{\text{mixt}} = S_{\text{solid}} + S_{\text{liquid}}$$

Just as tabulation of internal energy is facilitated by considering the internal energy per unit of mass, it is convenient to "intensify" the entropy. For example, for a simple compressible substance we can use the "specific entropy," or entropy per unit of mass; the symbol s is usually used for the intensified entropy, while S is used for the total (extensive) entropy;

$$s \equiv \frac{S}{M}$$

Then, for a simple compressible substance,

$$s = s(u, v)$$

The dimensions of S are energy/temperature, and those of s are energy/mass-temperature; that is, cal/°K or Btu/°R for S and cal/g-°K or Btu/lbm-°R for

s. These dimensions result from the choice of the Boltzmann constant in the definition of entropy [Eq. (6·8)], which in turn results from the desire to make the thermodynamic temperature scale agree with the empirical ideal-gas temperature scale.

The specific entropy of a liquid-vapor mixture can be expressed in terms of the quality and the specific entropies of the liquid and vapor,

$$s = (1 - x)s_f + xs_g \qquad\qquad\qquad\qquad (7·3)$$

The student may derive this equation following the steps used in obtaining Eq. (4·1).

In the next few sections we shall examine the nature of the functional relationships among entropy, energy, and volume for a simple compressible substance. Treatment of more general substances follows exactly these lines of argument, and the details will be omitted here. The first step is to establish a basic thermodynamic definition of temperature.

7·3 THE THERMODYNAMIC DEFINITION OF TEMPERATURE

Let us first review the concepts of temperature that we have used implicitly. If we bring two masses into contact, and there is some energy transfer as heat between them, we say that their temperatures were different. We also view the energy as passing from the "hotter" mass to the "colder" one. We say that the masses are in thermal equilibrium if they are at the same temperature, and no energy transfer as heat will occur when they are brought together. These notions show that temperature is basically thought of as an indicator of the direction of energy transfer as heat. Differences in temperature reflect lack of equilibrium, and this suggests that we might be able to make a basic definition of temperature through considerations about thermal equilibrium. Indeed, temperature is conceived as a property that two systems have in common when they are in thermal equilibrium.

Our approach will be to consider two masses, each in a thermodynamic equilibrium state. If we bring them together, and any energy transfer as heat takes place between them, then they were not initially at the same temperature. We then shall look for conditions under which *no* energy transfer as heat takes place when they are brought together, and try to find a *property* that has the same value for both masses under this condition of thermal equilibrium. The temperature is just such a property, and this approach will therefore lead us to the basic definition of temperature.

Consider two control masses, A and B, each initially in a state of thermodynamic equilibrium (Fig. 7·1), though A and B are not necessarily in equilibrium with each other. For simplicity assume that each mass is a simple compressible substance.

We shall let C denote the combined system A and B. Assuming that the allowed quantum states of A and B are independent, the entropy of the com-

Rigid wall

FIG. 7·1 *The combined system C is isolated*

bined system C is simply

$$S_C = S_A + S_B \tag{7·4}$$

Now, since A and B are each in some equilibrium state,

$$S_C = S_A(U_A, V_A) + S_B(U_B, V_B) \tag{7·5}$$

This expression holds as long as A and B are each in some equilibrium state, even when A and B are not in equilibrium with each other. Note that the individual masses of A and B are also specified and fixed.

We now imagine letting A and B interact through a rigid wall, which prevents changes in V_A and V_B. This rules out the possibility of any energy transfer as work between A and B, and any energy transfer must take place as heat. We also imagine isolating the combined system C, so that the only interactions are between A and B internal to C. Since system C is isolated, its entropy must not decrease; any interaction between A and B will serve to increase the entropy of C. S_C will attain its largest value when A and B are finally in thermal equilibrium, that is, when they are at the same temperature. Hence, the state of C that maximizes S_C is the equilibrium state we need in order to discover the thermodynamic definition of temperature.

Since C is isolated, the total internal energy $U = U_A + U_B$ must be "shared" by A and B. If we define r to be the fraction of the total internal energy contained by A, then

$$U_A = rU \qquad U_B = (1 - r)U \tag{7·6}$$

Since for a given isolation U, V_A, and V_B are fixed, the only free parameter left to vary S_C is r [see Eq. (7·5)]. For given U, V_A, and V_B, the value of r which maximizes S_C determines the distribution of internal energy between A and B in the equilibrium state. Figure 7·2 shows the variation of S_C with r schematically.

FIG. 7·2 *The entropy of the combined isolated system is a maximum when A and B are in equilibrium*

The point of maximum S is found by setting $dS_C/dr = 0$. Using the chain rule of differentiation, we differentiate Eq. (7·5),

$$\frac{dS_C}{dr} = \left(\frac{\partial S_A}{\partial U_A}\right)_{V_A} \frac{dU_A}{dr} + \left(\frac{\partial S_B}{\partial U_B}\right)_{V_B} \frac{dU_B}{dr}$$

or,

$$\frac{dS_C}{dr} = \left(\frac{\partial S_A}{\partial U_A}\right)_{V_A} U + \left(\frac{\partial S_B}{\partial U_B}\right)_{V_B} (-U) \qquad (7·7)$$

This vanishes only when

$$\left(\frac{\partial S_A}{\partial U_A}\right)_{V_A} = \left(\frac{\partial S_B}{\partial U_B}\right)_{V_B} \qquad (7·8)$$

Equation (7·8) fixes the state of maximum S_C, that is, the condition under which A and B will be in thermal equilibrium. Note that the derivatives in Eq. (7·8) are *properties* of A and B, respectively; the derivative on the left depends only on the state (U, V) of A, and that on the right depends only on the state of B.

When the *property* $(\partial S/\partial U)_V$ of A is equal to that for B, A and B are in thermal equilibrium. This suggests that we should define temperature in terms of this property. Any function of this property would have the qualitative feature that two systems in equilibrium had the same value of the function. What function should we choose? A choice which retains the other conceptual aspect of temperature, namely, that energy transfer as heat should take place from the warmer body to the cooler one, is†

$$\blacktriangleright \qquad T \equiv \frac{1}{(\partial S/\partial U)_V} \qquad (7·9)$$

As we shall show, this choice also makes the thermodynamic temperature scale coincide with the perfect-gas temperature scale, and hence makes the thermodynamic temperature equivalent to what we have been using for temperature all along. Equation (7·9) is the *thermodynamic definition of temperature* for a simple compressible substance. Since both S and U are extensive, their ratio, and hence T, is *intensive*. Note also that T is defined in terms of the equilibrium equation of state $S(U, V)$, and hence T does not have any meaning for a system not in a thermodynamic equilibrium state.

Let us next establish that energy transfer as heat takes place from the hotter to the cooler body. Equation (7·7) can be written as

$$dS_C = U \cdot dr \left(\frac{1}{T_A} - \frac{1}{T_B}\right) \qquad (7·10)$$

† Noting that the dimensions of S are energy/temperature, the derivative $\partial S/\partial U$ must have dimensions 1/temperature.

Now, if in the initial state $T_B \neq T_A$, then S_C must increase as a result of the interaction, and $dS_C > 0$. If $T_B > T_A$, this requires $dr > 0$, which corresponds to an increase in U_A and a decrease in U_B. Hence, the energy indeed flows from the warmer body (B) to the cooler one (A).

We can learn still more about the thermodynamic temperature from the analysis of the condition for equilibrium between A and B (Fig. 7·1). In order for the point at which $dS_C/dr = 0$ to be a *maximum*, and not a minimum or inflection point in the $S_C(r)$ curve, the *second* derivative d^2S_C/dr^2 must be negative. Differentiating Eq. (7·7) again with respect to r, we have

$$\frac{d^2S_C}{dr^2} = \left[\left(\frac{\partial^2 S}{\partial U_A{}^2}\right)_{V_A} U^2 + \left(\frac{\partial^2 S_B}{\partial U_B{}^2}\right)_{V_B} U^2\right] < 0 \qquad (7\cdot11)$$

Suppose A and B are identical systems. Then, the necessary condition for a maximum yields

$$\left(\frac{\partial^2 S}{\partial U^2}\right)_V < 0 \qquad \text{for } A \text{ or } B \qquad (7\cdot12)$$

This derivative is merely the first derivative of $1/T$, and hence $T(U, V)$ must be such that

$$\left(\frac{\partial(1/T)}{\partial U}\right)_V < 0$$

or

$$\left(\frac{\partial T}{\partial U}\right)_V > 0 \qquad (7\cdot13)$$

Equation (7·13) says that the temperature must be a monotone increasing function of the energy (Fig. 7·3); increasing the energy at fixed volume must increase the temperature. This is in accordance with experience cited previously.

A physical interpretation of temperature in terms of the microscopic concepts of entropy discussed in the last chapter is quite helpful. The reciprocal of temperature describes the sensitivity of the entropy to internal energy changes at fixed volume. If a small increase in internal energy greatly changes the microscopic randomness and the uncertainty about the microscopic state, the

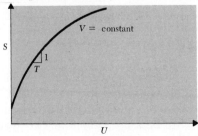

FIG. 7·3 *Temperature is a monotonically increasing function of internal energy*

quantity $1/T$ is large, and T is small. Absolute zero T corresponds to a state in which any infinitesimal increase in internal energy will make a finite increase in the microscopic randomness. At higher and higher temperatures $1/T$ becomes smaller and smaller, and hence the amount of additional microscopic randomness or uncertainty produced by adding some energy at constant volume becomes less and less at high temperatures. For simple compressible substances only positive absolute temperatures are of interest; if $T > 0$, any increase in internal energy (at constant volume) will result in an increase in entropy, that is, in an increase in the microscopic randomness and uncertainty. This seems quite reasonable, indeed.

We started with the idea that the entropy of a given amount of a simple compressible substance can be expressed as some function of its internal energy and volume, $S = S(U, V)$. If we take the differential of this function we obtain

$$dS = \left(\frac{\partial S}{\partial U}\right)_V dU + \left(\frac{\partial S}{\partial V}\right)_U dV \qquad (7 \cdot 14)$$

We now know that the derivative coefficient of dU in Eq. (7·14) is $1/T$, which we know as a function of state (presuming that the thermodynamic and empirical temperatures are indeed equivalent as we have stated and will shortly prove). If we can determine the derivative coefficient of dV in Eq. (7·14) as a function of measurable properties, Eq. (7·14) would become a differential equation for the entropy of a function of state. Then, by integration of this equation by appropriate analytical, numerical, or graphical means, we could determine the entropy as a function of the state of the substance, relative to the entropy in some arbitrary datum state. Our next task is therefore to examine $(\partial S/\partial V)_U$, which brings us to the thermodynamic definition of pressure.

7·4 THE THERMODYNAMIC DEFINITION OF PRESSURE

What is "the pressure" of a piece of matter? We think of pressure in mechanical terms as the force per unit area exerted by the matter on its boundaries. A microscopic interpretation of gas pressure in terms of molecular collisions with a wall is very vivid, even though we can't really see the molecules. Thermodynamics provides an entirely different way to define pressure, and in many ways this definition is more fundamental. Fortunately, the thermodynamic and mechanical pressures are equivalent under certain circumstances, so we can use force-measuring instruments to determine the thermodynamic pressure.

We discovered the thermodynamic definition of temperature by examining the conditions of thermal equilibrium. Following this line of thought, the thermodynamic definition of pressure is obtained from considerations of *mechanical* equilibrium. Pressure is conceived to be a property that two systems have in common when they are in mechanical equilibrium.

FIG. 7·4   *The combined system C is isolated*

Consider two control masses A and B, which together form an isolated system C. We presume A and B are free to expand or contract, thereby exchanging energy as work, and that they can also exchange energy as heat. The sign conventions for our analysis of these interactions are defined in Fig. 7·4. We again treat only the case of simple compressible substances.

The conditions of isolation require that the energy and volume of the combined system C remain fixed,

$$U_C = U_A + U_B = \text{constant} \tag{7·15a}$$
$$V_C = V_A + V_B = \text{constant} \tag{7·15b}$$

Assuming that A and B are each in some thermodynamic state, that the masses of A and B are fixed, and that their allowed quantum states are independent, the entropy of the combined system is again given by

$$S_C = S_A(U_A, V_A) + S_B(U_B, V_B) \tag{7·16}$$

Upon isolation of C, systems A and B will interact, exchanging both energy and volume. This interaction will lead to a state of equilibrium within C; for mechanical equilibrium the pressures of A and B must be equal, and for thermal equilibrium the temperatures must be equal. The conditions of equilibrium are obtained by seeking the state that maximizes the entropy of the isolated system C.

Since the total energy and volume are fixed, we cannot independently vary U_A, U_B, V_A, and V_B in seeking the maximum of S_C. It is therefore convenient to define the fraction of the energy and volume contributed by part A as r_U and r_V, respectively. Then,

$$U_A = r_U U \qquad U_B = (1 - r_U)U \tag{7·17a,b}$$
$$V_A = r_V V \qquad V_B = (1 - r_V)V \tag{7·17c,d}$$

The fractions r_U and r_V can be considered the two free variables to be adjusted in the maximization of S_C. $S_C(r_U, r_V)$ can be thought of as a *surface* above the $r_U - r_V$ plane; the form of this surface is shown in Fig. 7·5.

The state of maximum S_C is determined by the two conditions

$$\left(\frac{\partial S_C}{\partial r_U}\right)_{r_V} = 0 \qquad \left(\frac{\partial S_C}{\partial r_V}\right)_{r_U} = 0 \tag{7·18a,b}$$

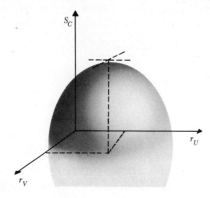

FIG. 7·5 *The S_C surface*

Using Eqs. (7·17), these two conditions give

$$\left(\frac{\partial S_A}{\partial U_A}\right)_{V_A} U - \left(\frac{\partial S_B}{\partial U_B}\right)_{V_B} U = 0 \tag{7·19a}$$

$$\left(\frac{\partial S_A}{\partial V_A}\right)_{U_A} V - \left(\frac{\partial S_B}{\partial V_B}\right)_{U_B} V = 0 \tag{7·19b}$$

Noting that the derivatives in Eq. (7·19a) are the reciprocal temperatures of A and B, Eq. (7·19a) is simply the requirement of thermal equilibrium, that is, that the temperatures of A and B must be equal. Equation (7·19b) is the condition of mechanical equilibrium, and these derivatives must somehow be related to the pressure. Noting that the dimensions of entropy are energy/temperature, the derivative $\partial S/\partial V$ has the dimensions of energy/volume-temperature = force-length/length^3-temperature = pressure/temperature. Hence, this derivative must be either plus or minus the pressure divided by T. The proper choice for sign can be obtained by noting that if A and B are not in equilibrium the system with the larger pressure should expand, and the entropy of C should thereby increase. The infinitesimal change in S_C associated with an infinitesimal dr_V is, when $T_A = T_B$,

$$dS_C = \left[\left(\frac{\partial S_A}{\partial V_A}\right)_{U_A} - \left(\frac{\partial S_B}{\partial V_B}\right)_{U_B}\right] V \, dr_V \geq 0$$

Hence, if $dr_V > 0$, which corresponds to expansion of A,

$$\left(\frac{\partial S_A}{\partial V_A}\right)_{U_A} > \left(\frac{\partial S_B}{\partial V_B}\right)_{U_B}$$

Since for $dV_A > 0$, $P_A > P_B$, the plus sign must be chosen. The thermodynamic definition of pressure is therefore given by

$$\blacktriangleright \quad \frac{P}{T} \equiv \left(\frac{\partial S}{\partial V}\right)_U \tag{7·20}$$

Since both S and V are extensive, P/T and hence P is *intensive*. Note that the thermodynamic pressure is defined in terms of the *equilibrium* equation of state $S = S(U, V)$, and hence P has no meaning for a substance not in a thermodynamic state.

Following the thoughts of our microscopic interpretation of temperature, we can interpret the pressure as a measure of the sensitivity of the entropy to volume changes at fixed internal energy. If a system of gas molecules expands at fixed internal energy, we become more uncertain about the locations of individual molecules, for they can roam over a larger space. Hence $(\partial S/\partial V)_U$ and P should always be positive, as is indeed the case for a gas. In a solid, an expansion at fixed energy may be accompanied by an ordering of the molecular structure, which reduces the randomness and uncertainty about the microscopic state. Hence in solids the pressure can be negative (which corresponds to tension).

The thermodynamic pressure P has the qualitative aspects of the mechanical pressure, but it is not obvious that they are identical. We shall show that they are identical shortly.

7·5 INTENSIVE REPRESENTATIONS AND SOME EXTENSIONS

We developed the definitions of T and P in terms of the extensive properties S, U, and V. Since the mass M is fixed for any piece of matter, we can divide numerators and denominators in these defining ratios by M, and thereby express T and P in terms of the intensive properties s, u, and v. The definitions of T and P in terms of $s(u, v)$ become

$$\blacktriangleright \qquad \frac{1}{T} \equiv \left(\frac{\partial s}{\partial u}\right)_v \tag{7·21}$$

$$\blacktriangleright \qquad \frac{P}{T} \equiv \left(\frac{\partial s}{\partial v}\right)_u \tag{7·22}$$

The differential of the specific entropy is therefore

$$\blacktriangleright \qquad ds = \frac{1}{T}\,du + \frac{P}{T}\,dv \tag{7·23}$$

This is a very important equation; it provides the means for evaluation of the entropy of substances from macroscopic laboratory data. It is called the *Gibbs equation* for a simple compressible substance.

The definitions above apply for simple compressible substances only, but extension to other classes of substances is quite straightforward. For example, the thermodynamic definition of temperature for a simple magnetic substance is

$$\blacktriangleright \qquad \frac{1}{T} \equiv \left(\frac{\partial s}{\partial u}\right)_{\mathbf{M}} \tag{7·24}$$

while for a simple dielectric substance it is

$$\blacktriangleright \qquad \frac{1}{T} \equiv \left(\frac{\partial s}{\partial u}\right)_{\mathbf{P}} \qquad\qquad (7 \cdot 25)$$

Following the development of the thermodynamic pressure, thermodynamic definitions for the electric and magnetic fields can be developed. The Gibbs equations for these substances can then be used to calculate the entropy as a function of state. For example, the Gibbs equation for a simple magnetic substance is, in intensive form,

$$\blacktriangleright \qquad ds = \frac{1}{T} du - \mu_0 \frac{v\mathbf{H}}{T} \cdot d\mathbf{M} \qquad\qquad (7 \cdot 26)$$

The development of this and other Gibbs equations are left as problems for the student.

The temperature T as used here is the "absolute" temperature, which would be measured as the Rankine (°R) or Kelvin (°K) scales. The relative temperatures (°F, °C) can be used when temperature differences are involved, but must not be used when temperature *levels* are needed [such as in Eqs. (7·21 to 7·26)].

Let's consider for a moment the possibility that the absolute temperature T might be negative for some system. Since $1/T$ measures the sensitivity of the entropy to energy changes at fixed "constraints" (fixed volume, magnetic moment, and so on), a negative temperature state would be one for which an increase in energy would reduce the entropy; by adding energy we could make the system become more ordered, that is, we could become less uncertain about the microscopic state. Most systems have more allowed quantum states at high energy than at low energy, and hence do not exhibit the peculiarity of negative absolute temperature. However, imagine a system for which there is an upper limit on the energy of allowed quantum states for individual particles. As the system energy is increased, more and more particles must occupy the state of greatest energy until finally at the system-state of maximum energy all of the particles are in their maximum energy state. This is a highly ordered condition; if we know that the total (macroscopic) energy is this highest possible amount, we know the microscopic state with no uncertainty. The entropy must therefore be zero in this state. Hence, as we add energy in approaching this state, the entropy would decrease, which corresponds to a situation of negative absolute temperature. Note that the negative temperatures would occur at higher energies than positive temperatures! Nuclear spin systems in crystals exhibit this negative temperature behavior. The spin state adjusts rapidly to changes in comparison to the lattice vibration, and hence the spin states can be treated as a separate thermodynamic system. The operation of solid-state masers depends upon the existence of such spin-system states of negative T.[†]

† A. E. Siegman, *Microwave Solid-State Masers*, McGraw-Hill Book Company, New York, 1964.

7·6 MACROSCOPIC EVALUATION OF ENTROPY

Later in this chapter we shall show that the thermodynamic and empirical temperatures are identical, and that the thermodynamic and mechanical pressures are identical for a substance in an equilibrium state. Let's accept these equivalences for the moment, and begin to do something quantitatively useful with the second law and entropy ideas. This will help the student to get his feet on the ground, and will make it easier for him to see where we are going and why.

Accepting these equivalences, we see that the coefficients of du and dv in the Gibbs equation [Eq. (7·23)] are directly measurable in the laboratory. The Gibbs equation therefore provides a differential equation from which the entropy of a substance can be quantitatively evaluated as a function of thermodynamic state, relative to an arbitrarily chosen reference state. Integration of this equation between any two states 1 and 2 yields

$$s_2 - s_1 = \int_1^2 \frac{du}{T} + \int_1^2 \frac{P}{T}\, dv \qquad (7·27)$$

The integrations can be carried out along any path connecting the two states. For example, suppose we take the path shown in Fig. 7·6a. We imagine plotting $1/T$ versus u and P/T versus v along this path as shown in Figs. 7·6b and 7·6c. The integrals under these curves can be computed numerically or graphically, and the difference $s_2 - s_1$ thereby evaluated from Eq. (7·27). If state 1 is the datum state, we set $s_1 = 0$, and s_2 then is the entropy relative to the datum state. It is *not* the *absolute entropy* as defined by Eq. (6·8). It is possible to evaluate the absolute entropy from macroscopic data with the help of an additional postulate about the limit of the entropy of a pure substance as $T \to 0$ (Chap. Eleven), or using statistical thermodynamics. However, only entropy *differences* and *changes* are required for most second-law analysis, and hence as long as we work with a single substance we can use its entropy as evaluated relative to the datum state.

As an example of this type of entropy evaluation, let's compute the entropy

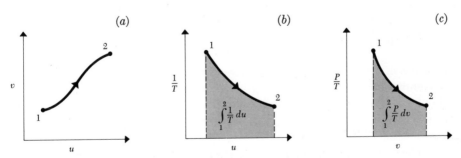

FIG. 7·6 *Computing an entropy difference from the Gibbs equation*

of saturated water vapor at 1 atm taking the saturated liquid at 1 atm as the datum state. The necessary u-v-P-T data are taken from Table B·1b (note we use the absolute temperature °R)

State 1   saturated liquid at 1 atm
$T = 671.59°\text{R}\ (212.00°\text{F})$
$v = 0.01672\ \text{ft}^3/\text{lbm}$
$u = 180.02\ \text{Btu}/\text{lbm}$
$P = 14.696\ \text{lbf}/\text{in.}^2$

State 2   saturated vapor at 1 atm
$T = 671.59°\text{R}\ (212.00°\text{F})$
$v = 26.80\ \text{ft}^3/\text{lbm}$
$u = 1077.5\ \text{Btu}/\text{lbm}$
$P = 14.696\ \text{lbf}/\text{in.}^2$

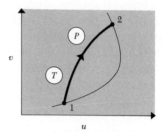

FIG. 7·7 *The path of integration (see also Fig. B·1)*

We could take any path of integration connecting two states. The path of constant pressure is easiest, for along this path both the temperature and pressure are constant (Fig. 7·7). The two integrals are then

$$\int_1^2 \frac{du}{T} = \frac{1}{T}(u_2 - u_1) = \frac{1077.5 - 180.02}{671.59} = 1.3363\ \text{Btu}/\text{lbm-°R}$$

$$\int_1^2 \frac{P}{T}\,dv = \frac{P}{T}(v_2 - v_1) = \frac{14.696 \times 144}{671.59}(26.80 - 0.01672)$$

$$= 84.4\ \text{ft-lbf}/\text{lbm-°R} = 0.1083\ \text{Btu}/\text{lbm-°R}$$

Hence,†

$$s_2 - s_1 = 1.4446\ \text{Btu}/\text{lbm-°R}$$

(Note that this is precisely the "entropy of vaporization" s_{fg} given in Table B·1b.) Hence, the specific entropy of saturated water vapor at 1 atm, relative to the saturated liquid at 1 atm, is 1.4446 Btu/lbm-°R. In Table B·1b we give the value of 1.7566 Btu/lbm-°R for the entropy at this state. This difference is due to a different choice of datum state; either would be correct, as long as we were consistent in any one analysis. Taking the entropy of state 1, relative to the triple-point datum, from Table B·1b as $s_1 = 0.3120$ Btu/lbm-°R, the entropy at state 2, relative to the triple point, would be

$$0.3120 + 1.4446 = 1.7566\ \text{Btu}/\text{lbm-°R}$$

Evaluation of the *absolute* entropy requires material from Chap. Eleven. But to complete the picture here, we state that the absolute entropy of state 1 is about 1.16 Btu/lbm-°R, and hence the absolute entropy of state 2 is

$$1.16 + 1.44 = 2.60\ \text{Btu}/\text{lbm-°R}$$

† Since the intervals are the same on the °R and °F scales, 1 Btu/lbm-°R = 1 Btu/lbm-°F; the latter units are often used.

This is essentially the value that would be computed from statistical thermodynamics using the basic definition of entropy.

The graphs and tables in Appendix B give the specific entropy, relative to some datum state, for a variety of substances. Most of these values were obtained by the type of integration outlined here. For some of the more exotic substances, such as cesium vapor (Fig. B·11) and the paramagnetic salt iron-ammonium alum (Fig. B·12), the entropy is based on a combination of statistical thermodynamics and macroscopic thermodynamic equations of the sort discussed in the next chapter.

With this background about the source of the entropy data given in Appendix B, we can begin to use these data in some simple quantitative second-law analyses. We shall want to study processes, and hence shall first discuss some important ideas about the nature of various processes.

7·7 REVERSIBLE AND IRREVERSIBLE PROCESSES

Processes that do not violate the second law can be classed as reversible or irreversible. The concept of a reversible process is very important in thermodynamics, and the ability to recognize, evaluate, and reduce irreversibilities in a process is essential to a competent engineering thermodynamicist.

Suppose the system of interest is an isolated system. The second law says that any process that would reduce the entropy of the isolated system is impossible. Suppose a process takes place within the isolated system in what we shall call the forward direction. If the change in state of the system is such that the entropy increases for the forward process, then for the backward process (that is, for the reverse change of state) the entropy would decrease. The backward process is therefore impossible, and hence we say that the forward process is *irreversible*. If the entropy is unchanged by the forward process, then it will be unchanged by the reverse process, and the process could go in either direction without violating the second law; such a process is called *reversible*. The key idea of a reversible process within an isolated system is that it does not "produce" any entropy.

Since a reversible process does not produce any entropy, the total molecular disorganization within the isolated system remains constant. It is impossible to tell which state in a reversible process came first; the reversible process leaves no "footprints in the sands of time." The reversible process is an idealization, like frictionless pulleys and resistanceless wires. It can be approached to a very high degree, and in fact there is some evidence that at very low temperatures electric current flow can become exactly reversible. Currents started in loops of superconducting materials have been observed to persist for very long times without measurable decay. These experiments are perhaps the closest man has come to truly realizing a reversible process, and may even be fully reversible. Some other processes that the student has probably idealized as being reversible in other courses are shown in Fig. 7·8. Note that each of the isolated systems of

(a) *Resistanceless current flow*

(b) *Frictionless motion*

(c) *Pneumatic spring*

FIG. 7·8 *Some familiar reversible processes*

(d) *Magnetic spring*

Fig. 7·8 happens to be an oscillator in which the oscillations persist indefinitely. At the end of each cycle the system is returned to its initial state, thereby "undoing" the state change of the first half cycle. Hence, if the entropy increased during a portion of the cycle, it would have to decrease during another portion in order to return to its initial value. But this would violate the second law, and thus we conclude that the entropy remains constant during each process. The processes are therefore (ideally) reversible.

An irreversible process is one that is not reversible, that is, one that *produces* entropy. All real processes (with the possible exception of superconducting current flows) are in some measure irreversible, though many processes can be analyzed quite adequately by assuming that they are reversible. Some processes that are clearly irreversible include mixing of two gases, spontaneous combustion, friction, and the transfer of energy as heat from a body at high temperature to a body at low temperature. These and some other obviously irreversible processes are shown in Fig. 7·9. Each process of Fig. 7·9 results in some increase in the entropy of the isolated system, that is, in some "entropy production." Qualitative microscopic interpretations of this entropy production will now be given.

In Fig. 7·9a an electric current flows through a resistance following the closing of a switch. We know from experience that the capacitor eventually becomes completely discharged, the wires become warmer, and finally the current flow ceases entirely. The electrons, which initially were concentrated on the plates of the capacitor, are now distributed throughout the system, and the dielectric in the capacitor has lost the molecular organization which gave it a net dipole moment. This randomization accounts for the entropy increase.

The spring-mass system in Fig. 7·9b oscillates at smaller and smaller amplitudes, until finally friction brings the mass to rest. Our experience tells us that the temperature of the system increased during the decay of the oscillation. The highly directed kinetic energy of the mass has been converted into randomly oriented motion of the molecules, and this extra randomness accounts for the entropy increase.

In Fig. 7·9c we see gas leaving a high-pressure container and flowing into one of lower pressure. The entropy increase required by the second law is reflected by the increased positional uncertainty.

Energy transfer as heat from a hot system to a cooler one is also irreversible (Fig. 7·9d). If this were not the case, we could expect to watch an isothermal system and eventually observe an energy transfer that would produce a non-uniformity of temperature. This would indeed be handy, for we could get hot water from ice for nothing. The energy transfer as heat tends to spread the energy over the system, and this increases the uncertainty about the microscopic state.

The system in Fig. 7·9e initially has oxygen on one side and nitrogen on the other. The molecules diffuse through one another, and eventually we have a homogeneous mixture. The mixing increases the randomness and uncertainty about the microscopic state, and this is reflected in the increase of entropy.

The spontaneous chemical reaction within the system of Fig. 7·9f is irreversible. Oxygen and hydrogen might explode in an isolated container and form water, but the reverse process never takes place. The spontaneous com-

(a) *Current flow through a resistance*

(b) *Motion with friction*

(c) *Unrestrained expansion*

(d) *Energy transfer as heat*

(e) *Diffusion*

(f) *Spontaneous chemical reaction*

FIG. 7·9 *Some irreversible processes*

bustion process converts electron and molecular binding energy into randomly oriented translational energy, and this randomization is evidenced by the increase in entropy.

Recognition of the irreversibilities in a real process is especially important in engineering. Irreversibility, or departure from the ideal condition of reversibility, reflects an increase in the amount of disorganized energy at the expense of organized energy. The organized energy (such as that of a raised weight) is easily put to practical use; disorganized energy (such as the random motions of the molecules in a gas) requires "straightening out" before it can be used effectively. And since we are always somewhat uncertain about the microscopic state, this straightening can never be perfect. Consequently the engineer is constantly striving to reduce irreversibilities in his systems in order to obtain better performance.

To summarize:

Processes that are usually idealized as *reversible* include

> Frictionless movement
> Restrained compression or expansion
> Energy transfer as heat due to infinitesimal temperature nonuniformity
> Magnetization, polarization
> Electric current flow through a zero resistance
> Restrained chemical reaction
> Mixing of two samples of the same substance at the same state

Processes that are *irreversible* include

> Movement with friction
> Unrestrained expansion
> Energy transfer as heat due to large temperature nonuniformities
> Magnetization or polarization with hysteresis
> Electric current flow through a nonzero resistance
> Spontaneous chemical reaction
> Mixing of matter of different composition or state

7·8 AN EXAMPLE OF A SECOND-LAW ANALYSIS

Let's now make these second-law ideas concrete by an example. Consider the isolated system shown in Fig. 7·10. Initially the system consists of 1.84 lbm

FIG. 7·10 *The system is isolated; the irreversible process produces entropy*

of saturated water vapor at 95 psia and 8.16 lbm of saturated liquid water at 10 psia. This system is clearly not in equilibrium initially, for there are severe pressure and temperature variations inside. The interactions that will occur spontaneously within the isolated system will smooth out these temperature and pressure differences; some of the vapor will condense, and this will drop the pressure and vapor temperature. The liquid will warm up, and finally the system will come to rest with a uniform temperature and pressure inside. Calculation of the final state requires only the ideas of equilibrium and a first-law analysis. The second law can be applied to see if the entropy increases within the isolated system; if it does, the process is irreversible, and the reverse process would be impossible. Intuition tells us that this is the case; indeed, so does the second law, which is really just a generalization of this kind of intuition. We shall carry out the first- and second-law analyses in some detail to illustrate the computation of entropy from the tabular and graphical equations of state and to confirm the expectation that the process does produce entropy.

Let's first evaluate the initial state. We assume that the liquid A and the vapor B are each in equilibrium states, and hence we can use the tables for the thermodynamic properties of water (Table B·1b) to evaluate their properties.

Liquid A   8.16 lbm of saturated liquid at 10 psia
$T = 653°R$ (193°F)
$u = 161.14$ Btu/lbm
$v = 0.01659$ ft³/lbm
$s = 0.2835$ Btu/lbm-°R

Vapor B   1.84 lbm saturated vapor at 95 psia
$T = 784°R$ (324°F)
$u = 1104.5$ Btu/lbm
$v = 4.652$ ft³/lbm
$s = 1.6068$ Btu/lbm-°R

The total energy, volume, and entropy of the system in its initial state are therefore

$$U_1 = 8.16 \times 161.14 + 1.84 \times 1104.5 = 3350 \text{ Btu}$$
$$V_1 = 8.16 \times 0.01659 + 1.84 \times 4.652 = 8.67 \text{ ft}^3$$
$$S_1 = 8.16 \times 0.2835 + 1.84 \times 1.6068 = 5.26 \text{ Btu/°R}$$

The next job is to determine the final state (2) using a first-law analysis. Assuming that the system is isolated, the energy balance gives

$$U_2 = U_1$$

Also, the volume is fixed and hence

$$V_2 = V_1$$

We assume that the entire system is in an equilibrium state at the end of the process. The internal energy and volume will therefore fix state 2. The specific internal energy and specific volume in the final state will be

$$u_2 = \frac{U_2}{M} = \frac{3350}{10} = 335 \text{ Btu/lbm}$$

$$v_2 = \frac{V_2}{M} = \frac{8.67}{10} = 0.867 \text{ ft}^3/\text{lbm}$$

Looking at Fig. B·1, we see that the final state is approximately 50 psia, $x = 0.1$. Returning to Table B·1b for more accurate data, we find

At 50 psia

$u_f = 249.9$ Btu/lbm $u_g = 1095.3$ Btu/lbm
$v_f = 0.0173$ ft³/lbm $v_g = 8.515$ ft³/lbm
$s_f = 0.4110$ Btu/lbm-°R $s_g = 1.6585$ Btu/lbm-°R

Then, if the quality x is 0.1, the final energy, volume, and entropy are

$$U_2 = 10(0.9 \times 249.9 + 0.1 \times 1095.3) = 3350 \text{ Btu}$$
$$V_2 = 10(0.9 \times 0.0173 + 9.1 \times 8.515) = 8.67 \text{ ft}^3$$
$$S_2 = 10(0.9 \times 0.4110 + 0.1 \times 1.6585) = 5.36 \text{ Btu/°R}$$

Note that the energy and volume are maintained as the first-law analysis requires (this checks the final state read from Fig. B·1).

Finally, the second law states that the entropy of this isolated system should increase, or remain constant if the process is reversible, that is, the amount of entropy production $\mathcal{P}_S$ cannot be negative,

$$\mathcal{P}_S \equiv S_2 - S_1 \geq 0$$

Noting that $S_2 > S_1$ from the calculations above, we are assured that the process is *irreversible*. The amount of entropy production for this process is†

$$\mathcal{P}_S = 5.36 - 5.26 = 0.1 \text{ Btu/°R}$$

7·9 TWO IDEALIZED SYSTEMS

Often the system of interest is not isolated. In order to investigate the reversibility, irreversibility, or impossibility of processes within the system, we can imagine that the system interacts with a hypothetical environment in which all processes are reversible. The system under study and this hypothetical environment then form an isolated system, and any increase in the entropy within the combined isolated system must be due to irreversibilities within the system under study. The amount by which the entropy of the combined system increases during the process is then the entropy production due to irreversibilities within the system under study. This type of irreversibility test requires elements from which the hypothetical reversible environment can be con-

† The fact that $\mathcal{P}_S$ is small compared to either S_1 or S_2 has no particular significance since the entropy datum of Fig. B·1 was arbitrarily chosen.

structed. Since the interactions between the system and its environment include heat and work, we need to conceive of two "reservoirs" to or from which energy can be transferred reversibly as work or heat.

We shall conceive of a *thermal energy reservoir* (TER) as some system of fixed mass that can undergo only heat interactions with its environment. Any energy transferred into the TER as heat will appear as an increase in its internal energy. The TER is further idealized as having a uniform internal temperature; a TER is always in an equilibrium state. We usually conceive of the TER as being very large, so that the temperature remains constant for the interactions we consider. Internal energy represents "disorganized" molecular energy, and energy transfer as heat can be viewed as "disorganized microscopic work." The TER can therefore be thought of as a source or sink for "disorganized energy."

In contrast, the *mechanical energy reservoir* (MER) is some system that possesses energy only in some fully organized mechanical form, such as in a raised weight. The only energy-transfer mode for a MER is reversible *work;* whatever force acts on the MER is independent of the direction or rate of change of the energy. The force on the MER is conceived to be adjustable by design to fit the analysis at hand. All motions within a MER are assumed to be frictionless, so that any energy put into the MER as work can be completely recovered as work. The MER can be thought of as a source or sink for "fully organized energy." A MER can have but one state for a given energy; given its energy, we know the position of the weight *exactly*, without uncertainty.

These two conceptual systems would be difficult to build exactly, but can be closely approximated and hence are reasonable concepts. A block of copper can be a good approximation to a TER; it has a large capacity to store internal energy, and can be idealized as being incompressible. A dead weight on the end of a frictionless pulley and a dead mass for the weight to gravitate toward forms a reasonable conceptualization for a MER (Fig. 7·11).

The MER and TER are useful concepts because they are two nonisolated systems for which we can easily compute the entropy change. The TER is a

(a) *The TER is a reservoir for "disorganized" energy*

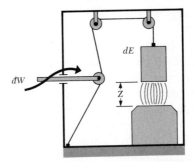

(b) *The MER is a reservoir for "organized" energy*

FIG. 7·11   *Two conceptual systems*

chunk of matter held at fixed volume. The infinitesimal increase in its entropy associated with an infinitesimal increase in its internal energy is, from Eq. (7·23),

$$dS = \frac{1}{T} dU \quad \text{for a TER} \tag{7·28}$$

An energy balance (Fig. 7·11a) reveals that the internal energy change is due solely to the energy transfer as heat *to* the TER

$$dU = đQ$$

and hence the entropy change of a TER can be calculated from

▶ $\quad dS = \dfrac{đQ}{T} \quad$ for a TER, $đQ$ is energy input $\qquad$ (7·29)

Thus, the disorganized transfer of energy to a TER will result in an increase in the randomness inside, that is, in an increase in our uncertainty about its microscopic state. The entropy of a TER can be decreased by removal of energy as heat ($đQ < 0$). This will reduce the randomness inside and hence the entropy will decrease ($dS < 0$).

In contrast, the MER is conceptually a *perfectly organized* system. It has *one* microscopic state for each energy; given the energy, the microscopic state of the MER is *precisely* known without any uncertainty. The probability of its single microscopic state is therefore exactly one and its entropy is therefore always exactly zero. Hence

▶ $\quad dS = 0 \quad$ for a MER $\qquad$ (7·30)

An energy balance on the MER (Fig. 7·11b) reveals that the energy transfer to the MER as work appears as an increase in the fully organized mechanical energy stored inside. This organization makes the energy fully recoverable as work.

Imagine an isolated system composed of two interacting MERs (they must be properly balanced to exert the same forces). If any change occurs in the state of the isolated system, the entropy will remain unchanged because the entropies of the subsystems comprising the isolated system remain unchanged. Hence a MER is clearly a reversible device.

Consider now an isolated system composed of two interacting TERs (Fig. 7·12). We know that energy transfer as heat will not take place "up the temperature hill," and hence heat transfer "down the temperature hill" is irreversible. However, in the limit where the temperature difference vanishes, the energy transfer process can be treated as reversible. To show this, let the

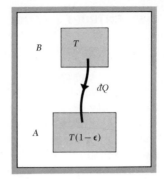

FIG. 7·12 *As* $\epsilon \to 0$ *the process approaches reversibility*

temperature of TER B be T, and that of TER A be $T(1 - \epsilon)$, where ϵ is a small number. The increase in entropy of the combined system C as a result of the transfer of an amount of energy as heat dQ from B to A is

$$dS_C = d(S_A + S_B) \geq 0 \tag{7·31}$$

and, considering the signs for positive energy transfer in Figs. 7·12 and 7·11, the entropy changes of A and B are

$$dS_A = + \frac{dQ}{T(1 - \epsilon)} = + \frac{dQ}{T}(1 + \epsilon + \epsilon^2 + \cdots) \tag{7·32a}$$

$$dS_B = - \frac{dQ}{T} \tag{7·32b}$$

Adding, we have

$$dS_C = \epsilon \frac{dQ}{T} + \cdots \geq 0 \tag{7·33}$$

Now, when the temperatures of A and B are very nearly equal ϵ will be very small, and we see that the entropy production, that is, dS_C, becomes very small in magnitude in comparison to dS_A or dS_B, and vanishes in the limit $\epsilon \to 0$. Hence, while the transfer of energy as heat across a finite temperature difference is irreversible and produces entropy, in the limit of zero temperature difference the process produces no entropy and hence becomes reversible. By reducing the temperature difference, the amount of entropy production can be made as small as one desires. Hence, we can consider the process of energy transfer as heat between a system at some temperature T and another (say a TER) at some infinitesimally different temperature to be a reversible process.

We shall next use the TER and MER to form ideal reversible environments in order to study the entropy production due to processes within a control mass.

7·10 ENTROPY CHANGE AND PRODUCTION FOR A CONTROL MASS

We can now derive an expression for the amount of entropy production as a result of an irreversible process within a control mass. Suppose the system A receives energy as heat and work during the process; we imagine that these energies come from a TER and a MER, respectively. In order to ensure the reversibility of all processes within the hypothetical environment, the temperature difference between the TER and the point on the control mass where the energy is received as heat must be infinitesimal. The control mass and its hypothetical environment form an isolated system, shown in Fig. 7·13.

Denoting the control-mass entropy by S, we have

$$dS_C = d(S_{TER} + S_{MER} + S) \geq 0$$

Now, the entropy of the MER does not change. Noting the difference in the direction of positive energy transfer as heat in Figs. 7·11 and 7·13, the entropy change for the TER is

$$dS_{TER} = \frac{-dQ}{T}$$

Therefore,

$$dS_C = dS - \frac{dQ}{T} \geq 0 \qquad\qquad (7 \cdot 34)$$

Hence the entropy change of the control mass must satisfy

$$\blacktriangleright \quad dS \geq \frac{dQ}{T} \qquad \begin{array}{l} \textit{control mass, } dQ \\ \textit{is energy input} \end{array} \qquad (7 \cdot 35)$$

The equality holds for the reversible process, the inequality for the irreversible process. Since the process within the ideal environment is reversible, any irreversibility must be due to the process within control mass A.

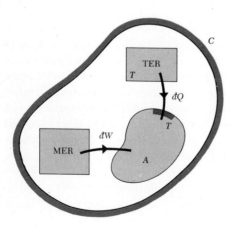

FIG. 7·13 *The combined system C is isolated, and the processes in the environment of A are all reversible*

In the special case where the process within A is reversible, the equality in Eq. (7·35) gives

$$\blacktriangleright \qquad dS = \frac{dQ}{T} \qquad \begin{array}{l} \textit{reversible process,} \\ \textit{control mass, } dQ \\ \textit{is energy input} \end{array} \qquad (7 \cdot 36a)$$

Integrating between an initial state 1 and a final state 2,

$$\blacktriangleright \qquad \Delta S = \int_1^2 \frac{dQ}{T} \qquad \begin{array}{l} \textit{reversible process,} \\ \textit{control mass, } dQ \\ \textit{is energy input} \end{array} \qquad (7 \cdot 36b)$$

The restrictions are listed because they are important and often forgotten. This equation is very important in thermodynamics, for it provides a means for evaluating the entropy change from laboratory measurements of temperature and energy transfer, provided that the experimental process can be made sufficiently close to reversible that dS_C is small compared to dS. Equation (7·36a) is taken as the definition of entropy in many classical macroscopic thermodynamic treatments.

· A reversible process of special importance is the *reversible adiabatic process* ($dQ = 0$). Applying Eqs. (7·36) we see that the entropy of a control mass undergoing a reversible adiabatic process will not change; such a process of constant entropy is called an *isentropic process*.

$$\blacktriangleright \qquad dS = 0 \left.\begin{array}{l} \\ \end{array}\right\} \quad \begin{array}{l} \textit{for any control mass,} \\ \textit{reversible adiabatic} \end{array} \qquad (7 \cdot 37a)$$

or

$$\blacktriangleright \qquad \Delta S = 0 \left.\begin{array}{l} \\ \end{array}\right\} \quad \textit{process} \qquad (7 \cdot 37b)$$

In a reversible adiabatic process the only energy-transfer mechanism is work. Reversible work constitutes perfectly ordered energy transfer, and will not increase the molecular randomness. For example, the process of gas compression in a piston-cylinder system can be made very nearly reversible and adiabatic, and this process is often treated as an isentropic process. As the gas is compressed its energy is increased. If the volume were not also reduced, this increased energy would increase the randomness and our uncertainty about the microscopic state. However, the reduction in volume means that we are more certain about the location of the molecules, and the constancy of the entropy can be regarded as a balance between the increased uncertainty due to the greater energy and the reduced uncertainty due to the more concentrated volume.† Another example of a (nearly) reversible adiabatic process is the rapid demagnetization of a paramagnetic salt at low temperatures. (This process is often used to produce very low temperatures.) Idealizing this process

† These arguments are not quite correct, but are made in the proper spirit. Actually, the quantum theory says that compression of the gas reduces the number of allowed states, and it is this which really compensates for the uncertainty increase due to energy addition.

as reversible and adiabatic, the reduction in uncertainty due to the removal of energy in the demagnetization process can be viewed as being balanced by the increase in uncertainty due to the disalignment of the magnetic dipoles. The second law says that the net effect is to maintain constant entropy during the reversible adiabatic demagnetization.

If the process within A is irreversible the entropy increase dS_C is directly chargeable to irreversibilities within A, and we call it the *entropy production*, due to the process within A. Hence, the amount of entropy production $d\mathcal{P}_S$ within system A of Fig. 7·13 is

$$d\mathcal{P}_S \equiv \underset{\substack{\text{increase in}\\\text{entropy}\\\text{storage}}}{dS} - \underset{\substack{\text{entropy}\\\text{inflow}}}{\frac{dQ}{T}} \tag{7·38}$$

Since the entropy production is a function of the process and not a function of the system states, the notation d is appropriate. Note that the entropy production represents the strength of the inequality in the second law. The second law says that the entropy production cannot be negative; the entropy production is zero for a reversible process:

$$\begin{aligned} d\mathcal{P}_S &> 0 \qquad \text{irreversible process} \\ d\mathcal{P}_S &= 0 \qquad \text{reversible process} \\ d\mathcal{P}_S &< 0 \qquad \text{impossible process} \end{aligned} \tag{7·39}$$

Since a transfer of energy as heat from the TER to the control mass results in a reduction of the entropy of the TER and an increase in the entropy of the control mass, it is convenient and logical to think of entropy "flowing" between the two as a result of their interaction. This is quite analogous to our concept of heat as energy flowing between the two. The magnitude of the entropy decrease for the TER is dQ/T, which would be the entropy increase of the control mass were the process reversible. Hence we call the term dQ/T the amount of *entropy transfer with heat* into the control mass. This allows us to focus only on the control mass in making future second-law analyses; wherever energy enters a control mass as heat, we consider there to be an entropy *inflow* with heat in the amount dQ/T, where T is the temperature of the control mass at the point where the energy dQ is received as heat. If energy is transferred *out* of the control mass, then we think of an entropy *outflow* with heat in the amount dQ/T, where T is the temperature of the control mass at the point where the energy dQ is removed as heat. If there is a net inflow of entropy with heat, the entropy of the control mass must increase by at least this amount. The excess of the actual control-mass entropy increase over the net entropy-inflow to the control mass represents the entropy that must have been "produced" within the control mass by irreversible action.

The microscopic view is very helpful in grasping the idea of entropy transfer with heat. We view heat as energy transfer that takes place as work on the microscopic scale, but in a random, disorganized way. We are very uncertain about the microscopic details of energy transfer as heat, and consequently do not know where or exactly when the wall molecules are going to push on system molecules in order to effect this energy transfer. Consequently, as a result of our uncertainty about exactly how the energy transfer takes place we become even more uncertain about the instantaneous microscopic state of the system. The entropy, the measure of our uncertainty as to microscopic detail, increases as a result of the disorganized energy-addition process.

7·11 EXAMPLES OF CONTROL-MASS SECOND-LAW ANALYSIS

Irreversible compression. Consider the control mass of Fig. 7·14a. The cylinder initially contains 0.2 lbm of freon-12 vapor at $-20°F$ (440°R) with an initial volume of 1.0 ft³. The piston is suddenly pushed in very rapidly, causing shock waves to propagate through the freon; after a short period of adjustment, the freon comes to equilibrium at the new volume (0.2 ft³). The process is sufficiently rapid that we can neglect any energy transfer as heat to the freon. Find the possible terminal states for this process.

There is no entropy flow with heat for this adiabatic process, and hence any increase in the freon entropy must be due to irreversible effects within the freon. Denoting the initial and final states by 1 and 2, respectively, the second law, as applied to the control mass, is

$$\mathcal{P}_S \equiv \underset{\substack{\text{increase in}\\\text{entropy storage}}}{S_2 - S_1} = M(s_2 - s_1) \geq 0$$

Thus, any state with specific entropy greater than the initial state will be a possible final state. From Fig. B·7,

$$T_1 = 440°R \ (-20°F) \qquad v_1 = 1.0/0.2 = 5 \text{ ft}^3/\text{lbm}$$
$$P_1 = 7.6 \text{ psia} \qquad s_1 = 0.184 \text{ Btu/lbm-°R}$$

Following up a line of constant entropy to the final specific volume of $0.2/0.2 = 1.0$ ft³/lbm, we find the state 2 corresponding to no entropy produc-

(a) *The rapid compression process forms a shock wave, which is an irreversible phenomenon*

(b) *The shaded band shows the possible final states*

FIG. 7·14

tion (reversible compression, isentropic process) as

$$T_{2s} = 93°F \qquad v_2 = 1.0 \text{ ft}^3/\text{lbm}$$
$$P_{2s} = 47 \text{ psia} \qquad s_{2s} = 0.184 \text{ Btu/lbm-°R}$$

The other possible final states lie along the line of final specific volume, as shown in Fig. 7·14b. Note that we can conclude that the pressure obtained by this process will be at least 47 psia, and possibly greater if the process is irreversible. A first-law analysis could be used to calculate the work required for the compression if state 2 is known. One would find that the *least* amount of work is required when state 2 is state 2s, that is, when the compression process is reversible. This conclusion would be of obvious importance in the design of a freon compressor for a large refrigeration system.

Adiabatic demagnetization. Iron-ammonium alum is placed in a magnetic field **H** of 10,000 gauss at 1°K. The magnetic field is suddenly removed. What is the lowest temperature that can be attained?

We assume the process is adiabatic. Therefore

$$\mathcal{P}_S \equiv S_2 - S_1 \geq 0$$

Looking at Fig. B·13, we see that the final state (2) must lie on the line **H** = 0 to the right of the point where $s = 2.8 \times 10^5$ erg/g-°K. The lowest temperature is therefore obtained with isentropic demagnetization, and is 0.04°K. The actual value of T_2 would be greater (Fig. 7·15).

7·12 EQUIVALENCE OF THE MECHANICAL AND THERMODYNAMIC PRESSURES

We can now show the conditions under which the mechanical and thermodynamic pressures are equal. Consider the control mass of Fig. 7·16. The entropy change of the control mass can be related to the energy and volume changes using the Gibbs equation (7·23), which in extensive form is

$$dS = \frac{1}{T} dU + \frac{P}{T} dV \qquad (7·40)$$

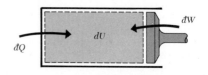

FIG. 7·15 *Adiabatic demagnetization is an effective way to obtain very low temperatures*

FIG. 7·16 *The control mass is a simple compressible substance*

An energy balance on the control mass of Fig. 7·16 gives

$$dU = dQ + dW \tag{7·41}$$

In Chap. Two we derived an expression for the energy transfer as work for fluid compression; there we used the mechanical pressure, which we denote for the moment as P_m. The work done *on* the substance is

$$dW = -P_m \, dV \tag{7·42}$$

Finally, the entropy production is, from Eq. (7·38),

$$d\mathcal{P}_s = \underset{\substack{\text{increase in}\\\text{entropy}\\\text{storage}}}{dS} - \underset{\substack{\text{entropy}\\\text{inflow}}}{\frac{dQ}{T}} \tag{7·43}$$

Using Eq. (7·40) to substitute for dS in Eq. (7·43), and Eq. (7·41) to substitute for dQ, we have

$$d\mathcal{P}_s = \frac{1}{T} \, dU + \frac{P}{T} \, dV - \frac{dU}{T} + \frac{dW}{T} = \frac{P \, dV + dW}{T}$$

Then, using Eq. (7·42), the second law requires

$$d\mathcal{P}_s = \left(\frac{P - P_m}{T}\right) dV \geq 0 \tag{7·44}$$

Now, if the process is reversible the amount of entropy production $d\mathcal{P}_s$ will be zero, and hence we conclude that $P = P_m$ *for a reversible process*. During any such reversible process the control mass must always be in an equilibrium state (otherwise there would be some irreversibility associated with the relaxation toward equilibrium). We conclude that the thermodynamic and mechanical pressures are identical *in any equilibrium state*.

If the process is irreversible, then $d\mathcal{P}_s > 0$, and hence

$$(P - P_m) \, dV > 0$$

If the substance is expanding, doing work, $dV > 0$, and hence $P > P_m$. The pressure measured during an irreversible expansion would therefore be less than the pressure that the system would have in equilibrium at the same energy and volume. Hence less work is done by the system than might be. In contrast, if the substance is being compressed, $dV < 0$, and $P < P_m$. The pressure exerted during compression is therefore greater than the equilibrium pressure. Hence more work must be done on the system than for the reversible process.

A microscopic interpretation will be helpful. Consider the compression of a gas in a piston-cylinder system. If the compression process is very rapid, the molecules will bunch up near the piston, exerting a larger pressure (P_m) than if they were distributed uniformly over the cylinder (P). Hence more

FIG. 7·17 *Work in reversible and irreversible processes*

work will be required for the rapid than for the slow compression. If the piston moves rapidly away from the gas, there will be fewer molecules near the piston than for a slower expansion $(P_m < P)$, and less work will be done by the gas. Figure 7·17 shows an hydraulic analogy that is helpful in grasping these ideas.

7·13 EQUIVALENCE OF THE THERMODYNAMIC AND EMPIRICAL TEMPERATURES

Now that we know $P = P_m$ in any equilibrium state, we can use the fact that the entropy is a function of state, together with certain experimental observations, to establish the correspondence between the thermodynamic and empirical temperature scales. The experimental evidence required is that the gases used in empirical thermometers apparently have the property that at very low pressures their internal energies u and their pressure-volume products depend solely on temperature (they behave like a "perfect gas"). This behavior is also predicted by quantum-statistical thermodynamic theory. The fact that the internal energy becomes a function only of temperature at very low pressures is nicely shown in Figs. B·1 and B·4. Conversely, at low pressures, specification of the internal energy is sufficient to determine the temperature, or the temperature is a function only of the internal energy. Consequently, for gases at sufficiently low pressures, we put

$$T = T(u)$$

Here T denotes the thermodynamic temperature. For the Pv product,

$$Pv = f(T) \tag{7·45}$$

where $f(T)$ represents some unknown function of the thermodynamic temperature.

In an equilibrium state the specific entropy is a function only of the specific internal energy and the specific volume,

$$s = s(u, v)$$

Then, from the calculus

$$\left\{ \frac{\partial[(\partial s/\partial u)_v]}{\partial v} \right\}_u = \left\{ \frac{\partial[(\partial s/\partial v)_u]}{\partial u} \right\}_v$$

Expressed in terms of the thermodynamic temperature and pressure,

$$\left[\frac{\partial(1/T)}{\partial v}\right]_u = \left[\frac{\partial(P/T)}{\partial u}\right]_v$$

Since the temperature of the low-pressure gas is independent of volume along a line of constant internal energy, the term on the left is zero, and consequently

$$\left[\frac{\partial(P/T)}{\partial u}\right]_v = 0$$

We see that P/T is independent of u along a line of constant v. However, since u depends only on T, the ratio P/T must be independent of T along this line. Therefore, we conclude that low-density gases have the property that

$$\left[\frac{\partial(P/T)}{\partial T}\right]_v = 0 \qquad (7\cdot46)$$

Using Eq. (7·45) in Eq. (7·46), we obtain

$$\frac{1}{v}\left[\frac{\partial(f/T)}{\partial T}\right]_v = \frac{1}{v}\frac{d(f/T)}{dT} = 0$$

The ratio $f(T)/T$ must therefore be *a constant*, which means that $f(T)$ must be of the form

$$Pv = f(T) = \text{constant} \times T$$

This is exactly the form that was arbitrarily selected for the empirical temperature; the empirical and thermodynamic temperature scales therefore must coincide, apart from a multiplicative constant. By judicious selection of the constant in the defining equation for the entropy, the two scales can be made identical. Henceforth we shall consider that the thermodynamic and empirical absolute temperatures† are exactly the same.‡

7·14 APPLICATIONS OF THE SECOND LAW TO ENERGY-CONVERSION SYSTEMS

We now have in hand all the tools necessary to study the possibility or limitations of any process imposed by the second law. One of the important areas of application of thermodynamics is in the study of energy-conversion systems. Nature has been generous in providing large sources of energy, but she managed to keep most of it tied up in randomly oriented microscopic forms and left man with the task of devising means for converting this energy to usable macroscopic forms. However, the second law places certain limitations

---

† On the Kelvin or Rankine scales.
‡ A more accurate experimental test of this could be made using the *Clapeyron equation*. This experiment will be discussed in the next chapter.

on the performance of energy-conversion systems; for example, we find that it is not possible to convert all the energy obtained from a nuclear reaction into useful mechanical work. The second law can be used to derive an expression for the maximum possible energy-conversion efficiency for any continuously operating converter, and the same limit holds for both steam power plants and thermoelectric converters. Such sweeping generality is indeed impressive, and very characteristic of thermodynamic theory.

We shall define a *heat engine* as any control mass to and from which energy is transferred as heat and from which energy is transferred as work. We further require that the processes undergone by the matter within the engine be cyclic, or continuous, such that after some period all the matter within the engine has been returned to its initial state.

A special type of heat engine is useful. Any heat engine to which energy is transferred as heat at one temperature and from which energy is transferred at a lower temperature is called a $2T$ *engine* (Fig. 7·18).

There are many ways by which one can devise a $2T$ engine, and it would be well to illustrate one at this point. Suppose we have a piston-cylinder system filled with a gas. By causing this system to excute the four-process cycle, shown schematically in Fig. 7·19, we can obtain work as a result of transfers of energy as heat to and from the engine. The process representation shows the temperature of the gas as a function of the piston position. Observe the cyclic nature of this process. By proper control of the piston displacement, the processes can in principle be carried out in such a way that the gas temperature is constant while energy is being transferred as heat. The processes inside the engine can in principle be made reversible. However, if we tried to reverse the engine (this is then called a heat pump), $T_{A'}$ would have to rise above T_A for there to be a transfer of heat to environment A. But if the process is carried out slowly enough $T_{A'}$ need be only an infinitesimal bit lower than T_A, and $T_{B'}$ only an infinitesimal bit higher than T_B, so that the heat-pump process can, in the limit, be made the exact reverse of the heat-engine process (Fig. 7·20); this we call a *reversible $2T$ engine* (R2T). This particular engine operates on a Carnot cycle and is thus called a *Carnot engine*. The reversible $2T$ engine is, of course, only an idealization, but it is fully as useful in thermodynamic theory as is the frictionless pulley in mechanics.

The *energy-conversion efficiency* of a heat engine is defined as the ratio of the useful work output to the energy input as heat,

$$\blacktriangleright \qquad \eta \equiv \frac{W}{Q_A} \qquad\qquad\qquad (7·47)$$

This ratio will not remain constant when the engine is reversed, except for a reversible $2T$ engine (see Fig. 7·21). Note that no energy-storage terms have been shown in any of these figures. The symbols Q and W are to be interpreted as being "for a cycle," and since the engines operate cyclicly, there is no change in the energy within an engine over a cycle.

FIG. 7·18   *A 2T heat engine*

Isothermal expansion

Adiabatic compression

Adiabatic expansion

Isothermal compression

FIG. 7·19   *A 2T-heat-engine cycle*

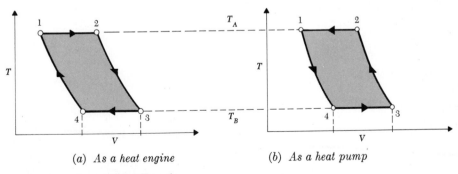

(a) As a heat engine   *(b) As a heat pump*

FIG. 7·20   *A reversible 2T engine*

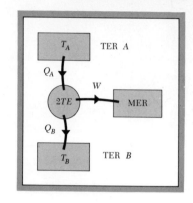

FIG. 7·21 *The efficiency of a reversible 2T heat engine is independent of the direction of operation*

FIG. 7·22 *Determining the efficiency of a 2T engine*

A simple expression for the limiting efficiency of a $2T$ engine can be derived by considering the system of Fig. 7·22. The engine receives energy as heat from a thermal energy reservoir at temperature T_A, and rejects energy as heat to a second TER at T_B. The energy output as work is stored in a mechanical energy reservoir. The combined system is isolated, and the second law says that the entropy of this isolated system can never decrease. Now, since the engine executes a cycle, all matter in the engine returns to its initial state, and hence its entropy is unchanged over one cycle. The MER undergoes no change in entropy. The entropy increases of the two TERs are

$$\Delta S_A = \frac{-Q_A}{T_A} \qquad \Delta S_B = \frac{Q_B}{T_B}$$

and hence the entropy produced when the engine executes one cycle is

$$\mathcal{P}_S = \left(\frac{Q_B}{T_B} - \frac{Q_A}{T_A}\right) \geq 0 \tag{7·48}$$

The equality holds only if the processes within the isolated system are reversible, that is, if the engine is an R2T.

$$\blacktriangleright \qquad \frac{Q_A}{Q_B} = \frac{T_A}{T_B} \qquad \text{for a reversible } 2T \text{ engine} \tag{7·49}$$

Applying the first law over the period of a cycle, we find

$$W = Q_A - Q_B \tag{7·50}$$

so that

$$\blacktriangleright \qquad \eta_{R2T} = \frac{Q_A - Q_B}{Q_A} = \frac{T_A - T_B}{T_A} \qquad \text{for } any \text{ reversible } 2T \text{ engine} \tag{7·51}$$

It is common practice to call this the *Carnot efficiency*, since the Carnot engine is one type of reversible $2T$ engine. However, we have said nothing at all about the nature of the engine, so the expression actually holds for *any* reversible $2T$ engine.

The inequality in Eq. (7·48) pertains to irreversible processes within the engine, that is, to an *irreversible $2T$* engine, for which

$$\frac{Q_B}{Q_A} > \frac{T_B}{T_A} \qquad \text{for } Q_A > 0$$

Thus

▶ $$\eta_{\text{irrev}} = \left(1 - \frac{Q_B}{Q_A}\right) < \left(1 - \frac{T_B}{T_A}\right) = \eta_{\text{Carnot}} \qquad (7\cdot52)$$

The Carnot efficiency is therefore an upper limit for the performance of any real heat engine. Highest efficiencies will be obtained when the ratio T_B/T_A is as small as possible; one would like to add the energy as heat at as high a temperature as possible and reject energy as heat at the lowest possible temperature. However, nature places physical limitations on man's capabilities. The energy which is rejected as heat must flow to an environment which is cooler than T_B; this means that we are limited to T_B of the order of 520°R (60°F). The energy transfer as heat must come into the engine from a region at a temperature greater than T_A. Temperatures of the order of 3500°R can be obtained by combustion reactions, but metallurgical considerations normally require that the device be kept much cooler. Modern steam power plants operate at about 1100°F (not on the Carnot cycle). Advanced nuclear power systems are being designed and tested in the range of 1500–2500°F. These high-temperature systems employ exotic metals and are not intended for long life or for production of low-cost electrical power. At 1500°F the Carnot-cycle efficiency is

$$1 - {}^{520}\!/_{1960} = 0.735$$

Even under such extreme conditions this most ideal cycle could convert only 73.5 percent of the energy transferred in as heat to useful work. Realistic devices of present technology operate in the range of 15–40 percent, and a heat engine having a thermal energy-conversion efficiency of even 50 percent has yet to be built.

It is evident that it would be impossible to devise a 100 percent efficient heat engine even if we really had reversible processes at our disposal. This can be seen by setting $Q_B = 0$ in Eq. (7·48), for we then find that Q_A must also be zero or negative for any cyclicly operating device. A $1T$ engine is therefore impossible, though it is not at all difficult to dream up a continuously operating device to which energy is transferred as work and from which energy is transferred as heat. It is also possible to make a system which will receive energy as heat, converting all this energy to work, but which will

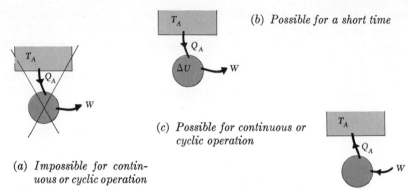

(b) *Possible for a short time*

(c) *Possible for continuous or cyclic operation*

(a) *Impossible for contin- uous or cyclic operation*

FIG. 7·23   *A 1T heat engine is impossible*

not operate indefinitely. For example, we can heat the gas in a piston-cylinder system and allow it to expand, removing the same amount of energy we put in, but eventually we would run out of cylinder, the piston would fall out, and the device would cease to operate. A short-lived converter with 100 percent efficiency is possible, but a continuously operating one is not. The statement that a continuously operating $1T$ engine is impossible is known as the *Kelvin-Planck statement* and is taken as the starting point in many classical developments of the second law. The restrictions placed on heat engines by the second law are illustrated in Fig. 7·23.

The second law also places limitations on systems that continuously transfer energy as heat from a region of low temperature to one of higher temperature (a refrigerator, or a heat pump). In particular, it may easily be shown

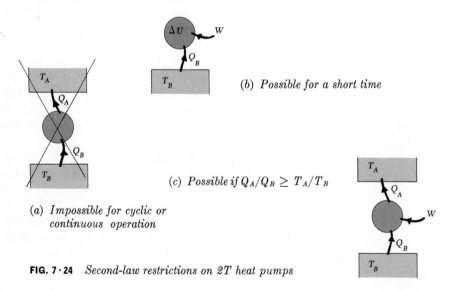

(b) *Possible for a short time*

(c) *Possible if* $Q_A/Q_B \geq T_A/T_B$

(a) *Impossible for cyclic or continuous operation*

FIG. 7·24   *Second-law restrictions on 2T heat pumps*

that it is impossible to devise any system that will do this cyclicly or continuously without any energy input as work. Such a device would constitute a refrigerator which requires no input power, and it certainly seems reasonable that this is an impossibility. However, it is possible to devise a system that will do this for a short time, or to have energy flow through a device from high temperature to low temperature without power input. The restrictions imposed by the second law on heat pumps are illustrated in Fig. 7·24. The statement that a zero-work heat pump is impossible is called the *Clausius statement*, and it too is often taken as the starting point for the development of the second law in classical thermodynamics. Its proof from entropy-production considerations is left as an exercise.

7·15   A REMARK ON THE THERMODYNAMIC TEMPERATURE

The fact that all reversible $2T$ engines operating between the same two temperatures have the same efficiencies can be used in principle to obtain a direct measurement of the thermodynamic temperature. We imagine using any reversible $2T$ engine as a thermometer and letting it operate between the unknown temperature T_A and the H_2O triple-point temperature $T_B \equiv 273.16°K$. We measure the energy transfers Q_A and Q_B and then use Eq. (7·49) to calculate the thermodynamic temperature of the test environment. It is important to appreciate that the thermodynamic temperature scale is independent of the nature of any thermometric substance; we can now look upon the gas thermometer as a means for measuring the thermodynamic temperature rather than as a means for defining an empirical temperature scale.

7·16   THE SECOND LAW FOR A CONTROL VOLUME

We began our discussions of the second law in the last chapter with a postulate that the entropy of an isolated system must never decrease. From this postulate we introduced the notions of entropy inflow and outflow with heat and of entropy production, and showed that the entropy production caused by processes within a control mass could never be less than zero. The entropy of a control mass can, of course, decrease, but only if some energy is removed as heat. We shall now extend these ideas to a control volume, for it is in this form that the second law is most often applied in engineering.

Consider the control volume of Fig. 7·25. We permit energy transfer as heat to take place at various points on the boundary, except where mass crosses the control surface. Energy transfer as work may also occur. For simplicity we assume that there are only the two mass flows shown and that they are one-dimensional at sections 1 and 2. To make the control-volume transformation we consider a control mass which occupies the control volume at time t and examine this control mass over an infinitesimal time interval dt. The change

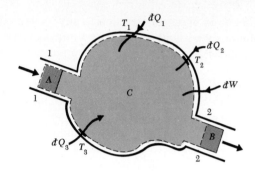

FIG. 7·25   *The control volume*

in its entropy is

$$dS_{CM} = S_{CM}(t + dt) - S_{CM}(t)$$

The entropy within the control mass at time t is exactly the entropy within the control volume at that time, since the two then coincide. The value of $S_{CM}(t + dt)$ can be expressed in terms of the entropy within the control volume at $t + dt$ and the entropies of the shaded portions A and B as

$$S_{CM}(t + dt) = S_{CV}(t + dt) + S_B - S_A$$

The entropies within A and B may be expressed in terms of the specific entropies of the substances flowing across the control surface, and we have

$$S_A = (A\rho\mathsf{V}\, dt)_1 s_1 \qquad S_B = (A\rho\mathsf{V}\, dt)_2 s_2$$

However, the terms $A\rho\mathsf{V}\, dt$ represent the elemental additions and removals of mass from the control volume at the respective sections. Thus

$$dS_{CM} = dS + (s\, dM)_2 - (s\, dM)_1$$

where $dS = S_{CV}(t + dt) - S_{CV}(t)$. The energy transfers as heat $đQ_i$ may now be considered as going to either the control mass or the control volume. The entropy production *for the control mass* is

$$đ\mathcal{P}_S \equiv \left\{ \underbrace{\left[dS + (s\, dM)_2 - (s\, dM)_1 \right]}_{\substack{\text{increase in entropy} \\ \text{within the control mass}}} - \underbrace{\sum_{\text{in}} \frac{đQ_i}{T_i}}_{\substack{\text{entropy} \\ \text{inflow}}} \right\}$$

Note that this equation is written in terms of the properties of the control volume, and hence can be viewed as an expression for the entropy production *for the control volume.*

$$\blacktriangleright \qquad đ\mathcal{P}_S \equiv \left\{ \underbrace{dS}_{\substack{\text{increase in} \\ \text{entropy within} \\ \text{the control} \\ \text{volume}}} + \underbrace{(s\, dM)_2}_{\substack{\text{entropy} \\ \text{outflow}}} - \left[\underbrace{(s\, dM)_1}_{\substack{\text{entropy} \\ \text{inflow}}} + \underbrace{\sum_{\text{in}} \frac{đQ_i}{T_i}}_{} \right] \right\} \qquad (7\cdot53)$$

Note that T_i should be interpreted as the temperature of the control surface at the point where dQ_i enters the control volume. The terms $s\, dM$ represent *convective entropy flow* associated with mass transfer across the boundaries of the control volume. The second law requires that the entropy production be positive,

$$d\mathcal{P}_S \geq 0 \qquad (7\cdot54)$$

For a control volume with several inflows and outflows, the definition of entropy production can readily be extended and expressed on a *rate* basis as

$$\blacktriangleright \qquad \dot{\mathcal{P}}_S \equiv \left\{ \frac{dS}{dt} + \left[\sum_{\text{out}} (s\dot{M}) + \sum_{\text{out}} \frac{\dot{Q}_i}{T_i} \right] - \left[\sum_{\text{in}} (s\dot{M}) + \sum_{\text{in}} \frac{\dot{Q}_i}{T_i} \right] \right\} \qquad (7\cdot55)$$

rate of   rate of   rate of
entropy   entropy   entropy inflow
storage   outflow

Here $\dot{\mathcal{P}}_S$ is the *rate of entropy production* within the control volume. The terms $s\dot{M}$ represent *rates of convective entropy transfer*, and the terms $\dot{Q}/T$ represent *rates of entropy transfer with heat*. The second law requires that the rate of entropy production be positive,

$$\dot{\mathcal{P}}_S \geq 0 \qquad (7.56)$$

The equality is again associated with reversible processes within the control volume, and the inequality with irreversible processes.

7·17 EXAMPLES OF SECOND-LAW ANALYSIS

A solar engine. It is proposed that solar energy be used to warm a large "collector plate"; this energy would, in turn, be transferred as heat to a fluid within a heat engine, and the engine would reject energy as heat to the atmosphere. Experiments indicate that about 200 Btu/hr-ft² of energy can be "collected" when the plate is operating at 190°F. Estimate the minimum collector area that would be required for a plant producing 1 kw of useful shaft power.

We first estimate the maximum energy-conversion efficiency of this system, using the Carnot efficiency as an upper limit. The atmospheric temperature is assumed to be 70°F. Then

$$\eta_{\text{max}} = 1 - \frac{70 + 460}{190 + 460} = 0.184$$

The efficiency of any real heat engine operating between the collector place and atmospheric temperature would be less than this, owing to irreversibilities in real devices. The minimum rate at which energy must be collected is related to the required power output and maximum energy-conversion efficiency,

$$\dot{Q}_{\text{min}} = \frac{\dot{W}}{\eta_{\text{max}}} = \frac{1 \text{ kw}}{0.184} = 5.44 \text{ kw} = 18,600 \text{ Btu/hr}$$

so the minimum area required is

$$A_{\min} = \frac{18,600}{200} = 93 \text{ ft}^2$$

A real system might be expected to need twice or three times this area, since its efficiency would probably be considerably less than 18.4 percent.

A compressor. Freon-12 enters an adiabatic compressor at 30 psia and 40°F and is compressed to 140 psia. What is the shaft-work input per lbm of freon-12 for the best adiabatic compressor which might be devised? See Fig. 7·26.

We make the following idealizations:

Steady flow steady state
Kinetic and potential energy changes negligible

An energy balance allows us to relate the work input per unit of mass W to the enthalpy rise across the compressor,

$$W = h_2 - h_1$$

The second law requires that the entropy production be positive. Since we have assumed that steady-flow steady-state conditions prevail, the entropy within the control volume is not changing, and because of our adiabatic idealization, no entropy flows with heat across the boundary. Only the convected entropy flows are involved, so we have

$$\dot{\Phi}_S = \dot{M}(s_2 - s_1) \geq 0$$
net rate of
entropy outflow

which yields

$$s_2 - s_1 \geq 0$$

The entropy of the fluid must increase as it passes through the device. This means that the outlet state must lie to the right of state $2s$ on the P-h diagram

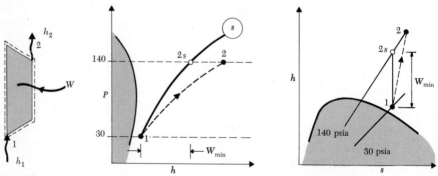

(a) *The control volume*   (b) *The process representation*

FIG. 7·26   *Compressor analysis*

of Fig. 7·26b (see Fig. B·7). It is evident that the least enthalpy change, that is, the least work input, is required by a device in which there is no entropy production. This work is $h_{2s} - h_1$, and its magnitude can be fixed with the aid of Fig. B·7. Denoting the work required by this ideal isentropic compressor by W_s, we find

$$W_s = h_{2s} - h_1 = 96 - 83 = 13 \text{ Btu/lbm}$$

The work required by a real irreversible adiabatic compressor would be greater than W_s. It is customary to define the *isentropic efficiency* of a compressor as

$$\blacktriangleright \qquad \eta_s = \frac{\text{work required by ideal isentropic compressor}}{\text{work required by actual compressor}} = \frac{W_s}{W_{\text{act}}}$$

Note that the isentropic efficiency compares an actual process to an ideal process and is not an energy-conversion efficiency. Both the actual and ideal devices are assumed to have the same inlet state and the same discharge pressure. A typical value for η_s might be 0.90. Then

$$W_{\text{act}} = \frac{W_s}{\eta_s} = \frac{13}{0.90} = 14 \text{ Btu/lbm}$$

The actual discharge enthalpy would be

$$h_2 = h_1 + W_{\text{act}} = 83 + 14 = 97 \text{ Btu/lbm}$$

This value, together with the discharge pressure, suffices to determine the discharge state.

An inventor's claim. An inventor claims to have devised a steady-flow compressor which requires no shaft-power input. He claims that CO_2 at 200 psia and 120°F can be compressed to 300 psia, where it will emerge at 20°F, simply by a transfer of energy as heat from his device. His patent application states that the device will handle 2 lbm of CO_2 per sec and is driven by a "cold

(b) *The process representation*

(a) *The control volume*

FIG. 7·27   *Analysis of the inventor's claim*

source" at $-140°F$. Energy is transferred as heat from this device to the cold space at the rate of 60 Btu/sec. He further states that the CO_2 enters and leaves the device at very low velocity, and that no significant elevation changes are involved. Could his claims be valid?

The device will be impossible if it violates either the first or second laws of thermodynamics. According to his claims, we may neglect kinetic and potential energies in the fluid streams and assume that steady-flow steady-state conditions prevail. We further assume that the flows are one-dimensional at the inlet and exit and that the CO_2 is in equilibrium states at these points. From Fig. B·6 we read the following:

$$T_1 = 120°F \qquad\qquad T_2 = 20°F$$
$$P_1 = 200 \text{ psia} \qquad\quad P_2 = 300 \text{ psia}$$
$$h_1 = 318 \text{ Btu/lbm} \qquad h_2 = 288 \text{ Btu/lbm}$$
$$s_1 = 1.315 \text{ Btu/lbm-°R} \quad s_2 = 1.240 \text{ Btu/lbm-°R}$$

An energy balance on the control volume, on a rate basis, gives

$$\dot{M}(h_2 - h_1) + \dot{Q} = 2 \times (288 - 318) + 60 = 0 \text{ Btu/sec}$$

His device is not an energy producer, so it does not violate the first law.

The entropy-production rate for the control volume is

$$\dot{\mathcal{P}}_S = \underbrace{\dot{M}(s_2 - s_1)}_{\substack{\text{net convective} \\ \text{entropy-outflow} \\ \text{rate}}} + \underbrace{\frac{\dot{Q}}{T_c}}_{\substack{\text{rate of} \\ \text{entropy outflow} \\ \text{with heat}}}$$

where T_c is the temperature of the cold space ($-140°F = 320°R$). Then

$$\dot{\mathcal{P}}_S = 2 \times (1.240 - 1.315) + \frac{60}{320} = -0.150 + 0.188 = +0.038 \text{ Btu/°R-sec}$$

The rate of entropy production is indeed positive, so his device does not violate the second law. We conclude that it is theoretically possible.

The availability of energy in a steady-flow device. A fluid enters a device at state 1 and emerges at state 2. The device can communicate with a large environment at temperature T_0, from which it can obtain energy as heat. What is the maximum available power output from this device?

This type of problem falls in the general area of *availability analysis*, a technique of great interest in advanced applied thermodynamics courses. The general approach here is to apply the first and second laws, thereby obtaining an upper limit on the amount of power which could be obtained from a device, given the inlet and discharge states.

The system we consider is shown in Fig. 7·28. We allow it to extract energy as heat from the environment at the rate $\dot{Q}_0$, and presume that it puts

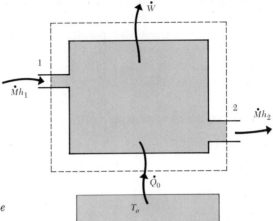

FIG. 7·28 *The control volume for the availability analysis*

out useful work at the rate $\dot{W}$. Assuming steady flow, steady state, and neglecting kinetic or potential energy of the flow streams, the first law analysis yields

$$\underset{\substack{\text{energy-inflow}\\\text{rate}}}{\dot{M}h_1 + \dot{Q}_0} = \underset{\substack{\text{energy-outflow}\\\text{rate}}}{\dot{M}h_2 + \dot{W}}$$

The entropy-production rate for the control volume is

$$\dot{\mathscr{P}}_S = \underset{\substack{\text{entropy-}\\\text{outflow}\\\text{rate}}}{\dot{M}s_2} - \underset{\substack{\text{entropy-inflow}\\\text{rate}}}{\left(\dot{M}s_1 + \frac{\dot{Q}_0}{T_0}\right)}$$

and the second law requires that $\dot{\mathscr{P}}_S \geq 0$. Combining the first and second equations, we have

$$\dot{M}(s_2 - s_1) - \frac{1}{T_0}[\dot{M}(h_2 - h_1) + \dot{W}] \geq 0$$

So,

$$\dot{W} \leq \dot{M}[(h - T_0s)_1 - (h - T_0s)_2]$$

The function $h - T_0s$ is called the *steady-flow availability function;* note that it is a function of both the fluid and the environment. The availability analysis tells us that the work output per lbm of fluid, $\dot{W}/\dot{M}$, cannot exceed the decrease in the availability function. If the equality holds, the processes within the control volume must all be reversible, including the energy-transfer process between the device and the environment at T_0. The maximum work output is therefore obtained for a *reversible* process.

The difference between the maximum possible useful work output and the actual work output is sometimes called the *irreversibility* of the process. In the analysis of complex engineering systems one can locate the primary sources of irreversibility, which all cost money, by calculating the amount of irreversibility associated with each component in the system or each step in the process. Efforts to improve performance can then be concentrated in areas where the greatest gains stand to be made. The student who goes on to more advanced courses in applied thermodynamics will likely find considerable use for this sort of availability-irreversibility analysis.

7·18 A SUMMARY OF THE FIRST AND SECOND LAWS

At this point it would be a good idea to summarize the working expressions for the basic laws, lest there be any confusion about what is applicable only to an isolated system or only to a control mass. The formalism of production is convenient and easy to recall; in general, *production* is defined as follows:

Production equals the increase in the amount stored within the system plus the excess of amount which flows out over that which flows in.

Similarly, the *rate of production* of something is defined as follows:

Rate of production equals the rate of increase in the amount stored within the system plus the excess of the outflow rate over the inflow rate.

We applied the production concept in formulating the mathematics of the second law; we stated that entropy can be produced but never destroyed. The formalism is equally useful in stating the ideas of the first law, for energy can be neither produced nor destroyed. We can therefore state the first and second laws of thermodynamics in a very compact and physically appealing way; for an infinitesimal process,

$$\blacktriangleright \quad d\mathcal{P}_E = 0 \tag{7·57}$$
$$\blacktriangleright \quad d\mathcal{P}_S \geq 0 \tag{7·58}$$

Alternatively, on a rate basis,

$$\blacktriangleright \quad \dot{\mathcal{P}}_E = 0 \tag{7·59}$$
$$\blacktriangleright \quad \dot{\mathcal{P}}_S \geq 0 \tag{7·60}$$

Table 7·1, a summary of these ideas for an isolated system, a control mass, and a control volume, uses the notation $\mathcal{K}$ for entropy transfer with heat,

$$\blacktriangleright \quad d\mathcal{K} \equiv \frac{dQ}{T} \tag{7·61}$$

Here dQ is an energy transfer as heat to the system under study and is received by the system at a point on the boundary where its temperature is T. The notation d is used, since $d\mathcal{K}$ represents an infinitesimal amount of entropy transfer with heat and does not, in general, represent the change of a property.

TABLE 7·1 SUMMARY OF THE WORKING FORMS OF THE FIRST AND SECOND LAWS

	First law	*Second law*
Basic principle	$đ\mathcal{P}_E = 0$ $\dot{\mathcal{P}}_E = 0$	$đ\mathcal{P}_S \geq 0$ $\dot{\mathcal{P}}_S \geq 0$
Isolated system 	$đ\mathcal{P}_E = dE$	$đ\mathcal{P}_S = dS$
Control mass 	$đ\mathcal{P}_E = dE - đQ - đW$	$đ\mathcal{P}_S = dS - đ\mathcal{K}$
Control volume 	$\dot{\mathcal{P}}_E = \dfrac{dE}{dt} - \dot{W} - \dot{Q}$ $+ \displaystyle\sum_{\text{out}} (e + Pv)\dot{M}$ $- \displaystyle\sum_{\text{in}} (e + Pv)\dot{M}$	$\dot{\mathcal{P}}_S = \dfrac{dS}{dt} - \displaystyle\sum_{\text{in}} \dot{\mathcal{K}}$ $+ \displaystyle\sum_{\text{out}} s\dot{M} - \displaystyle\sum_{\text{in}} s\dot{M}$

Note: $e \equiv u + \dfrac{V^2}{2g_c} + \dfrac{g_g}{g_c}z + Q\mathcal{E} + \cdots$ $đ\mathcal{K} \equiv \dfrac{đQ}{T}$ $\dot{\mathcal{K}} \equiv \dfrac{\dot{Q}}{T}$

SELECTED READING

Callen, H. B., *Thermodynamics*, secs. 1.1, 1.9, 2.4, 2.5, 2.7, John Wiley & Sons, Inc., New York, 1960.

Reif, F., *Fundamentals of Statistical and Thermal Physics*, secs. 3.5, 3.6, 3.10–3.12, McGraw-Hill Book Company, New York, 1965.

Tribus, M., *Thermostatics and Thermodynamics*, chap. 5, D. Van Nostrand Company, Inc., Princeton, N.J., 1961.

Van Wylen, G. J., and R. E. Sonntag, *Fundamentals of Classical Thermodynamics*, secs. 6.4, 6.7, 7.8, 7.9, 7.12, 7.13, chap. 8, John Wiley & Sons, Inc., New York, 1965.

QUESTIONS

7·1 What is the conceptual basis and definition of the thermodynamic temperature?

7·2 Is $-10°F$ a negative thermodynamic temperature?

7·3 Which have meaning in nonequilibrium states, which do not, and why: temperature, energy, entropy?

7·4 Suppose a substance could exist in equilibrium at negative temperatures; what would this mean with regard to the energy and entropy (on a microscopic scale)?

7·5 What is the thermodynamic definition of pressure?

7·6 What is a reversible process?

7·7 How is heat different from work?

7·8 What is an irreversible process?

7·9 One reversible $2T$ engine uses mercury as the working fluid, and another uses steam. When operating between the same two temperatures, how will their efficiencies compare?

7·10 Think of a device which receives energy as heat, rejects energy as work (these are the only energy transfers), yet does not violate the Kelvin-Planck statement.

7·11 Does a $1T$ engine violate the first law, the second law, or both?

7·12 What is entropy production? What is entropy inflow with heat?

7·13 Under what conditions will the entropy change of matter undergoing an adiabatic process be zero?

7·14 Suppose the thermodynamic temperature had been defined as $(\partial s/\partial u)_v$. Which way would heat flow, and would positive or negative temperatures be of most interest?

7·15 Give a qualitative microscopic explanation for the entropy change of a gas which undergoes reversible adiabatic expansion.

7·16 Give a qualitative microscopic explanation for the entropy change of a paramagnetic salt which undergoes reversible adiabatic magnetization.

7·17 What will happen to the entropy, energy, and temperature of a gas which is polarized reversibly and adiabatically at constant volume?

7·18 Under what circumstances would measurements of energy transfer as heat and temperature allow you to deduce the change in entropy of a control mass?

7·19 What happens to the entropy produced in a steady-flow steady-state system?

7·20 What is entropy?

PROBLEMS

7·1 Calculate the thermodynamic temperature of saturated water vapor at 100 psia from the u-s-v data in Appendix B and compare the result with the empirical temperature at this state.

7·2 Using the data on Fig. B·12, calculate the thermodynamic temperature for the paramagnetic substance iron-ammonium alum when M = 70 gauss and H = 1000 gauss and compare your result with that given by Fig. B·12.

7·3 Calculate the thermodynamic pressure for saturated water vapor at 100°F and compare your result with the tabulated saturation pressure at this state.

7·4 Derive the analog of Eq. (7·13) for a simple magnetic substance.

7·5 Using the method of Lagrange multipliers, show that the conditions for equilibrium for N interacting but independent pieces of simple compressible substances are that their temperatures and pressures all be identical.

7·6 Consider a control mass which executes a cycle, returning to its initial state. Prove that if dQ inflow is positive,

$$\oint \frac{dQ}{T} \leq 0$$

(This is the *inequality of Clausius*, and is an important intermediate theorem in classical developments of the second law.)

7·7 Consider two interacting systems, one at a negative T and the other at a positive T. Show that any energy transfer as heat will take place from the system at negative T to the one at positive T, and hence the negative T state is "hotter."

7·8 Consider two interacting systems at negative T. Show that any energy transfer as heat will take place from the system at the least negative value of T to the one at a more negative value of T. Which state is the "hotter"?

7·9 It has been proposed that energy be taken as heat from the atmosphere around Chicago and used to run a power plant. Energy would be rejected as heat to Lake Michigan. Estimate the maximum efficiency of conversion of thermal energy to electrical power which could be obtained in such a plant.

7·10 An inventor claims to have perfected an engine which will produce power from energy transferred as heat from a 1000°F flame. Energy will be rejected as heat to the ground at 60°F. He claims a 75 percent energy-conversion efficiency. As chief patent officer, would you issue him a patent, and if so, would you invest money in his operation?

7·11 An inventor claims his device is able to convert to work all energy transferred to it as heat, but he makes no claims as to how long his device will work. Could it work at all?

7·12 An inventor claims to have a device which receives 1000 watts of energy as heat but puts out only 750 watts of electrical power. The rest of the energy is put out as mechanical work and dissipated outside his device by friction. Discuss the validity of these claims.

7·13 Thermal power systems for use in space normally reject energy as heat by radiating to space. Since fluid-filled radiators are generally quite heavy, it has been suggested that this energy be converted to electricity and the current run through lighter resistors to dissipate the energy as heat. What do you think of this idea? Energy transfer as heat from a space vehicle must take place by radiation. The weight of a space radiator is proportional to its area, which is determined by the rate at which the energy must be radiated as heat; the rate of energy radiation is proportional to the product of area and the fourth power of the radiator temperature. Consider a reversible $2T$ engine giving a fixed amount of power and operating with fixed source temperature. Show that the least radiator weight is obtained when the radiator temperature is 0.75 times the source temperature.

7·14 The amount of solar energy received at the earth's surface is approximately 420 Btu/hr-ft². Not all of this energy can be used in a solar power plant because of the reradiation of energy by the collector surface. Assume that the reradiation is described by $\dot{Q} = A\sigma\epsilon T^4$, where A is the collector area, $\epsilon = 0.5$, and $\sigma = 1.71 \times 10^{-9}$ Btu/hr-ft^2-°R^4 is the Stefan-Boltzmann constant. Find the maximum collector surface temperature (at which all the incident solar energy is reradiated). Suppose the power plant has the Carnot efficiency. If T_0 is the environmental temperature to which energy is rejected as heat, and T_c is the collector temperature, at what temperature of T_c should the system operate to achieve the most power output with a collector of fixed size $(T_0 \approx 80°F)$?

7·15 Examine the examples in Sec. 5·2. Indicate which processes might be reasonably idealized as reversible and which are inherently irreversible.

7·16 Determine the amount of entropy production by the control mass of the thermal-mixing example in Sec. 5·2.

7·17 Calculate the entropy-production rate for the control volume of the nozzle example in Sec. 5·4 if $\dot{M} = 10,000$ lbm/hr.

7·18 Calculate the rate of entropy production for the heat-exchanger example in Sec. 5·4.

7·19 Mercury flows through an adiabatic device. At one end the mercury is a saturated vapor at 400°F, and at the other end it is a mixture of 0.30 quality at 40 psia. The flow rate is 10 lbm/sec. Determine the rate at which energy is transferred to the device as work (power input or output) and the direction of flow. Kinetic and potential energies are negligible.

7·20 Calculate the maximum possible output power (kw) from an adiabatic steam turbine handling 10 lbm/sec, where the inlet state is 100 psia at 500°F and the discharge pressure is 1 atm.

7·21 Mercury enters a small adiabatic turbine as a saturated vapor at 1200°F and is discharged at 100 psia. Determine the minimum possible quality of the discharge stream.

7·22 Determine the lowest temperature that could be obtained by adiabatic demagnetization of iron-ammonium alum (Fig. B·12) if the applied field **H** were suddenly dropped from 10,000 gauss to zero, assuming that the initial temperature is 2°K.

7·23 Devise a Carnot power cycle to operate with iron-ammonium alum, receiving energy at 2°K and rejecting energy at 1°K. State the processes that make up this cycle, and give a symbolic energy analysis of each process. What is the cycle efficiency?

7·24 Steam enters an adiabatic diffuser at 1200 ft/sec as a saturated vapor at 60 psia. What is the maximum possible discharge pressure?

7·25 Freon-12 enters an adiabatic nozzle at 100 psia, 120°F, and emerges at 10 psia. What is the maximum possible discharge velocity?

7·26 Compute the maximum amount of work that could be obtained from each lbm of freon-12 if the valve of Fig. 5·16 were replaced by an adiabatic turbine. Why is the valve usually used?

7·27 Compute the maximum percent liquifaction (by mass) of O_2 that can be achieved by expanding it adiabatically in a piston-cylinder system from the saturated vapor state at 10 atm to twice the volume.

7·28 Compute the minimum amount of power required by an adiabatic compressor that handles 10 lbm/min of freon-12, compressing it from −20°F, 10 psia to 60 psia.

7·29 Calculate the amount of useful power output which could be obtained from each component of the heat pump system of Fig. 5·16, assuming that the components were replaced by devices which keep the inlet and discharge states the same, and that the replacement components can interact with an environment at 60°F. Which components are the most costly in terms of the available energy which they "waste?" Where do you think that efforts should be spent on design improvements in order to realize the most appreciable gain?

CHAPTER EIGHT

THE
THERMODYNAMICS
OF STATE

8·1 INTRODUCTION

We now have the fundamental tools for thermodynamic analysis of engineering systems: the first law and second law. However, little quantitative work can be done without specific knowledge of state of the working substances. Therefore, before we analyze more complex systems we must spend some time on properties and the relations between properties.

Over the years a considerable body of equation-of-state information has been obtained by careful laboratory measurements, and these data are extremely important to the analyst. However, experiments are time-consuming and costly, and frequently we cannot wait for the availability of extensive data on a substance of interest. The first and second laws themselves can be extremely helpful in constructing a complete equation of state from a limited amount of data. Furthermore, thermodynamic theory is needed to provide relationships between the properties, so that those which are not directly measurable can be deduced. In this chapter we shall develop some of the more important relations between the intensive thermodynamic properties of some simple substances and indicate how these are used in building equations of state from basic laboratory data.

Equations of state can also be obtained from microscopic theories such as those of quantum-statistical mechanics, if a correct model is employed.† Relationships between the properties, derived by applications of the first and second laws, are essential in order to connect the results of these theories with measurable quantities.

8·2 THE GIBBS EQUATION

The equations of state may be expressed functionally in terms of the properties considered to be independent. In particular, for the simple com-

    † Figure B·12 was obtained in this manner.

pressible substance† we can put

$$s = s(u, v)$$

Taking the differential,

$$ds = \left(\frac{\partial s}{\partial u}\right)_v du + \left(\frac{\partial s}{\partial v}\right)_u dv$$

Then, using the thermodynamic definitions of temperature and pressure, we find

$$\blacktriangleright \qquad ds = \frac{1}{T} du + \frac{P}{T} dv \qquad (8 \cdot 1)$$

This is the *Gibbs equation*, which we derived in the same manner in the previous chapter. It is a differential equation of state which is extremely important in the thermodynamic theory of simple compressible substances. Since it relates the difference in the entropy between any two infinitesimally separated states to the infinitesimal differences in internal energy and volume between those states, the difference in entropy between two states can be found by integration,

$$s_2 - s_1 = \int_{u_1}^{u_2} \frac{du}{T} + \int_{v_1}^{v_2} \frac{P}{T} dv \qquad (8 \cdot 2)$$

In analyses not involving chemical reaction only the differences in entropy are involved. Consequently, we can select some state arbitrarily and refer the entropy for that substance to its value in this datum state. The charts and tables in Appendix B employ a variety of datum states. Having selected the datum state, we may perform the integrations of Eq. $(8 \cdot 2)$ from that point to any other state along any convenient path in the u-v plane. An illustration showing one simple integration is included in Sec. $7 \cdot 6$. Graphical or numerical integrations are usually employed, and we must, of course, know T and P as functions of u and v in order to perform the integration. In this manner we can determine the entropy of any substance, relative to the datum state.

Knowing the specific entropy of a substance as a function of the thermodynamic state, we can put lines of constant entropy on the graphical equations of state and enter values for the entropy in the tables. We can also use the entropy as a coordinate on a graphical equation of state; such graphs are particularly convenient in engineering analysis, especially where reversible adiabatic (isentropic, or constant-entropy) processes are involved. The temperature-entropy diagram is of special importance, for the area under a curve tracing out a reversible process on a T-s plane represents the energy transfer

† Remember that the simple compressible substance is one in which the only relevant reversible work mode is compression. The state postulate tells us that the thermodynamic state of a simple compressible substance is completely determined by specification of two independent thermodynamic properties.

$$Q_{12} = \int_{1 \atop \text{rev}}^{2} T\,ds$$

FIG. 8·1 *The area under a reversible process path on the T-s plane is the energy addition as heat for the process*

as heat to a unit of mass of the substance for the process (Fig. 8·1). Extensive use is made of T-s planes in engineering for both quantitative analysis and qualitative portrayal. We shall illustrate some of these ideas in numerical examples after we have developed some further relations between properties.

8·3 EQUATION OF STATE FOR THE PERFECT GAS

The *perfect gas*† is defined as any gas whose P-v-T relationship is of the form

▶ $$Pv = RT \qquad\qquad (8·3)$$

The gas constant R is related to the *universal gas constant* $\Re$ and the molal mass $\hat{M}$ by

▶ $$R = \frac{\Re}{\hat{M}} \qquad\qquad (8·4)$$

$\Re$ has the experimentally determined value

▶ $$\Re = 1545 \text{ ft-lbf/lbmole-}°\text{R}$$

The Boltzmann constant k is defined in terms of $\Re$ and Avogadro's number N_0 by

▶ $$k = \frac{\Re}{N_0} \qquad\qquad (8·5)$$

Sometimes k is called the gas constant per molecule. Values of $\hat{M}$ and R for several gases are given in Table B·6.

It is very important to realize that the idea of a perfect gas is an idealization to *real-gas* behavior. Thus the behavior of a real gas, such as air, will only be approximated by the perfect-gas equation.

A commonly employed microscopic model of the perfect, or ideal, gas is that the gas molecules consist of infinitesimally small, hard round spheres that take up negligible volume and that do not exert forces on one another except

† The student may wish to review the brief discussion of the perfect gas in Sec. 4·8.

FIG. 8·2 *In the ideal gas model the molecules are far apart and interact only upon collision*

upon collision. This model ignores both the finite volume that the molecules do in fact occupy and also the actual intermolecular forces that the molecules exert on each other at long range.

Under what conditions would we expect the above assumptions to be valid? If the molecules are far apart on the average, then there should be little long-range interaction. In addition, the molecules will not occupy much of the total volume. The molecules will be far apart when the gas has a low density, which corresponds to conditions of *low pressure* and *high temperature* (Fig. 8·2).

Just what pressure and temperature give ideal-gas behavior depends on the gas and the amount of deviation from Eq. (8·3) that one will accept. Figure 8·3 shows the deviation from perfect-gas behavior for several gases. Note that for the same pressure a higher temperature reduces the deviation from perfect-gas behavior.

The defining equation $Pv = RT$ can be put in other useful forms. If M is the mass of a sample of gas occupying volume V, multiplication by the mass yields

▶ $$PV = MRT \tag{8·6}$$

FIG. 8·3 *Test of the perfect-gas approximation for several gases (by permission from P. M. Morse, Thermal Physics, rev. ed., W. A. Benjamin, Inc., New York, 1964).*

Denoting the number of moles of the gas by $\mathfrak{N}$ and observing that the mass M is related to the number of moles and the molal mass $\hat{M}$ by

▶ $M = \mathfrak{N}\hat{M}$

we can express Eq. (8·6) as

▶ $PV = \mathfrak{N}\hat{M}RT = \mathfrak{N}\mathfrak{R}T$ (8·7)

Other forms are given in Table 8·1.

TABLE 8·1 FORMS OF THE PERFECT-GAS EQUATION

$Pv = RT$	R = particular gas constant
$Pv = \dfrac{\mathfrak{R}}{\hat{M}}T$	$\mathfrak{R}$ = universal gas constant
	$\hat{M}$ = molal mass, lb/lbmole
$P\hat{v} = \mathfrak{R}T$	$\hat{v} = \hat{M}v$, ft³/lbmole
$PV = \mathfrak{N}\mathfrak{R}T$	V = volume of $\mathfrak{N}$ lbmoles
$PV = MRT$	V = volume of M lbm

In Chap. Seven we showed that the thermodynamic and empirical (perfect-gas) temperatures were identical, using the additional information that the internal energy of gases used in empirical thermometers depends only on temperature as P approaches zero. It may easily be shown that the internal energy u of any substance obeying Eq. (8·3) is a function only of temperature. One proof can be made starting directly from the Gibbs equation,

$$ds = \frac{1}{T}\,du + \frac{P}{T}\,dv$$

Then, since ds is exact,

$$\left(\frac{\partial(1/T)}{\partial v}\right)_u = \left(\frac{\partial(P/T)}{\partial u}\right)_v = \left(\frac{\partial(R/v)}{\partial u}\right)_v = 0$$

T is therefore independent of v along any line of constant u, and consequently $T = T(u)$, or $u = u(T)$.

The differential of u is also expressible solely in terms of temperature changes. Recalling the definition of the specific heat at constant volume, we have

$$du = c_v\,dT \qquad\qquad (8·8)$$

Since u depends only on T, c_v must be a function only of temperature,

$$c_v = c_v(T)$$

The enthalpy is also a function only of temperature, since

▶ $h = u + Pv = u(T) + RT = h(T)$

Following the previous line of argument, we can show that

$$dh = c_P \, dT \tag{8·9}$$
$$c_P = c_P(T)$$

The differential equation for the entropy is the Gibbs equation,

$$ds = \frac{du}{T} + \frac{P}{T} \, dv = \frac{c_v}{T} \, dT + R \, \frac{dv}{v} \tag{8·10}$$

Alternatively, using $dh = du + P \, dv + v \, dP$,

$$ds = \frac{dh}{T} - \frac{v}{T} \, dP = \frac{c_P}{T} \, dT - R \, \frac{dP}{P} \tag{8·11}$$

We may now integrate these differential equations of state. Integrating Eq. (8·8),

$$\blacktriangleright \qquad u_2 - u_1 = \int_{T_1}^{T_2} c_v(T) \, dT \tag{8·12}$$

Integrating Eq. (8·9),

$$\blacktriangleright \qquad h_2 - h_1 = \int_{T_1}^{T_2} c_P(T) \, dT \tag{8·13}$$

Equations (8·10) and (8·11) integrate to give

$$\blacktriangleright \qquad s_2 - s_1 = \int_{T_1}^{T_2} \frac{c_v(T)}{T} \, dT + R \ln \frac{v_2}{v_1} \tag{8·14}$$

$$\blacktriangleright \qquad s_2 - s_1 = \int_{T_1}^{T_2} \frac{c_P(T)}{T} \, dT - R \ln \frac{P_2}{P_1} \tag{8·15}$$

In order to carry the algebraic equations of state further it would be necessary to know how the specific heats varied with temperature. An important relation between the specific heats is

$$\blacktriangleright \qquad c_P - c_v = R \tag{8·16}$$

which may easily be shown from Eqs. (8·3), (8·8), and (8·9). It is therefore necessary to determine only one of c_v or c_P for any ideal gas, and since c_P is more easily measured it is customary to work with c_P. Figure B·17 shows c_P and c_v for several gases. The curves labeled $P = 0$ correspond to the perfect-gas approximation, and could be used in the equations above.

An approximate equation that fits the experimental data over any fairly wide temperature range is

$$c_P = a + bT + cT^2$$

a, b, and c are experimentally determined coefficients. Table B·16 gives values for several gases. These equations fit the data with an average deviation of better than 1 percent and a maximum deviation of about 2 percent over the temperature range indicated.

It is convenient to define a property ϕ by

$$\phi(T) = \int_{T_0}^{T} \frac{c_P(T)}{T} \, dT \tag{8·17}$$

where T_0 is some reference temperature and ϕ is a function of temperature only. Using Eq. 8·15, one may express the entropy as:

▶ $$s_2 - s_1 = \phi_2 - \phi_1 - R \ln \frac{P_2}{P_1} \tag{8·18}$$

Values of the enthalpy and the property ϕ as functions of temperature have been obtained from measurements on many gases,† and a tabulation of these properties for air‡ is given in Table B·9. $T_0 = 0°R$ forms the datum for these compilations. Note that the simple quadratic variation of c_P is invalid as $T \to 0$, so the lower portion of the integration for $\phi(T)$ must be performed using other, more accurate, expressions.

The function $\phi(T)$ allows one to calculate the dependence of the entropy on T. In the air tables (Table B·9), the *reduced pressure* p_r and *reduced volume* v_r are defined as

$$\ln p_r \equiv \frac{\phi(T)}{R} \tag{8·19}$$

$$\ln v_r \equiv -\frac{1}{R} \int_{T_0}^{T} \frac{c_v}{T} \, dT \tag{8·20}$$

Note that both are dimensionless quantities and are functions of T only.

The reduced pressure is particularly useful in the analysis of isentropic processes. Setting the entropy difference to zero in Eq. (8·18), we obtain

$$\ln \frac{P_2}{P_1} = \frac{\phi_2 - \phi_1}{R} \qquad \text{for an isentropic process}$$

In terms of the reduced pressures, the right-hand side becomes

$$\ln p_{r_2} - \ln p_{r_1} = \ln \frac{p_{r_2}}{p_{r_1}}$$

and consequently we see that

$$\frac{P_2}{P_1} = \frac{p_{r_2}}{p_{r_1}} \qquad \text{for an isentropic process} \tag{8·21}$$

Similarly it may be shown that

$$\frac{v_2}{v_1} = \frac{v_{r_2}}{v_{r_1}} \qquad \text{for an isentropic process} \tag{8·22}$$

---

† See, for example, J. Keenan and J. Kaye, *Gas Tables*, John Wiley & Sons, Inc., New York, 1948.

‡ Air at low pressures may be treated as a mixture of perfect gases. In Chap. Ten we shall show that any such mixture behaves like a perfect gas.

FIG. 8·4 *The reduced pressure ratio is the same as the pressure ratio for an isentropic process*

To illustrate the use of the reduced pressure, suppose we want to compress air at 60°F isentropically from 1 atm to 5 atm, and need to know the final temperature (see Fig. 8·4). From Table B·9, at 60°F $p_r = 1.215$. Then

$$\frac{p_{r_2}}{p_{r_1}} = \frac{P_2}{P_1} = \frac{5}{1}$$

$$p_{r_2} = 6.08$$

Reading in Table B·9 for $p_r = 6.08$, we see that the final temperature is slightly greater than 360°F.

A simplified form of the perfect-gas equation of state is obtained if c_P is constant. For this special case it follows from Eq. (8·16) that c_v is also constant, and the equations of state are as follows for a perfect gas with constant specific heats:†

▶ $$Pv = RT \tag{8·23}$$

▶ $$u_2 - u_1 = c_v(T_2 - T_1) \tag{8·24}$$

▶ $$h_2 - h_1 = c_P(T_2 - T_1) \tag{8·25}$$

▶ $$s_2 - s_1 = c_v \ln \frac{T_2}{T_1} + R \ln \frac{v_2}{v_1} \tag{8·26}$$

▶ $$s_2 - s_1 = c_P \ln \frac{T_2}{T_1} - R \ln \frac{P_2}{P_1} \tag{8·27}$$

▶ $$s_2 - s_1 = c_P \ln \frac{v_2}{v_1} + c_v \ln \frac{P_2}{P_1} \tag{8·28}$$

▶ $$c_P - c_v = R \tag{8·29}$$

It is important to remember that these equations pertain only to *a perfect gas with constant specific heats*. They are especially useful in gas dynamics, where neat closed-form algebraic expressions for the properties of a one-dimensional gas-flow field can be derived.

To illustrate the use of these simplified equations, let's recompute the temperature rise for isentropic compression of air from 1 atm, 60°F, to 5 atm.

† Equation (8·28) follows from a combination of Eqs. (8·27) and (8·23).

Using Eq. (8·27), we set $s_1 = s_2$, and have

$$\frac{T_2}{T_1} = \left(\frac{P_2}{P_1}\right)^{R/c_P} = \left(\frac{P_2}{P_1}\right)^{(k-1)/k}$$

For air $k = 1.4$, and hence

$$\frac{T_2}{T_1} = \left(\frac{5}{1}\right)^{0.286} = 1.583$$

Then, with $T_1 = 520°R$,

$$T_2 = 1.583 \times 520 = 824°R$$

Recall that the gas table calculation of the previous example predicted a final temperature of 360°F, or 820°R. The slight difference represents the error associated with the assumption of constant specific heats.

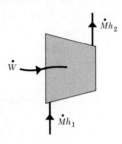

FIG. 8·5   *Adiabatic compressor analysis*

We could compute the work required to carry out the compression process. If it takes place in an adiabatic steady-flow compressor (Fig. 8·5), then an energy balance gives

$$\dot{W} = \dot{M}(h_2 - h_1)$$

Then, using Eq. (8·25),

$$\frac{\dot{W}}{\dot{M}} = h_2 - h_1 = c_P(T_2 - T_1) = 0.24 \times (824 - 520) = 73 \text{ Btu/lbm}$$

Note that the 4°R error associated with the constant specific heat assumption gives an error in the compressor work of 1 percent. Whether this error is tolerable for an engineering analysis would depend on the objectives of the analysis.

A useful relation between the pressures and volumes at two states can be derived from Eq. (8·28). Dividing by c_v, we have

$$\frac{s_2 - s_1}{c_v} = \ln\left[\left(\frac{v_2}{v_1}\right)^k \frac{P_2}{P_1}\right]$$

where k is the ratio of specific heats,

$$k = \frac{c_P}{c_v}$$

Taking the antilog, we obtain

$$P_2 v_2{}^k = P_1 v_1{}^k \exp\left(\frac{s_2 - s_1}{c_v}\right) \tag{8·30}$$

From the equation above we see that two states of the same entropy will have the same values for their property $P v^k$, provided that the idealizations we have made are satisfied. Only a *reversible* adiabatic process is isentropic, and this is an important restriction to bear in mind. Further, the gas must obey $Pv = RT$ and, in addition, have constant specific heats. If all these restrictions are met, it is indeed true that for a *perfect gas with constant specific heats undergoing a reversible adiabatic process*

$$\blacktriangleright \qquad P v^k = \text{constant} \tag{8·31}$$

We have now seen two examples of equations $P v^n = \text{constant}$. For the perfect gas with constant c_P the equation $P v^k = \text{constant}$ represents the isentropic process, and the equation $Pv = \text{constant}$ the isothermal process. The general process represented by $P v^n = \text{constant}$ is called the *polytropic process.* The polytropic process is a useful generalization;

Isobaric process $n = 0$
Isothermal process $n = 1$
Isentropic process $n = k$
Constant-volume process $n \to \infty$

Other processes can often be approximated with an appropriate value for the *polytropic exponent n.*

If $P v^n = \text{constant}$ during some process, it follows that for the perfect gas

$$\frac{P_2}{P_1} = \left(\frac{v_1}{v_2}\right)^n \tag{8·32}$$

$$\frac{T_2}{T_1} = \left(\frac{P_2}{P_1}\right)^{(n-1)/n} = \left(\frac{v_1}{v_2}\right)^{n-1} \tag{8·33}$$

The equations of state (8·23) to (8·29) allow calculation of the differences in internal energy, enthalpy, and entropy between any two states. Sometimes it is convenient to set the internal energy and entropy to be zero at some arbitrarily chosen datum state. In thermodynamic analyses not involving chemical reaction, we work exclusively with differences in internal energy, enthalpy, and entropy, so the use of a datum state is entirely permissible. However, entropy then differs from the true entropy by the value of the absolute entropy at the datum state. Since internal energy is relative anyway, no artificiality is introduced by the use of an internal energy datum. When chemical reactions are involved it becomes necessary to properly tie the internal energies and entropies of all elements and compounds together in a common way; we shall do this in Chap. Eleven.

Sometimes it is more convenient to select a datum state for enthalpy

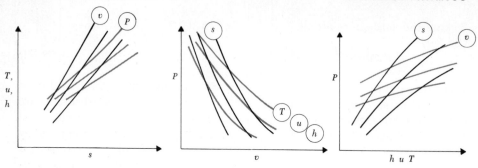

FIG. 8·6 *Graphical form of the perfect-gas equations*

rather than for internal energy. Since the values of h and u differ by Pv at the datum temperature, it is not permissible to select datums for both enthalpy and internal energy; only one of these may be set as zero at the datum state.

The equations of state for a perfect gas may be represented graphically on several thermodynamic planes, some of which are shown qualitatively in Fig. 8·6. Note that lines of constant T, u, and h coincide, so an h-s diagram would differ from the T-s diagram only by a scale stretching. Familiarity with the general nature of these graphical representations is especially helpful in the analysis of engineering systems involving idealized gases. The student should examine the figures in the Appendix, in particular B·1, B·2, and B·6, to see what regions on the plots exhibit perfect-gas behavior. These are regions in which h and T lines, or u and T lines, are the same. It is seen that these occur at high temperatures and low pressures, as previously discussed.

8·4 OTHER P-v-T EQUATIONS FOR GASES

A number of equations of state have been proposed in order to allow for real-gas behavior. The perfect-gas equation has the advantage of great simplicity, but we have seen from the figures in the Appendix that even at moderate pressures it does not accurately predict the true behavior of gases. On the basis of molecular arguments, Van der Waals suggested a modification of the perfect-gas equation that helps to account for weakly attractive intermolecular forces. A molecule about to strike the wall will experience a net attraction by molecules within the gas, and this will lessen the impulse which it delivers to the wall (Fig. 8·7). The attractive force is proportional to the number of molecules per unit of volume, as is the number of particles that strike the wall in a unit of time. Thus the effect of intermolecular attraction should be to lessen the pressure by an amount roughly proportional to the square of the gas density. This suggests that we should replace P in the perfect-gas expression by $P + (a/v^2)$, where a is a constant. In addition, the molecules of a dense gas occupy some volume, which suggests that v should be replaced by $v - b$, where b is a constant roughly indicative of the volume occupied by a unit of

FIG. 8·7   *Forces between gas molecules will tend to reduce the pressure*

mass in a dense (liquid) state. With these qualitative considerations, Van der Waals was led to propose the approximate equation which bears his name,

$$\left(P + \frac{a}{v^2}\right)(v - b) = RT \qquad (8\cdot 34)$$

The constants a and b have been determined for many gases as those which provide the best fit with experimental data. The fit is not very good over a wide range, and more accurate algebraic representations are usually employed where precise information is required.

The Van der Waals equation is a *cubic* in v, and consequently, to any given P and T there will correspond either one or three real values of v. When one plots the equation on a P-v plane the isotherms are found to appear as shown in Fig. 8·8. We know that for perfect-gas behavior $Pv = $ constant and the isotherms thus have a negative slope on the p-v plane. We therefore expect that the Van der Waals equation is not realistic in the region where the isotherms have a positive slope. However, there is one particular isotherm having an inflection point where $(\partial P/\partial v)_T = 0$; we might interpret this point as the critical point, and it can be determined very simply. We first rewrite Eq. (8·34) as

$$P = \frac{RT}{v - b} - \frac{a}{v^2}$$

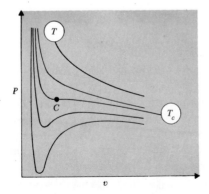

FIG. 8·8   *Van der Waals isotherms*

Both the slope and curvature of the critical isotherm must vanish at the inflection point. Thus

$$\left(\frac{\partial P}{\partial v}\right)_T = 0 = \frac{-RT_c}{(v_c - b)^2} + \frac{2a}{v_c^3}$$

$$\left(\frac{\partial^2 P}{\partial v^2}\right)_T = 0 = \frac{2RT_c}{(v_c - b)^3} - \frac{6a}{v_c^4}$$

$$a = \frac{27}{64}\frac{R^2 T_c^2}{P_c} \tag{8.35a}$$

$$b = \frac{RT_c}{8P_c} \tag{8.35b}$$

$$Z_c = \frac{P_c v_c}{RT_c} = \frac{3}{8} = 0.375 \tag{8.35c}$$

We see that the Van der Waals equation predicts that the constants a and b are determined solely by the critical state, and that $P_c v_c / RT_c$ has the same value for all substances. While this is not quite verified experimentally, it is true that Z_c has a value of the order of 0.25 to 0.3, as can be seen in Table B·8. Values of a and b for several gases are given in Table B·17.

The Van der Waals equation of state may be rewritten in terms of the *compressibility factor* $Z = Pv/RT$, a dimensionless thermodynamic property which can be graphed, or tabulated as a function of state. Equation (8·34) may be written as

$$\left(\frac{Pv}{RT} + \frac{27}{64}\frac{R^2 T_c^2}{P_c RTv}\right)\left(1 - \frac{RT_c}{8P_c v}\right) = 1$$

Now, we define the *reduced pressure*† and *reduced temperature* by

$$P^* = \frac{P}{P_c} \qquad T^* = \frac{T}{T_c}$$

The Van der Waals equation then becomes

$$\left(Z + \frac{1}{Z}\frac{27}{64}\frac{P^*}{T^{*2}}\right)\left(1 - \frac{1}{8Z}\frac{P^*}{T^*}\right) = 1$$

which suggests that a plot of the form

▶ $$Z = Z(P^*, T^*)$$

might correlate the P-v-T equation of state for real gases. This brings us to the principle of corresponding states.

It is found experimentally that the compressibility factor Z is very nearly the same function of the reduced pressure and temperature for many gases. This fact is known as the *principle of corresponding states;* it is not a basic principle in the sense of the first and second laws, but merely a convenient approximation. Figure 8·9 shows the correlation for a number of gases. The

† Not to be confused with the reduced pressure p_r used in the perfect-gas tables.

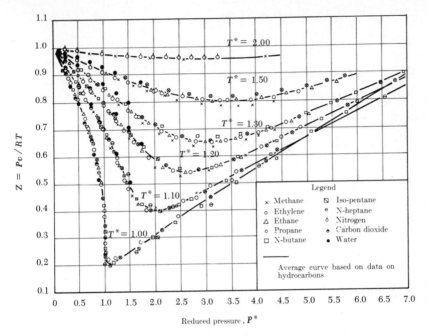

FIG. 8·9   *Demonstration of the principle of corresponding states*

Z-P^* plane is called a *generalized compressibility chart;* it is very useful in predicting the properties of substances for which more precise equation-of-state data have not yet been obtained, and also provides a convenient way to represent the properties of many substances within the memory of a digital computer. A more accurate generalized compressibility chart is included as Fig. B·14.

In terms of the generalized compressibility charts, we see that at very low pressures Z approaches unity, the value appropriate for the perfect-gas approximation. Also, we see that when the temperature is much larger than the critical temperature $(T^* \gg 1.0)$, perfect-gas behavior can be expected even out to large pressures $(P^* \gg 1.0)$.

As an example of the use of the generalized compressibility chart, let's find the specific volume of carbon dioxide at a pressure of 800 psia and a temperature of 100°F, and compare with the value obtained from Fig. B·6 and from the perfect-gas equation.

For CO_2 (from Table B·8),

$$T_c = 304.20°K \ (= 547°R)$$
$$P_c = 72.90 \text{ atm} \ (= 1070 \text{ psia})$$

so,

$$T^* = \frac{560}{547} = 1.02 \qquad P^* = \frac{800}{1070} = 0.748$$

From Fig. B·14, $Z = 0.70$. Then

$$v = \frac{ZRT}{P} = \frac{0.70 \times 35.1 \times 560}{800 \times 144} = 0.119 \text{ ft}^3/\text{lbm}$$

From Fig B·6 we interpolate to read

$$v = 0.120 \text{ ft}^3/\text{lbm}$$

From the perfect-gas equation we find a significant error:

$$v = \frac{RT}{P} = \left(\frac{ZRT}{P}\right)\frac{1}{Z} = \frac{0.119}{0.7} = 0.170 \text{ ft}^3/\text{lbm}$$

We conclude that the generalized compressibility chart gives reasonably accurate information and is particularly useful when the perfect-gas equation is not applicable and data for the substance of interest are not available.

A number of other algebraic P-v-T equations have been proposed, and perhaps the best known and most widely used is the Beattie-Bridgeman equation

$$\blacktriangleright \qquad P = \frac{\mathcal{R}T(1 - \epsilon)}{\hat{v}^2}(\hat{v} + B) - \frac{A}{\hat{v}^2} \qquad (8 \cdot 36)$$

A, B, and ϵ are functions of state,

$$A = A_0\left(1 - \frac{a}{\hat{v}}\right) \qquad B = B_0\left(1 - \frac{b}{\hat{v}}\right) \qquad \epsilon = \frac{c}{\hat{v}T^3}$$

where A_0, B_0, a, b, and c are constants which must be determined experimentally for each gas. Table B·17 gives these constants for a few gases. Values for many common gases have been determined and are available in the literature. However, much laboratory work remains to be done. For example, accurate thermodynamic properties of many high-temperature alkali-metal vapors, which are of interest for advanced thermal power systems, are not now generally available.

Generalized charts for the internal energy, enthalpy, and entropy of dense gases can be determined from ideal-gas specific heat data and real-gas P-v-T data with the help of thermodynamic relations. We shall see how this is done later in this chapter.

8·5 ALGEBRAIC EQUATION OF STATE FOR AN INCOMPRESSIBLE LIQUID

An algebraic equation of state can be developed for a *liquid* under the assumption that it is incompressible; that is, $v = $ constant. This idealized equation of state is of particular utility in analysis of liquid pumps, nozzles, heaters, and so on, operating well below the critical pressure or over limited pressure ranges. It is also applicable to a solid that is idealized as incompressible.

If the substance is essentially incompressible, its pressure can be increased a finite amount by an infinitesimal decrease in volume; such an increase can occur without a significant amount of energy transfer as work. The only means for reversibly changing the internal energy of such an idealized liquid is by transfer of energy as heat.† The incompressible liquid is therefore a degenerate case in which there are no reversible work modes, and consequently only one independent thermodynamic property. While the pressure is involved in energy transfers to the bulk fluid (flow work), which show up in increased bulk kinetic and potential energy, it is not involved in energy transfer to the "hidden microscopic modes," and consequently really is not a relevant thermodynamic property for this idealized liquid. The properties that are purely thermodynamic in nature include the internal energy, entropy, and temperature; from the state postulate we see that specification of any one of these suffices to fix the thermodynamic state.

We may express the internal energy as

$$u = u(T)$$

Differentiating and defining a specific heat for the liquid,

$$du = c\,dT$$

where

$$c = \frac{du}{dT} = c(T) \tag{8·37}$$

Integrating between two states,

$$\blacktriangleright \qquad u_2 - u_1 = \int_1^2 c(T)\,dT \tag{8·38}$$

To determine the entropy, imagine heating a unit of mass of the incompressible liquid reversibly. Application of the first and second laws then yields

$$đQ = du \qquad đQ = T\,ds$$

so that the Gibbs equation is

$$ds = \frac{du}{T}$$

as expected since $dv = 0$.

Substituting for du and integrating,

$$\blacktriangleright \qquad s_2 - s_1 = \int_1^2 \frac{c(T)}{T}\,dT \tag{8·39}$$

---

† The internal energy can also be changed by viscous friction, but this is not a reversible work mode. The fluid can also have kinetic energy due to its bulk motion and potential energy due to its position in a gravitational field.

If it is reasonable to assume that c is constant, Eqs. (8·38) and (8·39) further reduce to

▶ $\qquad u_2 - u_1 = c \cdot (T_2 - T_1)$ $\hfill$ (8·40)

▶ $\qquad s_2 - s_1 = c \ln \dfrac{T_2}{T_1}$ $\hfill$ (8·41)

We shall illustrate the use of these equations in a moment.

In control-volume analysis of engineering systems involving fluids, the matter of enthalpy invariably arises. In the case of this idealized liquid the enthalpy is a mixture of thermodynamic and mechanical properties. For an incompressible liquid with constant specific heat, we find

▶ $\qquad h_2 - h_1 = c \cdot (T_2 - T_1) + (P_2 - P_1)v$ $\hfill$ (8·42)

The enthalpy of an incompressible liquid, unlike the enthalpy of a perfect gas, is seen to be a function of both temperature and pressure. Note that for an incompressible substance $c_P = c_v = c$. This may be seen as follows; from the definition of enthalpy, $h = u + Pv$, so

$$dh = du + P \, dv + v \, dP$$

For the incompressible substance $dv = 0$, hence

$$dh = c \, dT + v \, dP$$

so,

$$c_P -\left(\frac{\partial h}{\partial T}\right)_P = c$$

Equations (8·40) to (8·42) are useful for estimating the properties of subcooled liquids when tabulations of the real thermodynamic properties are not available. Since the internal energy is a function only of temperature, the value of u for a subcooled liquid at T will be the same (idealizing the liquid as incompressible) as for the saturated liquid at the same temperature. A similar statement can be made for the entropy. The enthalpy can be computed in a number of ways, two of which we now describe.

Suppose we wish to estimate the values of u, h, and s for H_2O at 80°F and 1 atm pressure. This is a subcooled liquid state shown as 1 on Fig. 8·10. From Table B·1a we can read the values along the saturated liquid line as

$$h_3 = 48.02 \text{ Btu/lbm} \qquad v_3 = 0.01608 \text{ ft}^3/\text{lbm}$$
$$s_3 = 0.0932 \text{ Btu/lbm°R} \qquad P_3 = 0.5069 \text{ psia}$$

From Eq. 8·41 we see that s is a function of T only for the incompressible liquid. Therefore, our estimate of s_1 is made by moving *along a line of constant temperature* to state 3 so that $s_1 = s_3 = 0.0932$ Btu/lbm°R.

For the internal energy, which is also only a function of temperature:

$$u_1 = u_3 = h_3 - P_3 v_3 = 48.02 \text{ Btu/lbm}$$

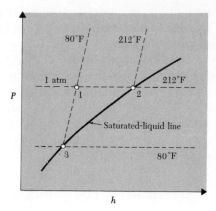

FIG. 8·10 *Estimation of liquid properties using the incompressible liquid equation of state*

The enthalpy at 1 is estimated by

$$h_1 - h_3 = u_1 - u_3 + v(P_1 - P_3) = v(P_1 - P_3)$$
$$= 0.01608 \times (14.7 - 0.5)^{144}\!/_{778} = 0.042 \text{ Btu/lbm}$$
$$h_1 = 48.02 + 0.042 = 48.06 \text{ Btu/lbm}$$

Alternatively, we could compute h_1 by working from state 2. In this case $h_2 = 180.07$ Btu/lbm and, since we are going along a line of constant pressure,

$$h_1 - h_2 = c(T_1 - T_2) = 1 \times (80 - 212) = -132 \text{ Btu/lbm}$$
$$h_1 = 180.07 - 132 = 48.07 \text{ Btu/lbm}$$

Since our first calculation involves the least extrapolation, we would probably consider it the better estimate if the disagreement had been significant.

The equations of state for an incompressible liquid must be portrayed graphically on a mixed plane, since there is only one independent thermodynamic property. The *P-h* plane is usually used, and a typical example is shown in Fig. 8·11.

The incompressible liquid is an approximation to the behavior of real

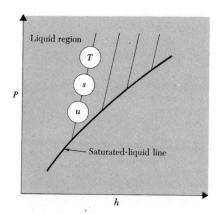

FIG. 8·11 *Graphical form of the incompressible liquid equation of state*

liquids just as the perfect-gas equation is an approximation to real-gas behavior. The approximations become poorer in both cases as we extend the range of application. Tables B·1 and B·3 provide information that can be used to estimate the compressibility of liquid water and mercury. Mercury is seen to be well approximated as an incompressible liquid. For example, the saturated liquid specific volume only changes from 1.25×10^{-3} ft³/lbm at 10 psia to 1.35×10^{-3} at 1000 psia. On the other hand, for water the saturated liquid specific volume changes by several percent between 14.7 psia and 1000 psia. Values for the thermodynamic properties of compressed liquid water are available in the literature.†

8·6 DIFFERENTIAL EQUATIONS OF STATE

The most easily measured properties are P, v, and T. However, we also know properties like h, s, u, and quantities like h_{fg}, s_{fg}. We shall now develop some relationships between properties that will permit them to be calculated from the most easily measured variables.

A list of the important properties for the simple compressible substance is given in Table 8·2. In this table we introduce the Helmholtz function, a, and the Gibbs function, g, two thermodynamic properties whose importance will be made clear in Chaps. Eleven and Twelve. The fact that a and g are properties, that is, functions of state, is itself very important, as we shall show next. The isentropic compressibility, a derivative property relating volume changes to pressure changes for an isentropic process, is also defined in Table 8·2. The isentropic compressibility is related to the speed at which pressure waves (sound) travel through a substance, and is consequently of considerable importance.

The Gibbs equation may be written in another useful form,

$$\blacktriangleright \qquad du = T\,ds - P\,dv \qquad\qquad\qquad (8·43)$$

Other differential equations of state can be obtained by combining the Gibbs equation with the differentials of the enthalpy, Helmholtz, and Gibbs functions. The enthalpy $h = u + Pv$ can be differentiated, yielding

$$dh = du + P\,dv + v\,dP$$

Combining with Eq. (8·43) results in a second differential equation of state,

$$\blacktriangleright \qquad dh = T\,ds + v\,dP \qquad\qquad\qquad (8·44)$$

This expresses enthalpy differences between two infinitesimally separated states in terms of the infinitesimal differences in the entropy and pressure. Moreover,

† J. H. Keenan and J. Keyes, *Thermodynamic Properties of Steam*, John Wiley & Sons, New York, 1936.

**TABLE 8·2   INTENSIVE THERMODYNAMIC PROPERTIES
OF A SIMPLE COMPRESSIBLE SUBSTANCE**

Property	*Definition*
Conceptual	
Internal energy u	Energy associated with molecular and atomic motions and forces
Entropy s	A measure of the average disorder on the microscopic scale
Defined	
Temperature T	$T \equiv 1/(\partial s/\partial u)_v$, equal to the empirical temperature
Pressure P	$P \equiv T(\partial s/\partial v)_u$, equal to the mechanical pressure
Specific volume v	Volume per unit of mass
Density ρ	Mass per unit of volume
Enthalpy h	$h \equiv u + Pv$
Helmholtz function a	$a \equiv u - Ts$
Gibbs function g	$g \equiv h - Ts$
Isobaric compressibility β	$\beta \equiv \dfrac{1}{v}\left(\dfrac{\partial v}{\partial T}\right)_P$
Isothermal compressibility κ	$\kappa \equiv -\dfrac{1}{v}\left(\dfrac{\partial v}{\partial P}\right)_T$
Isentropic compressibility α	$\alpha \equiv -\dfrac{1}{v}\left(\dfrac{\partial v}{\partial P}\right)_s$
Specific heat at constant volume c_v	$c_v \equiv \left(\dfrac{\partial u}{\partial T}\right)_v$
Specific heat at constant pressure c_P	$c_P \equiv \left(\dfrac{\partial h}{\partial T}\right)_P$

we see that the coefficients T and v are merely partial derivatives of $h(s, P)$,

$$\blacktriangleright \quad \left(\frac{\partial h}{\partial s}\right)_P = T \qquad\qquad (8\cdot 45a)$$

$$\blacktriangleright \quad \left(\frac{\partial h}{\partial P}\right)_s = v \qquad\qquad (8\cdot 45b)$$

Since $v > 0$, an isentropic increase in pressure will always result in an increase in the enthalpy. In other words, adiabatic compressors require work.

In a similar manner the Gibbs equation can be combined with the differential of the Helmholtz function $a = u - Ts$ to give

$$\blacktriangleright \quad da = -P\,dv - s\,dT \qquad\qquad (8\cdot 46)$$

The coefficients $-P$ and $-s$ are the partial derivatives of $a(v, T)$, so

▶ $$\left(\frac{\partial a}{\partial v}\right)_T = -P \tag{8·47a}$$

▶ $$\left(\frac{\partial a}{\partial T}\right)_v = -s \tag{8·47b}$$

Similarly, using the Gibbs function $g = h - Ts$, we may show that

▶ $$dg = v\,dP - s\,dT \tag{8·48}$$

Consequently,

▶ $$\left(\frac{\partial g}{\partial P}\right)_T = v \tag{8·49a}$$

▶ $$\left(\frac{\partial g}{\partial T}\right)_P = -s \tag{8·49b}$$

The importance of the Gibbs equation cannot be overemphasized. As an aid in being able to rederive it from first principles, we shall now make an alternative derivation. Consider a control mass consisting of a unit of mass of a simple compressible substance undergoing a reversible process, as shown in

FIG. 8·12 *System for derivation of the Gibbs equation*

Fig. 8·12. Applying the first law over an infinitesimal part of the process, we have

$$du = đW + đQ$$

Since the process is reversible, the second law gives

$$đQ = T\,ds$$

Moreover, the work is given by

$$đW = -P\,dv$$

Combining, we again obtain the Gibbs equation,

$$du = T\,ds - P\,dv$$

It should be easy to recall that $đQ = T\,ds$ for a reversible process, from which the Gibbs equation can be rederived if needed, or developed for other classes of substances.†

† While this derivation has used reversible processes, the Gibbs equation holds for any change of state regardless of the processes' reversibility.

8·7 SOME IMPORTANT PROPERTY RELATIONS

The four differential equations of state developed in Sec. 8·6 provide the basis for numerous important relationships among the thermodynamic properties of a simple compressible substance. Note that each is of the form

$$dz(x, y) = M \, dx + N \, dy$$

where

$$M = \left(\frac{\partial z}{\partial x}\right)_y \qquad N = \left(\frac{\partial z}{\partial y}\right)_x$$

Mathematically we would say that dz is an exact differential, which simply means that z is a continuous function of the two independent variables x and y. Since the order in which a second partial derivative is taken is unimportant, it follows that

$$\left(\frac{\partial M}{\partial y}\right)_x = \left(\frac{\partial N}{\partial x}\right)_y$$

This result may be applied to each of the four differential equations of state, giving

$$\blacktriangleright \qquad \left(\frac{\partial T}{\partial v}\right)_s = -\left(\frac{\partial P}{\partial s}\right)_v \qquad \text{from Eq. (8·43)} \qquad\qquad (8·50a)$$

$$\blacktriangleright \qquad \left(\frac{\partial T}{\partial P}\right)_s = \left(\frac{\partial v}{\partial s}\right)_P \qquad \text{from Eq. (8·44)} \qquad\qquad (8·50b)$$

$$\blacktriangleright \qquad \left(\frac{\partial P}{\partial T}\right)_v = \left(\frac{\partial s}{\partial v}\right)_T \qquad \text{from Eq. (8·46)} \qquad\qquad (8·50c)$$

$$\blacktriangleright \qquad \left(\frac{\partial v}{\partial T}\right)_P = -\left(\frac{\partial s}{\partial P}\right)_T \qquad \text{from Eq. (8·48)} \qquad\qquad (8·50d)$$

Equations (8·50) are known as the *Maxwell relations*. They are relations between the derivatives of the thermodynamic properties which must hold for any simple compressible substance; similar relations may be derived for other types of substances.

The internal energy of a simple compressible substance is generally expressible as

$$u = u(T, v)$$

Differentiating and bringing in the definition of the specific heat at constant volume, we find

$$du = c_v \, dT + \left(\frac{\partial u}{\partial v}\right)_T dv \qquad\qquad (8·51)$$

Equating Eqs. (8·43) and (8·51) and solving for ds,

$$ds = \frac{c_v}{T}\,dT + \frac{1}{T}\left[\left(\frac{\partial u}{\partial v}\right)_T + P\right]dv \tag{8·52}$$

Thinking of the entropy as a function of temperature and volume, we take its differential,

$$ds = \left(\frac{\partial s}{\partial T}\right)_v dT + \left(\frac{\partial s}{\partial v}\right)_T dv$$

and comparing this with Eq. (8·52), we see that

$$\left(\frac{\partial s}{\partial T}\right)_v = \frac{c_v}{T} \tag{8·53}$$

Using the third Maxwell relation, Eq. (8·50c),

$$\left(\frac{\partial s}{\partial v}\right)_T = \left(\frac{\partial P}{\partial T}\right)_v = \frac{1}{T}\left[\left(\frac{\partial u}{\partial v}\right)_T + P\right]$$

From this we obtain

▶ $$\left(\frac{\partial u}{\partial v}\right)_T = T\left(\frac{\partial P}{\partial T}\right)_v - P \tag{8·54}$$

This important equation expresses the dependence of the internal energy on the volume at fixed temperature solely in terms of the measurables T, P, and v. Since these properties are easily measured, Eq. (8·54) is very useful in the construction of equation-of-state information from laboratory data.

As an example let us apply Eq. (8·54) to the perfect gas. We have

$$Pv = RT$$
$$\left(\frac{\partial P}{\partial T}\right)_v = \frac{R}{v}$$

So, Eq. (8·54) gives

$$\left(\frac{\partial u}{\partial v}\right)_T = T\frac{R}{v} - P = P - P = 0$$

This implies that, for a perfect gas, the internal energy is independent of the density and depends only upon temperature.

From the previous discussion it follows that

$$ds = \frac{c_v}{T}\,dT + \left(\frac{\partial P}{\partial T}\right)_v dv \tag{8·55}$$

By considering the entropy as a function of the temperature and pressure and bringing in the differential of h in the form of Eq. (8·44), it may similarly be shown that†

$$ds = \frac{c_P}{T}\,dT - \left(\frac{\partial v}{\partial T}\right)_P dP \tag{8·56}$$

† This requires use of a Maxwell relation. The development is left for an exercise.

Subtracting Eq. (8·55) from Eq. (8·56) and solving for dP,

$$dP = \frac{c_P - c_v}{T(\partial v/\partial T)_P} dT - \frac{(\partial P/\partial T)_v}{(\partial v/\partial T)_P} dv$$

Then, considering P as a function of T and v, we see that

$$\frac{c_P - c_v}{T(\partial v/\partial T)_P} = \left(\frac{\partial P}{\partial T}\right)_v$$

It may be shown from the calculus (see Eq. 4·9) that

$$\left(\frac{\partial P}{\partial T}\right)_v = \frac{(\partial v/\partial T)_P}{-(\partial v/\partial P)_T}$$

Combining and solving for the difference in the specific heats,

$$\blacktriangleright \qquad c_P - c_v = -\frac{T[(\partial v/\partial T)_P]^2}{(\partial v/\partial P)_T} \qquad\qquad (8·57)$$

This is one of the more important equations of thermodynamics, and it tells us a great deal. For example, the derivative $(\partial v/\partial P)_T$ is negative for all stable substances, and consequently c_P can never be less than c_v. Furthermore, whenever the derivative $(\partial v/\partial T)_P = 0$, the two specific heats will be equal (for example, water at 4°C). Finally, experiments indicate that as T approaches absolute zero $(\partial v/\partial P)_T$ does not vanish, and so the two specific heats must approach one another at very low temperatures.

Equation (8·57) can be expressed in terms of the isothermal and isobaric compressibilities,

$$\blacktriangleright \qquad c_P - c_v = \frac{Tv\beta^2}{\kappa} \qquad\qquad (8·58)$$

It is difficult to measure c_v with any precision for a solid or liquid, and the above equation is quite useful for obtaining c_v from more easily measured quantities.

Let's verify Eq. (8·57) for the perfect gas. If

$$Pv = RT$$

then

$$\left(\frac{\partial v}{\partial P}\right)_T = -\frac{RT}{P^2} \qquad \left(\frac{\partial v}{\partial T}\right)_P = \frac{R}{P}$$

Substituting, we correctly find [Eq. (8·16)]

$$c_P - c_v = \frac{TR^2P^2}{P^2RT} = R$$

Equation (8·57) can also be used to compare c_P to c_v for copper (Table B·7),

$$c_P - c_v = \frac{Tv\beta^2}{\kappa}$$

at 200°K for copper

$$\beta = 45.6/°K$$
$$v = 7.029 \text{ cm}^3/\text{gmole}$$
$$\kappa = 0.748 \text{ cm}^2/\text{dyne}$$

Substituting,

$$c_P - c_v = \frac{200 \times 7.029 \times (45.6)^2}{0.748} = 3.9 \times 10^6 \text{ erg/gmole-°K}$$
$$= 0.093 \text{ cal/gmole-°K}$$

From Table B·7 at 200°K,

$$c_P - c_v = 5.41 - 5.32 = 0.09 \text{ cal/gmole-°K}$$

Since copper is practically incompressible, we indeed expect $c_P \approx c_v$.

By manipulating with the previous equations, we may show that the ratio of specific heats is related to the isentropic and isothermal compressibilities by

$$\blacktriangleright \qquad k \equiv \frac{c_P}{c_v} = \frac{\kappa}{\alpha} \tag{8·59}$$

The isentropic compressibility is related to the speed at which sound waves travel in the substance, and such speed measurements have been used as a means for determining the ratio of the specific heats.

A useful expression describing the variation of saturation pressure with saturation temperature can be derived with the help of Eq. (8·48). Since the liquid and vapor phases of a mixture in equilibrium have the same temperature and pressure, integration of Eq. (8·48) along an isotherm (a line of constant temperature) from the saturated-liquid line to the saturated-vapor line indicates that the two phases also have the same Gibbs function,† that is, $g_f = g_g$. Since g_f and g_g are functions of the saturation temperature only, it then follows that (Fig. 8·13)

$$\frac{dg_f}{dT_{\text{sat}}} = \frac{dg_g}{dT_{\text{sat}}}$$

Again using Eq. (8·48), we then find

$$v_f \left(\frac{dP}{dT}\right)_{\text{sat}} - s_f = v_g \left(\frac{dP}{dT}\right)_{\text{sat}} - s_g$$

or

$$\left(\frac{dP}{dT}\right)_{\text{sat}} = \frac{s_g - s_f}{v_g - v_f} = \frac{s_{fg}}{v_{fg}} \tag{8·60}$$

† This is a condition for equilibrium between phases of a mixture, as we shall show in Chap. Twelve.

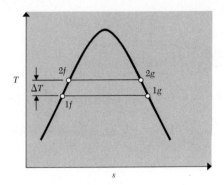

FIG. 8·13 *The Clapeyron equation relates saturation conditions to the slope of the saturation pressure–saturation temperature curve*

This expresses the change in the saturation pressure with respect to changes in temperature in terms of the properties of the saturated liquid and vapor. Now, since $g_f = g_g$,

$$h_f - Ts_f = h_g - Ts_g$$
$$s_g - s_f = \frac{h_g - h_f}{T}$$

Combining with Eq. (8·60), we find

$$\blacktriangleright \qquad \left(\frac{dP}{dT}\right)_{\text{sat}} = \frac{h_{fg}}{Tv_{fg}} \qquad\qquad (8·61)$$

This is known as the *Clapeyron equation;* it relates the variation of pressure with temperature along the saturated-vapor (or liquid) line to the enthalpy and volume of vaporization. The Clapeyron equation is extremely useful in constructing a graphical or tabular equation of state from a minimum of experimental measurements. It also tells us that $(dP/dT)_{\text{sat}}$ is positive, since enthalpies of vaporization are always positive, as are the volume changes undergone during the phase change. Consequently, the vapor pressure of any substance increases with temperature.

As an illustration, let's calculate h_{fg} for water at 225°F from data for P, T, and v only. We have, from Table B·1A,

$$v_{fg} = 21.15 \text{ ft}^3/\text{lbm}$$

To calculate $(dP/dT)_{\text{sat}}$, let's use the P and T data at 230°F and 220°F; from Table B·1,

$$\Delta P = 20.78 - 17.19 = 3.59 \text{ psia}$$

So,

$$\left(\frac{dP}{dT}\right)_{\text{sat}} \approx \frac{3.59 \text{ psia}}{10°R} = 0.359 \text{ psia/°R}$$

Then, using the Clapeyron equation,

$$h_{fg} = Tv_{fg}\left(\frac{dP}{dT}\right)_{sat}$$

$$= (225 + 460) \times 21.15 \times \frac{0.359 \times 144}{778} = 962 \text{ Btu/lbm}$$

This agrees with the value obtained by calorimetric measurements, as interpolated in Table B·1A.

A Clapeyron equation for fusion may be derived in an analogous manner. Denoting the saturated-solid state by a subscript s, the result would be

▶ $$\left(\frac{dP}{dT}\right)_{sat\,sol} = \frac{h_{sf}}{Tv_{sf}} \tag{8·62}$$

The enthalpy of melting $h_{sf} = h_f - h_s$ is positive for all known substances. The volume change $v_{sf} = v_f - v_s$ is positive for most substances, indicating that the freezing temperature increases with increasing pressure. However, water has the peculiar property that v_{sf} is negative and therefore has a fusion curve with a negative slope. Hence water will freeze at a lower temperature if the pressure is increased, or melt at a lower temperature if the pressure is increased.

In the absence of better data, the enthalpy of a real gas can be estimated using a combination of thermodynamic equations, perfect-gas theory, and the generalized compressibility correlation. Considering $h(T, P)$, we have

$$dh = \left(\frac{\partial h}{\partial T}\right)_P dT + \left(\frac{\partial h}{\partial P}\right)_T dP$$

The first partial derivative is simply c_P, and the second may be calculated solely from P-v-T data using an equation analogous to Eq. (8·54),

▶ $$\left(\frac{\partial h}{\partial P}\right)_T = v - T\left(\frac{\partial v}{\partial T}\right)_P \tag{8·63}$$

The derivation of this important relation follows that of Eq. (8·54), and is left as an exercise. The enthalpy can therefore be determined from

$$dh = c_P(T, P)\, dT + \left[v - T\left(\frac{\partial v}{\partial T}\right)_P\right] dP$$

We emphasize that in general c_P depends upon both T and P. However, at low pressures the perfect-gas limit is approached. The enthalpy of a perfect gas can therefore be viewed as

$$h_{pg}(T) = \int_0^T c_P(T, 0)\, dT \tag{8·64}$$

Now, we imagine carrying out the integrations from the reference state $T = 0$, $P = 0$. The path of integration is shown in Fig. 8·14. On the first part $dP = 0$. The contribution to h from this path is precisely the perfect-gas term, Eq. (8·64). On the second part $dT = 0$, and the contribution to h can be evaluated

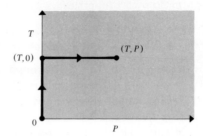

FIG. 8·14 *The path of integration*

solely from P-v-T data. Then,

$$\blacktriangleright \qquad h = h_{pg}(T) + \int_0^P \left[v - T\left(\frac{\partial v}{\partial T}\right)_P \right] dP \qquad (8\cdot65)$$

The temperature variation of c_P should of course be considered when evaluating h_{pg}. Note that Eq. (8·65) permits determination of $h(T, P)$ from P-v-T data and low-pressure c_P data.

The entropy can be found in a similar manner. We write Eq. (8·56) as

$$ds = \frac{c_P(T, P)}{T} \, dT - \left(\frac{\partial v}{\partial T}\right)_P dP$$

In the perfect-gas limit for small P,

$$ds_{pg} = \frac{c_P(T, 0)}{T} \, dT - \frac{R}{P} \, dP$$

We now subtract these two equations, and again carry out the integrations along the path of Fig. 8·14. Since there is no contribution from the dT terms on the second path, and they precisely cancel on the first path, we have

$$\blacktriangleright \qquad s - s_{pg}(T, P) = \int_0^P \left[\frac{R}{P} - \left(\frac{\partial v}{\partial T}\right)_P \right] dP \qquad (8\cdot66)$$

Since the integrand approaches zero as $P \to 0$, the integral presents no problems near the lower limit. Equation (8·66) permits calculation of the entropy of real gases from P-v-T data and low-pressure c_P data.

A more complete compressibility chart has been included in Appendix B as Figs. B·14a and B·14b. The corresponding enthalpies and entropies can be read from the generalized enthalpy and entropy charts, Figs. B·15 and B·16, which were developed from Eqs. (8·65) and (8·66). It should be emphasized that these charts are based on the principle of corresponding states, which is only an approximation. Whenever possible one should use equation-of-state data for the particular substance of interest; the generalized properties charts provide at least some way to work beyond the range of available data, which is often a necessity in modern engineering analysis.

As an example of the use of Figs. B·15 and B·16, consider a gas with the following known properties:

$\hat{M}$ = 31 lbm/lbmole P_c = 900 psia T_c = 540°R
c_P = 0.50 Btu/lbm-°R *at low pressure.*

It is desired to run the gas through a heat exchanger at an inlet pressure of 700 psia and an inlet temperature of 540°R. The exit conditions are 650 psia at 1000°R. How much energy must be added as heat to the gas and what will be the entropy change?

Let's first check the inlet state 1 to see if the perfect-gas model is appropriate. We have

$$\frac{P}{P_c} = \frac{700}{900} = 0.779$$

$$\frac{T}{T_c} = \frac{540}{540} = 1.000$$

Checking on Fig. B·14, we find $Z = 0.6$ so that the conditions are not those of the perfect gas ($Z = 1.0$), and we must use Fig. B·15 to calculate the enthalpy change. For the exit state 2 we have

$$\frac{P}{P_c} = \frac{650}{900} = 0.723$$

$$\frac{T}{T_c} = \frac{1000}{540} = 1.85$$

An energy balance gives the heat input per unit mass as

$$Q = h_2 - h_1$$

From Fig. B·15 at state 1

$$\frac{\hat{h}_{pg} - \hat{h}_1}{T_c} = 2.7 \text{ cal/gmole-°K} = 2.7 \text{ Btu/lbmole-°R}$$

Then,

$$h_1 = \frac{\hat{h}_{pg} - 2.7 T_c}{\hat{M}} = h_{pg1} - \frac{2.7 \times 540}{31} = (h_{pg1} - 47) \text{ Btu/lbm}$$

Similarly,

$$h_2 = h_{pg2} - \frac{0.55 \times 540}{31} = (h_{pg2} - 10) \text{ Btu/lbm}$$

So,

$$Q = h_2 - h_1 = (h_{pg2} - h_{pg1}) - 10 + 47$$
$$Q = c_P(T_2 - T_1) + 37 = 0.5 \times (1000 - 540) + 33 = 267 \text{ Btu/lbm}$$

Note that h_{pg} is evaluated using the *low-pressure* (ideal-gas) value for c_P. We see that had we used the perfect-gas approximation our error would have been some 15 percent. The entropy change can be calculated in a similar manner from Fig. B·16. We find

$$s_2 - s_1 = (s_2 - s_1)_{pg} + \frac{1.9 - 0.27}{31}$$

$$= 0.36 \text{ Btu/lbm-}°R$$

The student should carry out this calculation using Eq. (8·27) for $(s_2 - s_1)_{pg}$.

8·8 THERMODYNAMICS OF THE SIMPLE MAGNETIC SUBSTANCE

Thermodynamics is not restricted to simple compressible substances. In fact, some of the most interesting and important uses of thermodynamics involve other kinds of substances; we shall examine the simple magnetic substance to illustrate again the manner in which thermodynamics is used to obtain information about the properties of matter.

For a simple magnetic substance the state postulate tells us that there are only two independent intensive thermodynamic properties; we may take these as the internal energy and dipole moment per unit of mass, $v\mathbf{M}$. The magnetic

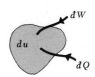

FIG. 8·15 *Deriving the Gibbs equation for a simple magnetic substance*

Gibbs equation may be obtained by considering a unit of mass of the material undergoing a reversible process between two infinitesimally separated thermodynamic states (Fig. 8·15). An energy balance gives

$$du = dQ + dW$$

The energy transfer as work per unit of mass [see Eq. (2·17)] is†

$$dW = \mu_0 v\mathbf{H} \cdot d\mathbf{M}$$

Since the process is reversible, the second law requires that

$$ds = \frac{dQ}{T}$$

Combining, the Gibbs equation is found to be

$$\blacktriangleright \qquad du = T\,ds + \mu_0 v\mathbf{H} \cdot d\mathbf{M} \qquad\qquad (8·67)$$

† The rationalized mksc system is employed throughout this section (see Appendix A). However, the equation-of-state information of Fig. B·12 is in the absolute magnetostatic system.

Inspecting the coefficients, it follows that

$$\blacktriangleright \qquad \mu_0 v \mathbf{H} = \left(\frac{\partial u}{\partial \mathbf{M}}\right)_s \tag{8.68}$$

$$\blacktriangleright \qquad T = \left(\frac{\partial u}{\partial s}\right)_\mathbf{M} = \frac{1}{(\partial s/\partial u)_\mathbf{M}} \tag{8.69}$$

The latter is merely the thermodynamic definition of temperature for magnetic systems.

It is convenient to define a magnetic enthalpy and a magnetic Gibbs function as

$$\blacktriangleright \qquad h \equiv u - \mu_0 v \mathbf{H} \cdot \mathbf{M}$$
$$\blacktriangleright \qquad g \equiv h - Ts$$

Specific heats at constant $\mathbf{M}$ and $\mathbf{H}$ are the analogs of c_v and c_P; they are defined as

$$\blacktriangleright \qquad c_\mathbf{M} \equiv \left(\frac{\partial u}{\partial T}\right)_\mathbf{M}$$

$$\blacktriangleright \qquad c_\mathbf{H} \equiv \left(\frac{\partial h}{\partial T}\right)_\mathbf{H}$$

A set of Maxwell relations for magnetic substances can be obtained. For example, the analog of Eq. (8·50c) is

$$\blacktriangleright \qquad \mu_0 v \left(\frac{\partial \mathbf{H}}{\partial T}\right)_\mathbf{M} = -\left(\frac{\partial s}{\partial \mathbf{M}}\right)_T \tag{8.70}$$

An expression relating the difference in specific heats may be found by the methods used in obtaining Eq. (8·57),

$$\blacktriangleright \qquad c_\mathbf{H} - c_\mathbf{M} = \frac{T\mu_0 v[(\partial \mathbf{M}/\partial T)_\mathbf{H}]^2}{(\partial \mathbf{M}/\partial \mathbf{H})_T} \tag{8.71}$$

If $(\partial \mathbf{M}/\partial \mathbf{H})_T$ is positive for any substance, as seems always to be the case, $c_\mathbf{H}$ must be larger than $c_\mathbf{M}$.

Superconductors are known to undergo a transition from superconducting to normally conducting states at well-defined values of the applied field. This "threshold field" is a function of temperature, and experimental data suggest that the equation of state might appear as shown in Fig. 8·16.

It may be shown from energy considerations that the energy which must be transferred as heat to effect a constant-T constant-$\mathbf{H}$ transition is equal to the difference in the magnetic enthalpies,

$$h_{sn} \equiv h_n - h_s$$

Here we use the subscripts n and s to denote the normal and superconducting states, respectively. Following the development of the Clapeyron equation, it may be shown that the threshold field is related to the temperature and to the

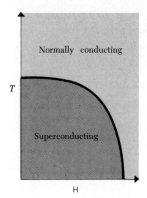

FIG. 8·16 *Phase transitions in superconductors at low temperaures*

enthalpy of transformation h_{sn} by

$$\left(\frac{d\mathbf{H}}{dT}\right)_{\text{threshold}} = -\frac{h_{sn}}{T\mu_0 v(\mathbf{M}_n - \mathbf{M}_s)}$$

In normally conducting states the magnetic moment $\mathbf{M}$ is zero. Superconduction occurs when the magnetization exactly cancels the applied field $\mathbf{H}$, so that electrons passing through the material experience no magnetic field. Setting $\mathbf{M}_n = 0$ and $\mathbf{M}_s = -\mathbf{H}$, the above equation reduces to

$$\blacktriangleright \qquad \left(\frac{d\mathbf{H}}{dT}\right)_{\text{threshold}} = \frac{-h_{sn}}{T\mu_0 v\mathbf{H}} \qquad (8\cdot72)$$

We see that the threshold field decreases with increasing temperature, which is indeed found to be the case.

8·9 ALGEBRAIC EQUATION OF STATE FOR THE CURIE SUBSTANCE

The Curie substance is any simple magnetic substance obeying the equation of state

$$\blacktriangleright \qquad \mathbf{M} = C\frac{\mathbf{H}}{T} \qquad (8\cdot73)$$

Paramagnetic salts at temperatures which are not too low and in fields which are not too strong behave in this general manner.

It may be shown that the internal energy is a function only of temperature for any simple magnetic substance for which $\mathbf{H}/T = f(\mathbf{M})$. Consider the magnetic Gibbs equation (8·67), written in the form

$$ds = \frac{1}{T}du - \mu_0 v\left(\frac{\mathbf{H}}{T}\right)d\mathbf{M}$$

If $\mathbf{H}/T = f(\mathbf{M})$, then since ds is exact,

$$\left[\frac{\partial(1/T)}{\partial\mathbf{M}}\right]_u = -\mu_0 v\left[\frac{\partial(\mathbf{H}/T)}{\partial u}\right]_\mathbf{M} = 0$$

T is therefore independent of $\mathbf{M}$ along a line of constant u, and $T = T(u)$. Inverting this relationship, we have $u = u(T)$. It must be emphasized that this holds only for the special circumstances where $\mathbf{H}/T = f(\mathbf{M})$ and is not true for paramagnetics in general.

The energy of a Curie substance is therefore given by

$$du = c_{\mathbf{M}}(T)\, dT$$

The entropy may be found from the magnetic Gibbs equation, which for the Curie substance is

$$ds = \frac{c_{\mathbf{M}}}{T}\, dT - \frac{\mu_0 v}{C}\, \mathbf{M} \cdot d\mathbf{M}$$

For a Curie substance with constant $c_{\mathbf{M}}$ the above equations integrate to give

$$\blacktriangleright \qquad u_2 - u_1 = c_{\mathbf{M}}(T_2 - T_1) \qquad\qquad (8\cdot74)$$

$$\blacktriangleright \qquad s_2 - s_1 = c_{\mathbf{M}} \ln \frac{T_2}{T_1} - \frac{\mu_0 v}{2C}\, (\mathbf{M}_2{}^2 - \mathbf{M}_1{}^2) \qquad\qquad (8\cdot75)$$

SELECTED READING

Lee, J., and F. Sears, *Thermodynamics*, 2d ed., chap. 2, secs. 7.1–7.7, Addison-Wesley Publishing Co., Inc., Reading, Mass., 1962.

Van Wylen, G., and R. Sonntag, *Fundamentals of Classical Thermodynamics*, chaps. 3 and 10, John Wiley & Sons, Inc., New York, 1965.

Wark, K., *Thermodynamics*, chap. 13, McGraw-Hill Book Company, New York, 1966.

Zemansky, M. W., *Heat and Thermodynamics*, 4th ed., chaps. 11, 13, and 14, McGraw-Hill Book Company, New York, 1957.

QUESTIONS

8·1 What role do equations of state play in the analysis of engineering systems?

8·2 Of what value are the differential equations of state?

8·3 Explain how the entropy can be found (relative to some datum state) without enumerating the quantum states.

8·4 What is the Gibbs equation?

8·5 Starting from the fundamental definition of a partial derivative, can you derive the chain rule of calculus?

8·6 Why is it essential to put a subscript on a partial derivative to indicate the property held constant?

8·7 Of what utility is the Clapeyron equation?

8·8 Explain how c_v can be determined without ever being measured directly.

8·9 On what diagram is c_P the slope of a line, and what line?

8·10 Considering the Clapeyron equation, what peculiar characteristic of H_2O makes ice skating possible?

8·11 Is the specific heat of a substance obeying $Pv = RT$ necessarily constant? Is it necessarily a function only of temperature?

8·12 If c_v is constant for a perfect gas, must c_P also be constant?

8·13 What are the meaning and utility of p_r and v_r in the air tables (Table B·9)?

8·14 Under what conditions does $Pv^k = $ constant?

8·15 What is the difference between c_v and $\hat{c}_v$?

8·16 When can $Pv = RT$ be expected to apply?

8·17 What is the approximate value of Pv/RT near the critical point?

8·18 Why is thermodynamics useful in the study of magnetic substances?

8·19 What is the principle of corresponding states?

PROBLEMS

8·1 Starting with the Gibbs equation, show that for a perfect gas undergoing an isentropic process $(T_2/T_1) = (P_2/P_1)^{(k-1)/k}$ where $k = c_P/c_v$.

8·2 A well-designed nozzle is idealized as isentropic. If the inlet conditions are 16 psia, 600°R and the exit pressure is 14.7 psia, find the exit velocity assuming the air obeys the perfect-gas equations of state and neglecting the inlet kinetic energy.

8·3 In designing the air conditioning system for an airplane, it is desired to determine the work required to compress air in an isentropic steady flow process from 0.5 atm to 5 atm. What is the exit temperature if the inlet temperature is 0°F?

8·4 Consider steam flow through an adiabatic valve at (a) an input state of 1000 psia, 850°F and an exit pressure of 300 psia, and (b) an input state of 60 psia, 800°F with an exit at 1 atm. Examine and discuss the validity of using the perfect-gas model in analyzing these two flows.

8·5 A test of an air compressor reveals that the compression stroke can be modeled by a polytropic process $(Pv^n = $ const) with $n = 1.35$. The initial temperature is 70°F, the initial pressure 13.5 psia. If the final pressure is 81.0 psia find the final temperature, the work done on the gas, and the heat transferred per lbm of air.

8·6 A fixed mass of a perfect gas is contained in a piston cylinder system. Initially the air occupies 1 ft³ at 70°F and 15 psia. After a compression process the pressure is 100 psia. Find (a) the mass of gas in the cylinder, (b) the final temperature, (c) the work required, (d) the change in u, (e) the heat transferred, if any, if the process is isothermal. Rework the above for a process of $Pv^{1.25} = $ constant.

8·7 Compute the complete algebraic equation of state for a perfect gas for which $c_v = a + bT$, where a and b are constants.

8·8 The general process represented by $Pv^n = $ constant is called the polytropic process. Consider a fixed mass of a perfect gas in a piston cylinder undergoing a process for which $Pv^n = $ constant. Show that the work done per lbm in such a process is given by $W = (P_2v_2 - P_1v_1)/(n - 1)$. If the process is isentropic, show that this reduces to $W = c_v(T_2 - T_1)$.

8·9 Derive expressions for the slopes of constant-pressure and constant-volume lines on a T-s plane for a perfect gas with constant specific heats and show that the volume line is steeper.

8·10 Derive the complete algebraic equation of state for a perfect gas for which $c_P = a + bT$, where a and b are constants.

8·11 Show that c_v is a function only of temperature for a Van der Waals gas. Derive an expression for $c_P - c_v$ for the gas. Is c_P also a function only of temperature? Derive algebraic expressions for the internal energy and entropy of a Van der Waals gas, with constant c_v, as a function of temperature and specific volume. Compare these with the perfect-gas equations.

8·12 Calculate the pressure as a function of molal volume for CO_2 at 400°K using the Beattie-Bridgeman equation of state. Cover the range 0–100 atm. Compare with values which would be obtained from the generalized compressibility chart.

8·13 Derive the complete algebraic equation of state for an incompressible liquid for which $c = a + bT$, where a and b are constants.

8·14 Estimate the enthalpy and entropy of mercury at room conditions relative to the datum used in Table B·3.

8·15 Using data from Appendix B, find the entropy, enthalpy, and internal energy for (*a*) water at 70°F, 100 psia, (*b*) mercury at 875°F, 800 psia, and (*c*) freon at 114 psia, −10°F.

8·16 The pump on a nuclear power system pressurizes the mercury from saturated liquid at 20 psia to 600 psia. Find the work required, treating the pump as adiabatic and the process as isentropic.

8·17 Using the generalized compressibility chart, determine the pressure required to fix a specific volume of 0.2 ft³/lbm at temperature of 120°F for CO_2. Compare with the CO_2 chart.

8·18 Nitrogen is stored in a thick-walled pressure tank at about 2200 psia. Find the specific volume at 2200 psia, 60°F using the generalized compressibility chart. Compare to the value of Fig. B·4. If the tank has a volume of 2.2 ft³ what is the mass of nitrogen stored?

8·19 It is desired to store 10 lbm of oxygen in a 1 ft³ tank at 300°F. To design the tank we need to determine the pressure under these conditions. Estimate the pressure in atmospheres from (*a*) the perfect-gas equation, (*b*) the Van der Waals equation, and (*c*) the Beattie-Bridgeman equation of state.

8·20 Determine the specific volume of steam at a pressure of 5000 psia and a temperature of 800°F from the generalized compressibility chart and compare to that value given in the steam tables. (Some power plants now operate at these pressures.)

8·21 Test the Clapeyron equation for *fusion* for CO_2 at −100°F using the data of Fig. B·6.

8·22 The vapor pressure is often approximated as an exponential function of temperature. Show how this approximation is suggested by the Clapeyron equation.

8·23 The Joule-Kelvin coefficient μ is defined by $\mu = (\partial T/\partial P)_h$. Prove that

$$\mu = \frac{1}{c_P}\left[T\left(\frac{\partial v}{\partial T}\right)_P - v \right]$$

Discuss how this equation might be used.

8·24 Show that the Joule-Kelvin coefficient for a perfect gas is zero.

8·25 Show that

$$\left(\frac{\partial c_v}{\partial v}\right)_T = T\left(\frac{\partial^2 P}{\partial T^2}\right)_v, \qquad \left(\frac{\partial c_P}{\partial P}\right)_T = -T\left(\frac{\partial^2 v}{\partial T^2}\right)_P$$

Discuss the use of these equations.

8·26 Prove that

$$\left(\frac{\partial u}{\partial P}\right)_T = -T\left(\frac{\partial v}{\partial T}\right)_P - P\left(\frac{\partial v}{\partial P}\right)_T$$

How might this be used?

8·27 Prove that

$$\left(\frac{\partial P}{\partial T}\right)_s = \frac{c_P}{Tv\beta}$$

Describe an experiment that would use this equation to determine c_P without any energy measurements.

8·28 Describe an experiment by which the latent heat of vaporization of a substance could be determined without any energy measurements.

8·29 Estimate the vapor pressure of mercury at 1600°F using the Clapeyron equation.

8·30 Using appropriate differential equations of state and taking the datum for entropy to be saturated liquid at 14.7 psia, determine the entropy of nitrogen at the following states, using those data of Fig. B·4 [graphical integrations are required for (b) and (c)]; use the most convenient differential equation of state: (a) saturated vapor, 14.7 psia; (b) 500°R, 14.7 psia; (c) the critical point.

8·31 Show that the isothermal compressibility is always greater than or equal to the isentropic compressibility.

8·32 The properties of ice at 1 atm may be found in the *Handbook of Chemistry and Physics*. Estimate the melting temperature of ice at 1000 psia.

8·33 Derive an expression analogous to Eq. (8·65) for $u - u_{pg}$. Derive an equation for $u - u_{pg}$ using this expression and the Beattie-Bridgeman equation.

8·34 Derive an expression analogous to Eq. (8·66) for $s - s_{pg}$ using Eq. (8·55). Derive an equation for $s - s_{pg}$ using this expression and the Beattie-Bridgeman equation.

8·35 Derive the analog of the Maxwell relations for a simple magnetic substance.

8·36 Derive the complete algebraic equation of state for a Curie substance for which $c_M = aT^2$, where a is a constant.

8·37 Consider a simple dielectric substance for which the polarization is related to the electric field and temperature by $\mathbf{E} = AT\mathbf{P}$, where A is a constant. Show that the energy of this dielectric is a function only of temperature. Derive a complete algebraic equation of state for the case where the specific heat at constant polarization $c_P \equiv (\partial u/\partial T)_P$ is constant.

8·38 Consider a simple surface for which the only possibly reversible work mode is surface extension. Derive the Gibbs equation $T\,dS = dU - \sigma\,dA$, where A is the surface area and σ is the surface tension. Derive the relation

$$\left(\frac{\partial U}{\partial A}\right)_T = \sigma - T\left(\frac{\partial \sigma}{\partial T}\right)_A$$

Show that if the surface tension is a function only of temperature, the energy per unit of area also depends only on temperature, and consequently that

$$\frac{U}{A} = \sigma - T\frac{d\sigma}{d_T}$$

The surface tension is easily measured, but it is difficult to measure the surface energy directly. How else might it be determined?

8·39 Consider a simple elastic solid for which the only significant possibly reversible work mode is pure strain. Develop the Gibbs equation $T\,ds = du - \sigma\,d\epsilon$, where s and u are the entropy and energy per unit of volume, σ is the stress (positive in tension), and ϵ is the strain. Following the development of the Maxwell relations, derive an expression for $(\partial\epsilon/\partial s)_\sigma$ in terms of $(\partial T/\partial\sigma)_s$. Take a rubber band, stretch it rapidly, and hold it to your lip. Which way does the temperature change? Check your result by rapidly releasing the strain. On the basis of your theory and experiment, will the elongation of a rubber rod under fixed stress increase or decrease when the rod is heated? (You might try to verify this prediction experimentally.) Unstressed metal rods normally expand when heated. What will happen to the temperature of a metal rod when it is rapidly stretched?

8·40 If the strain in the thin wire of Prob. 8·39 is small, it is convenient to put $l = l_0(1 + \epsilon)$, where l_0 is the unstretched length of the wire and ϵ is the strain (extension per unit length). The isothermal Young's modulus is $Y \equiv (\partial\sigma/\partial\epsilon)_T$. Show that if Y is constant so is $\alpha \equiv (\partial\sigma/\partial T)_\epsilon$. The volumetric specific heat at constant strain is $c_\epsilon \equiv (\partial u/\partial T)_\epsilon$ where u is the internal energy per unit volume. Derive algebraic equations for the energy and entropy per unit of volume (u and s) for a slightly stretched wire with constant Y and c_ϵ.

8·41 Consider an idealized liquid for which $P = A(v_0 - v)$, where A and v_0 are constants. Derive algebraic equations for energy, enthalpy, and entropy, assuming c_P is constant. Compare these with the equations for the incompressible liquid.

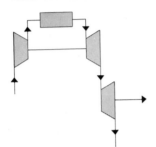

CHAPTER NINE

CHARACTERISTICS OF SOME THERMODYNAMIC SYSTEMS

9·1 ANALYSIS OF THERMODYNAMIC SYSTEMS

Thermodynamics is invaluable in the analysis of any system involving energy transfers; the most common and practical uses of thermodynamics in engineering are in analysis of systems containing some sort of working substance, usually in a liquid or gaseous phase, which is flowing or circulating through the device. In this chapter we shall examine the characteristics of a number of thermodynamic systems, mostly of this variety, and in addition, we shall look at the behavior of some more unusual devices which show promise of practical utility in the future. These characteristics may be predicted from a combination of thermodynamic analysis and experience with operating hardware. For the most part we shall consider systems sufficiently idealized that analysis of their performance is within the range of our studies thus far.

The systems of chief interest here are those which effect some sort of *energy conversion*. In power-generating systems we are interested in converting the internal energy of hydrocarbon fuel molecules, or the atomic energy of uranium or plutonium, into electrical or mechanical energy. In refrigeration systems we are interested in keeping some area cool by continual removal of energy as heat from that area. Most such systems involve a *working fluid*, such as water or air, which is circulated through the system in a *cycle*. In steam power plants (Fig. 9·1) the cycle is usually *closed*, while in gas power systems, such as the turbo-prop engine (Fig. 9·2), the cycle is often *open* (closed by the atmosphere).

The general methodology for energy analysis of a thermodynamic system was presented and illustrated in Chap. Five, and this chapter will afford additional practice with these important tools. In addition, we now have the many consequences of the second law at our disposal and are in a position to employ these in discussing the performance of thermodynamic systems. The second

247

FIG. 9·1   *Schematic of a simple steam power plant*

law places strong limitations on the performance of thermal energy-conversion and thermal transfer systems,† and we shall examine these in the following discussions.

The value of the process representation in the analysis of a thermodynamic system was emphasized in Chap. Five. Especially important is the temperature-

† Refrigerators, heat pumps, and so on.

FIG. 9·2   *Details of a turboprop engine*

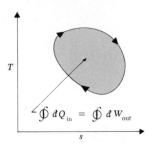

$$\oint dQ_{in} = \oint dW_{out}$$

FIG. 9·4 *The cyclic integral of T ds represents the net energy transfer as heat to the substance*

FIG. 9·3 *The T-s plane is particularly useful in showing amounts of energy transfer as heat*

entropy plane; when matter undergoes a reversible process, the sequence of states through which it passes traces out a line on the T-s plane (Fig. 9·3). Since the process is reversible, the energy transferred as heat *to* a unit of mass of the substance is represented by the area under the curve on the T-s plane. If the substance undergoes a cyclic process, there will be no net change in its internal energy over a cycle, and consequently the net energy transferred to a unit mass of the substance as heat during the cycle must equal the net energy transfer as work from the substance (work done), and both equal the area enclosed by the reversible path on the T-s plane (Fig. 9·4). The T-s process representation can therefore be a very graphic aid in comparing and evaluating thermodynamic systems, and we shall make extensive use of it in this chapter. Other thermodynamic planes are also quite descriptive, as will be seen.

9·2 THE CARNOT CYCLE

The *Carnot cycle* is the reversible cycle defined by two isothermal processes and two isentropic processes (Fig. 9·5). Since a reversible isentropic process is adiabatic, the only energy transfer as heat to a piece of substance undergoing a Carnot cycle occurs during the isothermal processes. The Carnot cycle constitutes a reversible $2T$ engine, and consequently the ratios of the energy transfers as heat defined in Fig. 9·5 are given by†

$$\blacktriangleright \qquad \frac{Q_H}{Q_C} = \frac{T_H}{T_C}$$

† This relation can easily be derived at will from $dQ_{rev} = T\,dS$, since

$$\frac{Q_H}{Q_C} = \frac{T_H(S_3 - S_2)}{T_C(S_4 - S_1)} = \frac{T_H}{T_C}$$

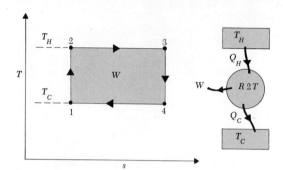

FIG. 9·5   *The Carnot engine*

Its energy-conversion efficiency is therefore

$$\blacktriangleright \qquad \eta = \frac{W}{Q_H} = \frac{Q_H - Q_C}{Q_H} = 1 - \frac{T_C}{T_H} \qquad\qquad (9\cdot1)$$

Highest efficiencies will be obtained when the ratio T_C/T_H is as small as possible. One would like to *add the energy as heat at as high a temperature as possible and reject energy as heat at the lowest possible temperature;* the practical limitations on T_H and T_C were discussed in Chap. Seven.

The Carnot cycle operates as a refrigerator when reversed (Fig. 9·6). The area enclosed by its *T-s* process path would represent the work required per cycle of operation, and we should like this to be as small as possible. This suggests that having T_H as close as possible to T_C is most desirable. A refrigeration cycle is rated in terms of its *coefficient of performance* (cop):

$$\blacktriangleright \qquad \text{cop}_{\text{refrig}} = \frac{Q_C}{W} \qquad\qquad (9\cdot2)$$

For the Carnot refrigerator,

$$\blacktriangleright \qquad \text{cop} = \frac{Q_C}{Q_H - Q_C} = \frac{T_C}{T_H - T_C} \qquad\qquad (9\cdot3)$$

Unlike the efficiency, the cop can range from zero to infinity. For a Carnot refrigerator extracting energy as heat from a cold space at 0°F and transferring

FIG. 9·6   *The Carnot refrigerator*

energy as heat to an environment at 60°F,

$$\text{cop} = \frac{460}{520 - 460} = 7.7$$

Real refrigeration systems operating between the same two temperatures would have coefficients of performance of the order of 2 to 3.

An interesting use of the refrigerator is as a *heat pump*. Here the objective is not to keep a region cool but instead to keep a region (such as a house) warm. The energy transfer to the hot space is then of prime interest, and it is customary to define the cop as

▶ $$\text{cop}_{\text{heat pump}} = \frac{Q_H}{W} \qquad\qquad (9 \cdot 4)$$

Then, for a Carnot heat pump,

▶ $$\text{cop} = \frac{Q_H}{Q_H - Q_C} = \frac{T_H}{T_H - T_C} \qquad\qquad (9 \cdot 5)$$

For example, a Carnot heat pump taking energy from the outdoors at 10°F and transferring energy into a home at 70°F would have a cop of

$$\text{cop} = \frac{530}{530 - 470} = 8.8$$

This means that the homeowner would be getting energy into the house equal to almost nine times the electrical energy showing up on his utility bill. A practical heat pump might have a cop of 3 to 4, but even this makes a heat pump far superior to direct electric-resistance heating from the point of view of utility costs.†

The Carnot cycle is very useful in estimating limits of efficiency for given operating temperatures; no real system limited by the same temperatures could exceed the performance of a Carnot cycle, since the efficiency of any irreversible $2T$ engine is less than Carnot-cycle efficiency. Unfortunately, it is very difficult to build a real device to operate on the Carnot cycle,‡ and its chief value is as a standard of comparison for real energy-conversion and refrigeration systems.

9·3 PATTERN PROCESSES

In thermodynamic analysis one often knows the initial state of a substance and can compute the work done or the energy transferred as heat only if something is known about the process undergone by the substance. The analyst frequently has to make appropriate idealizations in order to render the analysis

† The capital cost of the heat pump would, however, be significantly greater.
‡ The inherent difficulty in building an operating Carnot cycle arises from the difficulty of obtaining isothermal compression and expansion by proper control of the energy transfers as heat and work.

tractable; the idealized processes employed are frequently referred to as *pattern processes*. For example, if a gas is being compressed very slowly in a massive container, there would be plenty of time for energy to be transferred as heat, and a good idealization might be that the gas is always at the container temperature, that is, that the process is isothermal. In this case the isothermal process would be called the pattern process, and it represents a simplified model of what actually might occur.

When a substance undergoes a process very rapidly there will be little time for energy transfer as heat to occur, and we might make the idealization that the process is adiabatic. If, in addition, the irreversibilities discussed in Chap. Seven are not too important, it might also be appropriate to idealize that the process is reversible. The second law tells us that the entropy of matter undergoing a process which is both reversible and adiabatic will not change. Such an isentropic process is the pattern process normally employed for

> Restrained adiabatic compression or expansion of a gas in a piston-cylinder system
> Compression or expansion of a fluid in a steady-flow adiabatic compressor, turbine, or pump
> Frictionless adiabatic flow of a substance through a duct
> Adiabatic magnetization or demagnetization
> Adiabatic polarization or depolarization

The actual process may not be very close to the pattern process, and in such cases the analyst often introduces some sort of *performance parameter* to account at least partially for the departures from the idealized behavior. For example, in analysis of *turbines* we would introduce the *isentropic efficiency*, defined as

$$\blacktriangleright \qquad \eta_s \equiv \frac{W}{W_s} \qquad\qquad\qquad (9 \cdot 6)$$

Here W represents the work output which would be measured from an actual adiabatic turbine, and W_s is the theoretical work output of an isentropic-process turbine *operating with the same inlet state and discharge pressure*. The isentropic efficiency is not an energy-conversion efficiency, but rather a parameter which compares an actual device to an ideal (pattern) device. Second-law analysis indicates that $\eta_s \leq 1$. The value of η_s depends upon the design of the turbine blades, nozzle, and diffuser, and prediction of efficiencies requires some fairly sophisticated fluid-mechanical analysis. Small turbines have isentropic efficiencies of the order of 60 to 80 percent; large steam and gas turbines with isentropic efficiencies of the order of 96 percent have been built in recent years.

The designer of a power system would use an estimate of the turbine isentropic efficiency in his system analysis. This estimate would be based on experience with typical turbines of comparable power rating. The turbine manufacturer would have to meet this minimum efficiency specification as part of his contract, and in his engineering of the turbine he would make rather complex fluid-mechanical calculations in an attempt to predict the performance of trial designs. Having settled on the best design, he would fabricate a prototype, and test it to determine its operating characteristics, including its isentropic efficiency. If the efficiency is better than the original specified minimum, then the power system designer would certainly set higher minimum specifications in his next power plant design. So goes engineering.

To illustrate the evaluation of the isentropic efficiency, let's suppose that test data on a steam turbine yield

inlet state	outlet state
$T_1 = 700°F$	$T_2 = 450°F$
$P_1 = 500$ psia	$P_2 = 150$ psia

From the equations-of-state information for H_2O (Appendix B), we have

$h_1 = 1357.0$ Btu/lbm	$h_2 = 1245$ Btu/lbm
$s_1 = 1.6115$ Btu/lbm-°R	$s_2 = 1.63$ Btu/lbm-°R

An energy balance on the turbine, assuming it is adiabatic and neglecting kinetic and potential energy changes, gives (Fig. 9·7)

$$W = h_1 - h_2$$

where W is the work output per lbm of flow. Hence, if the turbine process were isentropic, we would have

$$W_s = h_1 - h_{2s}$$

where state $2s$ is fixed by the *inlet* entropy and the *exit* pressure (see Fig. 9·7).

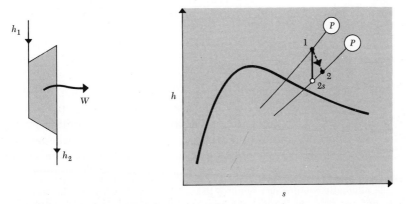

FIG. 9·7   *The isentropic efficiency can be determined from laboratory data*

Using Fig. B·2, the reference state $2s$ is

$$s_{2s} = s_1 = 1.6115 \text{ Btu/lbm-°R}$$
$$P_{2s} = P_2 = 150 \text{ psia}$$
$$h_{2s} = 1225 \text{ Btu/lbm}$$
$$T_{2s} = 415°F$$

Hence,

$$W = 1357 - 1245 = 112 \text{ Btu/lbm}$$
$$W_s = 1357 - 1225 = 132 \text{ Btu/lbm}$$
$$\eta_s = \frac{W}{W_s} = \frac{112}{132} = 0.85$$

Examples illustrating the use of the isentropic efficiency in design calculations are included with the system analyses in this chapter.

Compressors and pumps are handled in a similar way. The isentropic efficiency of an *adiabatic* compressor, or pump, is defined as

$$\blacktriangleright \qquad \eta_s \equiv \frac{W_s}{W} \qquad\qquad\qquad (9\cdot7)$$

Since the work required to produce a given pressure rise in an actual adiabatic compressor is greater than that for an isentropic compressor, η_s is always† less than 1, as we showed from the second law in Sec. 7·17. The ideal and actual devices are considered to have the same inlet state and the same discharge pressure. Small centrifugal hydraulic pumps have efficiencies of the order of 40–60 percent; the axial and centrifugal compressors employed in gas-turbine power plants and in jet engines have isentropic efficiencies in the range of 75–85 percent. The fact that small gas-turbine power systems have become practical realities in recent years is largely a result of advances in technology which have produced these levels of compressor efficiencies.

Isentropic efficiencies of *nozzles* are defined in terms of the discharge kinetic energy of the actual device compared to that for an ideal isentropic nozzle,

$$\blacktriangleright \qquad \eta_s \equiv \frac{(V^2/2g_c)}{(V^2/2g_c)_s} \qquad\qquad\qquad (9\cdot8)$$

The ideal and actual nozzles are considered to have the same inlet state and the same discharge pressure. Nozzle efficiencies are typically quite high (of the order of 90–95 percent); the main irreversibility is due to friction on the walls, and this is usually of minor importance, especially in very large nozzles.

Fluid flowing through a heat exchanger, nuclear reactor, or combustion

† If energy is transferred as heat from the actual compressor, η_s can exceed unity. Reversible adiabatic compression requires less work than irreversible adiabatic compression, but reversible isothermal compression requires even less work for a given pressure increase.

chamber is retarded by friction. However, in well-designed systems the resulting pressure drop can be made quite small, and consequently the pressure is very nearly equal at every point in the flow.† The pattern process for fluid being heated in steady flow is therefore one of *constant pressure*. The analyst will often assume some pressure drop, based on experience or other calculations, in order to make a slightly better calculation. However, the constant-pressure pattern process is usually quite satisfactory for preliminary system studies.

The use of pattern processes and component efficiencies allows us to make thermodynamic calculations of system performance without knowledge of the details of the hardware construction. We can learn a great deal about a proposed system from the process representation for fluid which circulates through the device. Temperature-entropy diagrams are particularly useful for reasons already mentioned. The *Mollier diagram* (*h-s* plane) is also very useful; vertical distances on this diagram are proportional to the energy transfer as work per lbm for an adiabatic compressor or turbine and to the energy transfer as heat for a steady-flow heater. Furthermore, the isentropic process conveniently appears as a vertical line, allowing the end state for an idealized adiabatic process to be found easily. In approaching a new system it is generally a good idea first to make a simple schematic flow diagram and then to sketch the process representation on an appropriate thermodynamic plane. Working out the process representation provides an understanding of how the system works and of any limitations imposed by the second law and orients thinking as to how to proceed with first-law analysis. We shall illustrate these ideas in the sections to follow.

9·4 A PARTICULAR VAPOR POWER SYSTEM

Thermodynamics developed as a result of nineteenth-century work with reciprocating steam engines. Present-day applications of thermodynamics go well beyond this single area, but vapor power systems remain a major source of electrical power and continue to grow in importance with the perfection of nuclear-reactor boilers.

Modern vapor power systems employ rotating rather than reciprocating machinery, for numerous practical reasons. The flow diagram and process representation for a simple *Rankine cycle* are shown in Fig. 9·8. We treat a somewhat idealized system for simplicity. Liquid is compressed by the pump and fed to the boiler. The boiler evaporates the fluid and delivers high-pressure vapor to the power-producing turbine. In the system shown, the turbine discharges to the atmosphere, and the only fluid which we might possibly afford to throw away in this manner is water.

To get some feeling for vapor power systems and to illustrate the general method of system analysis, we shall now analyze this system. Let us assume

† For a constant-area duct.

FIG. 9·8 *A simple Rankine vapor power system*

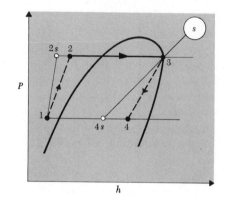

the following:

> Working fluid, water
> State 1, liquid at 80°F and 1 atm
> State 2, 100 psia
> State 3, saturated vapor at 100 psia
> State 4, 1 atm pressure
> $\eta_s = 0.60$ for pump, $\eta_s = 0.80$ for turbine
> Kinetic and potential energies negligible at states 1, 2, 3, and 4; pump and turbine adiabatic
> Steady flow steady state, water in thermodynamic equilibrium at 1, 2, 3, and 4

An energy balance on the pump yields

$$W_P = h_2 - h_1$$

where W_P is the shaft-work input for each unit of mass handled by the pump. Having no tabular or graphical equation-of-state information for subcooled liquid water, we shall treat it as an incompressible liquid.† Using Eq. (8·42),

---

† For the incompressible liquid undergoing an isentropic process $s_2 = s_1$ and therefore $T_{2s} = T_1$. Thus point $2s$ on Fig. 9·8 would lie directly on top of point 1 in the incompressible model.

the W_P for an ideal adiabatic pump would be (isentropic process)

$$W_{Ps} = v(P_{2s} - P_1)$$

From Table B·1, $v = 0.0161$ ft³/lbm. Then,

$$W_{Ps} = 0.0161 \times (100 - 14.7) \times \frac{144}{778} = 0.253 \text{ Btu/lbm}$$

The actual device then requires

$$W_P = \frac{W_s}{\eta_s} = \frac{0.253}{0.6} = 0.42 \text{ Btu/lbm}$$

The value of h_1 may be found using the incompressible-liquid equation of state in conjunction with the tabulated thermodynamic properties. This particular case was worked as an example in Sec. 8·5, where we found $h_1 = 48.06$ Btu/lbm. We therefore determine h_2 as

$$h_2 = h_1 + W_P = 48.06 + 0.42 = 48.48 \text{ Btu/lbm}$$

T_2 may be found from Eq. (8·42),

$$T_2 = T_1 + \frac{(h_2 - h_1) - v(P_2 - P_1)}{c}$$

$$= 80 + \frac{0.42 - 0.25}{1.0} = 80.2°\text{F}$$

Note the very small work requirement of the pump and the very slight temperature rise.

From Table B·1B we find $h_3 = 1187.2$ Btu/lbm. An energy balance on the boiler then gives

$$Q_B = h_3 - h_2 = 1187.2 - 48.48 = 1138.7 \text{ Btu/lbm}$$

where Q_B is the energy transfer as heat to the boiler per lbm of water.

An energy balance on the turbine yields

$$W_T = h_3 - h_4$$

where W_T is the shaft-work output per lbm of fluid. To determine state 4 we must first fix state 4s. From Table B·1B we read

$$s_3 = 1.6026 \text{ Btu/lbm-°R}$$
$$s_{f4} = 0.3120 \text{ Btu/lbm-°R} \qquad s_{g4} = 1.7566 \text{ Btu/lbm-°R} \qquad \text{(at 1 atm)}$$
$$s_{fg4} = s_{g4} - s_{f4} = 1.4446 \text{ Btu/lbm-°R} \qquad \text{(at 1 atm)}$$

Since $s_{4s} = s_3$,

$$s_{4s} = (1 - x_{4s})s_{f4} + x_{4s}s_{g4} = s_{f4} + x_{4s}s_{fg4}$$
$$x_{4s} = \frac{1.6026 - 0.3120}{1.4446} = 0.893$$

Again in Table B·1B we find

$$h_{f4} = 180.07 \text{ Btu/lbm}$$
$$h_{fg4} = 970.3 \text{ Btu/lbm} \qquad \text{(at 1 atm)}$$

Thus

$$h_{s4} = h_{f4} + x_{4s}h_{fg4} = 180 + 0.893 \times 970.3 = 1046 \text{ Btu/lbm}$$

Consequently,

$$W_{Ts} = h_3 - h_{4s} = 1187 - 1046 = 141 \text{ Btu/lbm}$$

Then

$$W_T = W_{Ts}\eta_s = 141 \times 0.8 = 112 \text{ Btu/lbm}$$
$$h_4 = h_3 - W_T = 1187 - 112 = 1075 \text{ Btu/lbm}$$

The discharge quality is then

$$x_4 = \frac{h_4 - h_{f4}}{h_{fg4}} = \frac{1075 - 180}{970} = 0.922$$

Note that the turbine-discharge temperature is 212°F, so that the steam which is thrown away is quite energetic.

To summarize, we have found

$$W_T = 112 \text{ Btu/lbm}$$
$$W_P = 0.4 \text{ Btu/lbm}$$
$$Q_B = 1139 \text{ Btu/lbm}$$

Part of the turbine work is required to drive the pump. One of the attractive features of vapor power plants is that this is a small fraction of the turbine-work output. In this particular case the back-work ratio is

$$\text{bwr} = \frac{W_P}{W_T} = \frac{0.4}{112} \approx 0.004$$

The energy-conversion efficiency of this plant is then

$$\eta = \frac{W_{\text{net}}}{Q_B} = \frac{112 - 0.4}{1139} = 0.099$$

Since $P_1 = P_4$ in this example, we could close the cycle with the addition of a condenser. Keeping states 1 and 2 fixed, this additional device would not influence the efficiency of the system. The energy that would be transferred as heat from the condenser can be determined by an overall energy balance, which yields

$$Q_C = Q_B - W_{\text{net}} = 1139 - 111.6 = 1027 \text{ Btu/lbm}$$

Most of the energy fed into the boiler as heat would be thrown away in the condenser; only 9.9 percent is converted to useful shaft work.

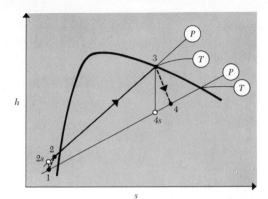

FIG. 9·9 *Process representation on the h-s plane*

The series of processes is also shown on an h-s plot in Fig. 9·9. This plot graphically shows the small back-work ratio as the respective enthalpy changes for the pump and turbine processes.

It is instructive to compare the energy-conversion efficiency of this system to that of a Carnot cycle operating between the same temperatures ($T_3 = 327.81°F$ and $T_1 = 80°F$). For the Carnot cycle

$$\eta = 1 - \frac{460 + 80}{460 + 328} = 0.315$$

Some of the difference can be attributed to irreversibilities in the turbine, but the major difference is due to the fact that the temperatures at which energy is transferred as heat to and from the working fluid are more widely separated for the Carnot cycle (see Fig. 9·10). Note that the area enclosed by the vapor-cycle process path is not equal to the net work output per lbm of fluid, since the processes which we treated were not all reversible. The performance of this plant is dismally poor by modern standards. In the next sections we shall

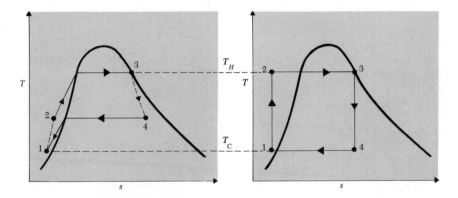

FIG. 9·10 *Comparison with a Carnot cycle*

examine some ways of obtaining better performance, making considerable use of process representations to show why improvements are obtained.

9·5 MODERN UTILIZATION OF THE RANKINE CYCLE

Two simple changes can provide considerable improvement in the energy-conversion efficiency of the system discussed in the previous section. Noting that the turbine work output would be enhanced if the turbine discharge pressure were lower, we might try to create a low-pressure region into which the turbine can discharge. This is accomplished with the addition of a condenser (Fig. 9·11), in which the steam can be condensed at a temperature closer to the environment temperature. For example, if river water is available at 60°F, then it would not be difficult to condense the steam at 100°F by transferring energy as heat to the cooler river water. The steam side of the condenser would operate at a pressure of 0.949 psia (Table B·1A), considerably less than atmospheric, and by inspection of the *h-s* diagram of Fig. 9·11 we see that the turbine work output per lbm of steam could be nearly doubled. The condensed H_2O (the *condensate*) would have to be pumped from this low pressure to the boiler inlet pressure, but as the work required to pressurize a liquid is very small compared to the work obtained in the expansion of a gas (the steam), a considerable net gain can be obtained.

Using a condenser permits continual circulation of the same working fluid, which means that purified water (which is less corrosive than tap water) can be used as the working fluid. This is a practical advantage of the *closed Rankine cycle*. A practical problem with condensing water at temperatures less than 212°F is that the pressure inside the condenser is less than 1 atm. This means that any leaks in the condenser shell will permit air to contaminate the working fluid, making it difficult to maintain the low condensing pressure. Consequently, condensing systems are always equipped with vacuum pumps that initiate the low pressure when the system is started and that remove small amounts of air which inevitably leak into the condenser. Steam-driven *jet pumps*, or jet

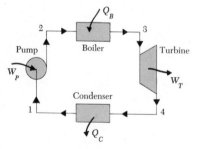

FIG. 9·11 *By condensing at a low pressure, the turbine work output can be markedly increased*

High
pressure
steam

Jet ejector

Low pressure
steam

FIG. 9·12 *Schematic of a steam condenser with jet ejector*

Cooling
water

Condensate

ejectors, are often used. In these devices a small amount of high-pressure steam is bled from the main line and fed through a venturi-like device in which the steam accelerates until its pressure is reduced to somewhat below the condensing pressure. The air can then be sucked up by the "venturi action," and the steam then slowed down with a resulting pressure rise and then discharged to the atmosphere. Figure 9·12 shows a schematic of a typical steam condenser and the jet pumps used to maintain the low pressure against leakage from the atmosphere.

When the turbine operates over a large pressure range the density variation within the turbine can be enormous. Such turbines are usually made in multiple stages, with each stage operating over a more modest pressure range (say 2:1). Sometimes the stages are separate machines on the same shaft, and sometimes the stages are all incorporated into a single large machine. Because of the wide density variation, the high-pressure stages are much smaller than the low-pressure stages, though the power outputs from the various stages are typically about the same.

If the quality of the steam in the turbine drops too low, the liquid droplets can impact upon the blades, causing serious damage. Hence it is usually the practice to maintain at least 90 percent quality ($x = 0.9$) in the low-pressure stage, and this places a lower limit on the condenser operating pressure. Cycle modifications which we are about to discuss (superheat and reheat) help solve this practical problem and permit turbine operation over wider pressure ranges.

We can think about the improvement offered by condensing in a somewhat different way. The open Rankine cycle (Fig. 9·8) is essentially closed by the atmosphere, and energy is rejected from the H_2O as heat at the condensing pressure of 212°F. By adding the condenser we permit the energy to be rejected from the closed Rankine system, which is a heat engine, at lower temperatures. Our discussions of the implications of the second law, and in particular of the Carnot cycle, indicate that improved efficiencies are obtained by rejecting energy as heat at as low a temperature as possible, and by adding energy as heat at as high a temperature as possible. The condenser in effect permits heat rejection at a lower temperature.

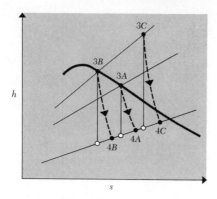

FIG. 9·13 *Note that superheating increases the turbine work output and reduces problems caused by low quality*

The energy addition as heat can also be put in at a higher (average) temperature by operating the boiler at a higher pressure. This will bring some practical problems of the sort discussed above, particularly in regard to the quality of the turbine steam. But we are not limited to saturated vapor at the boiler discharge. We can add further energy as heat to the steam, either in the boiler or in a separate heat exchanger (a *superheater*), and raise the temperature of the steam still further (at constant pressure in the pattern process). Figure 9·13 shows the *h-s* process representations for three turbines operating at the same discharge pressure. Turbine *A* operates over a small pressure range with saturated vapor at the inlet. *B* operates over a larger pressure range, also with saturated vapor at the inlet, and we see that the discharge quality is considerably lower in *B* than in *A*. However, the work output per lbm of fluid ($h_3 - h_4$) is greater in *B* than in *A*, so that while *B* is practically "worse" it is in principle "better" than *A*. Turbine *C* operates with superheated steam at the inlet, and is better than either *B* or *A*, for not only is the work output per lbm better but the turbine discharge steam can be maintained at a much higher quality. Hence, in modern power plants, the turbine operating conditions are almost always most like *C*.

Substantial gains in performance can be obtained by the simple modifications discussed above. To illustrate, let's analyze the system of Fig. 9·14. Note that we have set the turbine inlet state in the superheat region at 600 psia and 1000°F, and the condensing temperature at 80°F; these values are typical of modern power plants.

The idealizations we shall make in the analysis are that the pump and turbines are adiabatic devices, that the heating and cooling processes take place at constant pressure, and that the flow stream kinetic and potential energy changes are negligible. We shall also assume that the isentropic efficiencies of the pump and turbine are 0.8 and 0.9, respectively, typical values for reasonably large present-day machines.

By these assumptions, the pump inlet pressure is 0.506 psia (Table B·1A) and its discharge pressure is 600 psia. An energy balance on the pump yields for

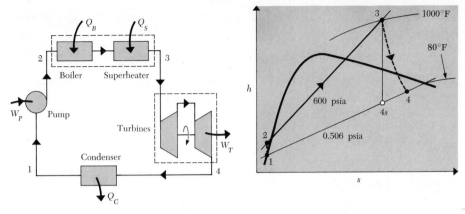

FIG. 9·14   *The model power system*

the pump work per lbm of liquid flow

$$W_P = h_2 - h_1$$

State 1 is fixed, and we shall establish state 2 and W_P, treating the liquid as incompressible. From Table B·1A,

$$h_1 = 48.02 \text{ Btu/lbm}$$

Using the incompressible-liquid equation of state,

$$h_{2s} = h_1 + v(P_2 - P_1) = 48.02 + 0.01607 \times (600 - 0.5)^{144}/_{778}$$
$$= 49.7 \text{ Btu/lbm}$$

Hence, were the pump isentropic,

$$W_{Ps} = 49.7 - 48.0 = 1.7 \text{ Btu/lbm}$$

For our actual pump,

$$W_P = \frac{W_{Ps}}{\eta_s} = \frac{1.7}{0.8} = 2.1 \text{ Btu/lbm}$$

This establishes the boiler inlet enthalpy as

$$h_2 = h_1 + W_P = 48.0 + 2.1 = 50.1 \text{ Btu/lbm}$$

The superheater discharge enthalpy is fixed by the specification of the turbine inlet state. From Table B·2

$$h_3 = 1516.7 \text{ Btu/lbm} \qquad s_3 = 1.7147 \text{ Btu/lbm-°R}$$

An energy balance on the boiler-superheater combination gives

$$Q_{\text{in}} \equiv Q_B + Q_S = h_3 - h_2$$

where Q_B and Q_S are the boiler and superheater heat inputs per lbm of flow. Hence,

$$Q_{in} = Q_B + Q_S = 1516.7 - 50.1 = 1466.6 \text{ Btu/lbm}$$

The student may make some appropriate assumptions about the boiler discharge state and calculate the amounts of Q_B and Q_S separately.

Now, an energy balance on all the turbine stages gives

$$W_T = h_3 - h_4$$

where W_T is the total turbine work output per lbm of steam. To establish state 4 we first must establish the reference state 4s. This state is fixed by its entropy and pressure. Looking at the h-s diagram, Fig. B·2, we see that state 4s lies in the vapor dome. Table B · 1A confirms this, for the saturated-vapor entropy at 80°F is 2.0360, which is indeed greater than s_3. We can use the value of $s_{4s} = s_3$ to calculate the quality at state 4s, and then use this quality to calculate h_{4s}. We have

$$s_{4s} = [(1 - x)s_f + xs_g]_{4s}$$

so

$$x_{4s} = \frac{s_{4s} - s_{f4s}}{s_{fg4s}} = \frac{1.714 - 0.093}{1.943} = 0.835$$

Then,

$$\begin{aligned} h_{4s} &= [(1 - x)h_f + xh_g]_{4s} \\ &= 0.15 \times 48.0 + 0.835 \times 1096.6 = 922 \text{ Btu/lbm} \end{aligned}$$

Note that we could have read this value from Fig. B·2, though not to the same accuracy. The work output from an isentropic turbine would therefore be

$$W_{Ts} = 1517 - 922 = 595 \text{ Btu/lbm}$$

The work output from our actual device is therefore

$$W_T = W_{Ts}\eta_s = 595 \times 0.9 = 535 \text{ Btu/lbm}$$

The actual turbine discharge enthalpy is therefore

$$h_4 = h_3 - W_T = 1517 - 535 = 982 \text{ Btu/lbm}$$

This enthalpy, together with the known pressure P_4, fixes state 4. From Fig. B·2 we see that the turbine discharge quality is about 0.90, which is probably acceptable.

Finally, the condenser heat transfer could be calculated from an energy balance on the condenser. This is left to the student as an exercise.

We now can calculate the plant performance. The net work output per lbm of fluid circulated is

$$W_{net} = W_T - W_P = 535 - 2.1 = 533 \text{ Btu/lbm}$$

Note that again a rather small amount of the turbine power is required by the pump. The plant energy-conversion efficiency is then

$$\eta = \frac{W_{net}}{Q_{in}} = \frac{533}{1467} = 0.363$$

This efficiency of 36.3 percent is a considerable improvement over the 8.9 percent of the previous example, and would cut the cost of power by about a factor of 4. This efficiency is typical of a relatively small central power station, and efficiencies of the order of 40 percent can be obtained with further cycle modifications to be discussed shortly.

The designer of a power plant would carry out the calculations described above, which we note were on a "per lbm" basis. After these are completed, the mass flow rate can be determined by the design power requirements for this system. For example, if 1 Mw is the electrical power output required, then

$$\dot{W}_{elect} = 10^6 \times 3.41 = 3.41 \times 10^6 \text{ Btu/hr}$$

If the efficiency of the electrical generator is, say, 0.98, then the plant shaft power would have to be

$$\dot{W} = 3.41 \times \frac{10^6}{0.98} = 3.5 \times 10^6 \text{ Btu/hr}$$

Since the turbine shaft work is 535 Btu/lbm, and the pump requires 2 Btu/lbm, the flow requirement is

$$\dot{M} = \frac{\dot{W}}{W_{net}} = 3.5 \times \frac{10^6}{533} = 6550 \text{ lbm/hr}$$

Hence the energy transfer rates for the several components are

$$\dot{W}_P = \dot{M}W_P = 6550 \times 2.1 = 13.7 \times 10^3 \text{ Btu/hr} = 5.4 \text{ hp}$$
$$\dot{W}_T = \dot{M}W_T = 6550 \times 535 = 3.50 \times 10^6 \text{ Btu/hr} = 1370 \text{ hp}$$
$$\dot{Q}_{in} = \dot{M}Q_{in} = 6550 \times 1467 = 9.6 \times 10^6 \text{ Btu/hr}$$

The power plant designer would then send out for bids on the components. The specifications might be as follows:

Pump
inlet 0.5 psia, sat liquid
discharge to 600 psia
minimum isentropic efficiency 0.8
design flow rate 6550 lbm/hr

Turbine
inlet 1000°F, 600 psia
discharge to 0.5 psia
minimum isentropic efficiency 0.9
design flow rate 6550 lbm/hr at 1800 rpm

Boiler-superheater
operating pressure 600 psia
inlet at 80°F, discharge superheated steam at 1000°F
design flow 6550 lbm/hr (nominal duty 10^7 Btu/hr)

It would then be up to the manufacturers of the components to design and deliver components meeting these specifications. The general plant designer would coordinate these designs to ensure that they fit into the space available in a reasonable and economic way. His specifications would probably include some piping sizes, component maximum sizes, weights, and so on, which he could estimate on the basis of previous experience with similar systems, with the help of appropriate engineering calculations.

9·6 OTHER RANKINE CYCLE MODIFICATIONS

A Rankine cycle modification normally employed in large central power stations is *reheat* (Fig. 9·15). The steam discharging from the first-stage turbine is reheated before being fed to the second-stage turbine, and as a study of the *h-s* diagram reveals, this provides the second-stage turbine with a larger possible enthalpy change. While the work output per lbm will be enhanced, the efficiency may be reduced or increased, depending on the reheat temperature range. To illustrate, suppose we reheat between the turbine stages in the example of the previous section, with a reheater pressure of 60 psia. We will reheat to 1000°F, and assume that the isentropic efficiencies of both turbine stages are 0.90. By appropriate thermodynamic analysis as illustrated previously we can establish the intermediate states as follows (see Fig. 9·15):

$h_3 = 1517$ Btu/lbm $h_4 = 1265$ Btu/lbm
$h_5 = 1532$ Btu/lbm $h_6 = 1110$ Btu/lbm

The work outputs per lbm for the two turbine stages are then

$W_{T1} = h_3 - h_4 = 1517 - 1265 = 252$ Btu/lbm
$W_{T2} = h_5 - h_6 = 1532 - 1110 = 422$ Btu/lbm

and the reheater energy input per lbm is

$Q_R = h_5 - h_4 = 1532 - 1265 = 267$ Btu/lbm

The boiler heat input and pump work are as before. The net work output and heat input per lbm are therefore

$W_{net} = 252 + 422 - 2.1 = 672$ Btu/lbm
$Q_{in} = 1467 + 267 = 1734$ Btu/lbm

Note that the work output has increased from 535 Btu/lbm to 672 Btu/lbm.

FIG. 9·15 *Reheat in the Rankine cycle*

(a) *The hardware*

(b) *T-s process representation*

(c) *h-s process representation*

The cycle efficiency is now

$$\eta = \frac{W_{\text{net}}}{Q_{\text{in}}} = \frac{672}{1734} = 0.387$$

The increase of 2.4 percentage points in efficiency amounts to nearly a 10 percent increase in efficiency, and hence nearly a 10 percent reduction in fuel costs for a given power output. In a small power station this gain might not offset the additional capital investment in system hardware, maintenance, and other items, but in a large power station the gain would most certainly be worth the investment. Large modern power plants normally employ several stages of reheat, each of which inches the efficiency upward by a small but not insignificant amount.

Another modification normally employed in large power stations is *extraction and regeneration*, or *feedwater heating* (Fig. 9·16). Part of the flow emerging from the first-stage turbine is bled off and condensed. The energy transferred from this fluid is added as heat to the low-temperature liquid emerg-

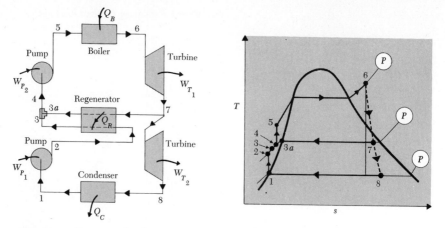

FIG. 9·16 *Regenerative Rankine cycle with a closed feedwater heater*

ing from the main pump. The only energy that must be added as heat from *outside* the system is that required to take the total stream from state 5 to state 6, and a considerable improvement in efficiency can be obtained.

Two basic types of regenerative heaters are used. Figure 9·16 shows a *closed* feedwater heater (the regenerator). Figure 9·17 shows the *open* feedwater heater, in which the extracted steam is mixed directly with liquid from the low-pressure condenser. To illustrate the effects of regeneration, let's add an open feedwater heater to the Rankine cycle (with reheat) analyzed above. The pressure between turbine stages will again be taken as 60 psia, and we shall extract just enough steam at the reheat pressure to heat the water emerging from the first pump to the saturation line. The pressure drop in the feedwater heater will be neglected. With these assumptions, we have enough information to fix the

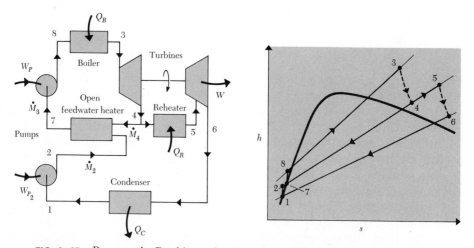

FIG. 9·17 *Regenerative Rankine cycle with an open feedwater heater*

states indicated on Fig. 9·17, by appropriate thermodynamic analysis, and these are tabulated below.

State	P, psia	T, °F	h, Btu/lbm
1	0.5	80	48.0
2	60	80.2	48.2
3	600	1000	1517
4	60	475	1265
5	60	1000	1532
6	0.5	115	1110
7	60	292	262
8	600	294	264

We next calculate the *extraction fraction*, $\dot{M}_4/\dot{M}_3$, from mass and energy balances on the open regenerator (what idealizations do the equations below imply?)

$$\dot{M}_2 h_2 + \dot{M}_4 h_4 = \dot{M}_3 h_7$$
$$\dot{M}_2 + \dot{M}_4 = \dot{M}_3$$

Combining,

$$\frac{\dot{M}_4}{\dot{M}_3} = \frac{h_7 - h_2}{h_4 - h_2} = \frac{214}{1217} = 0.175$$

Then,

$$\frac{\dot{M}_2}{\dot{M}_3} = 1 - 0.175 = 0.825$$

Energy balances on the components then allow us to express their energy transfers per lbm of *total* flow,

$$\frac{\dot{W}_{T1}}{\dot{M}_3} = h_3 - h_4 = 252 \text{ Btu/lbm}$$

$$\frac{\dot{W}_{T2}}{\dot{M}_3} = \left(\frac{\dot{M}_2}{\dot{M}_3}\right)(h_5 - h_6) = 0.825 \times 422 = 348 \text{ Btu/lbm}$$

$$\frac{\dot{W}_{P1}}{\dot{M}_3} = \left(\frac{\dot{M}_2}{\dot{M}_3}\right)(h_2 - h_1) = 0.825 \times 0.2 = 0.16 \text{ Btu/lbm}$$

$$\frac{\dot{W}_{P2}}{\dot{M}_3} = h_8 - h_7 = 2 \text{ Btu/lbm}$$

$$\frac{\dot{Q}_B}{\dot{M}_3} = h_3 - h_8 = 1253 \text{ Btu/lbm}$$

$$\frac{\dot{Q}_R}{\dot{M}_3} = \left(\frac{\dot{M}_2}{\dot{M}_3}\right)(h_5 - h_4) = 0.825 \times 267 = 220 \text{ Btu/lbm}$$

The net work output and heat input, per lbm of total flow, are then

$$\frac{\dot{W}_{net}}{\dot{M}_3} = 252 + 348 - 0.16 - 2 = 598 \text{ Btu/lbm}$$

$$\frac{\dot{Q}_{in}}{\dot{M}_3} = 1253 + 220 = 1473 \text{ Btu/lbm}$$

Note that these have both been reduced by the extraction process. The system energy-conversion efficiency is

$$\eta = \frac{\dot{W}_{net}}{\dot{Q}_{in}} = \frac{598}{1473} = 0.405$$

So, from the total performance point of view, the extraction and regeneration have improved the system. The student should particularly note the need for careful consideration of the mass flow rate variations in analyzing systems in which the flow rate is not the same everywhere in the system.

In theory, if an infinite number of extraction and regeneration stages could be employed, the external addition of energy as heat would take place at one temperature and the external removal of energy as heat would take place isothermally in the low-pressure condenser. The performance of this limiting

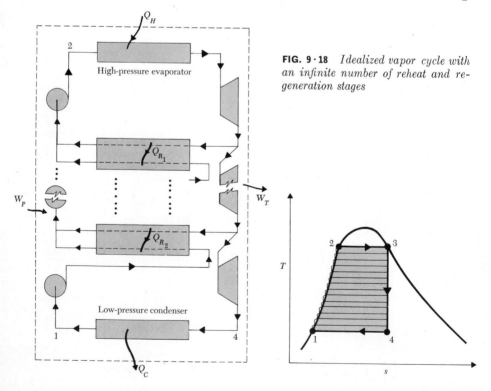

FIG. 9·18 *Idealized vapor cycle with an infinite number of reheat and regeneration stages*

system is then that of a reversible $2T$ engine, that is, of a Carnot cycle. This is very interesting, for the process representation does not look much like that of the Carnot cycle (see Fig. 9·18). In large central power stations employing reheat, regeneration, and extraction, efficiencies of the order of 35 to 40 percent have been obtained by using several (4 to 7) stages of regeneration. Extensive optimization calculations are normally a part of the design of any such system.

9·7 SOME THOUGHTS ON THE WORKING FLUID

We have used water as the working fluid in the vapor power cycle examples of this chapter. Indeed, water is the most common fluid in large central power stations, though by no means is it the only fluid used in vapor power systems. What are desirable properties for the working fluid? In view of our previous discussions, these would certainly seem to be important factors:

1 *High critical temperature*—to permit evaporation at a high temperature.
2 *Low saturation pressures at the maximum temperatures*—to minimize the pressure vessel and piping costs.
3 *Pressure just above 1 atm at condensing temperature*—to eliminate air leakage problems.
4 *Rapidly diverging pressure lines on the h-s diagram*—to minimize the back-work ratio and to make reheat modifications most effective.
5 *Large enthalpy of evaporation*—to minimize the mass flow rate for given power output.
6 *No degrading aspects*—noncorrosive, nonclogging.
7 *No hazardous features*—nontoxic, inflammable.
8 *Low cost and ready availability.*

It is evident that water is rather good only in regard to items 4, 5, 7, and 8 above. There are many other fluids that are better on the other items, as examination of the data in Appendix B will reveal. But, on an overall basis for ground-based power plants, water remains a predominant choice, and hence steam power engineering remains an interesting and important area of applied thermodynamics.

Vapor power cycles for use in space generally use other working fluids, such as mercury and rubidium. These fluids have reasonable vapor pressures at high temperatures, which is necessary because space power systems normally operate with maximum temperatures of 2000°F and condensing temperatures of 800 to 1400°F. These high condensing temperatures are required to minimize the weight of the condenser, which must be a radiator in a space environment. Vapor power cycles for very cold temperatures may work better with such fluids as CO_2 or freon. The environment, application, utilization, and budget must all be considered in selecting the working fluid for any power system.

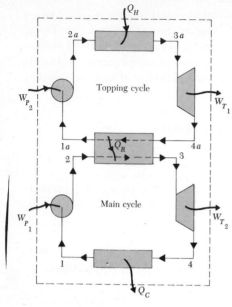

FIG. 9·19 *The binary vapor cycle*

9·8 OTHER VAPOR POWER CYCLES

In order to take advantage of the suitability of water in a relatively low-temperature Rankine cycle and the preference for other fluids, such as mercury, in high-temperature Rankine cycles, one can use the *binary vapor power system* (Fig. 9·19). Here two separate Rankine systems are combined, with the heat rejection from the high-temperature cycle being used as the energy source for the low-temperature cycle. Many systems of this type have been studied theoretically, but few have been put into operation. One operating system uses mercury in the high-temperature cycle (the *topping cycle*) and steam in the low-temperature cycle, and obtains efficiencies of around 40 percent. As the technology of the exotic fluids is developed for space applications, the ability to use fluids like potassium, rubidium, mercury, and sulfur in topping cycles may well lead to construction of more large central power stations operating on the binary cycle, and theoretical studies show that efficiencies of the order of 50 percent may be realizable in practical power systems of the future.

Another way of obtaining high efficiency is with the *supercritical vapor cycle* (Fig. 9·20). Here the fluid is heated at a pressure in excess of the critical

FIG. 9·20   *The supercritical vapor cycle*

pressure, and hence is transformed continuously from a liquid to a gas. With water the critical pressure is about 3200 psia, so a supercritical steam power plant is indeed a very high-pressure system. There is currently considerable interest in the development of supercritical vapor power systems.

9·9   VAPOR REFRIGERATION SYSTEMS

To refrigerate an area, we must expose that area to a fluid somewhat colder than the desired cold-space temperature. Energy can then be transferred as heat from the cold space to the colder fluid, and this will maintain the cold-space temperature against energy transfer as heat from the warm environment through the insulated cold-space walls. If we do not wish to discard the fluid, it must be circulated through the system in a manner that permits us to remove the energy taken from the cold space. This is generally done in a second heat exchanger, where energy is transferred as heat from the fluid to the environment. Of course the fluid at this point must be slightly warmer than the environment in order for this energy transfer as heat to take place.

Recalling that expansion of a low-quality mixture in a throttling valve produces a marked drop in the fluid temperature, we see that the expansion process provides an easy way to achieve a low fluid temperature. After this cold fluid has been evaporated by extracting energy from the region to be cooled, we must pressurize it again to raise its temperature above the environment temperature so that the heat-rejection process can take place. With these notions we have just reinvented the *vapor-compression refrigeration* cycle. The vapor-compression refrigeration cycle is the pattern cycle for the great majority of refrigeration systems (Fig. 9·21). The cycle is almost the reverse of the

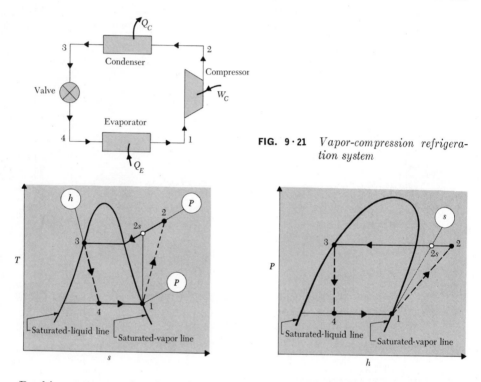

FIG. 9·21 *Vapor-compression refrigeration system*

Rankine power cycle; the difference is that a valve is used to produce the pressure drop, and no attempt is made to extract useful work from this expansion. The amount of work which could be obtained were the valve replaced by an isentropic turbine would be small in comparison with the compressor work requirement, since the volume changes are quite different. Furthermore, the quality of the mixture at state 4 is normally very low, and it is difficult to make a turbine operate for very long in this range. With the valve the cycle can never be reversible, since the throttling process is inherently irreversible.

To illustrate the thermodynamic considerations in the engineering of a refrigeration system, let's design a system for a specific task. Suppose we must maintain a cold space at 15°F in a 70°F environment. Suppose the estimated "heat leak" from the environment to the cold space is 100,000 Btu/hr. We must allow some temperature difference for the heat-transfer processes, so let's set the condensing temperature at 85°F and the evaporation temperature at 0°F. Freon-12 will be used as the working fluid, and following normal refrigeration practice we shall operate the compressor with 10°F superheat at the inlet (meaning 10°F above the saturation temperature at the compressor inlet pressure). The hardware and process representations are as in Fig. 9·21 except that point 1 is slightly in the superheated vapor region. On the basis of experience with reciprocating refrigeration compressors, we assume that a compressor having an isentropic efficiency of 0.85 can be provided.

We first establish the states. An energy balance on the compressor yields (the student should list the implicit idealizations in the margin)

$$W = h_2 - h_1$$

where W is the work input to the compressor per lbm of fluid circulated. By assumption, state 1 is fixed by its pressure and superheat (Fig. B·7, Table B·5):

$P_1 = 23.87$ psia (sat at 0°F)
$T_1 = 10°F$
$h_1 = 79 \, \text{Btu/lbm}$

For the ideal isentropic compressor, state $2s$ is fixed by the entropy (same as state 1) and the pressure,

$P_{2s} = 106$ psia (sat at 85°F) $T_{2s} = 110°F$
$h_{2s} = 90 \, \text{Btu/lbm}$

So, for the hypothetical isentropic compressor,

$$W_s = h_{2s} - h_1 = 90 - 79 = 11 \text{ Btu/lbm}$$

Hence, for our actual machine,

$$W = \frac{W_s}{\eta_s} = \frac{11}{0.85} = 13 \text{ Btu/lbm}$$

So, the discharge enthalpy is

$$h_2 = h_1 + W = 79 + 13 = 92 \text{ Btu/lbm}$$

This value, together with the discharge pressure (106 psia), fixes the compressor discharge state. Note that $T_2 = 120°F$.

State 3 is assumed to correspond to saturated liquid at 85°F, so $h_3 = 27$ Btu/lbm. To fix state 4, we note that an energy balance on the valve gives

$$h_3 = h_4$$

so that state 4 is fixed by the known enthalpy and pressure; from Fig. B·7,

$P_4 = 23.87$ psia $T_4 = 0°F$
$h_4 = 27 \, \text{Btu/lbm}$ $x_4 = 0.25$

Now, energy balances on the evaporator and condenser give, for their energy-transfer rates per lbm of mass flow,

$$Q_C = h_2 - h_3 = 92 - 27 = 65 \text{ Btu/lbm}$$
$$Q_E = h_1 - h_4 = 79 - 27 = 52 \text{ Btu/lbm}$$

and we had

$$W = h_2 - h_1 = 92 - 79 = 13 \text{ Btu/lbm}$$

The *coefficient of performance* of this refrigeration system is then

$$\text{cop} = \frac{Q_E}{W} = \frac{52}{13} = 4.0$$

Note that four times as much energy is pumped out of the cold space as is required by the compressor. Note also that all of the input energy ($Q_E + W$) is removed in the condenser (the overall energy balance also checks).

Now, our design requirement was for $Q_E = 100,000$ Btu/hr. Therefore, the required mass flow rate is

$$\dot{M} = \frac{\dot{Q}_E}{Q_E} = \frac{100,000}{52} = 1920 \text{ lbm/hr}$$

The rating of this unit in *tons of refrigeration* (1 ton = 12,000 Btu/hr, approximately the rate required to freeze 1 ton of ice in a day) is

$$\text{tonnage} = \frac{100,000}{12,000} = 8.3$$

The compressor power input will be

$$\dot{W} = \dot{M}W = 1920 \times 13 = 25,000 \text{ Btu/hr} = 9.85 \text{ hp}$$

Note that the hp/ton is 9.85/8.3 = 1.16. A good rule of thumb is that roughly 1 hp of power is required for each ton of refrigeration (over this sort of operating temperatures).

We might note that this system could be used as a heat pump, in which the 75°F environment into which energy is "pumped" as heat is a house. On a cold day (0°F outside) our heat pump would deliver to the house

$$\dot{Q}_C = \dot{M}Q_C = 1920 \times 65 = 125,000 \text{ Btu/hr}$$

which is indeed comparable with a household gas-fired furnace. However, the homeowner would only have to pay for the electrical power required to run the compressor, which in this case amounts to only 25,000 Btu/hr! The dollar savings over a few cold winters could well offset the high capital outlay required to purchase and maintain the heat pump equipment.†

† But then, if the neighbors are too close they may complain to the heat pump owner about his refrigeration of an already too cold out-of-doors!

Consideration of the Carnot cycle cop indicates that with refrigeration systems the best performance is obtained when the temperature difference over which the system operates is as small as possible. Hence, systems designed for a relatively small "lift" (the temperature to which the energy is "lifted" from the cold space) will have high cop's, while those intended for very cold refrigeration or for use in very hot environments will tend to have poorer performance. The cycle lift must always be somewhat larger than the difference between the cold space and environment temperature, for reasons noted above, but the performance can be improved markedly by good heat-exchanger design in the condenser and evaporator. The closer the condensing temperature can be brought to the environment, the better the performance. The 15°F temperature differences used in this example are typical of modern condensers and evaporators.

Another vapor refrigeration scheme is the *vacuum refrigeration system* that can be employed when refrigeration at temperatures slightly above 32°F is desired. The 32°F limit is set by the freezing point of water, the fluid used in such a system. In this system a steam ejector replaces the compressor, and the only moving parts are the pump impellers. The ejector maintains the flash

FIG. 9·22   *A vacuum refrigeration system*

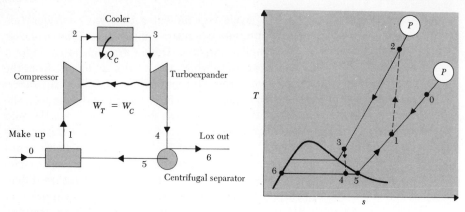

FIG. 9·23 *Oxygen liquefaction*

chamber at a low pressure, where the saturation temperature is at the desired low level. A low-temperature supply of water is thus maintained by the flash evaporation process and this water can then be run through an air conditioning system shown as the chiller in the figure. The system schematic and process representation (idealized) are shown in Fig. 9·22. The refrigeration occurs from the heat input to the chiller. The heat-rejection process occurs in the condensor and is noted as Q_C. Energy input as work is required by the pump.

An interesting application of vapor-compression refrigeration is in the production of liquid oxygen. The simplified system diagram and process representation for one type of lox plant are shown in Fig. 9·23. Note that for this system a turboexpender is used to replace the valve, so that useful work is extracted during the expansion process. However, in this case the expansion is from a superheated vapor state to a high-quality mixture state, whereas in the simple refrigerator the expansion occurs from a saturated liquid state to a low-quality mixture state.

FIG. 9·24 *The absorption refrigeration cycle*

The *absorption refrigeration cycle* is shown in Fig. 9·24. In this system the working fluid, usually ammonia (NH_3), is absorbed into water at low pressure. The liquid solution is then pumped to a high pressure, where the ammonia is driven off by heating. This arrangement permits the pressurization process to be applied to a *liquid* rather than to a vapor, and hence the pump work requirement is much less than in the conventional vapor-compression refrigerator.

9·10 SOME PROBLEMS AND ADVANTAGES OF ALL-GAS CYCLES

The cycles studied thus far in this chapter use a working fluid in both the liquid and gaseous phases. The chief advantage of this scheme is that the work required to pressurize the liquid is small in comparison to the work that can be obtained by expanding the gas (vapor), and hence the back-work ratio (bwr) is quite low. Hence, poor efficiency in the compression and expansion processes can be tolerated. If instead we choose to keep the working fluid in the gaseous phase throughout the cycle, then we shall be faced with the problem of a high back-work ratio; that is, the compression process will drain off a large fraction of the work obtained in the expansion process. The low bwr advantage of the Rankine cycle is the primary reason for the early development of vapor power system technology, which had reached a rather remarkable state of advancement by the end of the last century.

The first gas-power systems to be developed were simple internal combustion engines. In these systems the operating temperature ranges of the cycles are so wide that the low-temperature gas that must be compressed is much more dense than the expanding high-temperature gas, and hence only a moderate bwr is required. Because of the reciprocating nature of such engines, the metal parts are only exposed to these high temperatures (4000°F) momentarily, and with sufficient cooling the systems are practical. Gas-power cycles operating on steady-state bases (gas-turbine power systems) are restricted to lower maximum temperatures, and consequently the densities of the fluid which must be compressed and that which can be expanded are more nearly equal. This tends to produce a high bwr, and consequently high compressor and turbine isentropic efficiencies are required if any net work is to be obtained. Because of fluid-mechanical problems, it is more difficult to design an efficient compressor than an efficient turbine; in fact, it was not until the 1940s that compressor efficiencies sufficiently high to provide positive net work from the cycle were obtained. Since that time there have been major advances in the technology of centrifugal and axial flow compressors, and now gas-turbine power systems with efficiencies competitive with vapor power and reciprocating internal combustion systems can be built. Gas turbine systems have become the standard aircraft prime-mover, are used in many military vehicles, and will very likely become very important in buses, trucks, trains, and probably even automobiles in the very near future.

While all-gas systems have certain theoretical thermodynamic disadvantages, the practical advantages are numerous. The working fluid is clean and can be totally inert (helium is a popular fluid in nuclear gas power systems). Gas-bearing technology has been developed to the point where the working fluid can also be the lubricant, which simplifies the system operation and maintenance, and reduces costs. With the advent of fluidic control devices, even the control system can be operated with the working fluid, and hence a much more reliable integrated system can be obtained. The turbines are not beset by the erosive problems of wet vapor, and cavitation is not a problem in the compressor. The pressures can be relatively low, and hence heavy piping is not required. Hence, gas-turbine systems tend to be very compact and to have a higher power-to-weight ratio than vapor power plants. These practical advantages will certainly make gas-turbine power systems grow in importance in the next decade, particularly for prime-mover applications.

Atmospheric pollution problems are making a definite impact on the nature of prime-mover power systems, particularly for automobiles and trucks. In conventional spark-ignition engines the combination of momentary high temperatures with sudden quenching by contact with cold walls "freezes" harmful oxides and nitrides in the exhaust stream. These, in combination with unburned hydrocarbons resulting from rich (excess fuel) operation, are believed responsible for much of the smog in the great valleys of California. Cycles that run lean (excess air) and operate at lower peak temperatures, such as the gas turbine system, can substantially reduce the smog problem in such areas, and legislation designed to force the introduction of these systems is a definite possibility.

9·11 A PARTICULAR GAS-TURBINE POWER SYSTEM

In order to gain some appreciation for the problems of gas-turbine power production, let us analyze a very simple open-cycle system, shown in Fig. 9·25.

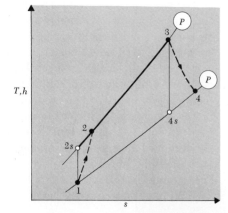

FIG. 9·25 *A simple gas-turbine power system*

We make the following idealizations:

Working fluid air, treated as a perfect gas
State 1, 60°F and 1 atm
State 2, 4 atm
State 3, 1000°F and 4 atm
State 4, 1 atm
$\eta_s = 0.65$ for compressor, $\eta_s = 0.87$ for turbine
Kinetic and potential energies negligible at states 1, 2, 3, 4; compressor and turbine adiabatic; steady flow steady state; equilibrium states at 1, 2, 3, and 4

The analysis consists of determining the various states and computing the energy transfers as heat and work per unit of mass of air. Energy balances on the three components yield

$$W_C = h_2 - h_1 \qquad W_T = h_3 - h_4 \qquad Q_H = h_3 - h_2$$

Noting that

$$\frac{R}{c_P} = \frac{c_P - c_v}{c_P} = \frac{k-1}{k}$$

we find from Eq. (8·27) that†

$$\frac{T_{2s}}{T_1} = \left(\frac{P_{2s}}{P_1}\right)^{(k-1)/k} \qquad \frac{T_3}{T_{4s}} = \left(\frac{P_3}{P_{4s}}\right)^{(k-1)/k}$$

Thus, since $(k-1)/k = 0.286$,

$$T_{2s} = T_1 \times 4^{0.286} = 520 \times 1.486 = 774°R$$

Using Eq. (8·25) to determine enthalpy changes,

$$W_{Cs} = h_{2s} - h_1 = c_P(T_{2s} - T_1) = 0.24 \times (774 - 520) = 61.0 \text{ Btu/lbm}$$

$$W_C = \frac{W_{Cs}}{\eta_s} = \frac{61.0}{0.65} = 93.9 \text{ Btu/lbm}$$

$$W_C = h_2 - h_1 = c_P(T_2 - T_1)$$

$$T_2 = T_1 + \frac{W_C}{c_P} = 520 + \frac{93.9}{0.24} = 911°R$$

$$Q_H = h_3 - h_2 = c_P(T_3 - T_2) = 0.24 \times (1460 - 911) = 131.5 \text{ Btu/lbm}$$

$$T_{4s} = T_3 \times 4^{-0.286} = \frac{1460}{1.486} = 983°R$$

$$W_{Ts} = h_3 - h_{4s} = c_P(T_3 - T_{4s}) = 0.24 \times (1460 - 983) = 114.2 \text{ Btu/lbm}$$

$$W_T = W_{Ts}\eta_s = 0.87 \times 114.2 = 99.4 \text{ Btu/lbm}$$

† Alternatively, one could use the air tables which include specific heat as a function of T. The work is then calculated to be 60.5 Btu/lbm.

$$W_T = h_3 - h_4 = c_P(T_3 - T_4)$$

$$T_4 = T_3 - \frac{W_T}{c_P} = 1460 - \frac{99.4}{0.24} = 1047°R$$

The *back-work ratio* is then

$$\text{bwr} = \frac{W_C}{W_T} = \frac{93.9}{99.4} = 0.945$$

The net work output is

$$W_{\text{net}} = W_T - W_C = 99.4 - 93.9 = 5.5 \text{ Btu/lbm}$$

and the system energy-conversion efficiency is

$$\eta = \frac{W_{\text{net}}}{Q_H} = \frac{5.5}{131.5} = 0.042$$

We see that compression of a gas takes quite a bit more work than compression of a liquid. Consequently, the back-work ratio for gas-power cycles will always be much larger than that for a Rankine cycle. Whereas we can tolerate poor isentropic pump efficiencies in a vapor power system, we must achieve high compressor isentropic efficiency in order to make gas-turbine cycles practicable. The compressor efficiency selected in this example was purposely low in order to emphasize this point. A rather substantial research-and-development effort on axial-flow compressors, beginning in the 1940's, has brought us to the level of about 85 percent for larger machines. With this value in our example,

$$W_C = \frac{61.0}{0.85} = 71.8 \text{ Btu/lbm}$$

$$T_2 = 520 + \frac{71.8}{0.24} = 820°R$$

$$Q_H = 0.24 \times (1460 - 820) = 153.6 \text{ Btu/lbm}$$

$$\text{bwr} = \frac{71.8}{99.4} = 0.723$$

$$W_{\text{net}} = 99.4 - 71.8 = 27.6 \text{ Btu/lbm}$$

$$\eta = \frac{27.6}{153.6} = 0.180$$

Note that this 20 percent gain in compressor efficiency would reduce the fuel consumption by a factor of more than 4. The importance of good turbomachinery design should now be apparent.

The pertinent energy transfers for this system are summarized below. For comparison we show the corresponding values for a cycle with isentropic compression and expansion. Note the large effect on system efficiency η due to irreversibilities in the compressor and turbine.

	W_C	W_T	W_{net}	Q_H	η
Ideal	61.0	114.2	53.2	164.5	0.32
Actual	71.8	99.4	27.6	153.6	0.18

The high level of the turbine outlet temperature (1047°R), compared to a Rankine cycle, may come as a surprise, and it may seem that there should be some way to use this energy. We have to live within the restrictions of the second law, but it is possible to make some gains. We shall discuss these shortly.

9·12   SOME REMARKS ON THE STEADY-FLOW COMPRESSION PROCESS

The compression process forms a key part of the gas-turbine power cycle. Gas compressors are also used in many other applications, and it will be profitable to digress from our study of power systems to discuss the gas-compression process in more detail.

We have indicated that the isentropic process is the usual pattern process for gas compression. This model is appropriate for devices in which the amount of energy transfer as heat is small in comparison to the energy transfer as work. But it is not necessarily true that the isentropic compressor is "best." In order to study this question, let us consider a model process in which we presume that the pressure and specific volume are related by

$$Pv^n = \text{const} \tag{9·9}$$

This model process is called the *polytropic process*, and n is the *polytropic exponent*. By choosing n to be various values we can study the work requirements for different compression processes. For example, if the working fluid is a perfect gas with constant specific heats, $n = k$ corresponds to an isentropic compression, and $n = 1$ corresponds to isothermal compression.

Consider now a compressor in which the fluid undergoes a *reversible* polytropic compression. An energy balance on the compressor (Fig. 9·26) gives

$$W + Q = h_2 - h_1 \tag{9·10}$$

For the reversible process, the energy transfer as heat can be related to the change in entropy of the fluid. Taking a unit mass of the fluid passing through

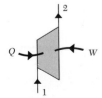

FIG. 9·26   *Polytropic compression analysis*

the compressor as the control mass, the second law requires that

$$Q = \int_1^2 T \, ds \qquad (9 \cdot 11)$$

where Q is the amount of energy transfer as heat to a unit mass of the fluid as it passes through the compressor. Now, the entropy, enthalpy, and pressure changes for any infinitesimal step of the process are related by (Eq. $8 \cdot 44$)

$$T \, ds = dh - v \, dP$$

Substituting in Eq. ($9 \cdot 11$), and integrating,

$$Q = h_2 - h_1 - \int_1^2 v \, dP \qquad (9 \cdot 12)$$

Upon combination with the energy balance, we have

$$W = \int_1^2 v \, dP \qquad (9 \cdot 13)$$

The student might compare this with the expression for the work done *by* a unit mass of fluid in a simple expansion process. Note that the smaller the specific volume the less is the work required to achieve a given pressure increase. This observation is behind our earlier remarks on the back-work ratios for Rankine cycles versus gas-power cycles.

Using the assumed polytropic relationship between P and v (Eq. $9 \cdot 9$), the integration of Eq. ($9 \cdot 13$) may be carried out, and the work expressed in terms of the initial state (P_1, v_1), the pressure ratio P_2/P_1, and the polytropic

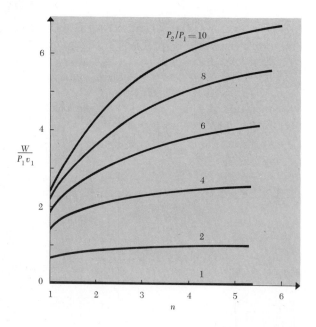

FIG. 9·27 *Work required for polytropic compression*

exponent n; one finds

$$W = \frac{n}{n-1} P_1 v_1 \left[\left(\frac{P_2}{P_1} \right)^{(n-1)/n} - 1 \right] \qquad n \neq 1 \qquad (9 \cdot 14a)$$

The case $n = 1$ must be handled separately; this yields

$$W = P_1 v_1 \ln \left(\frac{P_2}{P_1} \right) \qquad n = 1 \qquad (9 \cdot 14b)$$

Figure $9 \cdot 27$ shows the work required to achieve a given compression as a function of the polytropic exponent. Note that as n decreases less work is required, and that the least amount of work for $n \geq 1$ is obtained for $n = 1$, that is, for isothermal compression. Hence, for the compression process, the *isothermal* compressor is really a better ideal, and the *isothermal compression efficiency* η_T is often used to compare the work input for an actual compressor with that for an ideal, reversible isothermal compression process. Note that isothermal compression requires that $Q < 0$ (Fig. $9 \cdot 26$).

9·13 THE BRAYTON CYCLE AND ITS MODIFICATIONS

The pattern cycle for the gas-turbine power system studied in Sec. $9 \cdot 11$ is known as the *Brayton cycle*. The hardware schematic and process representation for a closed Brayton-cycle system is shown in Fig. $9 \cdot 28$. In the idealized Brayton cycle the compressor and turbine processes are isentropic, and pressure drop across the heat exchangers is neglected. If the working fluid is treated as a perfect gas with constant specific heats, a simple expression for the energy-

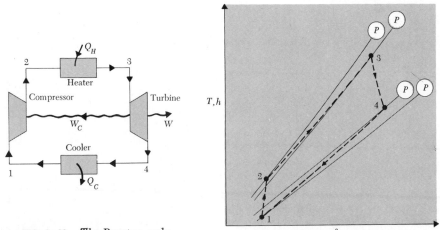

FIG. 9·28 *The Brayton cycle*

conversion efficiency may be obtained† in terms of the pressure ratio

$$\eta = 1 - \left(\frac{1}{P^*}\right)^{(k-1)/k} \tag{9·15}$$

where

$$P^* = \frac{P_2}{P_1} = \frac{P_3}{P_4}$$

This relationship for $k = 1.4$ is shown in Fig. 9·29. In particular, for the example of the last section, $P^* = 4$ and $\eta_{ideal} = 32.7$ percent, about twice what we obtained with the improved compressor. Note that high pressure ratios make the idealized Brayton cycle more efficient. However, compressor efficiency tends to drop off with increased pressure ratio, and this has a compensating effect in a real Brayton cycle. Pressure ratios in the range of 4 to 6 are typical of simple Brayton systems.

In gas-turbine systems intended for prime-mover use, it is usually important to keep engine weight small, which normally means maximizing the work output per lbm of fluid. Metallurgical considerations limit the turbine inlet temperature, and current systems operate at about 1600°F although some military gas turbines now have inlet temperatures as high as 1800°F. Within this temperature limitation there will be some pressure ratio that yields a maximum efficiency and another that yields the most work output per unit of mass of fluid, and these two ratios will not generally be the same. Figure 9·30 illustrates this in terms of the $T\text{-}s$ process representation. Recall that the work output per

† The development is as follows.
Energy balances: $W_T = c_P(T_3 - T_4)$, $W_C = c_P(T_2 - T_1)$, $Q_H = c_P(T_3 - T_2)$
Isentropic processes: $T_2/T_1 = T_3/T_4 = (P^*)^{(k-1)/k} = A$
Conversion efficiency:
$\eta = [(T_3 - T_4) - (T_2 - T_1)]/(T_3 - T_2) = (T_4A - T_4 - T_1A + T_1)/(T_4A - T_1A)$
$\eta = (T_4 - T_1)(A - 1)/[(T_4 - T_1)A] = 1 - 1/A$

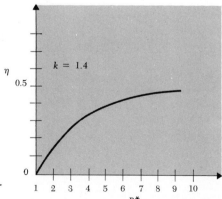

FIG. 9·29 *Idealized Brayton-cycle efficiency*

FIG. 9·30 *Two idealized Brayton cycles; the shaded cycle has a greater work output but a lower efficiency*

lbm of fluid is equal to the area enclosed by the T-s process path for a reversible process. The primed cycle on the figure has a greater work output per unit of mass than does the high-pressure cycle, but a lower energy-conversion efficiency. This is seen from the fact that in the primed cycle there is a greater input of energy at the lower temperatures while in the unprimed cycle all of the energy input as heat occurs at a high temperature, which leads to higher efficiency.

It may be shown that the pressure ratio yielding the most work per unit of mass for the idealized Brayton cycle of Fig. 9·30 is

$$P^*_{\text{opt}} = \left(\frac{T_3}{T_1}\right)^{k/[2(k-1)]} \tag{9·16}$$

Where a low power weight ratio is desirable it will be necessary to operate near to P^*_{opt}, and hence away from the maximum efficiency point.

We have seen that the turbine exhaust temperature of a simple Brayton cycle is quite high; if it exceeds the compressor outlet temperature *regeneration* is possible, as shown in Fig. 9·31 (the ideal cycle is shown there). In the regeneration process the high-temperature exhaust gas is used to preheat the gas coming

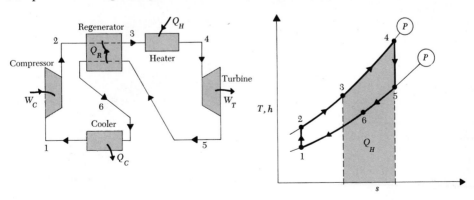

FIG. 9·31 *Idealized regenerative Brayton cycle*

from the compressor, thus reducing the required energy input from the external heat source. With a counterflow regenerator it is theoretically possible to heat the gas from state 2 to the temperature of state 5 with energy transferred as heat from the turbine exhaust gases. This would result in cooling of the exhaust gases to the compressor outlet temperature (state 2). Systems have been built in which more than 95 percent of the possible regenerative effect has been obtained. The amount of possible regeneration is the largest at low pressure ratios, and in contrast to the simple Brayton cycle, the regenerative cycle yields the highest efficiencies at low pressure ratios. It is much easier to build high-performance compressors for low pressure differences, and this fact makes the regenerative system even more attractive. Nuclear-powered gas-turbine systems employing regeneration have been built in the power range of 100–300 Mw, and automotive and shipboard gas turbines that produce 300–3000 hp are now in use. Efficiencies in the range of 20–30 percent are typical with regeneration.

To illustrate the effect of regeneration, let us put a regenerator into the improved Brayton-cycle example of the previous section. We could conceivably warm the fluid leaving the compressor at 820°R to the turbine outlet temperature (1047°R), but this would require an immense heat exchanger. However, 85 percent of this maximum possible temperature rise could be obtained with a heat exchanger of reasonable size. We therefore assume that the high-pressure gas leaves the regenerator at $820 + 0.85 \times (1047 - 820) = 1013°R$. The heater

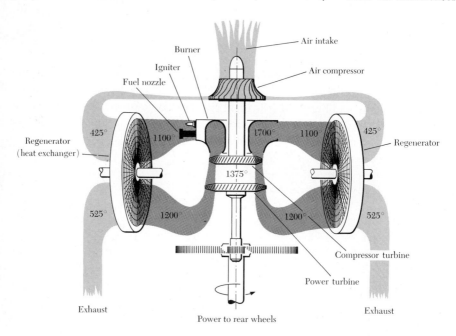

FIG. 9·32 *Schematic of an automotive gas turbine power system*

FIG. 9·33 *Idealized Brayton cycle with intercooling and reheat*

power would then be reduced to $Q_H = 0.24 \times (1460 - 1013) = 107$ Btu/lbm, which would give an energy-conversion efficiency of $\eta = 27.6/107 = 0.26$, a 50 percent improvement over the nonregenerative system. Thus, the regenerator would cut fuel costs by about 50 percent.

The development of compact and efficient regenerators is allowing the gas-turbine engine to move into the competitive automotive market. Of particular importance is the *rotary regenerator*, an unusual type of heat exchanger. A disk of porous metal is rotated through two semicircular ducts. Hot gases in one duct heat up the metal, which is then moved by the disk rotation to the other duct, where the energy is transferred as heat from the metal to the cooler gas. Such exchangers can be made very compact and highly efficient. There are, of course, numerous interesting engineering problems with such regenerators, such as sealing between the two ducts, thermal expansions that cause distortions, carryover of the hot gases directly into the cold gas duct, and so on. A remarkable development effort by the automotive companies in the past decade has now resolved most of these problems, and most operating automotive gas turbines are now equipped with rotary regenerators. Figure 9·32 shows a schematic of one manufacturer's system. Note particularly the dual turbine disks, and the operating temperatures revealed in their diagram. A competitor (or a student) can make a rather thorough assessment of their system from this information.

In larger gas-turbine power stations it is sometimes economical to employ *intercooling and reheat*. An idealized system with one intercooling stage and two stages of reheat is shown in Fig. 9·33. As shown in Fig. 9·34, intercooling

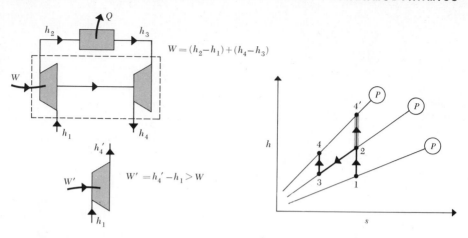

$$W = (h_2 - h_1) + (h_4 - h_3)$$

$$W' = h_4' - h_1 > W$$

FIG. 9·34 *Intercooling between compression stages reduces the work requirement*

between compressor stages reduces the compressor work requirement. Similarly, reheat between the turbine stages increases the work output per unit of mass for a given pressure ratio and turbine inlet temperature. The net work output per unit of mass therefore is increased by intercooling and/or reheat. However, the efficiency of a Brayton cycle with intercooling and/or reheat is *lower* than the simple Brayton-cycle efficiency, for more energy must be added as heat.† Intercooling and reheat do serve to *increase the potential for regeneration* by increasing the final turbine outlet temperature and at the same time reducing the compressor outlet temperature. Intercooling and reheat are therefore usually used in conjunction with regeneration. In theory, if an infinite number of reheat and intercooling stages are employed, and regeneration is also used,

† Thinking graphically, the portions of the cycle that are "patched on" to the simple Brayton cycle are lower temperature-ratio cycles, and therefore are less efficient.

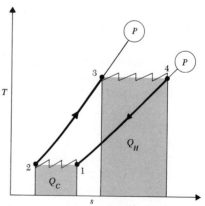

FIG. 9·35 *Idealized Brayton cycle with regeneration and infinite reheat and intercooling stages*

all the energy added externally occurs in the reheat exchangers when the fluid is at its maximum temperature, and all the energy rejection as heat takes place in the intercoolers, where the gas is at its lowest temperature. Thus the limiting case is a $2T$ engine (ideally reversible) having an efficiency given by the Carnot-cycle efficiency (see Fig. 9·35). This is very interesting, for the process representation is quite unlike that of a Carnot cycle. This limiting cycle is sometimes called the *Ericsson cycle*.

9·14 OTHER GAS POWER CYCLES

The *Otto cycle* is the pattern cycle for reciprocating *spark-ignition engines*. The pressure of the gas within the cylinder of an idealized spark-ignition engine is shown as a function of the piston position in Fig. 9·36. With the piston at top dead center (tdc), the intake valve opens and a fresh charge of fuel-air mixture is sucked in. At bottom dead center (bdc) the intake valve closes, and the return stroke causes the gas to be compressed. In the idealized system ignition occurs instantaneously at tdc, causing a rapid rise in temperature and pressure. The gas is then expanded on the outstroke, until at bdc the exhaust valve opens, and the gas "blows down" through the exhaust port. With a fourth stroke the gases are purged out. In the idealized Otto cycle the compression and expansion processes are considered reversible and adiabatic, that is, isentropic, and it is assumed that the pressure within the cylinder during the intake and exhaust strokes is equal to the atmospheric pressure. The work done by the piston on the gas inside the cylinder during the exhaust stroke is exactly equal to the work done on the piston by the gas during the intake stroke, so that useful work output results only from the excess of the work done by the gas during the expansion stroke over that done on the gas during the compression stroke.

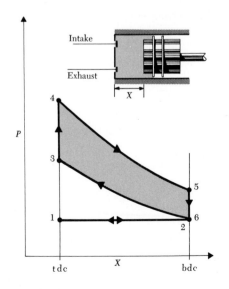

FIG. 9·36 *Pressures in an idealized spark-ignition engine*

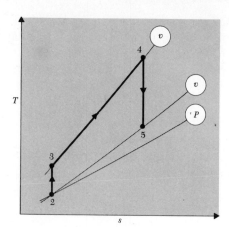

FIG. 9·37 *Idealized Otto-cycle process*
representation

The process representation for the fluid during the compression, ignition, and expansion parts of the cycle is shown in Fig. 9·37. The combustion process is idealized in terms of a simple energy addition (as heat), and the changes in the chemical composition of the mixture are neglected. If it is further idealized that the gas is a perfect gas with constant specific heats, appropriate thermo-dynamic analysis leads to a simple algebraic expression for the efficiency of the Otto cycle in terms of the compression ratio,

$$\eta = \frac{W_{\text{net}}}{Q_{34}} = 1 - \frac{1}{r^{k-1}} \tag{9·17}$$

where the compression ratio r is

$$r = \frac{v_2}{v_3} = \frac{v_5}{v_4}$$

This relationship for $k = 1.4$ is shown in Fig. 9·38.

A real spark-ignition engine will not meet the performance of the highly idealized Otto cycle. Combustion takes time, and for this reason it is initiated before tdc by "advancing the spark." Furthermore, there will be a pressure

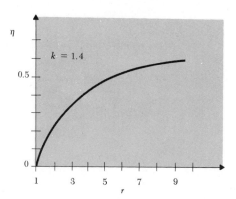

FIG. 9·38 *Otto-cycle efficiency*

drop across the valve during intake and exhaust; the piston must do work on the air to get it out, and this is more than the work done on the piston by the cylinder gases during the intake stroke. Heat transfer is involved, so the compression and expansion processes are not isentropic. The pressure-displacement diagram of a realistic spark-ignition engine is shown in Fig. 9·39.

From the curve of efficiency versus compression ratio it is clear that one would like to operate at high compression ratio, v_2/v_3. However, in the spark-ignition engine this is often difficult to do, for the fuel-air mixture may undergo *detonation* in which the fuel begins to burn beyond the area ignited by the spark. This causes high-pressure waves in the combustion chamber ("knocking") which may cause severe damage if allowed to continue over a period of time. Fuels with higher octane ratings have higher detonation temperatures, and the higher compression ratios of the automobiles of the late 1960s were due primarily to improved fuel rather than to improved engine technology.

One method of avoiding the detonation during compression with its limitation on the compression ratio is to inject the fuel *after* the compression process. Since there is no fuel in the cylinder during the compression process, higher compression ratios (and therefore higher air temperatures) can be reached without detonation. Then, upon injection of the fuel, it ignites spontaneously owing to the high air temperature. This ignition tends to occur fairly uniformly over the cylinder, without harmful blast waves. Such an engine is called a *compression-* (rather than spark-) *ignition* engine.

The *diesel cycle* is the pattern cycle for reciprocating compression-ignition engines. In the idealized system air is compressed to tdc, at which time fuel is injected, and it is idealized that the combustion process takes place at constant pressure for part of the expansion stroke. The remainder of the expansion stroke and the compression stroke are idealized as isentropic. The pressures within the cylinder of an idealized diesel engine are shown in Fig. 9·40. The process representation is shown in Fig. 9·41.

The efficiency of a diesel cycle may be worked out by thermodynamic

FIG. 9·39 *Pressures in a real spark-ignition engine*

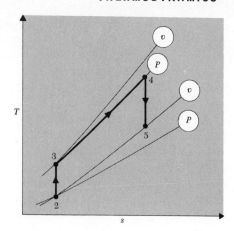

FIG. 9·40 *Pressures in an idealized diesel engine*

FIG. 9·41 *Idealized diesel-cycle process representation*

analysis. If it is assumed that the gas is a perfect gas with constant specific heats, an algebraic expression for the efficiency is obtained in terms of the compression and cutoff ratios,

$$\eta = 1 - \frac{1}{r^{k-1}} \frac{r_c^k - 1}{k(r_c - 1)} \qquad (9·18)$$

$$r = \frac{v_2}{v_3} \qquad \text{compression ratio}$$

$$r_c = \frac{v_4}{v_3} \qquad \text{cutoff ratio}$$

The idealized diesel-cycle efficiency is shown as a function of the compression and cutoff ratios in Fig. 9·42. Note that the efficiency for $r_c = 1$ is the same as

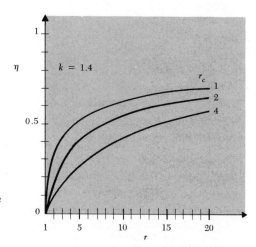

FIG. 9·42 *Idealized diesel-cycle efficiency*

for the Otto cycle, and that in general the diesel cycle has a lower efficiency than the Otto cycle *operating at the same compression ratio.*

Compression ratios of practical engines are limited by the pressures and temperatures which can be tolerated within the cylinders. In the spark-ignition engine combustion occurs as the gas is being compressed, while in the injection engines (compression-ignition) combustion begins as the gas is being expanded. As a result, diesel engines can operate at higher compression ratios (of the order of 15:1) than can spark-ignition engines (of the order of 8:1), and consequently can obtain comparable and even superior efficiencies.

A common modification on spark-ignition engines for aircraft operation is the *supercharger,* a steady-flow compressor used to compress the air before it enters the reciprocating engine. Supercharging an Otto engine will not improve its efficiency, which is only a function of its compression ratio. In fact, work must be provided to run the supercharger. However, the increase in density of the working fluid produced by the supercharger can result in greater power, since more fluid mass is circulated through the engine. The power/weight ratio is thereby increased.

A second modification, employed on the Wright turbosupercharged engine, is the *exhaust turbine.* The pressure in the cylinder of an Otto-cycle engine at bdc is greater than atmospheric pressure, and consequently work can be obtained by passing the gases through a steady-flow turbine. The result is (ideally) an increase in efficiency, since the work obtained from the turbine is greater than that required to drive the compressor.† A flow diagram and a process representation for the idealized *turbo-compound engine* is shown in Fig. 9·43. Recently there has been considerable interest in turbosupercharging of

† This may be seen easily by examining the *h-s* process representation for the turbo-supercharged cycle (Fig. 9·43), since the enthalpy changes are related to work for steady-flow adiabatic devices.

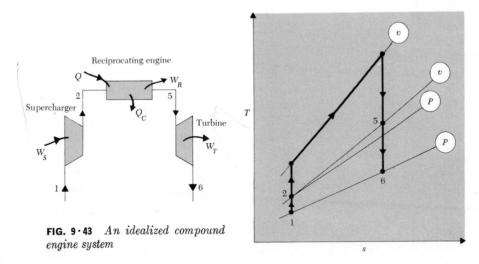

FIG. 9·43 *An idealized compound engine system*

diesel and spark-ignition engines. Here a free-running turbine is used to drive
the supercharger directly, and useful power is extracted solely from the reciprocating engine.

An interesting hybrid employs the *free-piston gas generator*. This device
consists of a pair of free-floating pistons synchronized to move in opposition.
Air is compressed between them as they move together, diesel fuel is injected
and ignites spontaneously, and the hot high-pressure gases are exhausted
through a power-producing turbine. The system schematic and process representation (idealized) are shown in Fig. 9·44. High isentropic efficiencies are
more easily obtained with reciprocating (rather than steady-flow) compressors,
and this is a practical advantage of the free-piston system.

Another cycle of interest is the *Stirling cycle*. This is of interest because it
offers the possibility of reaching (in the ideal cycle) the Carnot efficiency. It
consists of an isothermal compression 1-2, a constant volume heating 2-3, an
isothermal expansion 3-4, and a constant volume cooling 4-1. Note that heat is
rejected in process 1-2 and added to the system in process 3-4. Ideally, a regenerator could be placed in the system and the heat rejected in process 4-1 could
be used as the heat input in process 2-3. Under these conditions the ideal system
would have an efficiency equal to the Carnot efficiency for the two temperature
extremes. Stirling cycles using reciprocating hardware are currently being developed for automotive and small-power systems, and have even been considered
for artificial heart power. These systems use air, helium, or some other gas in a
closed cycle, using an external burner, nuclear reactor, radioisotope pile or other
suitable heat source, and rejecting energy as heat to a colder region via an
appropriate heat exchanger.   A scheme for artificial heart power uses a radioisotope pile at 1200°F, implanted in super-insulation in the abdominal cavity,
with the bloodstream acting as the cycle coolant.

The student should note that all these pattern cycles are highly idealized.
They have great merit as an aid to studying the actual systems, but one should

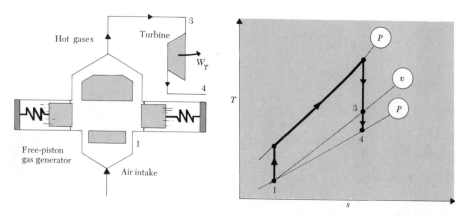

FIG. 9·44   *Idealized free-piston compound engine system*

not lose sight of the idealizations involved. Real spark-ignition engines do not have energy input exactly at constant volume. Real diesel systems do not have a constant pressure combustion process, which is merely a simple approximation to the process of heating due to fuel burning during the expansion process. We also remark that in these simplified pattern cycles the energy delivered to the air from the fuel is considered as a "heat input," and no chemical changes in the working fluids are considered. The chemical processes in real engines are of course important, and must be considered in accurate engineering calculations for such systems. We shall learn how to do this in Chaps. Eleven and Twelve.

9·15 AIR-CYCLE REFRIGERATOR

The reverse of the Brayton cycle can be used as a refrigeration cycle, and such systems are in common use aboard jet aircraft. Air is bled from the discharge of the main-engine compressor and expanded through a small turbine. The shaft power from the turbine is usually used to drive the fans circulating air through the cabin. The flow schematic and process representation for this *air-cycle refrigeration system* are shown in Fig. 9·45.

To illustrate air-cycle cooling as applied to aircraft, let's design a very simple cabin cooling system for a light jet airplane designed to cruise at 600 mph at an altitude of 10,000 ft. At this altitude the ambient temperature is approximately 35°F and the pressure is about 10 psia. We shall use the hardware and pattern cycle shown in Fig. 9·46.

It might be thought that we could easily cool the cabin by simply scooping in the cold ambient air. But let's see what happens when we try. An energy analysis of the scoop, in which flow relative to the airplane is diffused from 600 mph to very low speeds, can be used to calculate the temperature of the air after it has been brought nearly to rest. Assuming that the scoop is adiabatic, and making other simplifying idealizations (the student may list these in the

FIG. 9·45 *Air-cycle refrigeration*

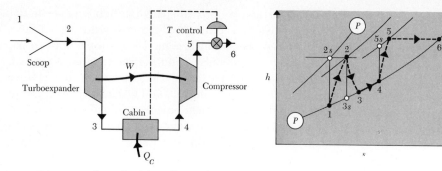

FIG. 9·46 *Our aircraft cooling system*

margin), we have

$$h_1 + \frac{V_1{}^2}{2g_c} = h_2$$

Treating the air as a perfect gas, the enthalpy difference may be expressed in terms of the temperature difference, and we have

$$T_2 = T_1 + \frac{V_1{}^2}{2g_c c_P}$$

Putting in the numbers (600 mph = 880 ft/sec),

$$T_2 = 495 + \frac{880^2}{2 \times 32.2 \times 0.24 \times 778} = 559°\text{R}$$

We see that in the process of slowing down the flow we convert the flow stream bulk kinetic energy into molecular kinetic energy, and consequently greatly increase the gas temperature. This temperature (99°F) is too hot for use as cooling air, and somehow the temperature must be reduced before the air is admitted to the cabin.

Suppose we drop the temperature of the air by expanding it through a turbine. Energy removed from the air will appear as turbine shaft work, which must somehow be absorbed; we will connect the turbine to a small compressor, which will take the air blown through the cabin and pump it to a higher pressure for ejection from the aircraft. The small turboexpander will have an isentropic efficiency of the order of 0.85 and a very crude compressor can be used, for it must only serve to deliver the turbine work to the air just before it leaves the aircraft. System control might be effected by discharging through a control valve, which could regulate the flow so as to maintain a preset cabin temperature.

We must determine the turboexpander inlet pressure. The scoop-diffuser might have a *pressure recovery factor* C_P of about 0.7 where (see Fig. 9·46)

$$C_P \equiv \frac{P_2 - P_1}{P_{2s} - P_1}$$

From the perfect-gas equation of state,

$$\frac{P_{2s}}{P_1} = \left(\frac{T_2}{T_1}\right)^{k/(k-1)}$$

So,

$$P_{2s} = 10 \times (559/495)^{3.5} = 15.2 \text{ psia}$$

Then, calculating P_2 from the assumed value of C_P,

$$P_2 = 10 + 0.7 \times (15.2 - 10) = 13.6 \text{ psia}$$

Let's assume that the cabin is designed to operate at 10 psia, which we take as the turbine discharge pressure. Analyzing the turbine in the usual way we find

$$T_3 = 512°R \ (52°F)$$
$$W_T = 11.3 \text{ Btu/lbm}$$

It would not take much air at 52°F to maintain the cabin of a small airplane at a comfortable 75°F. Suppose, for example, that the cabin "heat load" Q_C is 10,000 Btu/hr (about 3000 w). We analyze the cabin by assuming that the air leaves the cabin at the cabin temperature ($T_4 = 535°R$). Then, the required air-flow rate is

$$\dot{M} = \frac{\dot{Q}_C}{h_4 - h_3} = \frac{\dot{Q}_C}{c_P(T_4 - T_3)}$$

$$= \frac{10,000}{0.24 \times (535 - 512)} = 1800 \text{ lbm/hr}$$

At the scoop inlet density of 0.0546 lbm/ft³, and the scoop inlet velocity of 880 ft/sec, the scoop frontal area would have to be only

$$A = \dot{M}/(\rho_1 V_1) = \frac{1800/3600}{0.0546 \times 880} = 0.010 \text{ ft}^2$$

The turboexpander power output is

$$\dot{W}_T = M\dot{W}_T = 1800 \times 11.3 = 20,000 \text{ Btu/hr}$$

which is about 8 hp.

The student might complete the analysis of the other components in the system, and in particular examine the possibility of using this turbine power in a more direct way. The designer of such a system would carry out an extensive optimization analysis, experimenting with different system state points in an attempt to provide the necessary cooling for the least weight and cost.

9·16   A SIMPLE THRUSTING SYSTEM

Thermodynamics plays an important role in the analysis of propulsion systems. Let us consider one of the simpler types of thrust producers, shown in

High-pressure
storage tank

Plenum

Valve

FIG. 9·47

Nozzle

(a) A simple blowdown
thruster

(b) Pressures on the chamber
wall

(c) The control volume

Fig. 9·47. Gas at high pressure is bled from a storage bottle to a plenum chamber, from which it is exhausted through a nozzle. The pressure forces acting on the chamber walls are shown in Fig. 9·47a. Note that there is a net force which would tend to accelerate the walls opposite the direction of flow. This type of *blowdown thruster* is used in low-thrust situations where simplicity and reliability are key factors and where propellant weight is not vital. The attitude-control systems of our space vehicles have used nitrogen thrusters in the range of 2 to 100 lbf.

The thrust of a propulsion system is the force which the fluids exert on the container as a result of nonuniformities in pressure distribution. Examination of Fig. 9·47b would indicate that this force is roughly $P_0 A_t$, where P_0 is the chamber, or *stagnation*, pressure, and A_t is the throat area of the nozzle. An exact calculation of thrust requires application of the *momentum principle* to a control volume surrounding the gas and cutting across the exit plane of the nozzle. The momentum principle is a generalization of Newton's law arising from a control-volume transformation. We shall develop the momentum principle for a control volume in Chap. Thirteen, and here merely give the result of this transformation in Table 9·1. Here $\dot{\mathcal{P}}_M$ denotes the *rate of production of momentum*, as defined in the table.

Let us now apply the momentum principle to the control volume of Fig. 9·47c, assuming that the system is steady-flow steady-state, one-dimensional at the inlet and exit planes, and fixed in space. We write the momentum equation for the x direction, since this is the component of force we seek. The entering fluid has no momentum in this direction, and the rate of storage of momentum $d(\mathbf{M})/dt$ is zero by the steady-flow steady-state and no-acceleration idealiza-

TABLE 9·1 THE MOMENTUM PRINCIPLE

System	Momentum equation
Isolated system	$\dot{\mathcal{P}}_{\mathbf{M}} = \dfrac{d\,(\mathbf{M})}{dt} = 0$
Control mass	$\dot{\mathcal{P}}_{\mathbf{M}} = \dfrac{d\,(\mathbf{M})}{dt} = g_c\mathbf{F}$
Control volume	$\dot{\mathcal{P}}_{\mathbf{M}} = \dfrac{d\,(\mathbf{M})}{dt} + \displaystyle\sum_{\text{out}} \dot{M}\mathbf{V} - \sum_{\text{in}} \dot{M}\mathbf{V} = g_c\mathbf{F}$

$\mathbf{M}$ is total momentum of matter within the system. $\mathbf{V}$ is the momentum of a unit mass of matter crossing the boundaries. $\mathbf{F}$ is the total force exerted on the control volume.

tions. The only terms remaining are

$$\dot{M}\mathbf{V}_e = g_c(\mathbf{F}_x - P_e A_e) \tag{9·19}$$

Here $\mathbf{F}$ is the force exerted by the walls on the fluid, and $P_e A_e$ is the force acting across the exit plane. Often the exit pressure force is negligible, and

$$\mathbf{F}_x \approx \frac{\dot{M}\mathbf{V}_e}{g_c} \tag{9·20}$$

Thermodynamics becomes involved when we want to calculate the discharge velocity in order to determine the thrust. Consider the control volume of Fig. 9·48. We assume that the flow is steady, one-dimensional, and adiabatic and that the kinetic energy of the fluid in the plenum chamber is negligible. An energy balance then gives

$$h_0 = h + \frac{\mathbf{V}^2}{2g_c} \tag{9·21}$$

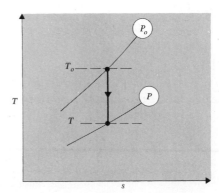

FIG. 9·48   *The thermodynamic analyses*

Let us further assume that the fluid is a perfect gas with constant specific heats. Then, using Eq. (8·25), we can relate the chamber (stagnation) temperature T_0 to the temperature and velocity at any flow section and express the result as

$$\frac{T}{T_0} = 1 - \frac{V^2}{2g_c c_P T_0} \qquad (9\cdot 22)$$

If we further idealize that the process undergone by the fluid is isentropic, then from Eq. (8·27), we have

$$\frac{P}{P_0} = \left(\frac{T}{T_0}\right)^{k/(k-1)} = \left(1 - \frac{V^2}{2g_c c_P T_0}\right)^{k/(k-1)} \qquad (9\cdot 23)$$

The process representation is shown in Fig. 9·48.

The dynamics and thermodynamics, plus conservation of mass, allow complete analysis of this thrusting system. Equations (9·21) and (9·22) hold at any section of the flow (provided our idealizations are reasonable), and in particular at the exit plane. They tell us that the more the gas is expanded in the nozzle, the higher will be the exit velocity, and consequently the greater will be the thrust.

As an example, suppose we consider a system with $P_e/P_0 = 0.1$ and a stagnation temperature of 80°F. For nitrogen $k = 1.4$ and $c_P = 0.24$ Btu/lbm-°F, so the temperature at the exit plane would be†

$$T = T_0 \left(\frac{P}{P_0}\right)^{(k-1)/k} = 540 \times 0.1^{0.286} = 279°R = -181°F$$

The exit velocity may now be calculated from Eq. (9·22),

$$V = \sqrt{2 \times 32.2 \times 0.24 \times 540 \times (1 - {}^{279}\!/_{540}) \times 778} = 1770 \text{ ft/sec}$$

The thrust calculation would require knowledge of the mass-flow rate. A useful measure of the performance of a propulsion system is the *specific impulse*, or thrust force per unit of mass-flow rate. For our system

$$SI = \frac{F_x}{\dot{M}} \approx \frac{V_e}{g_c}$$

so

$$SI = \frac{1770}{32.2} = 55 \text{ lbf/(lbm/sec)}$$

Hence, a 25 lbf nozzle will require about 0.5 lb of nitrogen per thrusting second.

Inspection of Eq. (9·23) indicates that there is a limit on the velocity which can be obtained by isentropic expansion of a gas. Since the pressure cannot fall below zero,

$$V_{max} = \sqrt{2g_c c_P T_0}$$

† This extreme cold would tend to freeze any water vapor in the gas, and such little ice crystals are believed to be the cause of the "fireflies" seen by astronauts.

which for our case amounts to 2540 ft/sec. Thus the best specific impulse which we could hope to obtain with the blowdown thruster is of the order of 80 lbf/(lbm/sec). We see that higher specific impulse with a gaseous flow requires higher stagnation temperatures. In the next section we shall examine the performance of some more powerful propulsion systems, indicating the sorts of specific impulses which they attain.

9·17 OTHER THRUSTING SYSTEMS

The earliest thrusting systems for aircraft propulsion were merely propellers driven by internal-combustion engines.† The *turboprop engine,* now used aboard commercial cargo aircraft, is an open-cycle gas-turbine engine in which the turbine drives the propeller.

The attainment of higher-speed flight requires higher jet velocities than can be obtained with large propellers, and the *turbojet engine* has become the workhorse of larger commercial and military aircraft. It is essentially a gas-

† The delay in developing the turboprop and the turbojet engine was in part because of difficulties in developing good compressors. In fact, the early Brayton cycles required more work to their compressors than the turbine would produce! These were, obviously, used for research and further development.

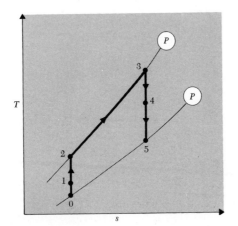

FIG. 9·49   *An idealized turbojet engine*

turbine plant in which the turbine power output is just sufficient to drive the compressor. The turbine exhaust is fed to a nozzle from which the flow is discharged at high velocity. A system schematic and idealized process representation are shown in Fig. 9·49. Military aircraft employ an afterburner, which is essentially a reheat device (Fig. 9·50). The afterburner provides greater nozzle-exhaust velocities and substantially increases the engine thrust. Specific impulses of the order of 60 lbf/(lbm/sec) are typical for modern jet engines. The afterburner increases this somewhat but greatly increases fuel consumption, and consequently, afterburners are "cut in" only for short periods of high thrust.

The choice of a propulsion system for aircraft involves many factors. Propeller systems are best suited to low-speed flight (300 mph); these engines derive their thrust by accelerating relatively large amounts of air to a modest velocity. In contrast, high-speed aircraft are best powered by jet engines, which provide thrust by accelerating smaller amounts of air to much higher velocities. In the high subsonic range (600 mph) the hybrid *turbofan engine* has provided the best choice where fuel economy is a prime factor. The turbofan is a jet engine which derives additional thrust from a *ducted propeller*, or *bypass fan*, which is driven off the main turbine shaft. The amount of thrust contributed by the two streams can be adjusted by varying the ratio of the bypass air-flow rate to the engine air-flow rate, and an optimum design thereby

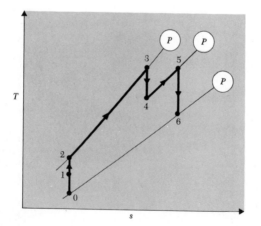

FIG. 9·50 *Idealized turbojet engine with afterburner*

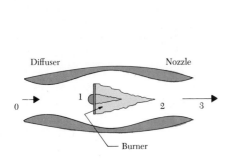

FIG. 9·51 *An idealized ramjet engine*

obtained for any particular type of mission. Bypass ratios in the range 0.5 to 2.5 are typical of current systems.

The *ramjet* is a carefully designed flow passage which uses the momentum of the onrushing air for compression, thereby entirely eliminating any moving parts. The aircraft must already be flying at a considerable speed before the ramjet engine can be started. Commercial supersonic transport craft could possibly employ turbojet engines for takeoff, ascent, descent, and landing and switch to ramjets for high-altitude supersonic cruising. A system schematic and process representation are shown in Fig. 9·51. Ideally the diffuser process is isentropic, but boundary-layer separation on the diffuser walls makes it difficult to achieve high isentropic efficiency in real supersonic diffusers.

Chemical-rocket engines are essentially open Rankine cycles in which the turbine is replaced by a rocket nozzle. Since a chemical rocket carries its own oxidizer, it is especially well suited for operation in space. Chemical rockets have specific impulses in the range of 150–300 lbf/(lbm/sec). A system schematic and highly idealized process representation are shown in Fig. 9·52.

It may be shown that the highest specific impulse is obtained for the lightest possible particles. Hydrogen has therefore been studied in conjunction with a nuclear-reactor energy source, and it appears that specific impulses of the order of 900 lbf/(lbm/sec) can be obtained. The nuclear hydrogen rocket (Fig. 9·53) will probably become an important engine for future space flights.

Ion engines offer the possibility of high specific impulses and will probably be used on long-term space voyages. An easily ionized element, such as cesium, is evaporated and then brought into contact with a suitable high-temperature surface. Electrons are removed at the surface, and the cesium ions and electrons are accelerated by appropriate electric fields and then mixed to form a neutral beam which is shot from the end of the engine. Specific impulses of the order of 10,000 lbf/(lbm/sec) are possible. A schematic of a proposed ion engine is shown in Fig. 9·54. Note that while the ion engine offers high specific impulse, the flow rate would be very small so that the thrust would be small. Consequently such a device would be used for accelerating a vehicle only after

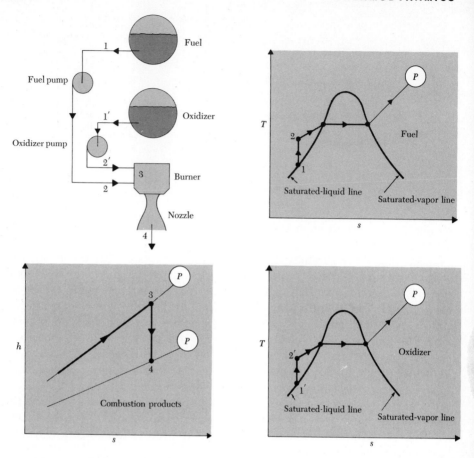

FIG. 9·52   *A chemical-rocket engine*

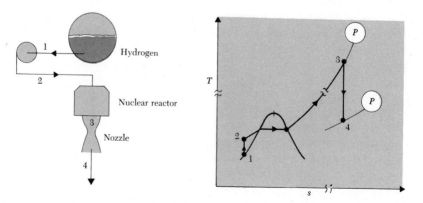

FIG. 9·53   *The hydrogen-rocket engine*

FIG. 9·54 *An ion engine*

the vehicle was already in space and away from the earth's gravitational field. The advantage of such a device is that a very high thrust per lbm expended is achieved so that for long flights extremely high accelerations can be achieved, which greatly shorten the flight time.

9·18   DIRECT ENERGY-CONVERSION SYSTEMS

The conventional devices for electric power generation which we have so far studied are typified by the Rankine vapor-power cycle and the Brayton gas-power cycle. All involve the circulation and state-manipulation of a working fluid which in a rather indirect way takes the energy from the fuel and helps us convert some of that energy to electrical power. This type of power generation has many heavy bulky components and many moving parts. In addition, we have seen that typical efficiencies are on the order of 30 to 35 percent.

Of growing importance is a class of energy-conversion systems called *direct energy-conversion* (DEC) devices. In these systems the electrical energy is obtained more directly from the fuel energy, without the need for circulating and manipulating a working fluid. DEC systems have been developed rapidly as a result of space-age demands, and there are many such systems that show great promise for consumer use. The absence of fluid-handling machinery means that many of the devices work with *no moving parts*, an obvious asset from the reliability point of view.

DEC methods rely on various physical phenomena that permit direct conversion of energy into electricity. Some of the methods use an energy input in the form of heat while others utilize solar radiation energy or chemical energy. Naturally, the direct conversion devices must still satisfy both the first and second laws of thermodynamics. Analyses of these newer systems require competence in several areas, including thermodynamics, electromagnetics, fluid mechanics, and solid-state physics, and with a few exceptions they are beyond the scope of this text. However, we shall now discuss some of these schemes in a qualitative way because they have definite and growing importance in engineering.

An interesting type of direct energy-conversion system already in use in space applications is the *thermoelectric converter*. In 1822, Seebeck found that an

FIG. 9·55 *A thermocouple circuit*

electromotive force (emf) is generated between two junctions, of dissimilar metals, at different temperatures. This effect forms the basis of the *thermocouple*, a temperature-measuring device (Fig. 9·55). For metals the emf is quite low, on the order of a few microvolts per degree of temperature difference. However, the semiconductor materials give much larger voltage outputs since the p- and n-type materials can be coupled to take advantage of the difference in behavior between the two materials.†

Since the thermocouple can be represented as a heat engine, the efficiency depends on T_h and T_c as well as on materials parameters of the semiconductors. Figure 9·56 shows a typical thermoelectric converter. Systems producing a few watts of power at efficiencies of 5 to 12 percent are reliable realities today.‡ For use at remote locations radioisotope heating has been used successfully as the heat source. Present systems do not come close to Carnot efficiency, but they do represent a reliable source of power with no moving parts.

In 1834, Peltier discovered that a current flow around a loop of two dissimilar metals warms up one end and cools down the other. Again this phenomenon can be enhanced by using semiconductor materials, and in this case a Peltier refrigerator can be made. In fact, one can buy commercial units using this effect. Figure 9·57 shows an example of a thermoelectric refrigerator. Recently a patent§ was issued for an electric blanket employing thermoelectric elements which can, in principle, be used either for heating or cooling.

† In n-type material heating causes electrons to diffuse to the cooler end of the material, so that the hot end becomes positively charged. In p-type material the cold end becomes positively charged by diffusion of the "holes."

‡ Thermoelectric converters powered by the waste heat from kerosene lamps are in wide use in rural areas of the Soviet Union, chiefly as a power source for radio receivers.

§ Patent No. 3080723.

FIG. 9·56 *A thermoelectric converter*

FIG. 9·57 *A thermoelectric refrigerator*

Unfortunately, rather high-amperage direct currents are presently required, and it is questionable just when such a blanket might become a consumer good.

A second type of direct energy power device is the *thermionic converter* (Fig. 9·58). The converter is essentially a heat engine using electrons as the working fluid, and therefore the Carnot efficiency is applicable as an upper limit. Direct conversion is possible if the "work function" of the anode (cold plate) is less than that of the cathode (hot plate). In order to operate satisfactorily, the vacuum diodes must have very close spacings (of the order of 0.02 mm), for otherwise the retarding potential arising from the distribution of electrons in the gap becomes too great for satisfactory operation. Diodes of this type have been operated with cathode temperatures of the order of 1500°K and with the anode at approximately 900°K, yielding power densities of the order of 2 to 10 watts/cm². The energy-conversion efficiency of these systems is of the order of 5 to 15 percent compared to a Carnot efficiency of 40 percent with these temperatures. The small spacings are difficult to maintain, especially with large cathode-anode temperature differences, and shortouts are frequent. The gas (plasma) diodes employ easily ionizable elements, such as cesium, whose positively charged ions tend to neutralize the retarding effects of the space charge, allowing larger spacings to be employed (1 mm). Efficiencies of the order of 18 percent have been obtained with this type of plasma diode operated at cathode temperatures of about 2500°K.

The thermionic converter is well suited for the production of electrical

FIG. 9·58 *A thermionic generator*

FIG. 9·59 *A proposed gas power cycle with thermoelectric topping*

power in space from a nuclear heat source. Since the energy which must be rejected as heat must be radiated to space, and high temperatures are required for low-weight radiators, space-systems designers can accept low efficiency in the interests of lightweight nonmechanical power-conversion equipment. The thermionic converter will probably also find application as a topping device for other power systems. Figure 9·59 shows a possible closed-cycle, nuclear-powered gas system using in-pile thermionic converter elements directly to generate electricity.

A somewhat different DEC system is the *photovoltaic device*. It is *not* a heat engine, and actually operates efficiently at a low (room) temperature using photons (light) as the primary energy source. In this device light falls on a surface and produces electrons by interaction within the surface. Semiconductor materials are utilized. Energy-conversion efficiencies on the order of 15 percent have been achieved in photovoltaic cells. The most well-known application of these devices has been on space vehicle solar panels. These solar cells are used to recharge batteries, which serve as the primary power source.

The *fuel cell* is a device in which a chemical reaction is harnessed directly to produce electrical power. Unlike a chemical battery, in which an electrolyte is decomposed into its basic components, a fuel cell utilizes a controlled reaction between components such as hydrogen and oxygen. Since the hydrogen and oxygen can be continuously supplied, the fuel cell does not run down as does a chemical battery. A schematic of a fuel cell is shown in Fig. 9·60. Gaseous hydrogen and oxygen at pressures of the order of 40 atm enter the cell and are brought into contact with porous electrodes. Between the electrodes is a liquid electrolyte, which serves to limit the reaction rate. Hydrogen diffuses through the porous anode, is absorbed on the surface, and then reacts with the OH^- ions in the electrolyte, forming water and yielding free electrons. Oxygen diffuses through the cathode, is absorbed by the surface, and reacts with the water to form OH^- ions. Thus water is continually being formed at the anode and decomposed at the cathode. The reaction rate is controlled by the rate of migration of OH^- ions through the electrolyte. Electrons flow out of the cell through a load and are returned to the cathode. The maximum cell emf is of the order of 1 volt and depends to a certain extent on the choice of reactants employed.

Fuel cells have been developed for operation in space vehicles and have many other possible applications. A major difficulty of present cells is the relatively short life span of the electrodes, especially when operated with relatively low-grade fuels. Their lifetime can be markedly increased by use of purified hydrogen, but the costs of the purifying operation are presently prohibitive from the standpoint of consumer use. However, fuel cells may become the power sources for electric cars of the future.

The fuel cell is not a heat engine (in fact the process is essentially isothermal), and consequently the Carnot efficiency is an irrelevant maximum for fuel-cell performance. However, given a supply of hydrogen and oxygen, more useful power can be obtained with a fuel cell than if the gases were allowed to react spontaneously and a Carnot cycle were run from the high-temperature flame. This is because the voltage of the cell tends to restrain the chemical reaction, much as a piston restrains spontaneous expansion of gas. The maximum theoretical efficiency of the fuel cell, based on the conversion of chemical to electrical energy, is 100 percent.

If a fluid that is a good electrical conductor flows through a magnetic field, an electric field is induced in the fluid, and power can be obtained. Such

FIG. 9·60   *A fuel cell*

a device is called a *magnetohydrodynamic* (mhd) *generator*.† While liquid metals such as mercury could be used, ionized gases (plasmas) are much more practical for the job of converting internal energy to electricity. The mhd generators now in existence use the products of combustion of fossil fuels, seeded with easily ionized elements, such as cesium, to form the plasma. In the future we can expect to see much more energetic plasmas produced as a result of controlled-fusion reactions. The gas is pressurized, heated, and passed through a nozzle (this looks quite a bit like the Brayton cycle). The high-velocity gases are ducted through a magnetic field, and an electric field perpendicular to the applied magnetic field is developed. A closed-cycle mhd system powered by a nuclear reactor is shown in Fig. 9·61.

Irreversibilities due to friction, ohmic losses, and heat transfer severely limit the practicability of small mhd generators; the most promising use therefore appears to be in conjunction with large central power stations; plants in

† In an mhd device the ionized gas flows at right angles to a magnetic field such that a force is generated at right angles to both the velocity of flow and the magnetic field. The force on the ions and electrons in the device drives them to opposite electrodes, giving rise to a current.

FIG. 9·61 *Idealized mhd power generator*

the 100-Mw range have been studied. The electrical conductivity of the gas decreases rapidly with decreasing temperature, which imposes a major limitation on the minimum-operating-temperature range. If the temperature falls too low the gas will deionize, and the device will open-circuit. The mhd system is therefore best suited to high-temperature operation and looks very attractive as a potential topping system for a binary power plant. The reject energy from the mhd system would thus be used as input energy to a conventional power system. If the plasma were at a temperature of say 4500°F, the potential efficiency of a binary cycle with energy rejection at 60°F would be

$$\eta = 1 - \frac{60 + 460}{4500 + 460} = 0.90$$

Design studies suggest efficiencies around 45 percent might be obtained in large practical systems.

An exotic type of refrigerator is the *magnetic refrigerator*, which takes advantage of the magnetic and superconducting properties of materials at low temperatures and has been built for laboratory use.† A sample of material is magnetized slowly while in contact with the "high-temperature" region, then suddenly (adiabatically) demagnetized, then demagnetized slowly while in contact with the low-temperature region, and finally magnetized adiabatically, returning to the initial state. Contact with the low- and high-temperature regions is made through superconductors. Lead is an electrical superconductor at low temperatures and a very poor thermal conductor. If a small field (only a few hundred gauss) is applied to the lead, it undergoes a transition to a normal electrical-conduction state, in which it is a good thermal conductor. A "thermal valve" can thereby be made. The schematic diagram and process representation for this type of magnetic refrigerator are shown in Fig. 9·62. The processes undergone by the magnetic substance are in the limit reversible, so that the limiting behavior is that of a Carnot cycle.

† C. V. Heer et al., *Review of Scientific Instruments*, vol. 25, no. 11, p. 1088.

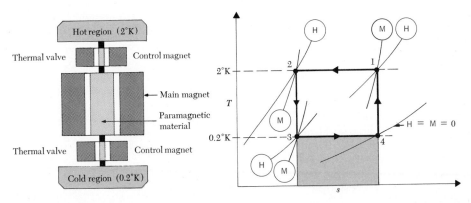

FIG. 9·62 *Low-temperature magnetic refrigeration*

9·19 CONCLUDING REMARKS

The student must remember that there are many criteria other than thermodynamics for choosing what systems should be used in a particular application. For space work a low efficiency may be acceptable if a high power/weight ratio can be achieved. Reliability is also of great importance, and the advantage of having no moving parts may offset a high initial cost. In any design a tradeoff will be necessary between the numerous parameters of interest before a final system is chosen. For power generation for large cities reliability and low fuel cost are important. The problems of site location, air and water pollution, and an aesthetic design of the plant all have to be considered—along with the thermodynamic analysis.

SELECTED READING

Lee, J., and F. Sears, *Thermodynamics*, 2d ed., chaps. 11–13, Addison-Wesley Publishing Co., Inc., Reading, Mass., 1962.

Obert, E., and R. Gaggioli, *Thermodynamics*, 2d ed., chaps. 15, 17, and 18, McGraw-Hill Book Company, New York, 1963.

Van Wylen, G., and R. Sonntag, *Fundamentals of Classical Thermodynamics*, chap. 9, John Wiley & Sons, Inc., New York, 1965.

Wark, K., *Thermodynamics*, chaps. 16 and 17, McGraw-Hill Book Company, New York, 1966.

QUESTIONS

9·1 What is the significance of the area under a line on a T-s plane?

9·2 Derive the Carnot-cycle efficiency from things which you remember.

9·3 What is an isentropic process? What processes might reasonably be idealized as isentropic?

9·4 What is an isentropic efficiency?

9·5 Give an argument for idealizing a steady-flow heating process as isobaric.

9·6 To what matter does the process representation of Fig. 9·5 pertain?

9·7 What is the reason for using reheat in a Rankine cycle?

9·8 How do the back-work ratios of the Rankine and Brayton cycles compare?

9·9 What is the reason for using a topping cycle?

9·10 What is the reason for supercharging an engine?

9·11 Why do intercooling and reheat lower the efficiency of a nonregenerative gas-turbine power system?

9·12 Explain with the aid of process representations why nonregenerative gas-turbine systems operate at higher pressure ratios than regenerative systems.

9·13 Is the thermoelectric converter a thermodynamic system?

9·14 What is the function of the valve in a vapor refrigeration system?

9·15 Can the cop of a heat pump ever exceed unity?

9·16 What is an afterburner?

9·17 Why does a ramjet not have a turbine?

9·18 What is a turboprop engine?

9·19 Why do jet engines have diffusers at the inlet?

9·20 Is a high or a low pressure ratio most desirable for a jet engine?

9·21 Can regeneration be used in jet engines?

9·22 Why does the hydrogen engine have a higher specific impulse than a chemical rocket?

9·23 Why is the ion engine not being considered for launchings, but being planned for long-term inflight propulsion?

PROBLEMS

9·1 Determine the isentropic efficiency of the turbine example of Sec. 5·4.

9·2 Determine the isentropic efficiency of the compressor in the heat-pump example of Sec. 5·4.

9·3 Air is to be compressed from atmospheric pressure at 60°F to 100 psia in a centrifugal compressor (isentropic efficiency about 0.70). The flow rate will be 500 lbm/min. Specify the hp requirement for the driving motor.

9·4 Air is to be supplied steadily at 10 lbm/sec, 120 psia, 70°F. Determine the necessary hardware. Specify the compressor efficiency, power input, and the heating (or cooling) requirements of any heat exchangers.

9·5 A steam turbine manufacturer has determined the following data for a small 10-kw turbine: inlet state 300 psia, 550°F; exit state 20 psia, 227°F. In the throttling calorimeter (see Prob. 5·29) on the turbine exit $P = 14.7$ psia, $T = 220$°F. Calculate the turbine isentropic efficiency.

9·6 Air enters an adiabatic nozzle at 1000°F and 20 psia and emerges at 1 psia. The isentropic efficiency of the nozzle is known to be 0.96. Determine the discharge velocity.

9·7 Oxygen flows through a flow-metering nozzle located in a 1-in.-diameter pipe. The nozzle throat diameter is ¼ in. The upstream pressure and temperature are 40 psia and 100°F, and the pressure at the nozzle throat is 10 in. of water lower than the upstream pressure. Determine the oxygen-flow rate, assuming $\eta_s = 0.94$.

9·8 What is the value of the efficiency of the adjacent reversible cycle?

9·9 Determine the energy-conversion efficiency that could be obtained in the example of Sec. 9·4 if the saturated liquid emerging at 212°F from the condenser is fed directly to the pump. Specify the flow rate and boiler-heat input for 1 Mw of output power.

9·10 Consider the system of Fig. 9·14. Keeping the turbine inlet and condensing temperatures fixed, and using pump and turbine isentropic efficiencies of 0.8 and 0.9, calculate the performance over the maximum range of boiler pressures and determine the boiler pressure yielding maximum cycle efficiency.

9·11 Determine the energy-conversion efficiency for a supercritical steam power plant where condensation occurs at 100°F and the high-pressure side is at 4000 psia. Assume that the maximum system temperature is 1000°F and that the overall isentropic efficiency of the turbines (several used in series) is 0.90. The pump efficiency is 0.60. Specify the heating rate and steam-flow rate for 100 Mw of power output.

9·12 A mercury-vapor power cycle for use in space operates on the Rankine cycle, except that a valve is added between the boiler and the turbine. Condensation occurs at 10 psia, and saturated liquid at this pressure enters the electromagnetic pump, which has an isentropic efficiency of 0.12. The boiler operates at 180 psia and delivers 0.98-quality vapor at this pressure. The valve drops the pressure to 100 psia before the fluid enters the turbine, which has an isentropic efficiency of 0.60. Make a thermodynamic analysis of this system and determine the energy-conversion efficiency, mercury-flow rate, reactor thermal power, and condenser heat-rejection rate for 10 kw of power output. What happens to the energy transferred as heat from the condenser?

9·13 Determine the performance of the system of Prob. 9·12 when the valve is wide open (no pressure drop).

9·14 The valve in Prob. 9·12 is necessary to reduce the moisture content of the vapor in the turbine. Suppose an effective zero-g boiler-superheater could be designed such that the valve could be eliminated and the boiler pressure reduced to 100 psia, keeping the turbine inlet state the same as in Prob. 9·12. Determine the performance of this system.

9·15 A cesium-vapor power plant for use in space operates with a boiler pressure of 50 psia and a condensing temperature of 1000°R. The maximum vapor temperature is 2200°R. The isentropic efficiencies of the pump and turbine are 0.65 and 0.70, respectively, and the system operates on the Rankine cycle. Determine the system performance. Compute the conversion efficiency, reactor heat-transfer rate, flow rate, condenser heat-rejection rate, and turbine hp for 10 Mw of power.

9·16 Suppose the cesium-vapor cycle of Prob. 9·15 is used as a topping cycle for the steam power cycle of Prob. 9·11. The flow rates of the two systems will not be the same as in these problems. Determine the efficiency of the combined plant, and specify the heat-transfer rates for the cesium boiler, the cesium-steam heat exchanger, and the steam condenser, and the pump and turbine hp for 300 Mw of total power, using the same component efficiencies.

9·17 Suppose the mercury-vapor cycle of Prob. 9·12 is used as a topping cycle for a Rankine steam power plant in which the evaporation occurs at 550°F and condensing occurs at 70°F. The steam-turbine inlet state has 75 F° of superheat. The isentropic efficiencies of the pump and turbine are 0.65 and 0.90 in the steam system. Determine the system efficiency, mercury and steam flow rates, the heat-transfer rates for the mercury and steam boilers and the condenser, and the pump and turbine hp for 300 Mw of total power output.

9·18 A supercritical CO_2 power plant powered by a low-temperature nuclear source has been proposed for operation in the Arctic. The high-pressure side is at 1100 psia, and condensation occurs at $-40°F$. Assuming pump and turbine efficiencies of 0.50 and 0.85 and a peak cycle temperature of 200°F, determine the system energy-conversion efficiency and the required reactor power and CO_2-flow rate for 2 kw net output.

9·19 The geothermal plant operated by a utility company in northern California utilizes steam produced by natural means underground. Steam wells are drilled to tap this steam supply which is available at 65 psia at 350°F. The steam leaves the turbine at 4-in. Hg absolute pressure. The turbine isentropic efficiency is 0.75. Calculate the efficiency of the plant. If the unit produces 12.5 Mw what is the steam flow rate? The 4-in. Hg exhaust pressure is maintained by using a condenser system that requires a cooling tower. How can you justify the capital expense for the condenser system?

9·20 A steam turbine plant has a single stage of regenerative feedwater heating using a closed feedwater heater. Steam enters the turbine at 400 psia and 800°F. The condenser operates at 1 psia. The bled steam is extracted at a temperature which is halfway between that in the *boiler* and the condenser. Assuming that the turbine stages have $\eta_s = 0.8$, and for the pumps $\eta_s = 0.6$, analyze the cycle in detail.

9·21 A potassium-steam binary vapor power cycle has been proposed as a means of achieving a high efficiency system.† The energy input to the potassium cycle will be from a nuclear reactor. The steam cycle design is based on the existing supercritical Eddystone power plant. The object of this series of problems is to analyze the system for efficiency.

The analysis will require location of thermodynamic data in the literature, an experience simulating the problems and frustrations of real engineering practice.

(a) Determine the efficiency of the potassium topping cycle under the following conditions: turbine inlet 1540°F, saturated vapor; turbine exit at 2.4 psia, turbine isentropic efficiency 0.7; condenser exit conditions 1100°F at 2.4 psia.

(b) Determine the efficiency of the steam cycle, which has two stages of reheat. At the inlet to the first turbine the conditions are 1050°F steam at 4000 psia. The steam exits the turbine at 786°F at 1133 psia. The first reheat stage goes to 1050°F at 1043 psia. The exit from the second turbine is at 705°F at 263 psia. The second stage of reheat goes to 1050°F at 251 psia. The steam leaves the third turbine at 1.5 psia. This turbine has an isentropic efficiency of 0.878. Condensation occurs at 1.5 psia and carries the steam to the saturated liquid state. Besides determining the overall efficiency, find the isentropic efficiencies of the first two turbines.

(c) Now, determine the efficiency of the combined cycles with the energy input as heat to the steam cycle supplied by the condensation process of the potassium cycle.

† W. R. Chambers et al., A Potassium-Steam Binary Vapor Cycle for Nuclear Power Plants, ORNL-3584 (1964).

(d) Now, add a single open feedwater heater to the potassium cycle to operate with bleed conditions of 26 psia at 1510°F. Assume the turbine efficiency remains 0.7. Find the cycle efficiency for the potassium cycle.

(e) Write a brief discussion of the advantages, based on your analysis, and disadvantages of this binary system.

9·22 It is proposed that warm water from the gulf stream (75°F) be used as an energy source for a power system for an oceanic research station. Cold water from 2000 ft below the surface will be used as the energy sink (35°F). Design a vapor power system using freon-12 for this operation, assuming a power requirement of 10 kw. Specify the freon flow rate, heat exchanger energy-transfer rates, compressor and pump power requirements. Assuming that the cold water leaves the condenser 10°F below the condensing temperature, and is discharged at the water surface, estimate the cold-water pumping power required. How might this pumping power be reduced?

9·23 Suppose geothermal steam is available at 75 psia, saturated vapor, at the rate of 100 lbm/hr. Design a power system to utilize as much of the energy of this steam as you can, assuming that the environmental temperature is 60°F. Specify the required component efficiencies, energy-transfer rates, intermediate states, and so on.

9·24 A major fact contributing to smog is that the high-speed combustion in conventional automobile engines tends to be relatively incomplete. In contrast, the combustion in a steady-flow burner is much more complete, and a significant reduction in automotive smog could be obtained by a national change to engines with continuous burners. Steam engines are now of considerable interest for this reason.

Using reasonable component efficiencies and operating parameters, design an automotive steam turbine power plant (closed cycle) for 100 hp. Specify the burner heat input rate, radiator heat output rate, and so on. Discuss the problems of load control and part-load performance.

9·25 Do Prob. 9·24 using a reciprocating steam engine with cam-driven valves. Assume adiabatic compression and expansion.

9·26 Large central power plants are often placed on rivers where a good low-temperature sink is available for heat rejection. Estimate and discuss the effects of such plants on the river environments. How much power could one generate on, say, the Mississippi and Sacramento rivers if the river temperature rise is to be held to 10°F? What is the effect of such "thermal pollution" on the ecology of our rivers?

9·27 Two identical bodies of constant specific heat are at the same initial temperature, T_1. A refrigerator operates between these bodies until one of them is cooled to a temperature of T_2. Derive an expression for the minimum amount of work required.

9·28 A 2-ton refrigerator system operates between 0°F and 100°F. Its cop is 0.8 of the Carnot cop for the same temperatures. What is the required work input in hp?

9·29 Using freon-12 as the refrigerant, determine the cop for a vapor compression refrigeration cycle with saturated vapor leaving the evaporator at 40°F and saturated liquid leaving the condenser at 80°F. The compressor has an isentropic

efficiency of 0.80. Compare to a Carnot refrigerator operating at 80°F and
40°F.

9·30 Using the table of refrigerants provided by the *American Society of Refrigerating
Engineers*, compare the suitability of the following refrigerants on the basis of
toxicity and flammability, pressures at operating temperatures of 5°F and 86°F,
and h_{fg} at 5°F. Comment on effect of a pressure less than atmospheric in the
evaporator. *Refrigerants:* Freon-11, -12, -27, Carrene 7, methyl chloride, ammonia,
CO_2.

9·31 It has been suggested that a used household refrigerator might be modified to
serve as a heat pump for heating a swimming pool. The purpose of this problem
is the evaluation of this suggestion. First estimate the performance of the refrigerator operating as a refrigerator. Assume the following:

> Working substance freon-12
> Motor 1 hp, 1750 rpm
> η_M = mechanical efficiency of motor = 0.95
> η_s = compressor isentropic efficiency = 0.85
> Compressor driven at motor speed
> η_{vol} = compressor volumetric efficiency† = 0.70
> Condensing temperature 120°F
> Evaporating temperature 0°F
> Compressor inlet 10F° superheat
> Condenser discharge saturated liquid

Making suitable idealizations and employing proper analysis methodology, determine the cycle state points, flow rate when the motor draws 1 hp of electrical
power, volume-flow rate (based on compressor inlet state), compressor-displacement rate, rate of heat transfer from cold space and to kitchen, heat-pump cop,
and refrigerator cop.

Now, if this device is used as a swimming-pool heat pump, the evaporator
temperature will be much higher, since the environment temperature will be
higher than the refrigerator cold space. Also, the condenser temperature can be
lower, owing to improved heat-transfer characteristics when water rather than
kitchen air is on the outside of the condenser coils. However, the flow rate will
be altered because of the different compressor inlet density. Analyze the heat-
pump operation, assuming the following conditions:

> $\eta_{vol} = 0.70$
> Motor speed 1750 rpm
> Condensing temperature 90°F
> Evaporating temperature 20°F
> Compressor inlet 10F° superheat
> Condenser discharge saturated liquid

Determine the cycle state point, flow rate, required motor power, heat-transfer
rate to pool, and heat-pump cop. The swimming-pool heating requirement will

† η_{vol} = (volume-flow rate based on inlet density)/(compressor-displacement rate).

be of the order of 25,000 to 50,000 Btu/hr. What is your evaluation of this suggestion?

9·32 A vacuum refrigeration system is to produce 100 tons of cooling. The water leaves the flash chamber at 45° and reaches a temperature of 65°F on leaving the chiller. Determine the pressure in the flash chamber and the mass flow rate through the chiller.

9·33 The objective of this problem is to make a realistic economic analysis of the "heat pump" concept for application to space heating in a region like your own. In a typical installation the system receives energy as heat from the air outside a house at a temperature somewhat below the prevailing atmospheric temperature, and rejects energy as heat to the air inside the house at a temperature somewhat above the inside air temperature. In order to keep the heat-transfer area in the condenser and evaporator from being too large, a reasonable temperature difference for heat transfer must be provided (say 10°F minimum).

(a) Choosing a suitable refrigerant, and making other assumptions as necessary, carry out the cycle analysis. Take the interior temperature as 70°F and use an outside temperature typical of your area on a cold winter day.

(b) Electrical energy costs about 2.4 cents/kw-hr. Gas costs vary widely across the country. Your local gas company can quote you a rough cost per 1000 Btu. Typical household furnaces manage to get about 0.7 of the energy released by combustion into the house. Discuss the relative merits of the heat pump and gas furnaces in your area. If the heat pump is more expensive to operate in your area, in what sort of areas might it be cheaper than gas?

9·34 Compression-distillation units for water purification offer certain advantages over the older type of heat-distillation units. A schematic flow diagram of a simple compression-distillation unit is shown in the sketch. A steady flow of impure water at 14.7 psia and 60°F (state 1) enters a heat exchanger in which it is evaporated. The purified saturated vapor is compressed and then fed back to the same exchanger for condensation and subcooling. Assuming that the compressor

Heat exchanger

isentropic efficiency is 0.7, and that the purified water emerges at 212°F, what is the pressure level of the condensing process, and what is the work input to the compressor per lbm of distilled water?

9·35 Air is to be compressed from 1 atm to 300 psia. Determine the work required for an isentropic compressor and for a highly cooled compressor in which the air undergoes an isothermal process. What is the isentropic efficiency of the isothermal compressor? What is the *isothermal efficiency* of the isentropic compressor ($\eta_T \equiv W_T/W$)? The inlet temperature is 60°F.

9·36 Determine the compressor efficiency for the example of Sec. 9·11 below which the plant would not be self-sustaining, all other things being equal.

9·37 Using the 0.85-efficient compressor, determine the efficiency of the system of Sec. 9·11 as a function of pressure ratio, keeping the turbine inlet temperature fixed. What pressure ratio must be achieved before the system can be started? Specify the flow rate, heating and cooling rates, compressor and turbine power, and pressure ratio (*a*) at the maximum efficiency point and (*b*) at the minimum flow-rate point for 300 hp of net shaft power.

9·38 Consider the two-stage compressor shown. Treating the gas as perfect with constant c_P, derive an expression for the work input per lbm in terms of P_1, P_2, P_4, η_1, η_2, T_1, and T_3. Then, for all other parameters fixed, find the value of P_2 which minimizes the work requirement. Show that when $T_3 = T_1$ and $\eta_1 = \eta_2$ the optimum condition is $P_2/P_1 = \sqrt{P_4/P_1}$.

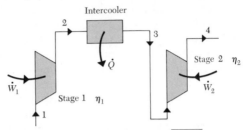

9·39 A reciprocating air compressor operates as shown in the sketch. The intake valve opens whenever the cylinder pressure drops to 1 atm, and the discharge valve opens when the cylinder pressure rises to 150 psia. The supply air is at 70°F, 15 psia. At top-dead center (tdc) the cylinder volume is 1 in.³, and at bottom-dead center (bdc) it is 40 in.³.

(*a*) Sketch the *indicator diagram* (pressure versus cylinder volume)

(*b*) Calculate the indicator state points and the net work input requirement (per lbm of air) assuming isentropic compression and expansion and adiabatic, constant pressure intake and exhaust.

(*c*) Calculate the overall (quasi-steady flow) isentropic efficiency.

(*d*) Calculate the air flow rate and power input requirement at 600 rpm.

9·40 Suppose that the cylinder of Prob. 9·39 is water-cooled.

(*a*) What will be the effect of this cooling on the flow rate supplied by the compressor?

(*b*) Approximating the compression process as polytropic, determine the minimum polytropic exponent for successful compression.

(*c*) Suppose that the maximum air temperature attained is 240°F, which is maintained during the discharge stroke, and that when the intake valve opens the air temperature is 120°F. Treating the compression and expansion processes as polytropic, analyze the compression cycle, calculating the net work input and heat output per cycle. Then, calculate the air flow rate, power input, and cooling rate at 600 rpm.

9·41 Derive an expression for the efficiency of a Brayton cycle analogous to Eq. (9·15) but including compressor and turbine isentropic efficiencies η_c and η_t.

9·42 Use the solution to Prob. 9·41 to derive an expression for the minimum compressor efficiency for which the Brayton cycle will work.

9·43 Develop expressions for the work output per lbm and the efficiency of an ideal Brayton cycle with regeneration assuming maximum possible regeneration. For fixed maximum and minimum temperatures, how do the efficiency and work outputs vary with pressure ratio? What is the optimum pressure ratio?

9·44 An ideal Brayton cycle gas turbine with regeneration but no reheat or intercooling operates at full load with an inlet temperature to the compressor of 60°F and an inlet temperature to the turbine of 1540°F. The compressor pressure ratio is 6.0. The cycle is also to be operated at part load at a pressure ratio of 3.0 with a turbine inlet temperature of 1100°F. Compare the thermal efficiency and net work output per lbm flow for the two operating points if the working fluid (air) is treated as a perfect gas and the maximum possible regeneration is obtained.

9·45 Rework Prob. 9·44 under the same conditions for full load and part load but without the regenerator. What do you conclude about the use of a regenerator?

9·46 Redo Prob. 9·44 using compressor and turbine isentropic efficiencies of 0.8 and 0.85, respectively, and a regenerator effectiveness ($\dot{Q}_{act}/\dot{Q}_{max}$) of 0.85.

9·47 A closed-cycle gas-turbine power plant, such as might be used to provide power for a remote experimental station, is shown below. Typical component performance factors might be compressor isentropic efficiency 0.80, turbine isentropic efficiency 0.82, and *regenerator effectiveness* $(T_3 - T_2)/(T_5 - T_2) = 0.85$.

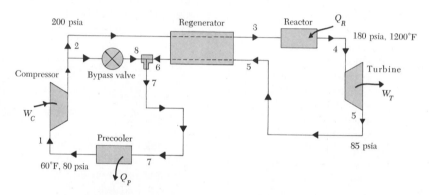

The objective here is to analyze this system for two cases: (*a*) bypass valve closed, that is, maximum output power, and (*b*) bypass valve opened such that the system is self-sustaining, but no net output power. The assumed compressor pressure ratio of 2.5:1 is typical for a regenerative gas-turbine power system. The function of the bypass valve is load control. Making suitable idealizations, determine the state points for the two operating conditions. Note that states 1 and 4 are fixed, and you can start from these. The working fluid in the system is nitrogen, which may be assumed to be a perfect gas with constant specific heats.

Calculate the overall energy-conversion efficiency, the reactor heat-transfer rate (kw), the compressor and turbine powers (hp), the precooler load (Btu/hr), and the flow rates (lbm/hr) for the case of (*a*) no bypass flow, net output power of 500 kw, and (*b*) same compressor flow, no net power (zero load, self-sustaining). What would be the efficiency for no bypass flow if the regenerator were eliminated (bigger reactor and precooler)?

9·48 A gas-turbine power plant for vehicular use consists of the components shown. Air enters at state 1 and is compressed, heated, and expanded in a two-stage turbine system. The first turbine is used to drive the compressor and the second to power the vehicle. A valve for load control is located between the two turbines.

The objective is to make a preliminary study of the feasibility of such a system. You may make the following idealizations:

All turbomachinery adiabatic (isentropic efficiencies as given)

Mass of fuel added in combustion negligible; to be treated simply as a device in which energy is added as heat to the air

Kinetic and potential energies negligible at the numbered state points

Air a perfect gas

Process in combustor isobaric ($P_2 = P_3$)

Maximum permissible air temperature 1600°F (metallurgical limit)

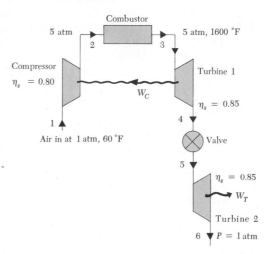

Determine states 5 and 6 for the two cases of (a) full power, valve wide open (state 4 = state 5), and (b) no power, no work from turbine 2 (state 5 = state 6). Show these on your scale T-s diagram and add them to your table. Determine the compressor work requirement, the work delivered by turbines 1 and 2 for these two cases, and the heat input required, all per lbm of air. Compute the full-load system efficiency, W_{shaft}/Q. For the case where the system is running at full power, delivering 300 hp, what air flow rate is required? If the energy transfer as heat to the air in the combustor is equivalent to 19,000 Btu/lbm of fuel, what fuel flow rate is required, what is the air-fuel ratio for this engine, and what is the full-load specific fuel consumption (lbm of fuel per hp-hr)?

9·49 A preliminary design is required for a gas-turbine power plant with a single stage intercooling and a regenerator with an effectiveness of 0.80 (see Prob. 9·47). The turbine inlet temperature is limited to 1400°F, the compressor inlet conditions are 520°R at 1 atm. Determine the *pressure ratio* for maximum efficiency, assuming $\eta_c = 0.85$ each stage, that the air emerges from the intercooler at 540°R, that each compressor stage has the same pressure ratio, and that $\eta_t = 0.9$.

9·50 An idealized air-standard Diesel cycle has a compression ratio of 15. The energy input is idealized as a heat transfer of 700 Btu/lbm. The inlet conditions are 70°F at 1 atm. Find the pressure and temperature at the end of each process in the cycle and determine the cycle efficiency.

9·51 The compression ratio on an ideal air-standard Otto cycle is 8.0. The inlet conditions are 1 atm at 70°F. The combustion process is idealized as a heat transfer of 700 Btu/lbm. Find the pressure and temperature at the end of each process and determine the cycle efficiency.

9·52 Discuss the inadequacies in the models of Probs. 9·50 and 9·51. Which idealizations are likely to be the weakest, and what effects will they have on the predicted performance?

9·53 An ideal Otto cycle operates with a compression ratio of 9:1 at intake conditions of 14.0 psia and 70°F. The cylinder volume initially is 125 in.³. If 4 Btu of energy is added as heat to the gas during the constant-volume heating process, calculate the cycle efficiency and the pressure and temperature at the end of each process.

9·54 An ideal Diesel cycle operates with a compression ratio of 15:1 at intake conditions of 14.0 psia and 70°F. The cylinder volume initially is 125 in.³. If 4 Btu of energy is added as heat to the gas during the constant-pressure heating process, calculate the cycle efficiency and the pressure and temperature at the end of each process.

9·55 A small turbojet engine for use in takeoff assist is to be designed to the following specifications:

> Static sea-level thrust, 1000 lbf
> Fuel, gasoline
> Size, maximum diameter not to exceed 18 in.

Since the engine is to be used for takeoff assist, it will be operated at sea level, and you may therefore assume that the temperature and pressure at the compressor inlet are 1 atm and 60°F. For a small engine of this type a compressor can probably be built to raise the pressure to 6.5 atm with an isentropic efficiency of 80 percent, so use these values there. A small turbine is needed to deliver the work required by the compressor, and one with an 80 percent isentropic efficiency can probably be made. However, the turbine inlet temperature should probably not exceed 2000°F, so take this as T_3 (see Fig. 9·49). If the supersonic nozzle is properly designed, it will exhaust the gas at a pressure of 1 atm, so assume this to be the case. The energy added as heat to the air in the combustor is 20,000 Btu/lbm of fuel.

The objective is to make a preliminary analysis of such an engine. Using the assumed values, calculate the compressor work requirement (Btu/lbm), the air-fuel ratio (lbm of air/lbm of fuel), and the state of the air entering the nozzle (P and T). You may neglect the mass of fuel added to the air. If the nozzle is adiabatic and frictionless and no shock waves occur, the flow in the nozzle may be idealized as being isentropic. Calculate the state of the gas leaving the nozzle and determine the exit velocity.

The Mach number in compressible flow is the ratio of the velocity at any point to the velocity of sound at that point,

$$M = \frac{\mathsf{V}}{a}$$

For a perfect gas, it may be shown that the speed of sound a† is

$$a = \sqrt{g_c k R T}$$

Calculate the speed of sound and the Mach number at the nozzle exit. At the throat the Mach number is 1. Calculate the velocity, temperature, pressure, and density of the air at the throat.

The specific impulse for this engine may be shown to be

$$SI = \frac{1}{g_c} (\mathsf{V}_5 - \mathsf{V}_1)$$

† Do not confuse a here with the Helmholtz function.

The velocity at the compressor inlet would be of the order of 200 ft/sec; assuming this value, calculate the specific impulse. Calculate the air-flow rate required to produce the specified 1000-lbf thrust. Calculate the density at the nozzle discharge and determine the flow area and nozzle diameter at this point. In a similar manner, calculate the throat area and diameter. Assuming that the free-flow area at point 1 is 80 percent of the frontal area and that the outside of the engine has the maximum diameter of 18 in., calculate the velocity and Mach number at the engine inlet. Calculate the fuel required to run this engine at full load for a 1-min takeoff-assist period.

9·56 An aerospace plane uses turbojet engines for takeoff and ramjet engines for upper-atmosphere flight. Assuming that the vehicle is flying at 5000 mph through the air at $-40°F$, determine the temperature of the air entering the combustion chamber of the ramjet engine.

9·57 Estimate the maximum specific impulses for the following thrusting systems:
(a) $T_0 = 3000°F$, $k = 1.3$, $c_P = 0.27$ Btu/lbm-°F
(b) $T_0 = 6000°F$, hydrogen
(c) Ion engine, cesium plasma ejected at 1 percent of the speed of light

9·58 Consider a blowdown thrusting system which will use hydrogen as the working fluid. The hydrogen will be stored in a high-pressure tank at 3000 psia, from which it will be bled to a chamber having a regulated pressure of 200 psia. The system temperature will be approximately 80°F. The thrusting nozzles will operate with an exit pressure of 10 psia. Determine the specific impulse. What flow rate is required for 40 lbf thrust? How large must the storage vessel be if the total thrusting requirement is 1000 lbf-sec?

9·59 Estimate the power requirements of a cesium-ion engine which produces 1 lbf of thrust. The ions are ejected at 5 percent of the speed of light. How much power is used for vaporization and how much for acceleration? What is the specific impulse of this engine? How might the required power be generated?

9·60 It has been proposed that a small rocket system for orientation of a space satellite could be built schematically as shown below. A two-phase substance would be stored in the tank. The vapor would be bled off to be ejected through the nozzle. Energy would be added as heat so that the temperature of the fluid in the tank remained constant. The valve would provide throttling as necessary prior to the passing of flow through the supersonic nozzle.

The purpose of this problem is the study of this system. Assume the following:

Substance, freon-12
Design restrictions: minimum temperature in system $-30°F$, minimum permissible quality in nozzle 0.98
Flow treated as steady between 1 and 4, state of vapor inside the tank constant (saturated vapor at tank temperature, 100°F)
Nozzle exhausts to free space, so $P_{amb} = 0$ (note that $P_4 > 0$)
Nozzle flow isentropic, V_2 negligible, valve adiabatic

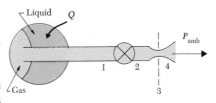

Sketch the process representation in the tank, starting from a completely liquid-filled tank and ending up with only saturated vapor. Sketch the representation of the processes between 1 and 4 on an h-s plane for the following three cases:

(a) No valve ΔP, state 4 at minimum quality

(b) State 4 at minimum temperature, minimum quality

(c) Intermediate case between (a) and (b)

Making suitable idealizations, compute the nozzle exit area A_4 and the flow rate required per lbm of thrust force for each of the three cases. Plot these quantities against the nozzle stagnation pressure P_2. The design requiring the least flow will be the lightest. Perhaps you will have to look at a couple of additional cases to pinpoint this optimum.

9·61 A stream of CO_2 at 20°F, 50 psia, 1200 ft/sec is needed for a chemical processing plant. The required flow rate is 2 lbm/sec. Design a system to obtain this flow. Bottled liquid CO_2 is available at room temperature (60°F).

9·62 A very low level thruster is required for a deep space probe. It has been suggested that subliming CO_2 be used. The CO_2 will be maintained at −60°F, and the required thrust is 0.01 lbf. Design a system to utilize the CO_2 vapor, which should not go below −140°F. Specify the nozzle exit area, the flow rate, intermediate states, other apparatus, and so on.

9·63 A refrigeration system capable of removing 10,000 watts is required for cooling a computer. The cold space will be maintained at 45°F, and the ambient temperature is 75°F. Allowing 10°F temperature difference on either side of the system for heat transfer, design a refrigeration system for this task. Specify component efficiencies, intermediate states, energy-transfer rates, and so on.

9·64 Design a desert power plant that uses solar energy as the energy source. The boiler temperature can be as high as 200°F, and the condenser temperature will be 100°F. The pressure within the system should be greater than atmospheric to avoid contamination by air. The total power requirement is 10 kw.

9·65 Design an Arctic power plant that uses solar energy as the power source. The boiler temperature can be as high as 100°F and the condenser temperature as low as −60°F. The internal pressure must exceed atmospheric to avoid contamination by air. The total power requirement is 5 kw.

9·66 A wind tunnel experiment requires air at 500°F, 0.01 atm, moving at 2200 ft/sec through a 0.2 ft² test section. Design a system to produce the desired flow from atmospheric air. Specify the hardware required, energy-transfer rates, flow rates, etc.

9·67 Oxygen is available at room temperature and 0.2 atm. Design a system in which the oxygen can be liquified at a rate of 10 lbm/min. The environmental temperature is 60°F, and the liquid oxygen can be stored at 10 atm.

9·68 A mercury vapor jet at 400 ft/sec, 1 atm, 1400°F is required for a commercial process. Design a system to obtain this jet from liquid mercury at room temperature; the required mass flow rate is 100 lbm/hr.

9·69 In a certain power system cesium vapor is available at 50 psia and 2000°R. Vapor is to be bled from this point at 0.2 lbm/min, and fed to an auxiliary apparatus at 2200°F, 0.3 psia. Design a system for this job.

9·70 A liquid having $c_P = c_v = 0.4$ Btu/lbm-°F is to be cooled in a parallel flow heat exchanger from 60°F to 30°F for a particular laboratory experiment. The liquid flow rate will be 100 lbm/hr. The cooling is to be accomplished using one of the following bottled gases:

(a) Air at 100 psia, 60°F

(b) Freon-12 at 72.4 psia, 60°F

(c) CO_2 at 500 psia, 60°F

(d) H_2O vapor at 20°F

The gas can be bled through the heat exchanger, and will be discharged to the atmosphere. No auxiliary hardware (other than a valve) can be used.

Only one of these gases will work for this purpose. Explain why each of the others is not satisfactory, using appropriate process sketches to make your points. For the gas that will work, specify the system configuration, gas flow rate, and so on. Use as little of the gas as possible with your system.

9·71 A dentist's drill of new design requires 0.01 hp. It will be driven by a small air turbine in the drill tip, with the discharged air used to blow chips away. The air must emerge from the drill at low velocity, atmospheric pressure, 75°F. Compressed air at 100 psia, 70°F is available to run the device.

Design a simple system which will work in the manner indicated. Sketch the *h-s* process representation for your system, and explain the concept of your design briefly, using this diagram. Then calculate the required air flow, power input to any heaters, pressure drop across any valves, and so on. Use the perfect-gas approximations and the following turbine operating conditions:

$$P_{\text{inlet}}/P_{\text{outlet}} = 3 \qquad \text{isentropic efficiency } 60\%$$

9·72 It has been proposed that power for an artificial heart be generated by a small reciprocating gas engine implanted in the chest. The body would act as the energy source (99°F) and energy would be rejected as heat to inhaled air (85°F). Investigate the feasibility of this proposal, presuming that 0.02 hp are required and that the cycle rate must be about 80 cycles/min.

9·73 A proposed scheme for powering an artificial heart imagines that breathed air will be expelled from the lungs through a simple mechanical engine. The body itself then powers the heart directly. Making suitable estimates and design calculations, investigate this proposal. The heart requires about 0.02 hp.

9·74 Small radioisotope heat sources are presently under development for implantation in the abdominal cavity. Temperatures of 1200°F seem possible with advanced types of insulation. Design a thermal power system using an inert gas to operate from this source, using the blood stream as the heat sink. Reciprocating machinery will be most practical, and the shaft power output should be 0.02 hp (for an artificial heart pump). Estimate the size of your design as best you can.

CHAPTER TEN

THERMODYNAMICS OF NONREACTING MIXTURES

10·1 DESCRIPTIONS OF MIXTURES

In the previous chapters we dealt only with a single substance, such as water, oxygen, or mercury. Occasionally we were concerned with systems containing two phases of a pure substance (for example, liquid and vapor H_2O). We have treated air as if it were a single substance, which is only reasonable at relatively low temperatures where its chemical structure is constant and at temperatures above the point at which one of the gases begins to condense. In this chapter we shall develop the thermodynamic theory for mixtures of substances, and explore various engineering applications of these ideas.

A *mixture* is any collection of molecules, ions, electrons, and so on. Each group of particles, distinguishable from the others by virtue of chemical structure, is called a *constituent* (or *species*) of the mixture. In mixtures where chemical reactions occur the amount of each constituent present cannot necessarily be varied independently. *Components* are those constituents the amounts of which can be independently varied. In this chapter we shall deal exclusively with nonreacting mixtures, in which each and every constituent is also a component.

A quantity of matter that is homogeneous in chemical composition and physical structure is called a *phase*. A phase can contain several components; for example, a mixture of gases would be a phase, and a mixture of the same substances in liquid form would be a different phase. A system having only one phase is called *homogeneous*, and a system with more than one phase is *heterogeneous*. A *pure substance* has the same chemical structure in all states, but may have several distinguishable phases.

The composition of a mixture may be described by specification of either the *mass* or the *number of moles* of each constituent. Two ways of specifying the composition independently of the quantity of the mixture are the *mass*

328

fraction,†

$$\blacktriangleright \qquad \Phi_i \equiv \frac{M_i}{\sum_i M_i} = \frac{M_i}{M} \tag{10 \cdot 1}$$

and the *mole fraction,*

$$\blacktriangleright \qquad \chi_i \equiv \frac{\mathfrak{N}_i}{\sum_i \mathfrak{N}_i} = \frac{\mathfrak{N}_i}{\mathfrak{N}} \tag{10 \cdot 2}$$

M and $\mathfrak{N}$ denote the total mass and total number of moles, respectively. The *molal mass* of the mixture is then

$$\hat{M} = \frac{\sum_i M_i}{\sum_i \mathfrak{N}_i} = \frac{\sum_i \hat{M}_i \mathfrak{N}_i}{\mathfrak{N}}$$

or

$$\blacktriangleright \qquad \hat{M} = \sum_i \chi_i \hat{M}_i \tag{10 \cdot 3}$$

For example, air is a mixture of approximately 3.76 moles of nitrogen for every mole of oxygen. The mole fractions are therefore

$$\chi_{N_2} = \frac{3.76}{4.76} = 0.79 \qquad \chi_{O_2} = \frac{1.00}{4.76} = 0.21$$

Then

$$\hat{M}_{air} = 0.79 \times 28.02 + 0.21 \times 32.00 = 28.97 \text{ lbm/lbmole}$$
$$= 28.97 \text{ g/gmole} = 28.97 \text{ kg/kgmole}$$

In this chapter we shall restrict ourselves to *simple compressible mixtures,* for which the only significant reversible work mode is volume change. According to the state postulate, the extensive thermodynamic state of any simple compressible mixture will be specified solely by its composition, energy, and volume. Its composition is specified by the set of mole numbers $\mathfrak{N}_1, \ldots , \mathfrak{N}_n$ of the n components. Thus the total entropy could be viewed functionally as

$$S = S(U, V, \mathfrak{N}_1, \mathfrak{N}_2, \ldots , \mathfrak{N}_n)$$

The derivatives of this function define the temperature, pressure, and electrochemical potentials. For temperature T

$$\blacktriangleright \qquad \frac{1}{T} \equiv \left(\frac{\partial S}{\partial U} \right)_{V, \mathfrak{N}_1, \ldots , \mathfrak{N}_n} \tag{10 \cdot 4}$$

For pressure P

$$\blacktriangleright \qquad \frac{P}{T} \equiv \left(\frac{\partial S}{\partial V} \right)_{U, \mathfrak{N}_1, \ldots , \mathfrak{N}_n} \tag{10 \cdot 5}$$

† The subscript i refers to any single unspecified constituent.

For the molal *electrochemical potential* $\hat{\mu}_i$ of the ith component,

$$\blacktriangleright \qquad -\frac{\hat{\mu}_i}{T} \equiv \left(\frac{\partial S}{\partial \mathfrak{N}_i}\right)_{U,V,\mathfrak{N}_1,\ldots,\mathfrak{N}_{i-1},\mathfrak{N}_{i+1},\ldots,\mathfrak{N}_n} \qquad (10 \cdot 6)$$

The definitions of temperature and pressure are equivalent to those introduced in Chap. Seven. The significance of the electrochemical potential will be explained in Chap. Twelve.

The Gibbs equation for a mixture is obtained by differentiation of the entropy,

$$\blacktriangleright \qquad dS = \frac{1}{T}\,dU + \frac{P}{T}\,dV - \sum_i \frac{\hat{\mu}_i}{T}\,d\mathfrak{N}_i \qquad (10 \cdot 7)$$

We shall use this important equation in Chap. Twelve. Note that if the composition does not change then each of the $d\mathfrak{N}_i$ are zero, and Eq. (10·7) reduces to Eq. (8·1), the Gibbs equation for a single substance.

10·2   MIXTURES OF INDEPENDENT SUBSTANCES

If we can idealize that the allowed quantum states of a given constituent are not influenced by the presence of the other constituents, the properties of the mixture may be determined from the "private" properties of its constituents. We call this a *mixture of independent substances*. Gas mixtures that are not too dense and some liquid and solid solutions (*ideal solutions*) may be treated in this manner.

In a mixture of independent substances each species has a "private" energy, and hence the total energy is

$$U = \sum_i U_i$$

Here U_i is the internal energy of the ith constituent.

Since the allowed quantum states of the constituents are independent, the mixture quantum states are determined from all possible combinations of constituent quantum states. As we saw in Chap. Six, the entropy of such a system is the sum of the entropies of its independent subsystems (the constituents). Hence,

The entropy of a mixture of independent substances is the sum of the entropies of the constituents,

$$S = \sum_i S_i$$

This fact is known as the *Gibbs rule*.

Let us consider a mixture of two independent substances A and B, each filling the total volume V. The entropy of the mixture can be expressed functionally as (for given amounts of A and B)

$$S = S_A(U_A, V) + S_B(U_B, V)$$

This will be true as long as each constituent is in a thermodynamic equilibrium state, even though the two constituents may not be in equilibrium with one another. We can find the condition of equilibrium between the constituents by isolating the mixture and finding the configuration of maximum entropy. The total internal energy, $U = U_A + U_B$, must remain fixed during this maximization. Differentiating the entropy with respect to U_A and keeping the volume and total internal energy fixed, we find

$$\frac{\partial S}{\partial U_A} = \left(\frac{\partial S_A}{\partial U_A}\right)_V + \left(\frac{\partial S_B}{\partial U_B}\right)_V \frac{dU_B}{dU_A} = \left(\frac{\partial S_A}{\partial U_A}\right)_V - \left(\frac{\partial S_B}{\partial U_B}\right)_V = 0$$

The condition of maximum entropy is then

$$T_A = T_B$$

We see that the equilibrium state will be one in which the temperatures of the two constituents are equal. This demonstration may be extended to mixtures of more than one constituent by the method of undetermined multipliers.

The pressure of the mixture is given by

$$P = T\left(\frac{\partial S}{\partial V}\right)_U = \sum_i \left[T\left(\frac{\partial S}{\partial V}\right)_U\right]_i = \sum_i P_i$$

Here P_i is the pressure which the ith constituent would have if it occupied the same volume as the mixture at the mixture temperature; P_i is called the *partial pressure* of the ith constituent. The fact that the total pressure is equal to the sum of the partial pressures for a mixture of independent substances is known as the *Dalton rule*.

A microscopic interpretation of the Dalton rule is helpful. The partial pressures represent the contribution to the average normal force per unit of area acting on the boundaries of the mixture system, resulting from impacts of the various constituents. The fact that the constituents are independent means that the average normal velocity of impacting particles of a constituent is not influenced by the presence of the other species.

To summarize, a mixture of independent substances in equilibrium has the following properties:

▶ $U = \sum_i U_i$ (10·8)

▶ $S = \sum_i S_i$ (10·9)

▶ $T_1 = T_2 = \cdots = T$ (10·10)

▶ $P = \sum_i P_i$ (10·11)

When the mixture has only one phase, it is convenient to work with the specific, or intensified properties. The specific internal energy of the mixture is

$$u = \frac{U}{M} = \sum_i \frac{M_i}{M} u_i = \sum_i \Phi_i u_i$$

or, on a molal basis,

$$\hat{u} = \sum_i \chi_i \hat{u}_i$$

The molal enthalpy of the mixture is

$$\hat{h} = \hat{u} + P\hat{v} = \sum_i \chi_i \hat{u}_i + \left(\sum_i P_i\right) \hat{v}$$

The molal enthalpy of the ith constituent may be written as

$$\hat{h}_i = \hat{u}_i + P_i \hat{v}_i = \hat{u}_i + P_i \frac{V}{\mathfrak{N}_i}$$

Since the molal specific volume of the mixture is

$$\hat{v} = \frac{V}{\sum_i \mathfrak{N}_i} = \frac{V}{\mathfrak{N}}$$

we can write

$$\hat{h} = \sum_i \chi_i \hat{u}_i + \sum_i \left(\frac{\mathfrak{N}_i}{\mathfrak{N}} P_i \frac{V}{\mathfrak{N}_i}\right) = \sum_i \chi_i \hat{h}_i$$

Similarly, it follows from Eq. (10·9) that

$$\hat{s} = \sum_i \chi_i \hat{s}_i$$

The molal specific heats of a mixture are defined as

$$\hat{c}_v \equiv \left(\frac{\partial \hat{u}}{\partial T}\right)_{\hat{v}, \chi_1, \chi_2, \dots, \chi_n}$$

$$\hat{c}_P \equiv \left(\frac{\partial \hat{h}}{\partial T}\right)_{P, \chi_1, \chi_2, \dots, \chi_n}$$

Thus

$$\hat{c}_v = \sum_i \chi_i \left(\frac{\partial \hat{u}_i}{\partial T}\right)_{\hat{v}} = \sum_i \chi_i \hat{c}_{v_i}$$

$$\hat{c}_P = \sum_i \chi_i \left(\frac{\partial \hat{h}_i}{\partial T}\right)_P = \sum_i \chi_i \hat{c}_{P_i}$$

We see that the molal internal energy, enthalpy, entropy, and specific heats for a mixture of independent substances are merely the sums of the contributions of each constituent evaluated at the mixture volume and temperature and weighted by their respective mole fractions. Equivalently, the contributions of the constituents may be evaluated at the mixture temperature and their respective *partial* pressures.

Summarizing,

$$\blacktriangleright \qquad \hat{u} = \sum_i \chi_i \hat{u}_i(T, P_i) \tag{10·12}$$

$$\blacktriangleright \qquad \hat{h} = \sum_i \chi_i \hat{h}_i(T, P_i) \tag{10·13}$$

$$\blacktriangleright \qquad \hat{s} = \sum_i \chi_i \hat{s}_i(T, P_i) \tag{10·14}$$

$$\blacktriangleright \qquad \hat{c}_v = \sum_i \chi_i \hat{c}_{v_i}(T, P_i) \tag{10·15}$$

$$\blacktriangleright \qquad \hat{c}_P = \sum_i \chi_i \hat{c}_{P_i}(T, P_i) \tag{10·16}$$

Since each of the constituents occupies the same volume, the ratio of the specific volumes of any two, based on their partial pressures and the mixture temperature, is inversely proportional to the ratio of their two masses,

$$\frac{v_i(T, P_i)}{v_j(T, P_j)} = \frac{V/M_i}{V/M_j} = \frac{M_j}{M_i} \tag{10·17}$$

As an example, let's find the specific heat at constant pressure for air, treating air as a mixture of nitrogen and oxygen.

We know that $\hat{c}_P = \sum_i \chi_i \hat{c}_{P_i}$

Now air can be treated as 1 mole of O_2 for every 3.76 moles of N_2. Thus

$$\chi_{O_2} = \frac{1}{4.76} = 0.21 \qquad \chi_{N_2} = \frac{3.76}{4.76} = 0.79$$

From Table B·6 we then find

$$\hat{c}_P = 0.21 \times 7.01 + 0.79 \times 6.95 = 6.96 \text{ Btu/lbmole-}°\text{R}$$

Note that the table gives a value of 6.95 Btu/lbmole-°R. Air actually contains some other gases, and if we account for these contributions to $\hat{c}_P$ the given value is obtained.

10·3 MIXTURES OF PERFECT GASES

Consider a mixture of perfect gases, each obeying the equation

$$PV = \mathfrak{N}\mathfrak{R}T \tag{10·18}$$

We idealize that this is a mixture of independent substances, so that the results of the preceding section may be applied directly. In particular, the partial pressure of the ith constituent is

$$P_i = \frac{\mathfrak{N}_i}{V} \mathfrak{R}T$$

The total pressure is then

$$P = \sum_i P_i = \left(\sum_i \mathfrak{N}_i\right) \frac{\mathfrak{R}T}{V} = \frac{\mathfrak{N}\mathfrak{R}T}{V}$$

The ratio of the partial pressure of any constituent to the total pressure, the *pressure fraction*, is therefore equal simply to its mole fraction,

$$\blacktriangleright \qquad \frac{P_i}{P} = \frac{\mathfrak{N}_i \mathfrak{R}T/V}{\mathfrak{N}\mathfrak{R}T/V} = \frac{\mathfrak{N}_i}{\mathfrak{N}} = \chi_i \qquad\qquad (10 \cdot 19)$$

The *partial volume* V_i of the ith constituent is defined as the volume that would be occupied by the ith constituent at the mixture temperature and pressure,

$$V_i = \frac{\mathfrak{N}_i \mathfrak{R}T}{P} = \frac{\mathfrak{N}_i}{\mathfrak{N}} V = \chi_i V$$

Since $\Sigma \chi_i = 1$, the total volume is equal to the sum of the partial volumes; this fact is sometimes called *Amagat's rule*.

The *volume fraction* of the ith constituent is defined as

$$\blacktriangleright \qquad \Psi_i \equiv \frac{V_i}{V} = \chi_i \qquad\qquad (10 \cdot 20)$$

So, for a perfect-gas mixture, the mole fraction is equal to both the pressure fraction and the volume fraction. This fact is extremely useful in laboratory analysis of gas composition.

Perfect-gas mixtures are sometimes specified by volume fractions and sometimes by mass fractions; either specification determines the other. For example, consider a mixture of O_2, H_2, and CO_2, specified as having volume fractions

$$\Psi_{O_2} = 0.15 \qquad \Psi_{H_2} = 0.60 \qquad \Psi_{CO_2} = 0.25$$

For a perfect-gas mixture the volume and mole fractions are identical (Eq. $10 \cdot 20$). The mixture calculation is carried out in Table $10 \cdot 1$. Then, the gas

TABLE 10·1   MIXTURE CALCULATION

Component	$\Psi_i = \chi_i$, $\dfrac{lbmole}{lbmole\ mixture}$		$\hat{M}_i$, $\dfrac{lbm}{lbmole}$		$M_i/\mathfrak{N}$, $\dfrac{lbm}{lbmole\ mixture}$	M_i/M, $\dfrac{lbm}{lbm\ mixture}$
O_2	0.15	×	32.0	=	4.80	0.282
H_2	0.60	×	2.016	=	1.21	0.071
CO_2	0.25	×	44.01	=	11.00	0.647
					$\hat{M} = 17.01$ lbm/lbmole	1.000

constant for the mixture is

$$R = \frac{\mathcal{R}}{\hat{M}} = \frac{1545}{17.01} = 90.9 \text{ ft-lbf/lbm-°R}$$

Note that while H_2 has the largest mole fraction it has the least mass fraction.

If instead the mass fractions were given, the mixture calculation would yield the mole fractions (Table 10·2).

TABLE 10·2 MIXTURE CALCULATION

Component	M_i/M, lbm lbm mixture		$\hat{M}_i$, lbm lbmole		$\mathfrak{N}_i/M$, lbmole lbm mixture	χ_i, lbmole lbmole mixture
O_2	0.282	÷	32.0	=	0.0088	0.15
H_2	0.071	÷	2.016	=	0.0353	0.60
CO_2	0.647	÷	44.01	=	0.0147	0.25
				$1/\hat{M} = $	0.0588 lbmole/lbm	1.00

Let's continue this example. Suppose the mixture pressure and temperature are 60 psia, 70°F. The density is then

$$\rho = \frac{P}{RT} = \frac{60 \times 144}{90.9 \times (70 + 460)} = 0.179 \text{ lbm/ft}^3$$

The partial pressures are

$$P_{O_2} = 0.15 \times 60 = 9 \text{ psia}$$
$$P_{H_2} = 0.60 \times 60 = 36 \text{ psia}$$
$$P_{CO_2} = 0.25 \times 60 = 15 \text{ psia}$$

If the mixture is heated, the mole fractions (and hence $\hat{M}$ and R) will remain unchanged, and we could treat this mixture as a single simple compressible substance in any engineering thermodynamic analysis.

Now, suppose we put the mixture in a closed tank with a "getter" that absorbs all of the oxygen. Assuming that the temperature remains 70°F, the pressure will be reduced. Since the constituent partial pressures depend only on the number of moles of the constituent, the volume, and the temperature, the H_2 and CO_2 partial pressures are unchanged, and the new total pressure is

$$P = P_{H_2} + P_{CO_2} = 36 + 15 = 51 \text{ psia}$$

The new *mass* fractions are

$$\frac{M_{H_2}}{M} = \frac{0.071}{1 - 0.282} = 0.099$$

$$\frac{M_{CO_2}}{M} = \frac{0.647}{1 - 0.282} = 0.901$$

The new *mole* fractions can be computed in the manner of the last table. However, here it is easier to compute them from the known partial pressures:

$$\chi_{H_2} = \frac{P_{H_2}}{P} = \frac{36}{51} = 0.706$$

$$\chi_{CO_2} = \frac{P_{CO_2}}{P} = \frac{15}{51} = 0.294$$

Let us now turn to mixing of perfect gases. Consider a system in an initial state where the constituents are separated, each at the *same temperature and pressure*, with each occupying its partial volume. The gases are allowed to mix within the isolated system. We would like to determine the final system state.

Denoting the final state by 2 and the initial state by 1, and using the fact that the energy of a perfect gas is a function of the temperature only, it follows from an energy balance on the isolated system that

$$\hat{u}_1 = \hat{u}_2$$

or, using Eq. (10·12),

$$\sum_i \chi_i \hat{u}_i(T_1) = \sum_i \chi_i \hat{u}_i(T_2) \tag{10·21}$$

Each of the internal energies would increase with an increase in T. Therefore, since the mole fractions are fixed, any temperature change would result in a change in the total internal energy. Since this is fixed, we conclude that the temperature will not change when the ideal gases are allowed to mix in an isolated container. Equivalently, there will be no heat transfer if the gases are allowed to mix in a constant-temperature, constant-volume container.

The pressures for the ith component initially and finally are therefore related by

$$\frac{P_{i2}V_{i2}}{P_{i1}V_{i1}} = \frac{\mathfrak{N}_i \mathfrak{R} T}{\mathfrak{N}_i \mathfrak{R} T} \tag{10·22}$$

but

$$V_{i2} = V_{\text{total}} = V \qquad \text{and} \qquad P_{i1} = P_{\text{initial}} = P_1$$

so

$$\frac{P_{i2}V}{P_1 V_{i1}} = 1$$

However, it is also true that

$$V = \sum_i V_{i1}$$

Thus

$$P_2 = \sum_i P_{i2} = \sum_i \frac{V_{i1}P_1}{V} = \frac{P_1}{V} \sum_i V_{i1} = P_1 \tag{10·23}$$

We see that the final pressure is equal to the initial pressure for this particular mixing process.

This mixing process is of course irreversible and must produce entropy. The entropy change of the ith constituent will be given by (see Eq. $(8 \cdot 18)$).

$$s_{i2} - s_{i1} = [\phi_{i2}(T) - \phi_{i1}(T)] - R_i \ln \frac{P_{i2}}{P_{i1}} \qquad (10 \cdot 24)$$

Note that the partial pressure is used to evaluate the entropy since the gases are assumed to be independent of one another and therefore the entropy of i is affected only by the partial pressure of i. Then, for the isothermal mixing process under consideration,

$$s_{i2} - s_{i1} = - R_i \ln \frac{P_{i2}}{P_1} = - R_i \ln \chi_i \qquad (10 \cdot 25)$$

On a molal basis this becomes

$$\hat{s}_{i_2} - \hat{s}_{i_1} = -\Re \ln \chi_i \qquad (10 \cdot 26)$$

The total change in entropy occurring when *different* gases are allowed to mix in an isolated system at constant temperature and pressure is therefore

$$S_2 - S_1 = -\Re \sum_i \Re_i \ln \chi_i = \Re \sum_i \Re_i \ln \frac{1}{\chi_i} \qquad (10 \cdot 27)$$

The mole fractions are all less than unity, and therefore the entropy change within the isolated system is positive. It should be noted that two samples of the same gas cannot be treated as independent substances, and therefore this result applied only to mixtures of different gases. There is *no* entropy change when samples of the same gas at the same pressure and temperature are mixed.

We remind the student that the mixing process discussed above is started with the gases in thermal and mechanical equilibrium with one another (same temperatures and pressures). If other initial conditions are prescribed, the temperature, pressure, or both may change. The final equilibrium state can of course be calculated by appropriate thermodynamic analysis, which includes energy and mass balances, use of the equations of state, and assumptions about the confinement of the gases during the mixing process.

10·4 APPLICATION TO AIR–WATER-VAPOR MIXTURES

Water vapor at pressures below 1 atm may be idealized as a perfect gas, and consequently, the theory developed in the previous sections has important application in the study of air–water-vapor mixtures. If the partial pressure of the water vapor corresponds to the saturation pressure of water at the mixture temperature, the mixture is said to be *saturated.*† A closed volume of air in

† Actually the presence of air alters the saturation pressure by a very small amount. We shall neglect this effect here; its magnitude is calculated in Chap. Twelve.

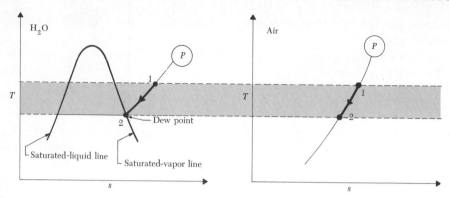

FIG. 10·1 *The dew point*

contact with water will, given sufficient time, become fully saturated, and then the partial pressure of the water vapor in the air will be given by the saturation pressure of water at the air temperature, as given by Table B·1. Air that has not been in contact with water for a sufficiently long period of time may not be saturated. The water in such a mixture would then be *superheated*.

If an air–water-vapor mixture that is not saturated is cooled at constant pressure, the mixture will eventually reach the saturation temperature corresponding to the partial pressure of the water vapor. This is called the *dew-point temperature* because it is associated with the formation of liquid droplets (dew). The constant-pressure cooling process and the dew point are shown in Fig. 10·1.

The composition of an air–water-vapor mixture is often indicated by the *specific humidity*, or *humidity ratio*, defined as the ratio of the mass of water vapor to the mass of air in the mixture,

$$\blacktriangleright \qquad \gamma \equiv \frac{M_w}{M_a} \qquad\qquad (10\cdot 28)$$

An alternate specification is the *relative humidity*, which is defined as the ratio of the partial pressure of the water vapor to the saturation pressure at the

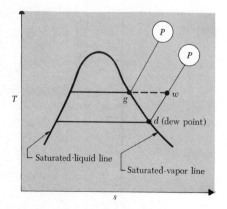

FIG. 10·2 *Saturation and partial pressure*

mixture temperature† (see Fig. 10·2),

$$\blacktriangleright \qquad \phi \equiv \frac{P_w}{P_g} \qquad\qquad (10\cdot29)$$

Since the mass ratios are inversely proportional to the specific-volume ratios [Eq. (10·17)],

$$\gamma = \frac{M_w}{M_a} = \frac{v_a(T, P_a)}{v_w(T, P_w)} \qquad\qquad (10\cdot30)$$

We have idealized the vapor as a perfect gas; then, since $T_g = T_w$,

$$\phi = \frac{P_w}{P_g} = \frac{v_g(T, P_g)}{v_w(T, P_w)} \qquad\qquad (10\cdot31)$$

$$\gamma = \phi \frac{v_a(T, P_a)}{v_g(T, P_g)} \qquad\qquad (10\cdot32)$$

Using the perfect-gas equation of state, and Eq. (10·30)

$$\gamma = \frac{R_a T/P_a}{R_w T/P_w} = 0.622 \frac{P_w}{P_a} \qquad\qquad (10\cdot33)$$

Then, combining with Eq. (10·31),

$$\blacktriangleright \qquad \phi = \frac{\gamma P_a}{0.622 P_g} \qquad\qquad (10\cdot34)$$

Finally, the total pressure is given by Dalton's rule as

$$\blacktriangleright \qquad P = P_a + P_w \qquad\qquad (10\cdot35)$$

To illustrate the use of this theory, suppose that the relative humidity of an air–water-vapor mixture is measured as 0.4 at a temperature of 70°F and 1 atm. We wish to determine the specific humidity, the dew point, and the partial pressure of the water vapor and air. We start with Eq. (10·29),

$$\phi = \frac{P_w}{P_g} = 0.40$$

Then, at 70°F, the pressure of saturated water vapor is

$$P_g = 0.363 \text{ psia} \qquad \text{(Table B·1A)}$$

Hence, the actual water partial pressure is

$$P_w = 0.40 \times 0.363 = 0.145 \text{ psia}$$

The air pressure must bring the total pressure up to 1 atm, and hence

$$P_a = 14.7 - 0.145 = 14.555 \text{ psia}$$

† In this section ϕ denotes only the relative humidity and should not be confused with the function $\phi(T)$ in the entropy expression for a perfect gas.

Then, using Eq. (10·33),

$$\gamma = 0.622 \frac{P_w}{P_a} = 0.622 \frac{0.145}{14.555} = 0.0062 \text{ lbm water/lbm air}$$

Finally, the dew point is the temperature of saturated water vapor at the partial water pressure,

$$T_{\text{DP}} = 44.8°\text{F} \; (T_{\text{sat}} \text{ at 0.145 psia, Table B·1A})$$

Hence, dew will form if the ambient temperature drops below 44.8°F. In a humid climate where $\phi = 0.90$ at a temperature of perhaps 85°F the dew point would be about 82.5°F. The impact of high humidity on human comfort should be obvious from these numbers.

The humidity can in principle be measured with an *adiabatic saturator*. This is a device into which flows the air–water-vapor mixture of unknown humidity, out of which flows a saturated air–water-vapor mixture at some lower adiabatic-saturation temperature, and to which water is added continuously. Schematic and process representations for an adiabatic saturator are shown in Fig. 10·3. The device is sufficiently long that equilibrium between the air–water-vapor mixture is obtained by the time the mixture reaches the exit. Thus the temperature of the mixture at state 3 will be the same as that of water at state 3, and we assume the water temperature is uniform, so that $T_2 = T_3$. Using the properties of perfect-gas mixtures and idealizing the device as adiabatic, energy and mass balances allow us to develop a useful expression:

Conservation of air and water

$$\dot{M}_{a1} = \dot{M}_{a3} \qquad \dot{M}_{w1} + \dot{M}_{w2} = \dot{M}_{w3}$$

Conservation of energy

$$\dot{M}_{a1}h_{a1} + \dot{M}_{w1}h_{w1} + \dot{M}_{w2}h_{w2} = \dot{M}_{a3}h_{a3} + M_{w3}h_{w3}$$

FIG. 10·3 *An adiabatic saturator*

By definition,

$$\gamma_1 = \frac{\dot{M}_{w1}}{\dot{M}_{a1}} \qquad \gamma_3 = \frac{\dot{M}_{w3}}{\dot{M}_{a3}}$$

Combining with the water mass balance,

$$\frac{\dot{M}_{w2}}{\dot{M}_{a1}} = \gamma_3 - \gamma_1$$

Substituting into the energy equation, one obtains

$$h_{a1} + \gamma_1 h_{w1} + (\gamma_3 - \gamma_1)h_{w2} = h_{a3} + \gamma_3 h_{w3} \qquad (10\cdot36)$$

Measurements of the pressure and temperatures allow determination of all the enthalpies and the specific humidity at state 3 from the equations of state of air and H_2O. The one remaining unknown in Eq. $(10\cdot36)$ is the specific humidity at state 1, which may then be calculated from the equation.

For example, suppose a mixture of air and water vapor enters an adiabatic saturation device at 90°F and 1 atm pressure, and the mixture leaves at 70°F and 1 atm. Let's find the specific and relative humidities at the inlet. Since the air leaving the device is saturated, we know that

$$\phi_3 = 1 \qquad P_{w3} = P_{g3} = 0.363 \text{ psia (at 70°F)}$$

Then, from Eq. $(10\cdot33)$,

$$\gamma_3 = 0.622 \frac{P_w}{P_a} = 0.622 \frac{P_w}{14.7 - P_w}$$

$$= 0.622 \times \frac{0.363}{14.7 - 0.363} = 0.0157 \text{ lbm } H_2O/\text{lbm air}$$

The enthalpies can be read in Appendix B. From Tables B·9 and B·1A,

$h_{a1} = 131.5 \text{ Btu/lbm}$
$h_{a3} = 126.7 \text{ Btu/lbm}$
$h_{w1} = 1100.9 \text{ Btu/lbm} \qquad \text{(sat. vapor at 90°F)}$
$h_{w3} = 1092.3 \text{ Btu/lbm} \qquad \text{(sat. vapor at 70°F)}$

To evaluate h_{w2}, we may use the incompressible-liquid equation of state. This must be properly tied to the other tabulated data for H_2O. If we take the base point at the liquid temperature, then we may write

$$h = h_f(T) + \frac{1}{\rho}[P - P_f(T)]$$

when the subscript f again denotes saturated liquid, and T is the liquid temperature (70°F). The pressure term may be neglected as a first approximation (the student should compute the error in the margin), and hence

$$h_{w2} = 38 \text{ Btu/lbm} \qquad \text{(sat. liquid at 70°F)}$$

Solving Eq. (10·36) for γ_1,

$$\gamma_1 = \frac{(h_{a3} - h_{a1}) + \gamma_3(h_{w3} - h_{w2})}{h_{w1} - h_{w2}}$$

$$= \frac{(126.7 - 131.5) + 0.0157 \times (1092.3 - 38)}{1100.9 - 38} = 0.01109$$

Eq. (10·33) may be written as

$$\gamma = 0.622 \frac{P_w}{(P - P_w)}$$

Solving for P_{w1},

$$P_{w1} = \frac{(0.01109/0.622) \times 14.7}{1 + (0.01109/0.622)} = 0.258 \text{ psia}$$

Finally, the relative humidity is, from Eq. (10·31),

$$\phi_1 = \left(\frac{P_w}{P_g}\right)_1 = \frac{0.258}{0.698} = 0.37$$

Now suppose that the makeup water (2) in the adiabatic saturator is not at the pool temperature (T_3). Equation (10·36) still applies, but h_{w2} would have a different value. Because of the high h_{fg} for water, h_{w1} is much larger than h_{w2}, and hence the γ_1 calculation is very insensitive to h_{w2}. For example, suppose T_2 is instead 60°F, for which $h_{w2} = 28$ Btu/lbm, instead of 38 Btu/lbm. The change in γ_1 is less than 1 percent. Hence, for air–water-vapor mixtures at 1 atm pressure the adiabatic-saturation temperature may be idealized as being independent of the makeup water temperature; with this idealization, the adiabatic-saturation temperature depends only on the temperature and humidity of the air–water-vapor mixture.

This idealization provides the basis for simple laboratory measurements of humidity using the *wet-bulb thermometer* (Fig. 10·4). Water brought up the

Air flow

Wicking

Water

FIG. 10·4 *A wet-bulb thermometer*

wick by capillary action is evaporated to the air flowing around the bulb, so that the air inside the wick becomes saturated at the temperature of the water in the wick. This temperature will be influenced by the rates of heat and mass transfer from the water to the air, which in turn depend on the configuration of the bulb, air velocity, and other factors. The wet-bulb temperature is therefore not a property of the gas mixture, since it depends upon the nature of the measuring instrument. However, it has been found experimentally that the wet-bulb temperature is very close to the adiabatic-saturation temperature for *air–water-vapor mixtures*, and thus it provides a satisfactory estimate for this property of the mixture.

The solution of Eq. (10·36) can be represented in a convenient graphical form, the *psychrometric chart* (Fig. B·13). This chart is based on an adiabatic-saturation process at 1 atm. More complete charts available in handbooks include correction factors for pressure; the values of specific humidity obtained from the chart of Fig. B·13 will be correct to within a few percent at pressures within 1 in. of mercury of atmospheric pressure. At lower or higher pressures the errors in using this chart become significant, and a more complete psychrometric chart should be consulted. Note that the dew point and adiabatic-saturation temperature (wet-bulb temperature) are identical for a saturated mixture. The dry-bulb temperature is simply the mixture temperature.

The *sling psychrometer* has both wet- and dry-bulb thermometers on a common swivel handle. The psychrometer is whirled round and round in the air, providing the necessary air flow over the wet bulb. When equilibrium is reached the wet- and dry-bulb temperatures are read.

As an example, suppose that wet- and dry-bulb temperatures measured in moist air at 1 atm of pressure are 70 and 90°F, respectively. We shall now find the specific and relative humidities and the thermodynamic properties of the mixture. From Fig. B·13 we read, for $T_{DB} = 90°F$ and $T_{WB} = 70°F$,

$$\gamma = 78 \text{ grains of vapor per lbm of dry air}$$
$$P_w = 0.25 \text{ psia}$$
$$\phi = 0.37$$
$$T_{DP} = 60°F$$

The partial pressure of the air is therefore

$$14.70 - 0.25 = 14.45 \text{ psia}$$

The mole fractions of air and water vapor are then

$$\chi_a = \frac{14.45}{14.70} = 0.983$$
$$\chi_w = \frac{0.25}{14.70} = 0.017$$

The mixture molal mass is then (see Table B·6)

$$\hat{M} = 28.97 \times 0.983 + 18.016 \times 0.017$$
$$\hat{M} = 28.8 \text{ lbm/lbmole} = 28.8 \text{ g/gmole}$$

Note that the presence of water vapor will always decrease the molal mass of the mixture from that for dry air. The mixture density is then

$$\rho = \frac{P}{(\Re/\hat{M})T} = \frac{14.70 \times 144}{(1545/28.8) \times 550} = 0.0718 \text{ lbm/ft}^3$$

Since the enthalpy of a perfect gas depends only on temperature, we may read the enthalpy of the water vapor from Table B·1a, even though it is not in a saturation state. Thus

$$h_w(90°F) = h_g(90°F) = 1100.9 \text{ Btu/lbm}$$

or

$$\hat{h}_w = 1100.9 \times 18.016 = 19,850 \text{ Btu/lbmole}$$

The enthalpy of the air may be obtained from the air tables (Table B·9), which assume perfect-gas behavior, as

$$h_a = 131.5 \text{ Btu/lbm}$$
$$\hat{h}_a = 131.5 \times 28.97 = 3810 \text{ Btu/lbmole}$$

The molal enthalpy of the mixture, relative to the datum states used in the steam and air tables, is then

$$\hat{h} = 0.983 \times 3810 + 0.017 \times 19,850 = 4080 \text{ Btu/lbmole}$$

so the enthalpy per lbm of *mixture* is

$$h = \frac{4080}{28.8} = 141.5 \text{ Btu/lbm}$$

The molal entropy of the water vapor could be obtained from superheat tables, but they do not extend down to 90°F. Instead we extrapolate from the saturation tables, treating the vapor as a perfect gas. Using Eq. (8·18), we find

$$\hat{s}(T, P) - \hat{s}_g(T) = -\Re \ln \frac{P}{P_g(T)}$$

Then, with the help of Table B·1a,

$$\hat{s}_w = 2.0087 \times 18.016 - 1.986 \ln \frac{0.25}{0.6982} = 38.14 \text{ Btu/lbmole-°R}$$

In determining the entropy of the air we must select a datum state. Table B·9 is based on 0°R (extrapolated perfect gas); consequently, we select 1 atm and 0°R for the entropy datum. Then, using Eq. (8·18),

$$s_a(T, P) = \phi(T) - R_a \ln \frac{P}{1 \text{ atm}}$$

From Table B·9,

$$\hat{s}_a = 0.6051 \times 28.97 - 1.986 \ln \frac{14.45}{14.7}$$

$$\hat{s}_a = 17.55 \text{ Btu/lbmole-}°R$$

Then the mixture entropy, relative to the indicated air and H_2O data, is

$$\hat{s} = 0.983 \times 17.55 + 0.017 \times 38.14 = 17.91 \text{ Btu/lbmole-}°R$$

$$s = \frac{17.91}{28.8} = 0.622 \text{ Btu/lbm-}°R$$

Finally, for c_P (see Table B·6),

$$\hat{c}_P = 0.983 \times 6.95 + 0.017 \times 8.07 = 6.98 \text{ Btu/lbmole-}°R$$

$$c_P = \frac{6.98}{28.8} = 0.242 \text{ Btu/lbm-}°R$$

The property values calculated above pertain to a unit mass of *mixture*. In practice a different base is often used; since the air flow rate is usually the same at the inlet and outlet of air conditioning systems, it is convenient to express the *mixture* enthalpy *per lbm of dry air*, which we shall here designate as h^*. In terms of the air and water enthalpies, h^* is readily shown to be

$$h^* = h_a + \gamma h_w \text{ Btu/lbm dry air} \tag{10·37}$$

Values of h^* are shown on most psychrometric charts. The datum state is somewhat peculiar, with h_a measured relative to $0°F$ (not $0°R$ as in the air tables) and h_w referenced to saturated liquid at $32°F$. In terms of h^*, the adiabatic-saturation equation [Eq. (10·36)] becomes

$$h_1^* + (\gamma_3 - \gamma_1)h_{w2} = h_3^*(T_{WB})$$

Note that h_3^* depends only upon the adiabatic-saturation temperature. Since the second term in this equation is typically very small compared to h^* (0.2 Btu/lbm dry air compared with 30 Btu/lbm dry air), a reasonable approximation for many engineering and meteorological applications is that

$$h^* \approx h^*(T_{WB})$$

With this approximation, lines of constant h^* coincide with lines of constant T_{WB}. Simplified psychrometric charts (such as Fig. B·13) portray the h^* information accordingly.

10·5 AIR CONDITIONING

The ideas just developed are applicable to the engineering aspects of air conditioning. We can use the psychrometric chart as the process diagram for these problems. For example, constant-pressure heating will not change the specific humidity but will change the relative humidity. Such a process is shown

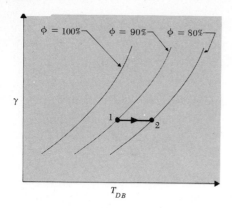

FIG. 10·5 *Heating reduces relative humidity*

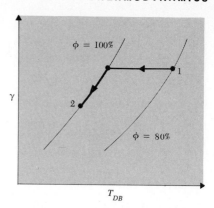

FIG. 10·6 *A cooling and condensation process*

FIG. 10·7 *Dehumidification*

FIG. 10·8 *Spray dehumidification*

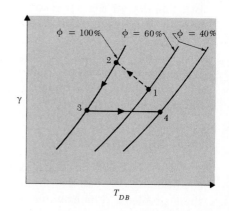

in Fig. 10·5 (see Fig. B·13). Constant-pressure cooling will not change the specific humidity unless the mixture is cooled to the adiabatic-saturation temperature. Further cooling would then result in condensation and a lowering of the specific humidity. Such a process is shown by Fig. 10·6.

Dehumidification may be accomplished by first cooling, allowing some vapor to condense, and then reheating the mixture. The hardware schematic and process representation (on the psychrometric chart) for a system to accomplish this are shown in Fig. 10·7. Some commercial air conditioners employ spray cooling, in which a chilled water is injected into the air, lowering its temperature below the original dew point, allowing a net dehumidification when the mixture is reheated. Such a system is shown in Fig. 10·8.

As an example, let's consider the processes required to take air at $\phi_1 = 100\%$, $T_{DB1} = 85°F$ to $\phi_3 = 50\%$, $T_{DB3} = 85°F$. We can imagine carrying out this process with the technique of Fig. 10·9. The amount of water to be removed can be determined directly from the psychrometric chart,

$$\gamma_1 - \gamma_3 = 184 - 90 = 94 \text{ grains/lbm dry air}$$

Another process of importance in air conditioning is the adiabatic mixing process in which two streams each of wet air are mixed. The final state is to be calculated; the control volume is shown in Fig. 10·10. The mass balance for the air gives

$$\dot{M}_{a3} = \dot{M}_{a1} + \dot{M}_{a2} \tag{10·38a}$$

The water mass balance can be written as

$$\dot{M}_{a3}\gamma_3 = \dot{M}_{a1}\gamma_1 + \dot{M}_{a2}\gamma_2 \tag{10·38b}$$

With appropriate idealizations (list these in the margin), the energy balance may be written as

$$\dot{M}_{a1}h_1^* + \dot{M}_{a2}h_2^* = \dot{M}_{a3}h_3^* \tag{10·38c}$$

If the inlet flow rates and states are known, Eqs. (10·38) form three equations

FIG. 10·9

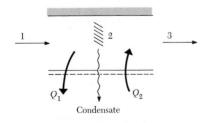

(a) *The system*

(b) *The process representation*

FIG. 10·10 *Adiabatic mixing of two wet air streams*

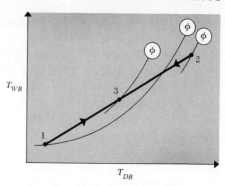

(a) *The system*

(b) *The process representation as psychrometric chart*

with $\dot{M}_{a3}$, γ_3, and h_3^* as three unknowns, and solution is straightforward. For example, suppose that 2000 cfm of air at 1 atm, 50°F, $\phi = 0.8$ is mixed with 1500 cfm of air at 1 atm, 100°F, $\phi = 0.6$. We must first determine the mass flow rates of *dry* air in the two streams. To do this we need the air specific volume, which is sometimes available on the psychrometric chart. Our chart does not include this, so we shall calculate it. At 50°F, with $\phi = 0.8$,

$$P_w = 0.80 \times 0.178 = 0.142 \text{ psia}$$

Then

$$v_1 = \frac{RT}{P_a} = \frac{53.3 \times 510}{(14.7 - 0.142) \times 144} = 12.97 \text{ ft}^3/\text{lbm dry air}$$

Similarly, for the 100°F air,

$$v_2 = \frac{53.3 \times 560}{(14.7 - 0.57) \times 144} = 14.62 \text{ ft}^3/\text{lbm dry air}$$

Therefore

$$\dot{M}_{a1} = \frac{2000}{12.97} = 154 \text{ lbm dry air/min}$$

$$\dot{M}_{a2} = \frac{1500}{14.62} = 102 \text{ lbm dry air/min}$$

Now, from the psychrometric chart we find

$\gamma_1 = 0.0061 \text{ lbm H}_2\text{O/lbm dry air}$
$\gamma_2 = 0.0254 \text{ lbm H}_2\text{O/lbm dry air}$
$h_1^* = 19 \text{ Btu/lbm dry air}$
$h_2^* = 52 \text{ Btu/lbm dry air}$

Then, from Eq. (10·38a),

$$\dot{M}_{a3} = 154 + 102 = 256 \text{ lbm dry air/min}$$

FIG. 10·11 *Swamp coolers provide low-cost air conditioning suitable for dry climates*

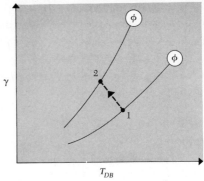

(a) *The system*   (b) *The process representation*

Next, from Eq. (10·38b),

$$\gamma_3 = \frac{(0.0061 \times 154) + (0.0254 \times 102)}{256}$$

$$= 0.0138 \text{ lbm } H_2O/\text{lbm dry air}$$
$$(= 97 \text{ grains } H_2O/\text{lbm dry air})$$

Finally, from Eq. (10·38c),

$$h_3^* = \frac{(19 \times 154) + (52 \times 102)}{256}$$

$$= 32 \text{ Btu/lbm dry air}$$

h_3^* and γ_3 fix state 3 on the psychrometric chart; we find

$$\phi_3 = 0.85 \qquad T_3 = 71°F$$

Another application of air conditioning to cooling houses in hot and dry climates is *evaporative cooling*. This involves either spraying water into air or blowing air through water-soaked pads. Such a device is shown in Fig. 10·11. This device is essentially an adiabatic saturator, except that complete saturation is not necessarily achieved. We have discussed the validity of the approximation that h^* is constant for this process (see Eq. (10·37) *et seq.*) and that h^* depends only upon the wet-bulb temperature. With these approximations, the process representation is shown in Fig. 10·11b. Assuming $T_1 = 105°F$, $\phi_1 = 0.1$, $T_2 = 80°F$, the psychrometric chart shows that the discharge air has a relative humidity of about 48 percent. This would be far more comfortable than the very hot dry inlet air. Simple *swamp coolers* of this type are consequently of great importance in desert areas.

SELECTED READING

Lee, J., and F. Sears, *Thermodynamics*, 2d ed., chap. 10, Addison-Wesley Publishing Co., Inc., Reading, Mass., 1962.

Van Wylen, G., and R. Sonntag, *Fundamentals of Classical Thermodynamics*, chap. 11, John Wiley & Sons, Inc., New York, 1965.

Wark, K., *Thermodynamics*, chaps. 11 and 19, McGraw-Hill Book Company, New York, 1966.

Zemansky, M. W., *Heat and Thermodynamics*, 4th ed., chap. 15, McGraw-Hill Book Company, New York, 1957.

QUESTIONS

10·1 What are mass fractions, volume fractions, and mole fractions, and under what circumstances is one equal to another?

10·2 How many independently variable properties are there for a mixture of two compressible electrically polarized gases?

10·3 What is a phase of a mixture?

10·4 What is a mixture of independent substances?

10·5 Under what circumstances are partial pressures equal to the total pressure times the mole fractions?

10·6 How would you compute the specific heat of a mixture of gases (nonperfect) from the known specific heats of its constituents?

10·7 Why is the datum state for enthalpy of a mixture arbitrary? Why can different datums be used for the different species as long as no chemical changes occur?

10·8 What is the meaning of the term "molal specific heat"?

10·9 Why does the entropy not change when two identical gases are allowed to mix?

10·10 What is a psychrometric chart?

10·11 What is the difference between relative humidity and specific humidity? Which do you think is most related to human comfort?

10·12 How can air be dehumidified?

10·13 A "swamp cooler" is simply a burlap sack dripping with water through which air is blown. What happens to the humidity and temperature of the air passing through it?

10·14 What are the basic principles employed in the thermodynamic design of air conditioning systems?

10·15 List ten different engineering systems in which the theory of this chapter is employed.

10·16 What would a typical dew point be during the summer months in your locality?

10·17 What is an adiabatic saturator?

10·18 What is a sling-psychrometer? How do you use it?

10·19 What are the reference conditions for enthalpy on the usual psychrometric chart?

PROBLEMS

10·1 Air is roughly 21 percent oxygen and 79 percent nitrogen (by volume). Calculate the specific heat of air from the data in Table B·6 and compare your result with the value given there.

10·2 A gas having a specific-heat ratio k of 1.500 is required for a certain gas-dynamic experiment. Specify a mixture that could be used.

10·3 Oxygen can be separated from air by fractional distillation, which amounts to cooling the air until either nitrogen or oxygen condenses. Which will occur first at 10 atm pressure?

10·4 One ft³ of helium at 1 atm and 80°F is mixed with 2 ft³ of oxygen at 1 atm and 100°F. Specify the partial pressures, mole fractions, mass fractions, and specific heats of this mixture at 2 atm and 150°F. Determine the difference in the enthalpy and entropy of the mixture between 50 and 100°F at 1 atm.

10·5 A gas has the following analysis by mass: O_2, 0.2; H_2, 0.08; CO_2, 0.25; and CO, 0.47. Determine the volumetric analysis and the gas constant of the mixture.

10·6 What are the specific heats per mole for a mixture consisting of 1 mole of carbon dioxide, 3 moles of helium, and 1 mole of oxygen?

10·7 How much will the enthalpy of a mixture of 20 percent freon-12 and 80 percent CO_2 (parts by mass) change when the mixture is heated at constant pressure (100 psia) from 140°F to 200°F?

10·8 At what temperature will fractional distillation occur in the mixture of Prob. 10·7 (100 psia), and which component will be first to condense?

10·9 8 ft³ of O_2 at 100°F, 100 psia are mixed adiabatically with 10 ft³ of H_2 at 60°F, 80 psia in a constant-volume container. What are the final pressure and temperature?

10·10 A 10-ft³ condenser chamber contains saturated air at 90°F, 27 in. Hg vacuum. Air leaks into the chamber until the temperature is reduced to 75°F and the vacuum reduced to 21 in. Hg. If the barometer reading is 20.02 in. Hg, find the amount of air that has leaked in.

10·11 A steady-flow mixing process occurs such that hydrogen at 70°F and methane at 150°F are mixed adiabatically to form a mixture which is 50 percent by volume hydrogen. All pressures are 1 atm and the hydrogen flow rate is 0.01 lb/sec. Determine the exit temperature.

10·12 Nitrogen and hydrogen are mixed in a steady-flow adiabatic device in the ratio of 4 lbm of hydrogen per lbm of nitrogen. The hydrogen enters at 20 psia, 100°F, and the nitrogen at 20 psia, 500°F. The pressure after mixing is 18 psia. Determine the exit temperature and the entropy production per lbm of mixture.

10·13 A mixture of air and water vapor containing 0.013 lbm of water vapor and 1 lbm of air occupies a tank at 14.7 psia and 90°F. Determine the dew point, relative humidity, and specific humidity.

10·14 Measurements with a sling-psychrometer have fixed $T_{WB} = 60°F$ and $T_{DB} = 75°F$ at 14.7 psia. Determine the relative humidity and specific humidity without using the psychrometric chart. Compare with the chart.

10·15 Air is supplied to a certain room from the outside, where the temperature is 30°F and the relative humidity is 60 percent. It is desired to supply the air to the room at 70°F and 60 percent relative humidity. How many pounds of water must be supplied to each lbm of air entering the room if these conditions are to be met?

10·16 The temperature of a certain room is 75°F and the relative humidity is 55 percent. The barometric pressure is 29.92 in. Hg. Find the partial pressures of the air and water vapor and the specific humidity of the mixture.

10·17 In a steady-flow device, air is heated to 90°F, without the addition of water, from a state where $T_{DB} = 60°F$, $T_{WB} = 55°F$. Find the relative humidity of the original mixture, the dew-point temperature, the specific humidity, the energy added, and the final relative humidity.

10·18 An air-water vapor mixture at 67°F, 50 percent humidity, 1 atm is heated at constant pressure to 82°F in part of a steady-flow air conditioner. Determine the inlet and discharge specific humidities, the discharge relative humidity, and the energy input as heat per lbm of dry air.

10·19 Two streams of air are mixed in a steady-flow adiabatic device. The first stream is at a temperature of 55°F with $\phi = 0.2$ and a flow rate of 650 ft³/min. The second stream is at 75°F with $\phi = 0.8$ and a flow rate of 900 ft³/min. If all pressures are 1 atm, find the outlet mixture relative humidity, temperature, and specific humidity.

10·20 Atmospheric air at 84°F and $\phi = 0.7$ flows over a set of cooling coils at a rate of 15,000 ft³/min. The condensed liquid leaves the system at 50°F. The air is then heated to 75°F, $\phi = 0.4$. Determine the rate of energy removal as heat in the cooling section, the condensate flow rate, and the energy input rate in the heating section.

10·21 For $T_{WB} = 70°F$ and $T_{DB} = 90°F$, determine the relative and specific humidities using the adiabatic-saturator model, and compare your results with those obtained from the psychrometric chart.

10·22 One thousand ft³/min of air at 75°F, 1 atm, and 70 percent relative humidity are to be cooled and dehumidified to 68°F and 55 percent relative humidity by cooling and reheating in a steady-flow air conditioner. Find the temperature to which the air must be cooled and the tonnage of refrigeration required.

10·23 Condensation on cold-water pipes often occurs in warm humid rooms. If the water temperature is 50°F and the room temperature is 75°F, what maximum relative humidity can be tolerated if condensation is to be avoided?

10·24 An air compressor takes in air from the atmosphere at 60°F and 75 percent relative humidity and discharges the air at 100 psia. The compressor isentropic efficiency is 82 percent. What are the relative and specific humidities of the discharged air?

10·25 Develop a psychrometric chart for a mixture of helium and water vapor at 2 atm. Show the 25, 50, 75, and 100 percent relative-humidity lines over the range 40–120°F.

10·26 Develop a psychrometric chart for helium-mercury mixtures at 60 psia for the range 300–500°F. Plot lines of 25, 50, 75, and 100 percent relative humidity.

10·27 Air at $T_{DB} = 110°F$, $T_{WB} = 70°F$ is humidified adiabatically with wet steam. The steam contains 16 percent moisture at 20 psia. What is the dry-bulb temperature of the humidified air when sufficient steam is added to humidify the air to 50 percent relative humidity? Assume 1 atm pressure.

10·28 An air–water-vapor mixture enters a cooler-dehumidifier at the rate of 1000 ft³/min. The mixture enters at 14.7 psia, 100°F, and $\phi = 0.8$. The absolute humidity on leaving is decreased to one third of that on entering. The relative humidity on leaving is 100 percent and the pressure is 14.7 psia. Determine the required heat-transfer rate.

10·29 Consider an evaporative cooler with atmospheric air (14.7 psia) at 100°F, $\phi = 0.1$. Cooling water at 50°F is sprayed into the air. If the air-water vapor mixture emerges at 80°F, what will be its relative humidity? What are the disadvantages of this approach to air conditioning?

10·30 A tank contains helium with mercury vapor. Initially the mixture is at 700°F and 2 psia. The mixture is cooled at constant pressure, and at 415°F mercury droplets are observed inside the tank. How much could the pressure of the original mixture have been increased in an isothermal compression before mercury condensation occurred at 700°F? What were the initial relative and specific mercury humidities?

10·31 A mixture of CO_2 and helium is cooled at constant volume from 40°F and 500 psia to −20°F, at which point CO_2 condensation is observed. What was the initial mixture composition?

10·32 A mixture of freon-12 and argon is cooled at constant volume from 200°F and 100 psia to −20°F, at which point freon condensation is observed. What was the initial mixture composition?

10·33 Specify a mixture of freon-12 and CO_2 such that both constituents will condense when the mixture temperature is 0°F. At what mixture pressure will this occur? What will happen when a mixture of this proportion is cooled at 100 psia? At 600 psia?

10·34 A mixture consists of 2.7 lbm of helium and 3.0 lbm of nitrogen at 10 psia, 80°F. The mixture is isentropically compressed to 100 psia. Find the change in entropy and enthalpy for the two components during this process.

10·35 A possible device to desalt sea water using solar energy is shown on the figure where typical operating conditions are also noted. Sea water is heated inside tubes in the condenser where it acts as the energy sink for the energy released in the condensation process. Because air cannot contain as much water at low

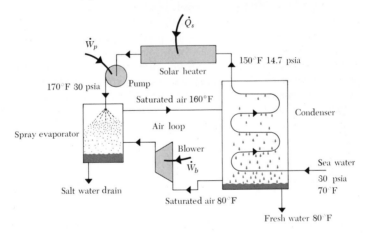

temperatures, the cooling of the air in the condenser causes a condensation process in which fresh water is released. The now warm salt water is further heated in solar collectors and pumped into a packed column evaporator. The air from the condenser is forced up through the evaporator and becomes saturated with water vapor at a high temperature. In effect the air acts as a transfer medium for water vapor.

The object of this problem is to determine the fresh water production per lbm of dry air circulated in the system. For a required output of 10,000 gallons of fresh water per solar (8-hr) day what air flow rate must be maintained through the condenser, what water flow rate on the water side of the condenser? Under the given conditions what is the energy input from the sun? If the collection rate is an average of 300 Btu/hr-ft² how many ft² of collector are required?

10·36 Air at 85°F and a relative humidity of 80 percent is to be processed in a steady-flow air conditioner, and delivered at 70°F, 50 percent humidity. The air flow rate is 200 ft³/min. Design a suitable system, specifying any energy-transfer rates, power requirements, temperatures, intermediate states, coolant flow rates, and so on.

10·37 Cooling air for a large computer must be supplied at the rate of 100 ft³/min. The temperature must be 50°F, and the humidity less than 0.0005 lbm H_2O/lbm dry air. Suppose the supply air is at 80°F and 50 percent relative humidity. Design a suitable air-conditioning system, specifying any energy-transfer rates, coolant flow rates, temperatures, intermediate system states, and so on.

10·38 A simple cooling system using CO_2 sublimation has been proposed for a short-term extravehicular space suit. The CO_2 will be sublimed from a small solid block at 10 psia, and mixed with the breathing gas at 70°F. The breathing rate is nominally 8 ft³/min, and the mixture must leave the suit at 90°F. The total energy-removal rate is to be 200 Btu/hr. Specify the required CO_2 sublimation rate, the mass requirement for 1 hr of operation, and the mass percent of CO_2 in the inlet mixture.

10·39 CO_2 must be removed from the oxygen in an astronaut life-support system. Suppose the breathing rate is 6 ft³/min, and that the exhaled mixture contains CO_2 with 10 percent volume fraction. Design a system to continuously remove 95 percent of the CO_2 from the discharged gas, assuming the mixture is delivered at 90°F to the conditioner and to the space suit at 70°F. Specify the volume flow of make-up oxygen required, the processes, power requirements, intermediate states, and so on within the conditioner.

10·40 Design a system to extract air from sea water at a depth of 100 ft. You may treat the water-dissolved air system as a mixture of independent substances. Finding the necessary solubility data will be good practice for your engineering career.

CHAPTER ELEVEN # THERMODYNAMICS OF REACTING MIXTURES

11·1 SOME CHEMICAL CONCEPTS AND TERMS

In this chapter we shall study mixtures that may be undergoing chemical reaction. The first law of thermodynamics forms the basis for quantitative analysis of chemical reactions. The second law of thermodynamics is used to identify the *direction* of chemical reactions. The *third law of thermodynamics* will be introduced in this chapter. This law is needed to connect properly the entropies of different species involved in the chemical reaction. Thermodynamics also allows us to determine the equilibrium composition of any mixture of chemical substances; this will be discussed in the next chapter. The prediction of *reaction rates* is beyond the scope of thermodynamics; the topic of chemical kinetics, which deals with reaction rates, will not be discussed in this text.

Associated with every chemical reaction is a *chemical equation*, derived by applying the conservation of atoms to each of the atomic species involved in some sort of a "unit reaction." The reaction begins with a collection of certain chemical constituents, called the *reactants*, and the chemical reaction causes a rearrangement of the atoms and electrons to form different constituents, called the *products*. The reaction between the constituent reactants hydrogen and oxygen to form the product water can be expressed as

$$2H_2 + O_2 \rightleftarrows 2H_2O \tag{11·1}$$

This expression indicates that two molecules of hydrogen and one molecule of oxygen can combine to form two molecules of water (the reaction may also go in the opposite direction). The coefficients in the chemical equation are called *stoichiometric coefficients* (2,1,2 in this example). The number of hydrogen atoms is conserved, as is the number of oxygen atoms. The chemical equation can also be interpreted as an equation relating the molal masses involved in a reaction; here two moles of hydrogen and one mole of oxygen combine to form two moles

355

of water. Note that the number of moles of the products may differ from that of the reactants.

A *stoichiometric mixture* of reactants is one in which the molal proportions of the reactants are exactly as given by the stoichiometric coefficients so that no excess of any constituent is present. A *stoichiometric combustion* is one in which all the oxygen atoms in the oxidizer react chemically to appear in the products.

The most common oxidizer is air, which for many purposes may be considered as a mixture of 21 percent oxygen and 79 percent nitrogen (mole or volume fractions). The chemical equation for stoichiometric combustion of methane (CH_4) with air is then

$$\underset{\text{reactants}}{CH_4 + 2(O_2 + 3.76N_2)} \leftrightarrows \underset{\text{products}}{CO_2 + 2H_2O + 7.52N_2} \tag{11·2}$$

If more air is supplied not all will be involved in the reaction, and the composition of the products will differ from that of a stoichiometric combustion. The additional air supplied is called *excess air*. The term *theoretical air* is also used; "200 percent theoretical air" is equivalent to 100 percent excess air. For example, if methane is burned with 125 percent theoretical air the chemical equation is†

$$\underset{\text{reactants}}{CH_4 + 1.25 \times 2(O_2 + 3.76N_2)} \rightleftarrows \underset{\text{products}}{CO_2 + 2H_2O + 0.5O_2 + 9.4N_2} \tag{11·3}$$

and the products mixture would not be stoichiometric. In order to *complete* a combustion reaction (to burn all the fuel), excess air is normally supplied. Internal combustion engines normally run *rich* (125 percent theoretical air) while gas-turbine engines normally run *lean* (250 percent theoretical air). Incomplete combustion results in the production of carbon monoxide (CO) instead of carbon dioxide (CO_2), a major contributor to urban smog.

Another important combustion parameter is the *air-fuel ratio* (AFR) in a reaction. For the stoichiometric combustion process of methane we have, on a molal basis,

$$AFR = \frac{\mathfrak{N}_{air}}{\mathfrak{N}_{CH_4}} = \frac{2 + 7.52}{1} = 9.52 \text{ moles air/mole fuel}$$

Since $\hat{M}_{air} = 28.95$ lbm/lbmole and $\hat{M}_{CH_4} = 16$ lbm/lbmole,

the AFR may also be expressed on a mass basis as

$$AFR = 9.52 \times \frac{28.95}{16} = 17.2 \text{ lbm air/lbm fuel}$$

† Note that this equation is balanced and that the stoichiometric coefficients are not necessarily integer. One can balance the equation (find the products' stoichiometric coefficients) by first considering the C atoms, then the H atoms, and finally the O atoms.

If a reaction occurs in an isolated vessel the internal energy of the products and reactants will be the same, and the entropy of the products will be greater than that of the reactants. Reactions can be made to occur at constant pressure and temperature by allowing the volume to change and transferring energy as heat from the reacting mixture. The internal energy of the products will then be different from that of the reactants. If the products have less internal energy (at constant P and T) the reaction is said to be *exothermic*, and energy must be transferred as heat from the mixture in order to keep the temperature constant. A reaction at constant P and T for which the opposite is true is called *endothermic*. The exothermic reaction is of particular utility in engineering as a means for supplying energy in the form of heat to thermal power systems.

11·2 FUEL ANALYSIS AND PRODUCT COMPOSITION

In an actual combustion process it may be necessary to determine experimentally both the products of combustion and their respective amounts. Often the fuel itself is unknown. The analysis of gaseous products of combustion is frequently made with an *Orsat apparatus*. A sample of the gas to be analyzed is brought into the Orsat analyzer at a known temperature and atmospheric pressure. The gas is then placed in contact with a liquid that absorbs CO_2, such as potassium hydroxide. The temperature and the total pressure are maintained constant during the measurement so that the volume of the gas decreases as CO_2 is absorbed. This decrease in volume is noted. The gas is then successively placed in contact with a liquid that absorbs O_2, such as pyrogallic acid, and then with a liquid that absorbs CO, such as cuprous chloride. The further decrease in volume of the gas sample is noted in each operation. The change in the volume of the gas sample during each separate absorption test is a measure of the volumetric fraction of that particular gas in the sample. Since the measurements are on a volumetric basis at a constant temperature and pressure and the gases are essentially ideal, the values obtained are also a measure of the mole fraction of each of the measured constituents. If additional gases (other than N_2 and H_2O) are expected to be present in significant amount in the sample, additional absorbers are required. At each stage of absorption the mixture is presumed to be saturated with water vapor. Since the temperature and pressure remain constant, the partial pressure of the water vapor is unchanged by the absorptions, and consequently an appropriate amount of H_2O condenses out with each absorption. The net effect is that indicated mole fractions are precisely those that would be obtained in a mixture *without* any water vapor (a *dry mixture*); the proof of this is left as a problem for the student. The gas remaining in the analyzer after the overall test is completed determines the nitrogen mole fraction of the *dry* mixture. The actual H_2O content is then determined from a mass balance.

As an example, suppose an Orsat analysis has provided us with the volume measurements given in Table 11·1.

TABLE 11·1 DRY MIXTURE COMPOSITION FROM ORSAT ANALYSIS

	$\Psi_i = \chi_i$
CO_2	0.11
O_2	0.03
CO	0.01
Subtotal	0.15
N_2	0.85
Total	1.00

We want to find the chemical equation and the AFR from these data. However, the fuel is unknown. Let's assume it is an equivalent hydrocarbon of the form

$$C_nH_m$$

We can use the Orsat data to determine n and m, and hence to discover the fuel. We assume the oxidant is air. Then, the chemical equation is assumed to be of the form

$$C_nH_m + a(O_2 + 3.76N_2) \rightleftarrows bCO_2 + cH_2O + dCO + eO_2 + fN_2$$

Since the dry mixture product mole fractions are known, it is convenient to write the chemical equation on the basis of 100 moles of dry mixture. Hence

$$b = 11 \qquad d = 1 \qquad e = 3 \qquad f = 85$$

Then, by conservation of N atoms,

$$a = \frac{85}{3.76} = 22.6$$

Conservation of oxygen atoms requires

$$2a = 2b + c + d + 2e$$

Hence,

$$c = 2 \times 22.6 - 2 \times 11 - 1 - 2 \times 3 = 16.2$$

Conservation of C atoms requires

$$n = b + d = 11 + 1 = 12$$

and conservation of H atoms requires

$$m = 2c = 32.4$$

Therefore, the fuel can be viewed as an equivalent hydrocarbon $C_{12}H_{32.4}$.

The chemical equation is then

$$C_{12}H_{32.4} + 22.6(O_2 + 3.76N_2) \rightleftarrows 11CO_2 + 16.2H_2O$$
$$+ CO + 3O_2 + 85N_2 \quad (11 \cdot 4)$$

We could calculate the AFR on a molal basis, but as the fuel molecular configuration is not really known, the result would be meaningless. We can, however, calculate the AFR on a mass basis. The molal mass of our effective $C_{12}H_{32.4}$ fuel is

$$\hat{M} = 12 \times 12.0 + 32.4 \times 1.0 = 176.4 \text{ lbm/lbmole}$$

Then,

$$\text{AFR} = \frac{\mathfrak{N}_{air}\hat{M}_{air}}{\mathfrak{N}_{fuel}\hat{M}_{fuel}} = \frac{(22.6 \times 4.76) \times 28.97}{1 \times 176.4} = 17.6 \text{ lbm air/lbm fuel}$$

Let's also calculate the percent excess air. The stoichiometric chemical equation is

$$C_{12}H_{32.4} + 20.1(O_2 + 3.76N_2) \rightleftarrows 12CO_2 + 16.2H_2O + 75.5N_2 \quad (11 \cdot 5)$$

Then, the percent excess air is

$$\frac{22.6 - 20.1}{20.1} = 0.124$$

corresponding to "112.4 percent theoretical air."

Because of the high water content in typical combustion products, and the very corrosive effects of high-temperature condensate, knowledge of the dew point of products of combustion is often important. If the product composition is known, the partial pressure of water is readily determined, and this corresponds to the saturation pressure of H_2O at the dew point.† For example, for the products mixture of the previous example,

$$\chi_{H_2O} = \frac{16.2}{11 + 16.2 + 1 + 3 + 85} = 0.139$$

Then, by Eq. (10·19),

$$P_{H_2O} = 0.139 \times 14.7 = 2.04 \text{ psia}$$

Inspecting Table B·1b, we see this corresponds to a saturation (dew-point) temperature of about 126°F.

11·3 STANDARDIZED ENERGY AND ENTHALPY

In order to carry out thermodynamic calculations for chemical reactions we need to know the equations of state for all species involved. Equations of state for many substances have been worked up from a combination of laboratory data, thermodynamic relations, and quantum-statistical analyses; we

† To a very good approximation. See Sec. 12·6.

are already familiar with the examples given in Appendix B. In the preparation of these equations of state it is customary to select some arbitrary datum state at which the internal energy (or alternatively, the enthalpy) and the entropy are taken to be zero. These equations of state may be used in any thermodynamic analysis involving one substance only (or mixtures of non-reacting substances), since differences in internal energy and entropy between two states are all that ever enter into consideration. However, with chemically reacting systems it is necessary to use a common basis for evaluation of the thermodynamic properties of all substances involved in any particular analysis. For example, suppose we arbitrarily selected some state T_0 and P_0 as the datum for H_2, O_2, and H_2O. Then, any reaction carried out at this temperature and pressure would appear to result in no change in the internal energy or entropy of the mixture, an obviously incorrect situation.

It might be thought that since energy is a monotonically increasing function of temperature, the energy of all substances at the absolute zero of temperature would be zero. This is certainly not the case, because a considerable amount of energy may be associated with molecular and nuclear binding forces and other energy modes. It does not appear practical to speak of the "absolute energy" of matter. A datum must be selected that will allow us to properly tie together the energy of different substances so that we can make proper energy analyses of chemical reactions.

The procedure we follow is to select some arbitrary datum (temperature and pressure) at which we give zero values to the enthalpy of the basic elements.† It would be nice if this could be absolute zero temperature and, say, 1 atm pressure, but this would require accurate low-temperature data not generally available at the present time. A more practical datum conventionally adopted for chemical thermodynamic tabulations is 25°C (77°F) and 1 atm pressure. This is called the *standard reference state*. By convention, we make the enthalpy of every *elemental* substance zero at the standard reference state.‡ By elemental substance we mean the substance composed of only one kind of atom in the form in which it exists in equilibrium at the standard reference state. For example, the enthalpy of mercury (Hg, liquid) is zero at the standard reference state, as is the enthalpy of oxygen (O_2, gas) at this temperature and pressure.§

---

† It is customary to give the enthalpy, rather than the internal energy, a zero value at the datum state; this then fixes the value of the energy at the datum state, since absolute values for P and v are measurable.

‡ Recall that different isotopes of an element have the same chemical properties. If no nuclear reactions are involved, the enthalpy of each isotope can be considered zero at this standard state.

§ These may not agree with the graphical and tabular equations of state often presented. The standard reference state is used primarily in chemical thermodynamic literature, as for example, in some places in the *Handbook of Chemistry and Physics*. The user of equation-of-state information should always check the datum, especially if he is analyzing a chemical reaction.

The *enthalpy of formation* of a compound is defined as the difference between the enthalpy of the compound, h°_{comp}, and the enthalpy of the elemental substances from which it is formed, all evaluated at the standard reference state. It is conventionally denoted by Δh°_f and, on a molal basis, is

$$\blacktriangleright \qquad \Delta \hat{h}^\circ_f \equiv \hat{h}^\circ_{\text{comp}} - \Sigma \nu_i \hat{h}^\circ_i \qquad\qquad (11 \cdot 6)$$

Here $\hat{h}^\circ_i$ is the molal enthalpy of the ith elemental substance involved in the formation reaction, and ν_i is the number of moles of the ith elemental substance involved in forming a single mole of the compound. The enthalpy of formation can be evaluated by appropriate measurements of energy transfers as heat and work and is a frequently tabulated property. Since by convention the elemental substances have zero enthalpy at the standard reference state, the enthalpy of a compound at the standard reference state is merely its enthalpy of formation. The enthalpy at other states may be established using this datum-point enthalpy. We call this the *standardized enthalpy*, meaning simply that it is properly related to the enthalpy of other elements and compounds. Values for Δh°_f can be determined by laboratory measurement or by advanced methods of statistical thermochemistry (see Table B·12). Knowing Δh°_f for any substance, the standardized enthalpy can be calculated by simple adjustment of the enthalpy data for that substance. Table B·13 was constructed in this manner. Note that the enthalpy of formation and standardized enthalpy often have negative values as a result of the choice of reference state.

The term "heat of formation" is used sometimes to refer to the enthalpy of formation and sometimes to mean the negative of the enthalpy of formation; the user of any tabulation must be sure which (if either) the tabulator had in mind. The term arises because it may be shown that the energy which must be transferred as heat from the mixture to keep the temperature and pressure constant is equal to the enthalpy of formation.

11·4   HEATS OF REACTION, HEATING VALUES

We now have practically all the tools necessary for analysis of the energetics of chemical reactions. Of particular interest is the combustion of fuels, where it is common practice to write the energy balance on a per-mole-of-fuel basis. Consider the combustion of a hydrocarbon fuel C_nH_m with air in a steady-flow burner (Fig. 11·1). It is common to assume that the products contain only H_2O, CO_2, and N_2, with additional O_2 if excess air is supplied. For a stoichiometric reaction the chemical equation is

$$C_nH_m + \left(n + \frac{m}{4}\right)(O_2 + 3.76N_2) \rightleftarrows nCO_2 + \frac{m}{2}H_2O + \left(n + \frac{m}{4}\right)3.76N_2$$

Note that in this form the stoichiometric coefficients give the amounts of species in the products and reactants per mole of fuel. Now, the energy balance

FIG. 11·1   *The energy terms are per mole of fuel*

on a per-mole-of-fuel basis is

$$\hat{H}_R = \hat{H}_P + \hat{Q}$$

where for brevity we have denoted the *total* enthalpies of the products and reactants, *per mole of fuel*, by $\hat{H}_P$ and $\hat{H}_R$, respectively. $\hat{Q}$ is then the energy transfer as heat from the combustor per mole of fuel burned. It is common practice to evaluate $\hat{H}_R$, $\hat{H}_P$, and $\hat{Q}$ considering the reaction to occur *at the standard reference state* (1 atm, 77°F), for this provides a sensible way to compare various fuels.

Under these conditions we have

$$\blacktriangleright \qquad \hat{H}_P^\circ = \left(\sum_i \mathfrak{N}_i \hat{h}_i\right)_{\text{products}} \qquad\qquad (11\cdot 7a)$$

$$\blacktriangleright \qquad \hat{H}_R^\circ = \left(\sum_i \mathfrak{N}_i \hat{h}_i\right)_{\text{reactants}} \qquad\qquad (11\cdot 7b)$$

where the mole numbers $\mathfrak{N}_i$ are simply the stoichiometric coefficients in the chemical equation. Then,

$$\blacktriangleright \qquad \hat{Q}^\circ. = \hat{H}_R^\circ - \hat{H}_P^\circ \qquad\qquad (11\cdot 8)$$

$\hat{Q}^\circ$ is termed the *heating value* or *heat of reaction* of the fuel. Note that $\hat{Q}^\circ$ represents the energy that must be transferred as heat from the system, per mole of fuel, in order to maintain the system at constant temperature. The term *enthalpy of combustion* is sometimes used for the *negative* of $\hat{Q}^\circ$, which is then denoted by $\hat{H}_{RP}^\circ$. (The superscript is often omitted, and we include it here to emphasize that the reaction is taken at the standard reference state.)

$$\blacktriangleright \qquad \hat{H}_{RP}^\circ = -\hat{Q}^\circ = \hat{H}_P^\circ - \hat{H}_R^\circ \qquad\qquad (11\cdot 9)$$

The H_2O in the products may appear in either the liquid or vapor phase. When the H_2O is in its *liquid* phase $\hat{Q}^\circ$ is termed the *higher heating value* (HHV), while when H_2O vapor is considered, $\hat{Q}^\circ$ is called the *lower heating value* (LHV). Noting that condensation releases h_{fg}, which adds to $\hat{Q}^\circ$, we see that HHV > LHV.

To illustrate, let's evaluate the quantities discussed above for ethane (C_2H_6). The chemical equation is

$$C_2H_6 + 3.5(O_2 + 3.76N_2) \rightleftarrows 2CO_2 + 3H_2O + 13.15N_2$$

Using enthalpy data from Table B·12,

$$\hat{H}_R^\circ = 1 \times (-36{,}401) + 3.5 \times 0 + 3.5 \times 3.76 \times 0$$
$$= -36{,}401 \text{ Btu/lbmole fuel}$$
$$\hat{H}_P^\circ = 2(-169{,}183) + 3(-122{,}976) + 13.15 \times 0$$
$$= -707{,}294 \text{ Btu/lbmole fuel}$$

Note that we consider the H_2O to be *liquid*. Then,

$$\hat{Q}^\circ = (-36{,}401) - (-707{,}294) = 670{,}893 \text{ Btu/lbmole fuel}$$
$$\hat{H}_{RP}^\circ = -\hat{Q}^\circ = \hat{H}_P - \hat{H}_R = -670{,}893 \text{ Btu/lbmole fuel}$$

Since we treated the H_2O as liquid, the higher heating value is

$$\text{HHV} = 670{,}893 \text{ Btu/lbmole}$$

To find the lower heating value, we need the molal enthalpy of water vapor at 77°F. Interpolating in Table B·1A,

$$h_{fg} = 1050.3 \text{ Btu/lbm at } 77°\text{F}$$

so,

$$\hat{h}_{fg} = 1050.3 \times 18.016 = 18{,}921 \text{ Btu/lbmole}$$

Hence, for water vapor at the standard reference state,

$$\hat{h}^\circ = -122{,}976 + 18{,}921 = -104{,}055 \text{ Btu/lbmole}$$

Alternatively, we could have read from Table B·13

$$\hat{h}^\circ = -103{,}968 \text{ Btu/lbmole}$$

which is less exact because of the perfect-gas approximations employed. Then, with water vapor in the products,

$$\hat{H}_P^\circ = 2(-169{,}183) + 3(-104{,}055) = 650{,}531 \text{ Btu/lbmole}$$

and hence the lower heating value is

$$\text{LHV} = (-36{,}401) - (-650{,}531) = 614{,}130 \text{ Btu/lbmole fuel}$$

Often the heating values are quoted on a mass basis. Since the molal mass of ethane is 30.07 lb/lbmole, the lower heating value can be expressed as

$$\text{LHV} = \frac{614{,}130}{30.07} = 20{,}400 \text{ Btu/lbm}$$

11·5   SOME ILLUSTRATIVE CALCULATIONS

We shall now go through a sequence of example calculations to illustrate the matters discussed above and to introduce some new ideas.

Let's first find the LHV and $\hat{H}_{RP}$ for methane (CH_4) burned with air in a stoichiometric reaction at 77°F and 1 atm. The chemical equation is

$$CH_4 + 2(O_2 + 3.76N_2) \rightleftarrows CO_2 + 2H_2O + 7.52N_2$$

An energy balance on the control volume (see Fig. 11·1) on a per-mole-of-fuel basis, gives

$$\hat{H}_R = \hat{H}_P + \hat{Q}$$

Now,

$$\text{LHV} = \hat{Q} = \hat{H}_R - \hat{H}_P$$

Using the chemical equation,

$$\text{LHV} = \hat{h}_{CH_4}^\circ + 2\hat{h}_{O_2}^\circ + 7.52\hat{h}_{N_2}^\circ - \hat{h}_{CO_2}^\circ - 2\hat{h}_{H_2O}^\circ - 7.52\hat{h}_{N_2}^\circ$$

where the H_2O is in vapor form. Using data from Tables B·12 and B·13,

$$\begin{aligned} \text{LHV} &= -32,179 + 0 + 0 - (-169,183) - 2(-103,968) - 0 \\ &= 344,940 \text{ Btu/lbmole } CH_4 \end{aligned}$$

Note the difference with the molal LHV of ethane computed in the previous section. However, the molal mass of methane is only 16.04 lb/lbmole, and hence on a mass basis

$$\text{LHV} = \frac{344,940}{16.04} = 21,500 \text{ Btu/lbm}$$

which is quite similar to that of ethane. Most hydrocarbon fuels have lower heating values in the range 10,000 to 22,000 Btu/lbm.

The enthalpy of combustion of methane is

$$\hat{H}_{RP}^\circ = -\text{LHV} = -344,940 \text{ Btu/lbmole } CH_4$$

In order to study the effect of temperature on $\hat{H}_{RP}$, let's now consider the same reaction at an elevated temperature, say 2000°R. Now,

$$\begin{aligned} \hat{H}_{RP} &= \hat{H}_P - \hat{H}_R \\ &= \hat{h}_{CO_2} + 2\hat{h}_{H_2O} + 7.52\hat{h}_{N_2} - \hat{h}_{CH_4} - 2\hat{h}_{O_2} - 7.52\hat{h}_{N_2} \end{aligned}$$

But now all enthalpies must be evaluated at 2000°R. The pressure is unimportant, for we treat all constituents as perfect gases with $h = h(T)$. The nitrogen contributions cancel in the equation above since the product and reactant temperatures are identical. From Table B·13 we can find all but $\hat{h}_{CH_4}$ at 2000°R. We can calculate $\hat{h}_{CH_4}$, assuming perfect-gas behavior.

$$\hat{h}(2000°R) - \hat{h}(537°R) = \int_{537°R}^{2000°R} \hat{c}_P(T) \, dT$$

Over this wide temperature range the variation in $\hat{c}_P$ must be considered. Specific heat data for methane are given in Table B·16,

$$\hat{c}_P(T) = 3.381 + 0.018044T - 4.3 \times 10^{-6}T^2 \qquad \text{cal/gmole-°K} \ (T \text{ in °K})$$

Substituting and integrating, taking proper care in the unit conversion, we find

$$\hat{h}(2000°R) = \hat{h}(537°R) + 20{,}086 \text{ Btu/lbmole}$$

So, for CH_4,

$$\hat{h}(2000°R) = -32{,}179 + 20{,}086 = -12{,}093 \text{ Btu/lbmole}$$

Then, combining with the enthalpy data in Table B·13,

$$\hat{H}_{RP} = -152{,}194 + 2(-90{,}797) - (-12{,}093) - 2(11{,}439)$$
$$\hat{H}_{RP} = -344{,}574 \text{ Btu/lbmole}$$

At 77°F we found $\hat{H}^{°}_{RP} = -344{,}940$. We see that the enthalpy of combustion is only slightly changed with temperature, which is true for many hydrocarbon fuels. This fact is often useful in making simplified combustion calculations.

Let us further extend the calculations. Suppose the reactants enter at 77°F at 1 atm and leave at an unknown temperature at 1 atm. We wish to determine this exit temperature.

Whereas in the previous calculations we considered exothermic reactions at constant temperature, we now assume that the burner is adiabatic. Our procedure will be to make an energy balance and solve for the enthalpy of the products in terms of the enthalpies of the reactants. The enthalpy, composition, and pressure of the products will then suffice to fix the exhaust temperature. We make the following idealizations:

Products contain only CO_2, H_2O, N_2, and O_2
Oxygen, nitrogen, methane, and CO_2 are perfect gases
The products of combustion constitute a mixture of independent perfect gases
Steady flow steady state
Adiabatic control volume
Equilibrium at inlets and exhaust
Kinetic and potential energies negligible

With these idealizations, an energy balance on the control volume (Fig. 11·2) yields

$$(\Re\hat{h})_{CH_4} + (\Re\hat{h})_{O_2} + (\Re\hat{h})_{N_2} = (\Re\hat{h})_{prod} \tag{11·10}$$

where $\Re$ denotes the molal mass flow rate. The chemical equation is again

$$CH_4 + 2(O_2 + 3.76N_2) \rightleftarrows CO_2 + 2H_2O + 7.52N_2 \tag{11·11}$$

Note that 10.52 moles of products are formed by combustion of 1 mole of fuel.

FIG. 11·2 *The control volume is adiabatic*

Hence,

$$\frac{\mathfrak{N}_{CH_4}}{\mathfrak{N}_{prod}} = \frac{1}{10.52} = 0.095$$

$$\frac{\mathfrak{N}_{O_2}}{\mathfrak{N}_{prod}} = \frac{2}{10.52} = 0.190$$

$$\frac{\mathfrak{N}_{N_2}}{\mathfrak{N}_{prod}} = \frac{7.52}{10.52} = 0.715$$

So, the energy balance can be written as

$$\hat{h}_{prod} = 0.095\hat{h}_{CH_4} + 0.190\hat{h}_{O_2} + 0.715\hat{h}_{N_2}$$

which is equivalent to an energy balance written on a per-mole-of-products basis. Since the state of the reactants is known, the energy balance becomes an equation for $\hat{h}_{prod}$. Using the data of Table B·12, we have

$$\hat{h}_{prod} = 0.095(-32{,}179) + 0 + 0 = -3057 \text{ Btu/lbmole}$$

We now need to determine what temperature will give this value of $\hat{h}_{prod}$. The product enthalpy is related to the individual species enthalpies by (see Eq. 10·13)

$$\hat{h}_{prod} = \chi_{N_2}\hat{h}_{N_2} + \chi_{CO_2}\hat{h}_{CO_2} + \chi_{H_2O}\hat{h}_{H_2O}$$

Calculating the constituent mole fractions,

$$\chi_{N_2} = \frac{7.52}{10.52} = 0.715$$

$$\chi_{CO_2} = \frac{1}{10.52} = 0.095$$

$$\chi_{H_2O} = \frac{2}{10.52} = 0.190$$

Hence,

$$\hat{h}_{prod}(T) = 0.715\hat{h}_{N_2}(T) + 0.095\hat{h}_{CO_2}(T) + 0.190\hat{h}_{H_2O}(T)$$

The component enthalpies are given in Table B·13. A trial and error solution will determine what temperature will give the correct product enthalpy (-3057 Btu/lbmole). The results are tabulated in Table 11·2. Interpolating between 4000 and 4200°R, we find $T = 4187°$R for $\hat{h} = -3057$ Btu/lbmole.

TABLE 11·2 PRODUCT ENTHALPY CALCULATION

	χ_i	$T = 4000°R$		$4200°R$	
		$\hat{h}_i$	$\chi_i \hat{h}_i$	$\hat{h}_i$	$\chi_i \hat{h}_i$
CO_2	0.095	$-123{,}981$	$-11{,}780$	$-121{,}050.5$	$-11{,}500$
H_2O	0.190	$-67{,}747$	$-12{,}880$	$-65{,}227.9$	$-12{,}400$
N_2	0.715	$27{,}599.9$	$19{,}700$	$29{,}338.6$	$20{,}980$
			$-4{,}960$		$-2{,}920$

The product temperature is called the *adiabatic flame temperature*, the temperature reached in an adiabatic steady-flow combustion process.

A typical combustion process would not have reactants exactly at the standard state. To illustrate the effects of the deviations, let's modify the previous example. Suppose the air enters at 90°F and 40 psia, and the methane enters at 60°F and 20 psia. First, we evaluate the standardized enthalpies of the reactants. Since the inlet temperatures are not far from 77°F, the constant specific heat assumption is reasonable here. Then (see Eq. 8·25),

$$\hat{h} = \hat{h}° + \hat{c}_P(T - T_0)$$

So, using data from Table B·6,

$$\hat{h}_{O_2} = 0 + 7.01(90 - 77) = 91.1 \text{ Btu/lbmole}$$
$$\hat{h}_{N_2} = 0 + 6.95(90 - 77) = 90.3 \text{ Btu/lbmole}$$
$$\hat{h}_{CH_4} = -32{,}179 + 8.53(60 - 77) = -32{,}325 \text{ Btu/lbmole}$$

As before, $\hat{h}_{prod}$ is calculated from the energy balance; one finds $\hat{h}_{prod} = -2983$ Btu/lbmole. The temperature can be determined from our previous calculations. Interpolating between 4000°R and 4200°R, we find $T = 4193°R$. Note that the modest change in inlet conditions has only slightly affected the burner discharge temperature.

The typical combustion process would utilize excess air to ensure that complete combustion takes place. Excess air will also cause a decrease in the adiabatic flame temperature since energy will be required to increase the temperature of the nonreacting air. In fact, excess air is often introduced to control the adiabatic flame temperature and maintain it within the limits set by the materials in the system.

Again let us consider the combustion of methane in a steady-flow burner. The oxidizer will be air, and we suppose that twice as much air is supplied as is necessary for the combustion (200 percent "theoretical air"). The air will enter at 90°F and 40 psia and the methane at 60°F and 20 psia. The products of combustion emerge at 1 atm. The chemical equation is [compare with Eq. (11·11)]

$$CH_4 + 4(O_2 + 3.76N_2) \rightleftarrows CO_2 + 2H_2O + 2O_2 + 15.04N_2 \qquad (11·12)$$

The energy balance again produces Eq. (11·10), which we use as the basis for the discharge-temperature calculation. The reactant enthalpies were calculated for these inlet states in the previous example, and are summarized below.

$$\hat{h}_{CH_4} = -32,325 \text{ Btu/lbmole}$$
$$\hat{h}_{O_2} = 91.1 \text{ Btu/lbmole}$$
$$\hat{h}_{N_2} = 90.3 \text{ Btu/lbmole}$$

Now, the mole fractions of the reactants mixture are indicated by the chemical equation

$$\frac{\mathfrak{N}_{CH_4}}{\mathfrak{N}_{prod}} = \frac{1}{20.04} = 0.0499$$

$$\frac{\mathfrak{N}_{O_2}}{\mathfrak{N}_{prod}} = \frac{4}{20.04} = 0.1996$$

$$\frac{\mathfrak{N}_{N_2}}{\mathfrak{N}_{prod}} = \frac{4 \times 3.76}{20.04} = 0.7505$$

The standardized enthalpy of the product mixture is then

$$\hat{h}_{prod} = 0.0499 \times (-32,325) + 0.1996 \times 91.1 + 0.750 \times 90.3$$
$$= -1527 \text{ Btu/lbmole}$$

This value will be used to establish the temperature of the exhaust gases.

The mole fractions of the species in the product mixture are, from the chemical equation,

$$\chi_{CO_2} = \frac{1}{20.04} = 0.0499$$

$$\chi_{H_2O} = \frac{2}{20.04} = 0.0998$$

$$\chi_{O_2} = \frac{2}{20.04} = 0.0998$$

$$\chi_{N_2} = \frac{15.04}{20.04} = 0.7505$$

The products of enthalpy may again be written as

$$\hat{h}_{prod}(T) = \chi_{CO_2}\hat{h}_{CO_2}(T) + \chi_{H_2O}\hat{h}_{H_2O}(T) + \chi_{O_2}\hat{h}_{O_2}(T) + \chi_{N_2}\hat{h}_{N_2}(T)$$

Data for the standardized enthalpies of the constituents in the product mixture may be obtained from Table B·13. Calculation of the product temperature again requires iteration, which is summarized in Table 11·3. Interpolating, we

TABLE 11·3 PRODUCT ENTHALPY CALCULATION

		2600°R		2700°R	
	χ_i	$\hat{h}_i$	$\chi_i \hat{h}_i$	$\hat{h}_i$	$\chi_i \hat{h}$
CO_2	0.0499	-144025	-7187	-142631	-7117
H_2O	0.0998	-84397	-8423	-83279	-8311
O_2	0.0998	$+16586$	$+1655$	$+17458$	$+1742$
N_2	0.7505	$+15686$	$+11773$	$+16517$	$+12396$
			$\hat{h}_{prod} = -2182$		$\hat{h}_{prod} = -1290$

find $T_{prod} = 2674°R$. Note the dramatic decrease in flame temperature caused by excess air.†

11·6 ABSOLUTE ENTROPY AND THE THIRD LAW OF THERMODYNAMICS

Thus far in this chapter we have considered only the first-law aspects of chemical reactions, emphasizing combustion of hydrocarbon fuels by air. We always assumed complete combustion in the examples above, and made certain assumptions about the products of reaction. The second law provides the basis for theoretical prediction of the true composition of a product mixture, and hence it plays a very important role in chemical thermodynamics. To apply the second law we need to relate properly the entropies of all elements and compounds.

Let us first recall the meaning of zero entropy. A state of zero entropy is one for which one single system quantum state is always observed. We would know the microscopic state of a system at zero entropy precisely, with zero uncertainty. Imagine now that we add one quantum of energy to the system and that this permits it to suddenly take any one of a very large number of quantum states. Assuming each quantum state is equally likely, the entropy change would be

$$\delta S = k \ln \Omega - 0$$

where Ω is the number of quantum states available to the system with the single quantum of energy. The internal energy change δU would be simply ϵ, the very small amount of energy added. Since Ω is likely to be very large, a tiny increase in energy would give a huge increase in entropy. Recalling the

† The serious student should be aware of the availability of extensive tables for computation of hydrocarbon combustion reactions. In particular, the Keenan and Kaye *Gas Tables* (see Selected Reading List) are very useful, for they include product enthalpy information for 200 percent and 400 percent theoretical air for combustion of a general fuel $(CH_2)_n$.

thermodynamic definition of temperature, Eq. (7·9), we are led to suspect that T must be very small when the entropy is zero.

We can illustrate this by a numerical example. Consider 1 cm³ of matter having a mass of the order of 1 g and a molal mass of the order of 20 g/gmole. This system would contain roughly 3×10^{22} atoms. The quantum of energy added might be possessed by any one of the atoms, so the entropy in the slightly energized state will be approximately

$$S \approx \text{k} \ln N \approx 1.38 \times 10^{-23} \text{ joule/}^\circ\text{K} \times \ln (3 \times 10^{22})$$
$$\approx 70 \times 10^{-23} \text{ joule/}^\circ\text{K}$$

We imagine adding a quantum of energy by means of a photon having a wavelength equal to 1 cm (this is a reasonable estimate for the least energetic photon that might be captured by 1 cm³ of matter). Its energy is

$$\epsilon = \frac{\text{hc}}{\lambda} = \frac{6.62 \times 10^{-34} \text{ joule-sec} \times 3 \times 10^8 \text{ m/sec}}{0.01 \text{ m}}$$
$$\epsilon \approx 2 \times 10^{-23} \text{ joule}$$

The temperature is therefore estimated to be

$$T \approx \frac{1}{\delta S/\epsilon} \approx \frac{1}{70 \times 10^{-23}/2 \times 10^{-23}} \approx \frac{1}{35} \, ^\circ\text{K}$$

This should be interpreted as the "average" temperature over the range $0 < S < 70 \times 10^{-23}$ joule/°K. Since the temperature is a monotonic function of the entropy, the temperature at the zero entropy state may be expected to be even smaller.

On the basis of these considerations we make the following macroscopic postulate:

The temperature of any pure substance in thermodynamic equilibrium approaches zero as the entropy approaches zero.

Conversely, since the temperature is a monotonic function of the entropy,

The entropy of any pure substance in thermodynamic equilibrium approaches zero as the temperature approaches zero.

Expressed mathematically, for a pure substance in equilibrium,

$$\blacktriangleright \qquad \lim_{T \to 0} S = 0 \tag{11·13}$$

This particular form of the postulate is called the *third law of thermodynamics*. The third law was developed in the early 1900s, primarily through the efforts of Nernst, and consequently is often called the *Nernst theorem*.

A considerable body of experimental data supporting the third law now exists. We can calculate the absolute entropy of a substance from the measured thermodynamic properties by integrating the differential equations of state from absolute zero; for gases this requires passage from the solid state through the liquid state and vaporization to get to the gaseous phase. It is also possible to calculate the entropy of gases using statistical thermodynamics. The close agreement of the entropies calculated on these different ways provides some of the strongest evidence in support of the third law.

Some exceptions to the agreement between the macroscopically determined and statistically determined absolute entropies have been claimed, and there is some disagreement as to the validity and generality of the third law, though no one denies its usefulness. According to Fast,[†] all the exceptions seem to be satisfactorily explained. First of all, the substance must be "pure," since presence of any additional species would immediately give a positional entropy, even at zero temperature. Second, it is necessary to extrapolate to absolute zero and data down to very low temperatures must be provided. Other apparent exceptions arise from the fact that thermodynamic equilibrium is not maintained as the temperature is reduced. None of these contradicts the third law which holds only at absolute zero for pure substances in equilibrium states.

The third law permits determination of the absolute entropy of every substance, including elemental substances (Hg, O_2, . . .) and compounds. These entropies are all properly tied to a common base and may therefore be used in analyzing chemical reactions. The absolute entropies of several substances are given in Tables B·12 and B·13.

11·7 A SECOND-LAW APPLICATION

To illustrate one application of the second law, consider again the last example of Sec. 11·5. There we presumed (without justification) that the reaction could in fact occur; let us now test this presumption with the aid of the second law. Applying the second law to the control volume (Fig. 11·2), we find

$$\dot{\mathcal{P}}_s = (\mathfrak{N}\hat{s})_{\text{prod}} - (\mathfrak{N}\hat{s})_{CH_4} - (\mathfrak{N}\hat{s})_{O_2} - (\mathfrak{N}\hat{s})_{N_2} \geq 0 \qquad (11·14)$$

where $\hat{s}$ represents the absolute molal entropy. If the entropy production is positive, the reaction is possible; if it is zero, the reaction is reversible, that is, could go in either direction; if a negative value is calculated, the assumed reaction could not occur.

The absolute molal entropies of the reactant gases will be calculated by extrapolation from the entropies at standard reference state; we treat the gases as perfect, with constant specific heats over the small temperature range of the extrapolation. Equation (8·27) is equivalent to

$$\hat{s} = \hat{s}^0 + \hat{c}_p \ln \frac{T}{T_0} - \mathfrak{R} \ln \frac{P}{P_0} \qquad (11·15)$$

[†] J. D. Fast, *Entropy*, p. 85, McGraw-Hill Book Co., New York, 1962.

ϕ — tabulated in B-13

or $\hat{s} = \hat{s}^0 + \int_{T_0}^{T} \hat{c}_p \frac{dT}{T} - R \ln \frac{P}{P_0}$ if ϕ is not tabulated use 11-15 for small temp. ranges where $\hat{s}^0$ is the entropy in the standard reference state (T_0, P_0). The partial pressures of the O_2 and N_2 in the air are proportional to their mole fractions. Thus

$$P_{O_2} = 0.21 \times 40 = 8.4 \text{ psia}$$
$$P_{N_2} = 0.79 \times 40 = 31.6 \text{ psia}$$

The absolute molal entropies of the incoming constituents are then, for CH_4,

$$\hat{s} = 44.47 + 8.53 \times \ln \frac{520}{537} - 1.986 \times \ln \frac{20}{14.7} = 43.58 \text{ Btu/lbmole-}°\text{R}$$

for O_2,

$$\hat{s} = 48.986 + 7.01 \times \ln \frac{550}{537} - 1.986 \times \ln \frac{8.4}{14.7} = 50.27 \text{ Btu/lbmole-}°\text{R}$$

and for N_2,

$$\hat{s} = 45.755 + 6.95 \times \ln \frac{550}{537} - 1.986 \times \ln \frac{31.6}{14.7} = 44.41 \text{ Btu/lbmole-}°\text{R}$$

The molal entropy of the products is computed in Table 11·4, using the data from Table B·13.

TABLE 11·4 PRODUCT ENTROPY CALCULATION

	χ_i	2600°R $\hat{s}_i$	2600°R $\chi_i\hat{s}_i$	2700°R $\hat{s}_i$	2700°R $\chi_i\hat{s}_i$
CO_2	0.0499	69.245	3.455	69.771	3.482
H_2O	0.0998	59.414	5.926	59.837	5.972
O_2	0.0998	61.287	6.116	61.616	6.149
N_2	0.7505	57.436	43.106	57.750	43.321
			$\hat{s}_{prod} = 58.603$		$\hat{s}_{prod} = 58.924$

Interpolating,

$$\hat{s}_{prod} = 58.603 + \frac{2674 - 2600}{2700 - 2600} \times (58.924 - 58.603)$$
$$= 58.839 \text{ Btu/lbmole-}°\text{R}$$

Substituting into Eq. (11·14),

$$\frac{\dot{\mathcal{P}}_s}{\dot{\mathfrak{N}}_{prod}} = 58.839 - 0.0499 \times 43.58 - 0.1995 \times 50.27 - 0.7505 \times 44.41$$
$$= 13.313 \text{ Btu/lbmole-}°\text{R} \geq 0$$

Since a positive entropy-production rate is obtained, the process assumed does not violate the second law. Note that the reaction is not reversible (because it produces entropy).

We assumed that the products of combustion contain no CO, NO, or other compounds and that the reaction was "complete." The second-law structure also provides a means for determining the equilibrium composition of a reacting mixture, and we shall consider this problem in the next chapter.

SELECTED READING

Keenan, J., and J. Kaye, *Gas Tables*, John Wiley & Sons, Inc., New York, 1948.

Lee, J., and F. Sears, *Thermodynamics*, 2d ed., chap. 14, Addison-Wesley Publishing Co., Inc., Reading, Mass., 1962.

Van Wylen, G., and R. Sonntag, *Fundamentals of Classical Thermodynamics*, chap. 13, John Wiley & Sons, Inc., New York, 1965.

Wark, K., *Thermodynamics*, chap. 14, McGraw-Hill Book Company, New York, 1966.

Zemansky, M. W., *Heat and Thermodynamics*, 4th ed., chaps. 17 and 18, McGraw-Hill Book Company, New York, 1957.

QUESTIONS

11·1 What are reactants, products, and chemical equations?

11·2 What is a stoichiometric mixture?

11·3 Why is it essential that the enthalpies and entropies of all substances be tied to a common base when chemical reactions are considered?

11·4 Is the energy of a substance ever really zero? Is its entropy?

11·5 What basic principles are employed in a calculation of the temperature following combustion in an adiabatic steady-flow device?

11·6 What is the heat of formation?

11·7 What is the enthalpy of formation?

11·8 What is the enthalpy of reaction?

11·9 What do the terms excess air and theoretical air mean?

11·10 What is the difference between exothermic and endothermic?

11·11 What does an Orsat analysis determine?

11·12 What are the values of T and P at the standard reference state?

11·13 To what does the Nernst theorem refer?

11·14 Does the first law hold true for a chemical reaction? Does the second law?

11·15 What is the difference between the higher heating value and the lower heating value?

11·16 Why does the introduction of excess air reduce the adiabatic flame temperature?

PROBLEMS

11·1 Write out the chemical equation for the reaction of octane (C_8H_{18}) with a stoichiometric reaction with air. Determine the theoretical air/fuel ratio for this reaction on both a molal and mass basis.

11·2 Write out the chemical equation for the reaction of octane (C_8H_{18}) with (a) 100 percent excess air and (b) 250 percent theoretical air.

11·3 Write the chemical equation for the reaction of n-butane (C_4H_{10}) with a stoichiometric reaction with air. Determine the theoretical air/fuel ratio for this reaction on both a molal and mass basis.

11·4 An oil fuel contains 84 percent C and 16 percent H_2 by mass. Find the stoichiometric air for complete combustion of 1 lbm of fuel. Determine the air/fuel ratio.

11·5 Compute the air/fuel ratio by mass used in an engine if the exhaust gas dry analysis in percent by volume is CO_2, 0.124; O_2, 0.032; CO, 0.001; H_2, 0.002.

11·6 Determine the dew point of the products when octane (C_8H_{18}) is burned with 400 percent theoretical dry air if the pressure is 14.7 psia.

11·7 Compute the standardized enthalpy and entropy of a mixture of equal parts by mass of CO_2 and H_2O at 2 atm pressure and 100°F.

11·8 Determine from the *Handbook of Chemistry and Physics* the standardized enthalpy of ozone and atomic oxygen at 18°C and 2 atm.

11·9 Determine the dew point of the products when n-butane (C_4H_{10}) reacts with stoichiometric dry air if the pressure is 18 psia. What is the effect on the dew point if 100 percent excess air is supplied to the reaction?

11·10 Liquid benzene (C_6H_6) is burned in a stoichiometric reaction with dry air. Determine the air/fuel ratio and the dew point of the products if the total pressure is 13.5 psia. Redo the problem if 200 percent excess air is used.

11·11 Redo the previous problem for the stoichiometric case if the air has an initial relative humidity of 60 percent and the inlet pressure is 14.7 psia at 77°F.

11·12 Determine the products of combustion and the air/fuel ratio by mass when a liquid fuel that is 84 percent carbon by weight and 16 percent hydrogen is burned with 50 percent excess air.

11·13 Propane (C_3H_8) reacts with air such that an Orsat analysis yields as products of combustion the following percentages: CO_2, 11.5; O_2, 2.7; CO, 0.7. Determine the reaction equation and the percent theoretical air for the reaction.

11·14 An unknown hydrocarbon fuel undergoes combustion such that the products have the following percentage composition as measured by an Orsat apparatus: CO_2, 9.0; CO, 1.1; O_2, 8.8; N_2, 81.1. Determine the reaction equation, air/fuel ratio, and the percent theoretical air on a mass basis.

11·15 How much energy is released when 1 mole of propane (C_3H_8) reacts with 80 percent theoretical air when both the inlet and exit states of the combustion are at the standard reference state? How much energy is released in a stoichiometric reaction?

11·16 Determine the enthalpy of combustion at 77°F for ethane (C_2H_6) when gaseous ethane reacts, assuming liquid water in the products. Do the same for acetylene (C_2H_2). Determine your answer in Btu/lbm fuel.

11·17 Set up a table showing the enthalpy of combustion at standard reference conditions, assuming that water appears as a liquid in the product, for hydrogen, carbon monoxide, methane, ethane, and propane.

11·18 The enthalpy of combustion for gaseous propane is 955,000 Btu/mole at standard reference conditions if the water products are liquid. From this information, determine the lower heating value of this fuel at standard reference conditions.

11·19 Calculate the enthalpy of combustion for the water-gas reaction, CO (g) + H_2O (g) $\rightarrow$ CO_2 (g) + H_2 (g), at standard reference conditions and at 1000°R.

11·20 Estimate the adiabatic flame temperature for a stoichiometric reaction of n-butane (C_4H_{10}) with air.

11·21 Redo the previous problem for the adiabatic flame temperature if the reaction occurs with 400 percent theoretical air.

11·22 It is desired to burn liquid n-butane (C_4H_{10}) with sufficient excess air so that the inlet temperature to a gas turbine will not exceed 1750°R. Specify the required excess air to limit the temperature to this value assuming that the standard reference condition exists at the inlet to the combustor.

11·23 Determine the adiabatic flame temperature that would be obtained from complete combustion of C_8H_{18} (octane) with theoretical air if (1) the inlet conditions are 1 atm at 77°F, and (2) if the inlet conditions are 1000°R. (Note an average $c_P = 7.90$ Btu/lbmole-°R for C_8H_{18} in this temperature range, $\hat{h}^o_{C_8H_{18}} = -89{,}680$ Btu/lbmole).

11·24 Estimate the adiabatic flame temperature when methane (CH_4) at 77°F reacts with 80 percent theoretical air also at 77°F. (Note that CO will be present in the products since the reaction is one of incomplete combustion.)

11·25 Determine the adiabatic flame temperature for propane burning in air (a) stoichiometrically, (b) with twice the stoichiometric air, and (c) with four times the stoichiometric air. Assume complete combustion in each case.

11·26 Propane (C_3H_8) and oxygen in stoichiometric proportions react in a steady-flow water-cooled burner. The reactants both enter at 90°F and 2 atm and emerge at 850°F. The products-flow rate is 250 lbm/hr. What is the rate of energy transfer as heat to the cooling water? Assume that the products contain only CO_2 and H_2O.

11·27 Acetylene is burned in a constant-pressure water-cooled burner at 30 psia. Twice the stoichiometric amount of air is provided, and the reactants enter at 40°F. The products emerge at 200°F, and the total flow rate is 10 lbm/min. Water enters the cooling jacket at 60°F and 10 psia and emerges at 1 atm and 180°F. What water-flow rate must be provided? The products contain only CO_2, H_2O, O_2, and N_2.

11·28 Gaseous acetylene at 77°F is burned with 400 percent theoretical air that enters the combustion chamber at 1000°R. The products of combustion leave at 2000°R. Calculate the heat loss from the combustion chamber per lbmole of acetylene burned.

11·29 A turboprop engine has the following characteristics:

> compressor pressure ratio, 6
> maximum cycle temperature, 2200°R
> η_C compressor isentropic efficiency, 0.85
> η_T turbine isentropic efficiency, 0.90
> Fuel, n-octane (C_8H_{18})

The engine propels a plane at 400 mph at an altitude of 40,000 feet (4.4 psia, −48°F). Analyze the cycle on a per-lbm basis, making suitable assumptions. Calculate all intermediate state points, and the engine specific fuel consumption, lbm fuel/hp-hr.

11·30 A commercial heater must provide 1000 ft³/min of hot gas at 400°F, 1 atm pressure. Design an appropriate system, specifying the fuel, flow rates, and so on.

11·31 The burner for a large power station must provide boiler heating at the rate of 3×10^8 Btu/hr. The maximum flame temperature is to be 1500°F, and the products can leave the boiler at no less than 1200°F. Design a burner system, specifying the fuel, flow rates, and so on.

11·32 The burner in a small engine must handle 10 lbm/sec of air, heating it to 1600°F. Any liquid hydrocarbon fuel may be used. Design a burner system, specifying the fuel requirements.

11·33 Design a small air-breathing jet engine to provide 200 lbf of thrust for a flying belt operation. Specify the fuel requirements per minute of flying time. What range might such a device obtain?

11·34 Orsat analyses are treated as though the gas sample contained no H_2O (dry gas analysis). Show that the presence of water vapor in the sample does not affect the results of the Orsat analysis.

CHAPTER TWELVE

EQUILIBRIUM

12·1 THE GENERAL APPROACH

In this chapter we shall discuss the problem of predicting the configuration of systems in thermodynamic equilibrium. For example, the theory will permit us to predict the equilibrium composition of a mixture of chemicals in an isolated vessel, will give us an upper bound on the voltage output of a fuel cell, and will tell us how many phases of an alloy can exist together at any particular temperature and pressure. It is clear that the concept and theory of thermodynamic equilibrium have very wide-ranging applications that are particularly important to physical chemists, metallurgists, solid-state physicists, and many engineers.

The first and second laws provide the framework for the theory of thermodynamic equilibrium. In this theory the second law is used in a very quantitative manner. For isolated systems the equilibrium state is one of maximum entropy, and we have used this condition several times in the previous chapters. In this chapter we shall develop corresponding conditions for equilibrium of nonisolated systems with environments that maintain constant system temperature and pressure. The isolated system formed by the system under study and the environment will reach its maximum entropy when the system and environment are in equilibrium with one another. We shall show that in this case the *Gibbs function* of the *nonisolated* system is a *minimum*, and hence minimum Gibbs function gives the equilibrium state for a system exposed to an isothermal isobaric environment. Other similar criteria can be developed for systems in contact with other types of environments, using the first and second laws as the starting point.

In the first portion of the chapter we shall treat mixtures of nonreacting substances. This material culminates in the *Gibbs phase rule*, a consequence of the theory which permits one to predict the number of coexisting phases that may be present in such an equilibrium mixture. The remainder of the chapter is devoted to equilibrium in reacting mixtures, with particular emphasis on mixtures of perfect gases.

12·2 EQUILIBRIUM

Consider an isolated system consisting of a two-phase mixture, such as a gaseous water-vapor–nitrogen mixture in contact with liquid water containing nitrogen in solution. We seek the conditions of equilibrium between the two phases (see Fig. 12·1). Assuming that the allowable quantum states for the

FIG. 12·1   *A and B represent two phases*

two phases are independent, the entropy of the system will be the sum of the entropies of the two phases. We imagine isolating the system; the equilibrium state will be the one of maximum system entropy, selected from all possible states having the same total internal energy, volume, and mass of each component. We denote the entropy of the combined system by S_C and have

$$S_C = S_A(U_A, V_A, \mathfrak{N}_{1A}, \ldots, \mathfrak{N}_{nA}) + S_B(U_B, V_B, \mathfrak{N}_{1B}, \ldots, \mathfrak{N}_{nB})$$

The isolation constraints require

$$U_A + U_B = \text{constant}$$
$$V_A + V_B = \text{constant}$$
$$\mathfrak{N}_{iA} + \mathfrak{N}_{iB} = \text{constant}$$

Thus we are free to vary only $U_A, V_A, \mathfrak{N}_{1A}, \ldots, \mathfrak{N}_{nA}$ in seeking the maximum of S_C. The condition

$$\left(\frac{\partial S_C}{\partial U_A}\right)_{V_A, \mathfrak{N}_{1A}, \ldots, \mathfrak{N}_{nA}} = 0$$

leads directly to

$$\blacktriangleright \quad \frac{1}{T_A} = \frac{1}{T_B} \qquad T_A = T_B \tag{12·1}$$

The condition

$$\left(\frac{\partial S_C}{\partial V_A}\right)_{U_A, \mathfrak{N}_{1A}, \ldots, \mathfrak{N}_{nA}} = 0$$

requires that

$$\frac{P_A}{T_A} = \frac{P_B}{T_B}$$

and since the temperatures are equal,

▶ $\qquad P_A = P_B$ (12·2)

The condition

$$\left(\frac{\partial S_C}{\partial \mathfrak{N}_{iA}}\right)_{U_A, V_A, \mathfrak{N}_{1A}, \ldots, \mathfrak{N}_{(i-1)A}, \mathfrak{N}_{(i+1)A}, \ldots, \mathfrak{N}_{nA}} = 0$$

indicates that

$$\left(\frac{\hat{\mu}_i}{T}\right)_A = \left(\frac{\hat{\mu}_i}{T}\right)_B \qquad i = 1, 2, \ldots, n$$

But since the temperatures must also be equal, a necessary condition for equilibrium between the phases is

▶ $\qquad \hat{\mu}_{iA} = \hat{\mu}_{iB}$ (12·3)

These results may be extended to mixtures with more than two phases; necessary conditions for equilibrium are

The temperature of every phase must be the same.
The pressure of every phase must be the same.
The electrochemical potential of each component must have the same value in every phase.

Consider again the system of Fig. 12·1. Suppose that the two phases are in thermal and mechanical equilibrium, and that the electrochemical potentials of all but constituent i are equal in both phases. The entropy change of the combined system associated with any interaction will then be simply

$$dS_C = dS_A + dS_B = \left(\frac{\hat{\mu}_{iB}}{T} - \frac{\hat{\mu}_{iA}}{T}\right) d\mathfrak{N}_{iA}$$

where $d\mathfrak{N}_{iA}$ represents an infinitesimal number of moles of constituent i transferred from B to A. Since the combined system is isolated, the second law requires that $dS_C \geq 0$, and

$$(\hat{\mu}_{iB} - \hat{\mu}_{iA}) d\mathfrak{N}_{iA} \geq 0$$

The equality is associated with reversible transfer between the two phases, which can occur only if $\hat{\mu}_{iA} = \hat{\mu}_{iB}$. For the inequality to hold,

if $\hat{\mu}_{iB} > \hat{\mu}_{iA}$ $\qquad$ then $\qquad$ $d\mathfrak{N}_{iA} > 0$
$\quad$ $\hat{\mu}_{iB} < \hat{\mu}_{iA}$ $\qquad$ then $\qquad$ $d\mathfrak{N}_{iA} < 0$

We conclude that the electrochemical potential acts as a driving force for mass transfer. Any species will try to move from the phase having the higher electrochemical potential for that species to the phase having lower electrochemical potential. This fact forms the basis for predictions and analysis of the solubility or insolubility of one species in another. It is also useful in studying the distribution of free electrons between dissimilar metals in contact.

12·3 EVALUATION OF THE ELECTROCHEMICAL POTENTIAL

Consider a single phase. Increasing the mass of the phase and keeping the temperature, pressure, and component proportions unchanged will not change the energy, volume, or entropy per unit of mass of the phase. In other words, because a phase is homogeneous any sample taken from it will have the same intensive state. The condition may be expressed by

$$U(T, P, \lambda\mathfrak{N}_1, \ldots, \lambda\mathfrak{N}_n) = \lambda U(T, P, \mathfrak{N}_1, \ldots, \mathfrak{N}_n)$$
$$V(T, P, \lambda\mathfrak{N}_1, \ldots, \lambda\mathfrak{N}_n) = \lambda V(T, P, \mathfrak{N}_1, \ldots, \mathfrak{N}_n)$$
$$S(T, P, \lambda\mathfrak{N}_1, \ldots, \lambda\mathfrak{N}_n) = \lambda S(T, P, \mathfrak{N}_1, \ldots, \mathfrak{N}_n)$$

Here λ is any factor. Of particular interest in mixture thermodynamics is the Gibbs function,

$$\blacktriangleright \qquad G \equiv U + PV - TS \qquad (12\cdot4)$$

Because of the relations above, it also follows that the Gibbs function of a phase is such that

$$G(T, P, \lambda\mathfrak{N}_1, \ldots, \lambda\mathfrak{N}_n) = \lambda G(T, P, \mathfrak{N}_1, \ldots, \mathfrak{N}_n)$$

Differentiating with respect to λ,

$$\sum_i \frac{\partial G(T, P, \lambda\mathfrak{N}_1, \ldots)}{\partial(\lambda\mathfrak{N}_i)} \mathfrak{N}_i = G(T, P, \mathfrak{N}_1, \ldots, \mathfrak{N}_n)$$

This must hold for all values of λ; setting λ equal to unity,

$$\sum_i \mathfrak{N}_i \frac{\partial G(T, P, \mathfrak{N}_1, \ldots, \mathfrak{N}_n)}{\partial\mathfrak{N}_i} = G(T, P, \mathfrak{N}_1, \ldots, \mathfrak{N}_n) \qquad (12\cdot5)$$

We shall return to this result in a moment.

Taking the differential of the Gibbs function,

$$dG = dU + P\,dV + V\,dP - T\,dS - S\,dT$$

Now, the Gibbs equation for the mixture is (see Eq. 10·7)

$$T\,dS = dU + P\,dV - \sum_i \hat{\mu}_i\,d\mathfrak{N}_i$$

Upon combining we find

$$dG = V\,dP - S\,dT + \sum_i \hat{\mu}_i\,d\mathfrak{N}_i \qquad (12\cdot6)$$

We therefore recognize the electrochemical potentials as

$$\blacktriangleright \qquad \hat{\mu}_i = \left(\frac{\partial G}{\partial \mathfrak{N}_i}\right)_{P,T,\mathfrak{N}_1,\ldots,\mathfrak{N}_{i-1},\mathfrak{N}_{i+1},\ldots,\mathfrak{N}_n} \qquad (12\cdot7)$$

Equation $(12\cdot5)$ then simplifies to

$$\blacktriangleright \qquad G = \sum_i \hat{\mu}_i \mathfrak{N}_i$$

A particularly important case is that of the *pure phase*, containing one constituent. The above equation then yields

$$\blacktriangleright \qquad \hat{\mu} = \frac{G}{\mathfrak{N}} = \hat{g} \qquad (12\cdot8)$$

Hence, *the electrochemical potential for a pure phase is simply the Gibbs function of the phase.*

Let's illustrate these ideas by consideration of a mixture of H_2O liquid and vapor at 14.696 psia. The conditions for phase equilibrium are

$$T_f = T_g \qquad P_f = P_g \qquad \mu_f = \mu_g$$

We have tacitly used the first two throughout this text. Let's test the third. Since $\mu = g = h - Ts$ for each pure phase, from Table B·1B we find

$$\mu_f = 180.07 - 671.67 \times 0.3120 = -29.5 \text{ Btu/lbm}$$
$$\mu_g = 1150.4 - 671.67 \times 1.7566 = -29.5 \text{ Btu/lbm}$$

The electrochemical potentials of the two phases in equilibrium are indeed identical.

We now introduce a special conceptual system analogous to the TER and MER used in Chap. Seven. A *constituent reservoir* (CR) is conceived as a large region of constant volume which can be connected to a system under study by a rigid, semipermeable, diathermal membrane (Fig. 12·2). The membrane is conceived to be permeable only to one constituent, and hence the CR becomes a warehouse for a pure phase of that constituent. Energy transfer as heat across the membrane permits the CR to reach thermal equilibrium with a system. The CR is assumed to have no internal irreversibility, and to possess a uniform

FIG. 12·2 *Evaluating the electrochemical potential with the help of a constituent reservoir*

internal state. Since its volume is fixed, any entropy changes will be given by [see Eq. (10·7)]

$$dS_{CR} = \frac{dU_{CR}}{T} - \frac{\hat{\mu}_i}{T}\,d\mathfrak{N}_i \tag{12·9}$$

Consider now a single-phase mixture in contact with a CR containing a pure phase of component 1. The combined system is isolated (Fig. 12·2), and its equilibrium state will be that which maximizes its entropy, subject to the constraints that

$$U_M + U_{CR} = \text{constant}$$
$$V_M = \text{constant}$$
$$V_{CR} = \text{constant}$$
$$\mathfrak{N}_{iM} = \text{constant} \qquad i = 2, 3, \ldots, n$$
$$\mathfrak{N}_{1M} + \mathfrak{N}_{1CR} = \text{constant}$$

Here the subscript M denotes the mixture and CR denotes the reservoir. Because of the constraints, only U_M and $\mathfrak{N}_{1M}$ can be varied in seeking the maximum of S_C, the entropy of the combined system. Necessary conditions for equilibrium are therefore

$$\left(\frac{\partial S_C}{\partial U_M}\right)_{\mathfrak{N}_{1M}} = 0$$
$$\left(\frac{\partial S_C}{\partial \mathfrak{N}_{1M}}\right)_{U_M} = 0$$

The first of these leads to

$$\left[\left(\frac{\partial S}{\partial U}\right)_{V,\mathfrak{N}_1,\ldots,\mathfrak{N}_n}\right]_M = \left[\left(\frac{\partial S}{\partial U}\right)_{V,\mathfrak{N}}\right]_{CR}$$

which means that

$$T_M = T_{CR}$$

The second condition gives

$$\left[\left(\frac{\partial S}{\partial \mathfrak{N}_1}\right)_{U,V,\mathfrak{N}_2,\ldots,\mathfrak{N}_n}\right]_M = \left[\left(\frac{\partial S}{\partial \mathfrak{N}}\right)_{U,V}\right]_{CR}$$

Since $T_M = T_{CR}$, this requires

$$\hat{\mu}_{1M} = \hat{\mu}_{CR}$$

But the reservoir is a pure phase, so that $\hat{\mu}_{CR} = \hat{g}_{CR}$. This result may be shown to hold in general, and thus

$$\blacktriangleright \qquad \hat{\mu}_i = \hat{g}_i(T, P^*) \tag{12·10}$$

where P^* is the pressure that would exist in a pure phase of the ith component in contact with the mixture through a rigid diathermal membrane permeable only to the ith component. In principle this provides a means for measuring the electrochemical potential of every component in a mixture.

12·4 ELECTROCHEMICAL POTENTIALS IN A MIXTURE OF PERFECT GASES

We can obtain a simple expression for the electrochemical potential of a constituent in a mixture of perfect gases. The Gibbs function for the mixture is

$$
\begin{aligned}
G &\equiv U + PV - TS \\
&= \sum_i \mathfrak{N}_i \hat{u}_i + V \sum_i P_i - T \sum_i \mathfrak{N}_i \hat{s}_i = \sum_i \mathfrak{N}_i \hat{g}_i(T, P_i)
\end{aligned} \tag{12·11}
$$

In particular, for a two-constituent mixture,

$$
G = \mathfrak{N}_1 \hat{g}_1(T, P_1) + \mathfrak{N}_2 \hat{g}_2(T, P_2)
$$

Then, using Eq. (12·7),

$$
\begin{aligned}
\hat{\mu}_1 &= \left(\frac{\partial G}{\partial \mathfrak{N}_1}\right)_{T,P,\mathfrak{N}_2} \\
&= \hat{g}_1(T, P_1) + \left[\mathfrak{N}_1 \left(\frac{\partial \hat{g}_1}{\partial P_1}\right)_T \left(\frac{\partial P_1}{\partial \mathfrak{N}_1}\right)_{\mathfrak{N}_2,P,T} + \mathfrak{N}_2 \left(\frac{\partial \hat{g}_2}{\partial P_2}\right)_T \left(\frac{\partial P_2}{\partial \mathfrak{N}_1}\right)_{\mathfrak{N}_2,P,T} \right]
\end{aligned} \tag{12·12}
$$

The partial pressures are related to the mole fractions by Eq. (10·19)

$$
P_1 = P \frac{\mathfrak{N}_1}{\mathfrak{N}_1 + \mathfrak{N}_2} \qquad P_2 = P \frac{\mathfrak{N}_2}{\mathfrak{N}_1 + \mathfrak{N}_2}
$$

Hence

$$
\left(\frac{\partial P_1}{\partial \mathfrak{N}_1}\right)_{\mathfrak{N}_2,P} = \frac{P}{\mathfrak{N}_1 + \mathfrak{N}_2} - \frac{P\mathfrak{N}_1}{(\mathfrak{N}_1 + \mathfrak{N}_2)^2} = \frac{\mathfrak{N}_2 P}{(\mathfrak{N}_1 + \mathfrak{N}_2)^2}
$$

$$
\left(\frac{\partial P_2}{\partial \mathfrak{N}_1}\right)_{\mathfrak{N}_2,P} = -\frac{P\mathfrak{N}_2}{(\mathfrak{N}_1 + \mathfrak{N}_2)^2}
$$

From Eqs. (8·49a) and (8·3) it follows that

$$
\left(\frac{\partial \hat{g}_1}{\partial P_1}\right)_T = \frac{\Re T}{P_1} \qquad \left(\frac{\partial \hat{g}_2}{\partial P_2}\right)_T = \frac{\Re T}{P_2}
$$

Thus the term within brackets in Eq. (12·12) is

$$
\mathfrak{N}_1 \frac{\Re T}{P_1} \left(\frac{\mathfrak{N}_2 P}{\mathfrak{N}^2}\right) - \mathfrak{N}_2 \frac{\Re T}{P_2} \left(\frac{\mathfrak{N}_2 P}{\mathfrak{N}^2}\right) = \Re T \frac{\mathfrak{N}_2}{\mathfrak{N}} \left(\frac{\mathfrak{N}_1}{\mathfrak{N}} \frac{P}{P_1} - \frac{\mathfrak{N}_2}{\mathfrak{N}} \frac{P}{P_2}\right)
$$

and vanishes by Eq. (10·19); hence Eq. (12·12) reduces to

$$
\hat{\mu}_1 = \hat{g}_1(T, P_1)
$$

Thus, *the molal electrochemical potential of a constituent is equal to its molal Gibbs function, evaluated at the mixture temperature and its partial pressure.* This result may be shown to be true for every constituent in a mixture of perfect gases,

$$\blacktriangleright \qquad \hat{\mu}_i = \hat{g}_i(T, P_i) \qquad\qquad \tag{12·13}$$

An alternative expression can be obtained using Eq. (8·18). We have

$$\hat{\mu}_i = \hat{g} = \hat{h}(T) - T\hat{s}(T, P_i)$$

Now, from Eq. (8·18)

$$\hat{s}(T, P_i) = \hat{s}(T, P) - \Re \ln \frac{P_i}{P}$$

so,

$$\hat{\mu}_i = \hat{h}(T) - T\hat{s}(T, P) + \Re T \ln \frac{P_i}{P}$$

Hence, in a mixture of perfect gases,

$$\hat{\mu}_i = \hat{g}_i(T, P) + \Re T \ln \chi_i \tag{12·14}$$

This latter form is particularly convenient in analysis of reacting perfect-gas mixtures.

As an example of calculating the chemical potential of a perfect gas, consider 1 lbmole of oxygen and 3.76 lbmoles of nitrogen at a total pressure of 20 psia at 600°R. To calculate the electrochemical potential of the O_2, we start with

$$\hat{\mu}_{O_2} = \hat{g}_{O_2}(T, P) + \Re T \ln \chi_{O_2}$$

Now

$$\chi_{O_2} = \frac{1}{4.76} = 0.21$$

$$\hat{g}_{O_2} = \hat{h}_{O_2} - T\hat{s}_{O_2}$$

but

$$\hat{s}_{O_2} = \hat{\phi}_{O_2} - \Re \ln \frac{P}{P_0}$$

where

$$P_0 = 1 \text{ atm}$$

Then, using data from Table B·13,

$$\hat{g}_{O_2}(T,P) = 443.2 - 600 \times \left(49.762 - 1.986 \ln \frac{20}{14.7} \right)$$

$$= -29{,}048 \text{ Btu/lbmole}$$

and

$$\hat{\mu}_{O_2} = -29{,}048 + (1.986)(600) \ln (0.21)$$

$$= -30{,}903 \text{ Btu/lbmole}$$

12·5 THE GIBBS PHASE RULE

Since the molal Gibbs function is an intensive property, the electrochemical potential must also be intensive (this can be seen from the definition). Consequently it depends on the proportions of the mixture but not on the amounts of each component present.   Within a given phase the temperature and pressure may be independently varied (by heating and compression), and in addition, the proportions within the phase may be varied by altering the mole fractions. However, the mole fractions must add up to unity, and therefore only $n - 1$ of these are independently variable. Thus, within a given phase we may think of the electrochemical potential as being uniquely determined by specifications of T, P, and all but one of the mole fractions,

$$\hat{\mu}_i = \hat{\mu}_i(T, P, \chi_1, \chi_2, \ldots, \chi_{n-1})$$

With this functional relation, and with the condition that the electrochemical potentials of a component must have the same value in all coexisting phases, we can now establish an important rule governing the number of possible coexisting phases.

Consider a mixture of phases of a single component. The electrochemical potential of each phase is a function of temperature and pressure. We denote these by

$$\hat{\mu}'(T, P), \hat{\mu}''(T, P), \hat{\mu}'''(T, P), \ldots$$

Henceforth the primes refer to phases. Now, suppose we have an equilibrium mixture of two phases of the substance. Then, from the condition of equilibrium,

$$\hat{\mu}'(T, P) = \hat{\mu}''(T, P)$$

This condition provides a relation between T and P which must be satisfied for all equilibrium mixture states that contain two phases. It may be rewritten functionally as

$$T = T(P)$$

showing that the temperature and pressure of a mixture of two phases of a single substance are not independently variable.

Suppose the mixture is in an equilibrium state with three phases of the same substance present. The equilibrium condition is then

$$\hat{\mu}'(T, P) = \hat{\mu}''(T, P) = \hat{\mu}'''(T, P)$$

This amounts to two equations in the variables T and P, which suffice to determine the unique value of T and P at which the three phases can coexist. Thus, while it is possible to have a two-phase mixture of a substance over a range of temperatures, a mixture of three specified phases can exist only at a single temperature and pressure, called the *triple point*. A substance that can exist

FIG. 12·3 *Phase diagram for H_2O. The shaded portions are different solid phases*

in several phases may have several triple points; six are evident in the phase diagram for water of Fig. 12·3.

While a single substance can exist in many phases, only three phases can coexist in equilibrium. Coexistence of four phases would require that three conditions of equilibrium in two variables (P and T) be satisfied, and no solution would be possible in general.

We might restate these observations as follows: given a mixture of a single component, the number of properties from the set (T, P) which may be independently fixed is equal to 3 minus the number of phases. This is a special case of the Gibbs phase rule.

Consider now a mixture of n components in p phases. For each component there will be a total of $p - 1$ equations of equilibrium of the form

$$\hat{\mu}_i'(T, P, \chi_1', \ldots, \chi_{n-1}') = \hat{\mu}_i''(T, P, \chi_1'', \ldots, \chi_{n-1}'')$$

Thus there will be a total of $n(p - 1)$ conditions of equilibrium which must be satisfied. The state of each phase is described by its temperature, pressure, and $n - 1$ mole fractions. The set of possible intensive variables which might conceivably be varied is therefore

$$\blacktriangleright \qquad (T, P, \chi_1', \chi_2', \ldots, \chi_{n-1}', \chi_1'', \ldots, \chi_{n-1}^p)$$

and is exactly $p(n - 1) + 2$ in number. But because of the $n(p - 1)$ equilibrium conditions, the number of these which are freely variable is only

$$f = p(n - 1) + 2 - n(p - 1)$$

or

$$\blacktriangleright \qquad f = n - p + 2 \qquad\qquad\qquad\qquad\qquad (12·15)$$

Here f denotes the number of independently variable intensive properties *from the list above*. This result is known as the *Gibbs phase rule*.

For the single-component mixture discussed earlier, we have the following:

$f = 2$ for one phase
$f = 1$ for two phases
$f = 0$ for three phases
No more than three phases permitted

It should be pointed out that the number of independently variable extensive properties from the set

$$(U, V, \mathfrak{N}_1, \ldots, \mathfrak{N}_n)$$

is always $n + 2$. The Gibbs rule does *not* pertain to this set, but rather to the set of *intensive* properties listed above.

To illustrate application of the phase rule, consider a two-component mixture. The largest number of coexisting phases possible is four ($n = 2$, $p = 4$, $f = 0$). This will occur only at particular values of pressure, temperature, and phase composition. At a given pressure three phases may coexist in states for which the following conditions are satisfied:

$$\hat{\mu}_1'(T, P, \chi_1') = \hat{\mu}_1''(T, P, \chi_1'') = \hat{\mu}_1'''(T, P, \chi_1''')$$
$$\hat{\mu}_2'(T, P, \chi_1') = \hat{\mu}_2''(T, P, \chi_1'') = \hat{\mu}_2'''(T, P, \chi_1''')$$

This set of four independent equations contains the five variables T, P, χ_1', χ_1'', χ_1''', and in principle could be reduced to the form

$$T = T(P)$$

Thus at a given pressure three phases could coexist only at one temperature and mixture composition ($n = 2$, $p = 3$, $f = 1$). With two phases ($n = 2$, $p = 2$, $f = 2$) the equilibrium conditions are functionally equivalent to

$$T = T(P, \chi_1')$$

Hence the temperature at which two phases can coexist is to be determined by pressure and the mole fraction of one component in one of the phases. In a single-phase mixture ($n = 2$, $p = 1$, $f = 3$) the temperature, pressure, and one mole fraction can be arbitrarily prescribed.

A typical phase diagram for a liquid-vapor binary† mixture is shown in Fig. 12·4. The graph is made on a plane of constant pressure from the three-dimensional T-P-χ_1 space. If a liquid mixture originally at A is heated, evaporation will occur when state B is reached. The first vapor to escape will have the composition of D. A mixture at state C would actually contain liquid at state B and vapor at state D, much as a two-phase single-component mixture contains saturated liquid and saturated vapor.

† Having two components.

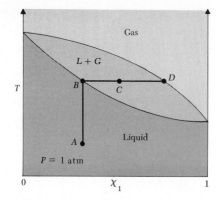

FIG. 12·4 *Typical phase diagram for a liquid-vapor binary mixture*

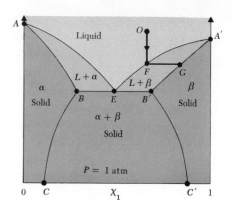

FIG. 12·5 *Typical phase diagram for a solid-liquid binary mixture*

Phase diagrams for solid-liquid binary solutions often appear as shown in Fig. 12·5. Again only a single constant-pressure plane is shown. Two solid phases, labeled α and β, exist. The curves ABC and $A'B'C'$ are called *solidus* curves, and the curve AEA' is the *liquidus* curve. Suppose we start cooling a liquid having the composition of state 0. When F is reached, the β-phase solid will start to precipitate with the composition G. The only composition for which the condensed solid would have the identical composition as the liquid is the *eutectic* solution (E).

The line BEB' represents the locus of three phase states. The Gibbs phase rule requires that all such states have a common temperature for a given pressure, and consequently the line is an isotherm.

It is difficult to sketch the three-dimensional T-P-χ_1 phase space. If we could, the eutectic point would trace out a curved line, and at a particular pressure a vapor phase would be encountered. The phase rule tells us that there would be a unique point in the phase space at which this would occur. No more than four coexisting phases could ever be found.

Phase diagrams for solid-liquid systems may be familiar from courses dealing with metallurgy. If so, you may recall that a eutectic solution makes good alloy castings, because it freezes very uniformly. You probably also wondered why certain multiple-phase lines were isotherms, while others were not. Now it can be seen that thermodynamics provides a sound theoretical basis for these things in the phase rule.

12·6 ALTERATION OF THE SATURATED-VAPOR PRESSURE BY AN INERT GAS

As a further application of the thermodynamic theory of equilibrium, consider a vessel containing a liquid, above which is a mixture of its vapor

FIG. 12·6 *The system*

and an inert gas (see Fig. 12·6). We treat the inert gas and vapor as a mixture of independent substances.   Liquid will evaporate until the gas space is saturated; we wish to learn how much the presence of the inert gas alters the saturated-vapor pressure from that which would be obtained without the inert component.

The conditions of equilibrium between phases require that the chemical potential of each component have the same value in all phases. The liquid constitutes one phase and the gas mixture the other. We assume that no inert gas is present in the liquid, so it constitutes a pure phase. The electrochemical potential of the pure liquid phase [see Eq. (12·8)] is

$$\hat{\mu}_f = \hat{g}_f(T,P)$$

where $\hat{g}_f(T,P)$ denotes the Gibbs function of the liquid as a function of the temperature T and total pressure P. Under our perfect-gas idealizations the electrochemical potential of the vapor in the mixture [see Eq. (12·13)] is

$$\hat{\mu}_g = \hat{g}_g(T,P_g)$$

where $\hat{g}_g(T,P_g)$ denotes the molal Gibbs function of the vapor as a function of T and the vapor pressure P_g. Imagine increasing the amount of the inert gas present, keeping the temperature constant. Since the electrochemical potentials $\hat{\mu}_f$ and $\hat{\mu}_g$ remain equal, they must change in the same amount, and we have

$$\left(\frac{\partial \hat{g}_f}{\partial P}\right)_T dP = \left(\frac{\partial \hat{g}_g}{\partial P_g}\right)_T dP_g$$

In Chap. Eight we showed [Eq. 8·49a)] that

$$\left(\frac{\partial g}{\partial P}\right)_T = v(P,T)$$

Therefore the change in the partial pressure of the vapor is related to the change in the total (liquid) pressure by

$$dP_g = \frac{\hat{v}_f(P,T)}{\hat{v}_g(P_g,T)} dP$$

If the molal volume of the vapor is very large compared to that of the liquid, such as is the case with water at room temperatures, the vapor-pressure change will be very small compared to the change in the total pressure, and in many engineering calculations it is satisfactory to neglect alteration of the vapor pressure by the presence of an inert gas.

If we idealize that the specific volume of the liquid is constant and bring in the perfect-gas equation of state to evaluate $\hat{v}_g$, we obtain

$$\mathcal{R}T \frac{dP_g}{P_g} = \hat{v}_f \, dP$$

Integrating between two configurations 1 and 2,

$$\mathcal{R}T \ln \frac{P_{g2}}{P_{g1}} = \hat{v}_f \cdot (P_2 - P_1)$$

or

$$\frac{P_{g2}}{P_{g1}} = \exp\left[\frac{\hat{v}_f(P_2 - P_1)}{\mathcal{R}T}\right]$$

For example, consider starting with a vessel containing nothing but water and water vapor at 60°F. The initial vapor pressure will be equal to the saturation pressure of pure H_2O, which we find from Table B·1A as 0.256 psia. The liquid specific volume is 0.016 ft³/lbm, and hence $v_f = 0.016 \times 18.016 = 0.288$ ft³/lbmole. Imagine adding enough inert gas, such as air, to bring the total pressure up to 1 atm, cooling as necessary to keep the temperature constant. The final water-vapor pressure P_{g2} will be given by

$$\frac{P_{g2}}{P_{g1}} = \exp\left[\frac{0.288 \times (14.7 - 0.26) \times 144}{1545 \times 520}\right] = e^{0.00075} = 1.00075$$

Thus the change in saturation pressure produced by the presence of the inert gas is very small for air–water-vapor mixtures at 1 atm and may be neglected in engineering calculations. This will be true whenever $\hat{v}_f/\hat{v}_g \ll 1$. However, if $\hat{v}_f$ is an appreciable fraction of $\hat{v}_g$, the presence of an inert constituent in the gas phase can markedly influence the saturation pressure.

12·7 GENERAL CONDITIONS FOR CHEMICAL EQUILIBRIUM OF A MIXTURE

An extremely important aspect of the theory of chemical reactions is the determination of the equilibrium composition of a mixture of chemically reactive constituents. In this section we derive some general conditions for chemical equilibrium from basic thermodynamic considerations. These conditions will be expressed in terms of thermodynamic properties of the mixture; however, a system that is not in equilibrium is not in a thermodynamic state, and there is some difficulty in ascribing properties such as temperature and entropy in the absence of equilibrium. A similar problem arose when we discussed equilibrium between phases of a mixture. There we assumed that each phase was separately in a thermodynamic equilibrium state, though the combined system of phases was not. The same approach is adopted here. To discuss the properties of a mixture not in chemical equilibrium, that is, not having the composition of the equilibrium mixture, we imagine shutting off the reaction, and evaluate the properties of the mixture as if it were a mixture of nonreacting gases in a thermodynamic equilibrium state. By this procedure we shall be able to establish the conditions of chemical equilibrium, and thereby the composition in the true equilibrium state.

Restricting our considerations to a mixture of simple compressible substances, we apply the first and second laws of thermodynamics to the mixture, which we assume to be at temperature T and pressure P. The energy balance gives

$$dU = dQ + dW$$

and the entropy production is

$$d\mathcal{P}_s = dS - \frac{dQ}{T} \geq 0$$

Since the pressure is uniform,

$$dW = -P\,dV$$

Combining the above three equations, we obtain

$$T\,d\mathcal{P}_s = T\,dS - dU - P\,dV \geq 0 \tag{12.16}$$

Equation 12.16 tells us that any reaction that takes place must be such as to produce entropy. In particular, a reaction taking place in an insulated constant-volume vessel, where $dU = 0$ and $dV = 0$, must be such that

▶ $$dS \geq 0 \tag{12.17}$$

If we want to determine the equilibrium composition of a mixture reacting under these conditions, we need only determine the mixture entropy as a function of composition; the equilibrium composition for an isolated reaction is then the one which maximizes the entropy (Fig. 12.7).

We are more often interested in finding equilibrium compositions under other conditions. The condition for equilibrium in a reaction taking place at constant volume and temperature can be expressed in terms of the *Helmholtz*

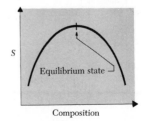

FIG. 12·7 *Equilibrium at constant volume and energy*

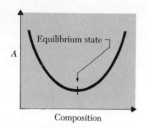

FIG. 12·8 *Equilibrium at constant volume and temperature*

function,

▶ $A \equiv U - TS$ (12·18)

The differential of the Helmholtz function is

$dA = dU - T\,dS - S\,dT$

Upon combination with Eq. (12·16) we obtain

▶ $dA + S\,dT + P\,dV \leq 0$ (12·19)

Hence, a reaction occurring at constant temperature and volume must be such as to decrease the Helmholtz function. The equilibrium composition of a mixture reacting in an isothermal constant-volume vessel is therefore the one having the least value of the Helmholtz function for that volume and temperature (Fig. 12·8).

The most interesting situation is the reaction at constant pressure and temperature. To find the conditions for equilibrium under these conditions we need to bring in a function whose differential will involve the terms $T\,dS - dU - P\,dV$ in such a way as to cancel them out of Eq. (12·16) and replace them by differentials of pressure and temperature (which are then zero). The Gibbs function fills this need,

$G \equiv U + PV - TS$ (12·20)

Differentiating,

$dG = dU + P\,dV + V\,dP - T\,dS - S\,dT$

Combining with Eq. (12·16), we find

▶ $dG - V\,dP + S\,dT \leq 0$ (12·21)

FIG. 12·9 *Equilibrium at constant pressure and temperature*

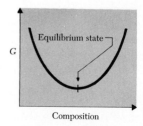

Therefore, any reaction proceeding at constant temperature and pressure will be such that the Gibbs function of the mixture will continually decrease, until it reaches its minimum value at the final, equilibrium composition (Fig. 12·9).

The Gibbs function is instrumental in allowing us to determine the equilibrium composition of any reactive mixture of known pressure and temperature, regardless of whether or not these were kept constant during all of the reaction. Since the electrochemical potential relates the change in the Gibbs function of a mixture (considered as nonreacting) to changes in the amounts of its constituents [see Eq. (12·7)], it too is very important in chemical thermodynamics.

12·8 DEGREES OF REACTION FREEDOM:
THE SIMPLE REACTIVE MIXTURE

Any reaction that takes place in a reactive mixture will be limited by the fact that atoms are conserved (that is, by the chemical equation). For example, consider the mixture CH_4, O_2, H_2O, CO, and CO_2. If no material is added to the mixture, any change in the composition must result from chemical reaction. Denoting a change in mole number by $d\mathfrak{N}$, the constraining conditions are,† for conservation of C,

$$d\mathfrak{N}_{CH_4} + d\mathfrak{N}_{CO} + d\mathfrak{N}_{CO_2} = 0 \qquad (12\cdot22a)$$

for conservation of O,

$$2d\mathfrak{N}_{O_2} + d\mathfrak{N}_{H_2O} + d\mathfrak{N}_{CO} + 2d\mathfrak{N}_{CO_2} = 0 \qquad (12\cdot22b)$$

and for conservation of H,

$$4d\mathfrak{N}_{CH_4} + 2d\mathfrak{N}_{H_2O} = 0 \qquad (12\cdot22c)$$

We have three constraints and five constituents. Thus only two *degrees of reaction freedom* exist for the mixture. For instance, we could consider CH_4 and CO as the two independent components; then, from Eqs. (12·22), we find

$$
\begin{aligned}
d\mathfrak{N}_{H_2O} &= -2d\mathfrak{N}_{CH_4} & (12\cdot23a) \\
d\mathfrak{N}_{CO_2} &= -d\mathfrak{N}_{CH_4} - d\mathfrak{N}_{CO} & (12\cdot23b) \\
d\mathfrak{N}_{O_2} &= \tfrac{1}{2}d\mathfrak{N}_{CO} + 2d\mathfrak{N}_{CH_4} & (12\cdot23c)
\end{aligned}
$$

It is evident that the number of degrees of reaction freedom of a mixture is equal to the number of possible compounds minus the number of kinds of atoms represented. We shall call a mixture having one degree of reaction freedom a *simple reactive mixture*. For example, the mixture CH_4, O_2, H_2O, and CO_2 is a simple reactive mixture.

† As in calculus, $d\mathfrak{N}$ always denotes an infinitesimal *increase* in $\mathfrak{N}$. Each mole of CH_4 contains the same number of carbon atoms as one mole of CO, and twice as many hydrogen atoms as one mole of H_2O.

12·9 EQUATIONS OF REACTION EQUILIBRIUM

Consider a simple reactive mixture having a chemical equation of the form

▶ $\qquad \nu_1 C_1 + \nu_2 C_2 \leftrightarrows \nu_3 C_3 + \nu_4 C_4$ $\hfill$ (12·24)

where $C_1, \ldots, C_4$ denote the chemical constituents, and $\nu_1, \ldots, \nu_4$ are the stoichiometric coefficients. From Eq. (12·7) it follows that the difference in the Gibbs function of the mixture (considered as nonreacting) between any two states having the same temperature and pressure, but infinitesimally different compositions, is

$$dG_{T,P} = \hat{\mu}_1 \, d\mathfrak{N}_1 + \hat{\mu}_2 \, d\mathfrak{N}_2 + \hat{\mu}_3 \, d\mathfrak{N}_3 + \hat{\mu}_4 \, d\mathfrak{N}_4 \qquad (12·25)$$

However, in our reacting mixture the changes in mole numbers are related through the chemical equation, and

$$d\mathfrak{N}_2 = \frac{\nu_2}{\nu_1} \, d\mathfrak{N}_1 \qquad (12·26a)$$

$$d\mathfrak{N}_3 = -\frac{\nu_3}{\nu_1} \, d\mathfrak{N}_1 \qquad (12·26b)$$

$$d\mathfrak{N}_4 = -\frac{\nu_4}{\nu_1} \, d\mathfrak{N}_1 \qquad (12·26c)$$

From Eqs. (12·25) and (12·26), we see that for any reaction at constant temperature and pressure, since G must decrease,

▶ $\qquad (\hat{\mu}_1 \nu_1 + \hat{\mu}_2 \nu_2 - \hat{\mu}_3 \nu_3 - \hat{\mu}_4 \nu_4) \, d\mathfrak{N}_1 \leq 0$

It then follows that

If

$\hat{\mu}_1 \nu_1 + \hat{\mu}_2 \nu_2 > \hat{\mu}_3 \nu_3 + \hat{\mu}_4 \nu_4$

then $d\mathfrak{N}_1 < 0$ and the reaction proceeds to the right, and if

$\hat{\mu}_1 \nu_1 + \hat{\mu}_2 \nu_2 < \hat{\mu}_3 \nu_3 + \hat{\mu}_4 \nu_4$

then $d\mathfrak{N}_1 > 0$ and the reaction proceeds to the left.

The condition of chemical equilibrium for a simple reactive mixture is therefore

▶ $\qquad \hat{\mu}_1 \nu_1 + \hat{\mu}_2 \nu_2 = \hat{\mu}_3 \nu_3 + \hat{\mu}_4 \nu_4 \hfill$ (12·27)

This is called the *equation of reaction equilibrium;* it is a relation among the intensive properties of the products and reactants. We see that in order to determine the composition of a mixture after chemical equilibrium has been attained we must know the electrochemical potentials as functions of temperature, pressure, and the mole fractions.

The conditions for equilibrium of more complex mixtures are obtained in a similar manner. For example, for the first mixture considered in the previous section, CH_4, O_2, H_2O, CO, and CO_2, the change in the Gibbs function for any infinitesimal reaction at constant temperature and pressure would be

$$dG_{T,P} = \hat{\mu}_{CH_4} \, d\mathfrak{N}_{CH_4} + \hat{\mu}_{O_2} \, d\mathfrak{N}_{O_2} + \hat{\mu}_{H_2O} \, d\mathfrak{N}_{H_2O} + \hat{\mu}_{CO} \, d\mathfrak{N}_{CO} + \hat{\mu}_{CO_2} \, d\mathfrak{N}_{CO_2}$$

Using the constraining conditions, Eqs. (12·23), we find

$$dG_{T,P} = (\hat{\mu}_{CH_4} + 2\hat{\mu}_{O_2} - 2\hat{\mu}_{H_2O} - \hat{\mu}_{CO_2}) \, d\mathfrak{N}_{CH_4}$$
$$+ (\tfrac{1}{2}\hat{\mu}_{O_2} + \hat{\mu}_{CO} - \hat{\mu}_{CO_2}) \, d\mathfrak{N}_{CO}$$

At equilibrium the Gibbs function must be a minimum with respect to each and every independent variation of the mixture composition. In other words, dG must be zero for any $d\mathfrak{N}_{CH_4}$ and any $d\mathfrak{N}_{CO}$. This requires the *two* equations of reaction equilibrium,

$$\hat{\mu}_{CH_4} + 2\hat{\mu}_{O_2} = 2\hat{\mu}_{H_2O} + \hat{\mu}_{CO_2} \qquad (12\cdot28a)$$
$$\hat{\mu}_{CO_2} = \tfrac{1}{2}\hat{\mu}_{O_2} + \hat{\mu}_{CO} \qquad (12\cdot28b)$$

These equations can be directly associated with the two chemical equations

$$CH_4 + 2O_2 \rightleftarrows 2H_2O + CO_2 \qquad (12\cdot29a)$$
$$CO_2 \rightleftarrows \tfrac{1}{2}O_2 + CO \qquad (12\cdot29b)$$

In general, one equation of reaction equilibrium will be obtained for each degree of reaction freedom. The coefficients of the electrochemical potentials for each equation of reaction equilibrium will be identical with the coefficients of the constituent in the associated simple chemical equation. It should be mentioned that the job of determining what constituents to put in the mixture list is not a simple one and generally requires considerable experience.

12·10 REACTIONS IN PERFECT-GAS MIXTURES

The equation of reaction equilibrium provides the means for determining equilibrium composition of reacting perfect-gas mixtures. Previously we found that the electrochemical potential of one constituent of a perfect-gas mixture is given by

$$\hat{\mu}_i = \hat{g}_i(T, P) + \mathfrak{R}T \ln \chi_i \qquad (12\cdot30)$$

Since the equation of reaction equilibrium will involve the Gibbs functions of the constituents, it is convenient to define the Gibbs-function change for a complete unit reaction ΔG_r

$$\blacktriangleright \qquad \Delta G_r = \sum_{\text{prod}} \nu_i \hat{g}_i - \sum_{\text{react}} \nu_i \hat{g}_i \qquad (12\cdot31)$$

For the special reaction of Eq. (12.27),

$$\Delta G_r \equiv \nu_3 \hat{g}_3(T, P) + \nu_4 \hat{g}_4(T, P) - \nu_1 \hat{g}_1(T, P) - \nu_2 \hat{g}_2(T, P) \qquad (12\cdot32)$$

Combining Eqs. (12·27), (12·30), and (12·31), we have

$$\Delta G_r + \Re T \ln \frac{\chi_3^{\nu_3}\chi_4^{\nu_4}}{\chi_1^{\nu_1}\chi_2^{\nu_2}} = 0 \tag{12·33}$$

If ΔG_r is known, this equation plus equations indicating the relative abundances of the elements in the mixture may be solved simultaneously to obtain the constituent mole fractions in the equilibrium mixture.

The value of ΔG_r will depend on both temperature and pressure. However, the pressure effect is easily separated. Denoting P_0 as an arbitrarily chosen reference pressure, it follows from Eq. (8·18) and the definition of the Gibbs function that

$$\bar{g}(T, P) = \bar{g}(T, P_0) + \Re T \ln \frac{P}{P_0} \tag{12·34}$$

Hence, substituting into Eq. (12·32),

$$\Delta G_r(T, P) = \Delta G_r(T, P_0) + \Re T \ln \left(\frac{P}{P_0}\right)^{\nu_3 + \nu_4 - \nu_1 - \nu_2}$$

Note that $\Delta G_r(T, P_0)$ is a function only of T for a selected reference pressure. Equation (12·33) then may be written as

$$\left(\frac{\chi_3^{\nu_3}\chi_4^{\nu_4}}{\chi_1^{\nu_1}\chi_2^{\nu_2}}\right)\left(\frac{P}{P_0}\right)^{\nu_3 + \nu_4 - \nu_1 - \nu_2} = \exp\left[\frac{-\Delta G_r(T, P_0)}{\Re T}\right]$$

Since the right-hand side is a function only of temperature, the left-hand side is independent of pressure. We define the *equilibrium constant* for the reaction by

$$\blacktriangleright \quad K(T) \equiv \left(\frac{\chi_3^{\nu_3}\chi_4^{\nu_4}}{\chi_1^{\nu_1}\chi_2^{\nu_2}}\right)\left(\frac{P}{P_0}\right)^{\nu_3 + \nu_4 - \nu_1 - \nu_2} \tag{12·35}$$

Note that the equilibrium constant is a dimensionless property of the equilibrium mixture and is a function only of the mixture temperature.†

The term ΔG_r is sometimes called the *free-energy change* for the reaction. The reference pressure P_0 is normally taken as 1 atm; values of ΔG_r (298°K, 1 atm) are tabulated in handbooks under the name "standard free-energy change" for the reaction. Note that

$$\blacktriangleright \quad K(T) = \exp\left[\frac{-\Delta G_r(T, P_0)}{\Re T}\right] \tag{12·36}$$

† It does, however, depend on the choice of P_0. In other texts $K(T)$ is normally defined as

$$\frac{\chi_3^{\nu_3}\chi_4^{\nu_4}}{\chi_1^{\nu_1}\chi_2^{\nu_2}} P^{\nu_3 + \nu_4 - \nu_1 - \nu_2}$$

which gives it the dimensions of pressure to the $\nu_3 + \nu_4 - \nu_1 - \nu_2$ power. Since tabulations in the literature always employ P in atmospheres, the numerical values of these equilibrium constants will agree with Eq. (12·35) for $P_0 = 1$ atm.

The equilibrium constant can be calculated if ΔG_r is known. Values of K for several reactions are given in Table B·14 in the form $\log_{10} K$. Equation (12·35) is often called the *law of mass action;* it is not a law in the sense of the first and second laws of thermodynamics, but is merely a definition of the equilibrium constant.

The equilibrium composition of a given simple reactive mixture of perfect gases can be determined from the equilibrium constant. Perfect-gas mixtures with more degrees of reaction freedom require one additional equilibrium constant for each additional degree of freedom.

Two other quantities appearing in the literature on chemical thermodynamics are the enthalpy and entropy changes for a complete unit reaction,

▶ $\qquad \Delta H_r \equiv \nu_3 \hat{h}_3 + \nu_4 \hat{h}_4 - \nu_1 \hat{h}_1 - \nu_2 \hat{h}_2$

▶ $\qquad \Delta S_r \equiv \nu_3 \hat{s}_3 + \nu_4 \hat{s}_4 - \nu_1 \hat{s}_1 - \nu_2 \hat{s}_2$

Note that ΔG_r may be calculated as:

$$\Delta G_r = \Delta H_r - T \, \Delta S_r$$

For a mixture of perfect gases ΔH_r will depend only on temperature, since the enthalpies are functions only of temperature. However, ΔS_r will depend on both temperature and pressure.

12·11   CALCULATION EXAMPLES

Equilibrium constant calculation. Consider the reaction $CO_2 \rightleftarrows CO + \frac{1}{2}O_2$ at 1000°R. We must first calculate ΔG_r, using Eq. (12·31), and then we can calculate K (1000°R) from Eq. (12·36). Now, by definition

$$\hat{g} = \hat{h} - T\hat{s}$$

Using molal enthalpy and entropy data from Table B·13, at 1000°R, 1 atm

$\qquad \hat{g}_{O_2} = 3362.4 - 1000 \times 53.477 = -50,115 \text{ Btu/lbmole}$

$\qquad \hat{g}_{CO} = -44,254.3 - 1000 \times 51.646 = -95,900 \text{ Btu/lbmole}$

$\qquad \hat{g}_{CO_2} = -164,531 - 1000 \times 57.212 = -221,743 \text{ Btu/lbmole}$

So

$\qquad \Delta G_r = \hat{g}_{CO} + \frac{1}{2}\hat{g}_{O_2} - \hat{g}_{CO_2}$

$\qquad\qquad = -95,900 + \frac{1}{2} \times (-50,115) - (-221,743)$

$\qquad\qquad = +100,786 \text{ Btu/lbmole}$

Then,

$\qquad \ln K = \dfrac{-100,786}{1.986 \times 1000} = -50.6$

$\qquad \log_{10} K = \dfrac{1}{2.30} \ln K = \dfrac{-50.6}{2.30} = -22.0$

Note this agrees well with the value interpolated from Table B·14.

Equilibrium composition. As a further example, let us determine the equilibrium composition of a mixture of CO, CO_2, and O_2 at 3000°K and 10 psia. We suppose that the mixture contains one carbon atom for every five oxygen atoms. The chemical equation is

$$CO_2 \rightleftarrows CO + \tfrac{1}{2}O_2 \tag{12·37}$$

so the equilibrium constant is

$$K(T) = \frac{\chi_{CO}\chi_{O_2}^{\frac{1}{2}}}{\chi_{CO_2}} \left(\frac{P}{P_0}\right)^{1+\frac{1}{2}-1}$$

From Table B·14 at 3000°K

$$\log_{10} K = -0.469 \qquad K = 0.340$$

Then Eq. (12·35) becomes

$$\frac{\chi_{CO}\chi_{O_2}^{\frac{1}{2}}}{\chi_{CO_2}} = 0.340 \times \left(\frac{10}{14.7}\right)^{-\frac{1}{2}} = 0.412 \tag{12·38a}$$

The sum of the mole fractions must be unity,

$$\chi_{CO} + \chi_{O_2} + \chi_{CO_2} = 1 \tag{12·38b}$$

A third condition is given by the fact that one carbon atom is present for every five oxygen atoms,

$$\frac{\chi_{CO_2} + \chi_{CO}}{2\chi_{CO_2} + \chi_{CO} + 2\chi_{O_2}} = \frac{1}{5} \tag{12·38c}$$

Equations (12·38) form a set of three simultaneous equations for the three unknown mole fractions. Their solution must be obtained by some numerical scheme; we find

$$\chi_{CO} = 0.128$$
$$\chi_{O_2} = 0.625$$
$$\chi_{CO_2} = 0.247$$

This gives the equilibrium composition of a mixture of CO, CO_2, and O_2 at 3000°K and 10 psia.

Effect of pressure. Let us redo the previous example but at a pressure of 30 psia. Since $K = K(T)$ the equilibrium constant has the same value as before. Applying Eq. (12·35), we have

$$\frac{\chi_{CO}\chi_{O_2}^{\frac{1}{2}}}{\chi_{CO_2}} = 0.340 \left(\frac{30}{14.7}\right)^{-\frac{1}{2}}$$

Equations (12.38b) and (12·38c) are again required as constraints. The solution now gives

$$\chi_{CO} = 0.0891$$
$$\chi_{O_2} = 0.615$$
$$\chi_{CO_2} = 0.296$$

Note that the equilibrium composition is affected by pressure and that increased pressure tends to reduce the number of moles (and hence the number of molecules) in the equilibrium mixture. This is generally the effect of increased pressure in reacting gas mixtures.

Effect of temperature. Let us again consider the CO, O_2, CO_2 mixture, this time at $5000°K$ and 10 psia. For variety let's write the reaction as

$$CO + \tfrac{1}{2}O_2 \rightleftarrows CO_2 \qquad\qquad (12\cdot39)$$

which interchanges the role of products and reactants from our previous approach. Note, however, that the equilibrium composition is independent of the direction of the reaction. Table B·14 does not explicitly give $K(T)$ for this reaction. However, ΔG_r for the reaction of Eq. (12·39) is simply the negative of that for the reaction of Eq. (12·37). Hence the $K(T)$ for one reaction is simply the *reciprocal* of the $K(T)$ for the other (see Eq. 12·36), and the logarithms of K are simply the *negatives* of one another. Hence, for the reaction of Eq. (12·39), Table B·14 implies

$$\log_{10} K = -1.387$$
$$K = 0.0410$$

To add further variety, let's handle the constraints in a somewhat different manner. For brevity set

$$\chi_{CO_2} = a$$

Then, solving the constraints, Eq. (12·38b) and (12·38c), simultaneously, we find

$$\chi_{O_2} = \frac{4 - a}{6}$$

$$\chi_{CO} = \frac{2 - 5a}{6}$$

Now, Eq. (12·35) gives

$$\frac{\chi_{CO_2}}{\chi_{CO}\chi_{O_2}{}^{1/2}} = 0.041 \times \left(\frac{10}{14.7}\right)^{1/2} = 0.0339$$

In terms of a,

$$\frac{a}{\{[(2 - 5a)/6] \times [(4 - a)/6]^{1/2}\}} = 0.0339$$

This single equation can be solved graphically, or by iteration, which is particularly easy if time-shared computation is available. One finds $a = 0.009$, so that $\chi_{CO} = 0.326$, $\chi_{CO_2} = 0.009$, and $\chi_{O_2} = 0.665$. The reaction given in Eq. (12·39) is exothermic when proceeding from left to right. Note that in our higher-temperature example less CO_2 is formed and the reaction is thus less complete. It is a general observation that exothermic reactions are less complete at higher temperatures and endothermic reactions are more complete at higher temperatures.

12·12   VAN'T HOFF EQUATION

The dependence of the equilibrium constant on temperature can be related to the enthalpy change for a complete unit reaction. Differentiating Eq. (12·36)

$$\frac{dK}{dT} = \frac{1}{\Re T^2}\left[\Delta G_r(T, P_0) - T\frac{d\Delta G_r(T, P_0)}{dT}\right]K$$

The fourth differential equation of state derived in Chap. Eight was

$$dg = -s\,dT + v\,dP$$

Applying this to the changes for a complete unit reaction at fixed pressure we find

$$\frac{d\Delta G_r(T, P_0)}{dT} = -\Delta S_r$$

From the equations above and the definition of the specific Gibbs function it also follows that

$$\Delta G_r = \Delta H_r - T\,\Delta S_r$$

Hence the derivative of the equilibrium constant may be expressed as

$$\frac{1}{K}\frac{dK}{dT} = \frac{\Delta H_r(T)}{\Re T^2}$$

or

$$\blacktriangleright \qquad \frac{d(\ln K)}{dT} = \frac{\Delta H_r(T)}{\Re T^2} \qquad\qquad (12\cdot40)$$

This is called the *van't Hoff equation* and it is very important in chemical thermodynamics. It permits determination of the enthalpy change for a complete unit reaction solely from equilibrium-composition data. Conversely, it permits us to evaluate changes in the equilibrium constant (a second-law parameter) solely from energy balance (first-law) data.

Equation (12·40) shows that for endothermic reactions ($\Delta H_r > 0$) K will increase with increasing temperature, while for exothermic reactions ($\Delta H_r < 0$) K will decrease with increasing temperature. Since ΔH_r is only weakly dependent on temperature, we can integrate Eq. (12·40) from reference state 1 assuming that ΔH_r is constant to obtain:

$$\ln\frac{K}{K_1} = -\frac{\Delta H_r}{\Re}\left(\frac{1}{T} - \frac{1}{T_1}\right) \qquad\qquad (12\cdot41)$$

Note that $\ln K$ is linear in $1/T$ in this approximation and consequently plots of $\ln K$ versus $1/T$ are often used to determine $\Delta H_r/\Re$ from experimental data.

As an example let us look at a reaction of interest in magnetohydrodynamics: the determination of ΔH_r for the ionization reaction of cesium. We have

$$Cs \rightleftarrows Cs^+ + e^-$$

From the data of Table B·14

$$T_1 = 4000°K \qquad \log_{10} K_1 = 4.07 \qquad K_1 = 11,800$$
$$T = 4500°K \qquad \log_{10} K = 4.43 \qquad K = 25,900$$

Assuming that ΔH_r is approximately constant, we have from Eq. (12·41)

$$\Delta H_r = -\mathfrak{R} \ln \frac{25,900/11,800}{1/4500 - 1/4000}$$

$$\Delta H_r = 5.5 \times 10^4 \text{ cal/gmole-°K}$$

If this result is converted to ev/molecule we have

$$\Delta H_r = 5.5 \times 10^4 \frac{\text{cal}}{\text{gmole-°K}} \frac{\text{gmole}}{6.023 \times 10^{23} \text{ molecules}}$$
$$\times \frac{4.186 \text{ joules}}{\text{cal}} \frac{\text{ev}}{1.06 \times 10^{-19} \text{ joules}}$$

$$\Delta H_r = 3.6 \text{ ev/molecule}$$

Since ΔH_r is positive the reaction is endothermic and requires 3.6 ev to ionize each molecule. This is in fact the *ionization potential* of cesium at these elevated temperatures.

12·13 APPLICATION TO THE FUEL CELL

Consider a fuel cell burning hydrogen and oxygen, as shown in Fig. 12·10. The maximum electrical energy output per mole of water formed and the maximum cell voltage can be determined with the theory developed in this chapter.

We assume steady flow, steady state, and negligible kinetic- and potential-energy changes for the fluids, and consider only the electrostatic potential

FIG. 12·10 *The fuel cell*

energy of the electrons. The cell temperature and fluid temperatures are assumed to be equal. An energy balance, made over an infinitesimal time period, then gives

$$(\hat{h}\ d\mathfrak{N})_{\mathrm{H_2O}} - (\hat{h}\ d\mathfrak{N})_{\mathrm{H_2}} - (\hat{h}\ d\mathfrak{N})_{\mathrm{O_2}} + dQ + \mathsf{e}(\mathcal{E}_b - \mathcal{E}_a)\ dN_e = 0$$

where e denotes the charge on an electron, and dN_e is the number of electrons passing through the control volume. Applying the second law, we obtain

$$d\mathcal{P}_s = (\hat{s}\ d\mathfrak{N})_{\mathrm{H_2O}} - (\hat{s}\ d\mathfrak{N})_{\mathrm{H_2}} - (\hat{s}\ d\mathfrak{N})_{\mathrm{O_2}} + \frac{dQ}{T} \geq 0$$

The equality will hold if the processes within the cell are reversible. Otherwise the inequality must be used. Combining the first- and second-law equations, we obtain

$$\mathsf{e}(\mathcal{E}_b - \mathcal{E}_a)\ dN_e \leq -[(\hat{g}\ d\mathfrak{N})_{\mathrm{H_2O}} - (\hat{g}\ d\mathfrak{N})_{\mathrm{H_2}} - (\hat{g}\ d\mathfrak{N})_{\mathrm{O_2}}] \tag{12·42}$$

The chemical equation is

$$\mathrm{H_2} + \tfrac{1}{2}\mathrm{O_2} \rightleftarrows \mathrm{H_2O}$$

Since stoichiometric reaction is assumed, Eq. (12·42) may be written as

$$dE_{\mathrm{elect}} = (\mathcal{E}_b - \mathcal{E}_a)\mathsf{e}\ dN_e \leq -\Delta G_r\ d\mathfrak{N}_{\mathrm{H_2O}} \tag{12·43}$$

Here dE_{elect} represents the useful electrical energy output. The value of ΔG_r for this reaction is equivalent to $-238{,}000$ joules/mole of $\mathrm{H_2O}$. Hence the maximum possible electrical energy output of such a cell is 238,000 joules for each mole of water produced.

The maximum cell voltage can be obtained by considering the reactions at the electrodes. At the anode

$$\mathrm{H_2} + 2\mathrm{OH^-} \rightarrow 2\mathrm{H_2O} + 2e^-$$

and at the cathode

$$\tfrac{1}{2}\mathrm{O_2} + \mathrm{H_2O} + 2e^- \rightarrow 2\mathrm{OH^-}$$

The net amount of water production associated with the transfer of two electrons through the load is one molecule. The number of electrons passed for each mole of water formation is then $2N_0$, where N_0 is Avogadro's number. Dividing Eq. (12·43) by $-2\mathsf{e}N_0$ (a positive quantity), it becomes

$$\mathcal{E}_a - \mathcal{E}_b \leq -\frac{\Delta G_r}{2N_0\mathsf{e}} = \frac{-238{,}000}{2 \times 6.023 \times 10^{23} \times (-1.602 \times 10^{-19})}$$

$$\mathcal{E}_a - \mathcal{E}_b \leq 1.23 \text{ volts}$$

The efficiency of the fuel cell is defined as the actual energy output per mole of water formation to the maximum possible output calculated above.

Like the isentropic efficiency of a compressor, it compares the actual output to the output of an idealized device and is not an energy-conversion efficiency.

12·14 CURRENT METHODS AND APPLICATIONS
OF THE THERMODYNAMIC THEORY OF COMBUSTION

The equilibrium composition of a perfect-gas mixture with more than one degree of reaction freedom requires simultaneous solution of a larger set of algebraic equations, with additional equations coming from the additional reaction equations and their associated equilibrium constants.

The standardized enthalpy and absolute entropy, together with the equilibrium constant, provide a sound theoretical basis for computation of states of reacting mixtures and energy analyses of control volumes in which reactions occur. Usually it is necessary to resort to digital-computer calculations, and rather elaborate computer programs for combustion analysis have been developed by groups engaged in serious combustion calculations. Hand calculations for a large class of hydrocarbon reactions are now possible with the aid of charts and tables.† Some of these charts employ slightly different datum states and methods, but the fundamental ideas are the same as we have presented here.

Some typical problems in present technology in which this sort of theory is employed include the reacting gas effects in the high-temperature air around a reentry body, reactions in the boundary layers on rocket nozzle walls, air pollution control devices, waste utilization and disposal furnaces, new metal smelting procedures, and new low-contaminant gas welding devices. These are but a few of the challenging areas open to qualified thermodynamicists.

SELECTED READING

Lee, J., and F. Sears, *Thermodynamics*, 2d ed., chap. 14, Addison-Wesley Publishing Co., Inc., Reading, Mass., 1963.

Van Wylen, G., and R. Sonntag, *Fundamentals of Classical Thermodynamics*, chap. 13, John Wiley & Sons, Inc., New York, 1965.

QUESTIONS

12·1 What is the chemical potential?
12·2 What is the phase rule?
12·3 Can two phases of ice plus liquid and vapor H_2O exist in equilibrium in any state?

---

† Many tables use F for the Gibbs function. See for example the *JANAF Interim Tables of Thermochemical Data*, vols. 1–4, Dow Chemical Company, Midland, Mich., 1960.

12·4 Why is a triple point better than a two-phase point as the fixed point on a temperature scale?

12·5 What is the greatest number of coexisting phases for a three-component (tertiary) mixture?

12·6 What happens to the pressure of a vapor above its liquid when an inert non-dissolving gas is introduced with the vapor? Does the vapor condense or does more evaporate when the inert gas is added at constant temperature?

12·7 What is the condition for equilibrium in a mixture of reacting substances held at constant temperature and pressure?

12·8 How is the chemical potential related to the Gibbs function of a mixture (considered as nonreactive)?

12·9 What is meant by degree of reaction freedom?

12·10 What is a simple reactive mixture?

12·11 What is the enthalpy of formation?

12·12 What is the standard free energy of formation?

12·13 What is the enthalpy of reaction?

12·14 To what kind of reactive mixture does the equilibrium constant pertain?

12·15 How can you tell what will happen when some substances are put together in a constant-pressure constant-temperature chamber?

12·16 How would you go about calculating the composition of air, considered as a mixture of O_2, O, N_2, N, and NO, at $3000°K$?

12·17 Partial pressures can be measured by simple volumetric means. How, then, can the enthalpy of reaction be determined without any energy measurements?

12·18 How many equilibrium constants would be needed for the determination of the equilibrium composition of a mixture of CO_2, CO, O_2, O, H_2O, OH, N_2, NO, and NO_2?

12·19 Can thermodynamics be used to determine the output voltage of a battery?

PROBLEMS

12·1 Using data in Appendix B, verify that $g_g = g_f$ for mercury at 60 psia.

12·2 The Gibbs function of formation is defined as the difference between the Gibbs functions of the compound and its forming elements at standard reference conditions. Determine the Gibbs function of formation for CO_2 and H_2O (liquid).

12·3 Consider the alloy phase diagram shown.

(a) What states are also states on the phase diagrams of the single components?

(b) How many phases coexist in region ACE?

(c) How many phases coexist on the line EB?

(d) How many phases are present at point E? How many independent intensive properties does the system have at E?

12·4 Consider the phase diagram for NaCl-H₂O. Explain why ice melts when salt is sprinkled on it. What is the lowest temperature that might be reached if ice, salt, water, and water vapor initially at 0°C are mixed at constant pressure in an insulated container?

12·5 Air frequently becomes trapped in refrigeration systems. If the gas in a freon-12 system contains 10 percent air (by mass), how much will the freon-12 saturation pressure be changed when the system temperature is 80°F?

12·6 A laboratory analysis shows that CO_2 becomes 10 percent dissociated into CO and O_2 at 4300°R when the total pressure is 1 atm. Find the equilibrium constant from this information and compare to that given in Table B·14.

12·7 Determine the degree of dissociation of CO_2 at 5000°R, 1 atm if 100 percent excess oxygen is supplied to the reaction.

12·8 Hydrogen is to be burned with oxygen to produce a 3000°F flame. Neglecting dissociation, determine the composition of the product gases and specify the ratios of the oxygen- and hydrogen-flow rates. $P = 1$ atm, and the burner is adiabatic.

12·9 Find the mole fractions of O present in equilibrium oxygen at 1000°K and at 5000°K ($P = 1$ atm).

12·10 Find the mole fractions of N present in equilibrium nitrogen at 1000°K and 5000°K ($P = 1$ atm).

12·11 Assuming that air is composed of O_2, O, N_2, N, and NO, and that only O_2 and N_2 are present in significant amounts at room temperatures in the ratio 3.76 moles of N_2 per mole of O_2, determine the composition of equilibrium air at 1000°K and 1 atm.

12·12 Using the data in Table B·13, calculate the equilibrium constant for the reaction $CO_2 \rightleftarrows CO + \frac{1}{2}O_2$ at 1000°K and compare your result with the value given in Table B·14.

12·13 Using the data in Table B·13, calculate the equilibrium constant for the dissociation of O_2 at 2500°K and compare your result with the value given in Table B·14.

12·14 Using the data in Table B·13, calculate the equilibrium constant for the gaseous reaction $CO_2 + H_2 \rightleftarrows CO + H_2O$ at 298°K. Derive an expression which would let you obtain this instead from Table B·14 in terms of the equilibrium constants for simpler reactions.

12·15 Using the data in the *Handbook of Chemistry and Physics* and the van't Hoff equation, determine the value of the equilibrium constant for the reaction

$C + 2H_2 \rightleftarrows CH_4$ at 500°C. Assume that ΔH_r does not vary appreciably over the low-temperature range.

12·16 For the reaction $H_2O \rightleftarrows H_2 + \frac{1}{2}O_2$ the equilibrium constant is known to be $\log_{10} K = -3.531$ at 3600°R. Estimate the constant at $T = 4000°R$ using the van't Hoff equation.

12·17 From the equilibrium constants given in Table B·14, estimate the ΔH_r for the reaction $CO_2 \rightleftarrows CO + \frac{1}{2}O_2$ at $T = 2000°K$. Compare to a calculated value for ΔH_r based on Table B·13.

12·18 1 mole of CO reacts with 1 mole of O_2 in a steady-flow process. Both inlet conditions are 77°F at 1 atm. The final products are a mixture of CO, CO_2, O_2 at 1 atm. Determine the equilibrium compositions at 3000°K and 2800°K.

12·19 For Prob. 12·18, determine the heat transfer from the system for the cases where the temperature of the products is 3000°K and 2800°K. At what exit temperature is the system adiabatic?

12·20 Calculate and plot the percentage of ionization in cesium at 10^{-2} and 10^{-4} atm over the range of ionization (the electrons may be treated as a monatomic perfect gas with $\hat{M} = 5.48 \times 10^{-4}$ g/gmole).

12·21 Calculate and plot the percentage of ionization in sodium at 10^{-2} and 10^{-4} atm over the range of ionization (the electrons may be treated as a monatomic perfect gas with $\hat{M} = 5.48 \times 10^{-4}$ g/gmole).

12·22 Determine the number of free electrons and ions per cm^3 in argon seeded with 1 percent cesium (by mass) at 1 atm and 1000°K (the electrons may be treated as a monatomic perfect gas with $\hat{M} = 5.48 \times 10^{-4}$ g/gmole). Neglect argon ionization.

12·23 Determine the number of free electrons and ions per cm^3 in argon seeded with sodium at 1 atm and 1000°K (the electrons may be treated as a monatomic perfect gas with $\hat{M} = 5.48 \times 10^{-4}$ g/gmole). Neglect argon ionization.

12·24 Work the previous two problems. Which seed seems most desirable to attain a plasma with high electrical conductivity?

12·25 Determine the maximum energy output per mole of CO_2 for a fuel cell operating on CO and O_2 at 298°K and 1 atm. Assume that the products contain only CO_2.

12·26 A particular plasma gas dynamics experiment requires a plasma at 800°K, 1 atm having 10^{14} free electrons per cm^3. Specify an inert carrier gas, an easily ionizable seed, and the mass fractions that would produce the desired plasma.

CHAPTER THIRTEEN

AN INTRODUCTION TO COMPRESSIBLE FLOW

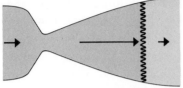

13·1 THE MOMENTUM PRINCIPLE

We have had experience to this point with analyzing various power systems using the first and second laws of thermodynamics. We can find the exit velocity from a nozzle just from an application of the first law if the entrance and exit states are fixed. But as yet we do not know why supersonic nozzles are designed with a converging-diverging shape, such as is shown in Fig. 13·1. Such design constitutes a problem in *compressible fluid flow*.

Subsonic

Supersonic

FIG. 13·1 *A supersonic nozzle. The Mach number is greater than 1 at the exit*

Thermodynamics is an important tool in working with compressible flows. To analyze such problems completely, momentum equations are required along with conservation of mass, energy, equations of state, and the second law. Consequently, the study of compressible flow provides an excellent opportunity to integrate thermodynamics with fluid mechanics.

The student is now familiar with all of the basic principles used to solve compressible flow problems. These are:

1 Conservation of mass
2 Conservation of energy (the first law of thermodynamics)
3 The second law of thermodynamics
4 The momentum principle

407

The student is presumably well grounded in applications of the momentum principle (Newton's second law) to systems of *fixed mass* (any control mass). Before we can analyze some compressible flow systems it is necessary to extend Newton's second law to the control volume. Special forms of the control-volume momentum principle are usually used in elementary fluid mechanics courses, and the student should relate our development to the special cases he might have encountered previously.

To derive the control-volume momentum principle we start with the momentum equation as applied to a control mass (Fig. 13·2). Let $\mathbf{F}$ denote the *net* force, that is, the sum of all surface and body forces, acting on the control mass at time t. Note that $\mathbf{F}$ is in general a vector with three components. $\mathbf{F}$ is related to the rate of change of the momentum of the control mass by Newton's law,

$$\blacktriangleright \qquad g_c\mathbf{F} = \frac{d}{dt}\left(\mathbf{M}_{CM}\right) \qquad\qquad (13\cdot1)$$

The momentum $\mathbf{M}$ is also a vector. For a continuous body the momentum may be expressed as an integral of the velocity $\mathbf{V}$ over the mass within the control volume,

$$\mathbf{M} = \int_{CM} \rho\mathbf{V}\,dV \qquad\qquad (13\cdot2)$$

Note that $\rho\,dV$ represents an element of mass within the space occupied by the control mass (CM). Newton's law then says

$$g_c\mathbf{F} = \frac{d\mathbf{M}_{CM}}{dt} \qquad\qquad (13\cdot3)$$

The control-volume equation is obtained simply by expressing $d\mathbf{M}_{CM}/dt$ in terms of integrals related to the *control volume* (CV) rather than to the con-

Control volume

Surface area A_3

Surface area A_1

Control mass at time $t+\Delta t$

III

A_3

II

I

A_1

F

FIG. 13·2 *The control volume coincides with the control mass at time t*

Control mass at time t

trol mass (CM). From the basic definition of a derivative,

$$\frac{d\mathbf{M}_{CM}}{dt} = \lim_{\Delta t \to 0} \frac{\mathbf{M}_{CM}(t + \Delta t) - \mathbf{M}_{CM}(t)}{\Delta t} \tag{13·4}$$

Now, we choose the control mass at t as that matter within the control volume at time t. Then, since they contain the same matter at time t, their momenta are equal,

$$\mathbf{M}_{CM}(t) = \mathbf{M}_{CV}(t)$$

However, at time $t + \Delta t$ they do not contain the same matter, and hence

$$\mathbf{M}_{CM}(t + \Delta t) \neq \mathbf{M}_{CV}(t + \Delta t)$$

But we can relate $\mathbf{M}_{CM}(t + \Delta t)$ to $\mathbf{M}_{CV}(t + \Delta t)$ and other terms with the help of Fig. 13·2. Note that

$$\mathbf{M}_{CM}(t + \Delta t) = \mathbf{M}_{II}(t + \Delta t) + \mathbf{M}_{III}(t + \Delta t)$$
$$\mathbf{M}_{CV}(t + \Delta t) = \mathbf{M}_{I}(t + \Delta t) + \mathbf{M}_{II}(t + \Delta t)$$

where I, II, and III refer to the three regions in space shown in Fig. 13·2. Hence,

$$\mathbf{M}_{CM}(t + \Delta t) = \mathbf{M}_{CV}(t + \Delta t) + \mathbf{M}_{III}(t + \Delta t) - \mathbf{M}_{I}(t + \Delta t)$$

Substituting into Eq. (13·4), and regrouping terms

$$\frac{d\mathbf{M}_{CM}}{dt} = \lim_{\Delta t \to 0} \left(\frac{\mathbf{M}_{CV}(t + \Delta t) - \mathbf{M}_{CV}(t)}{\Delta t} \right)$$
$$+ \lim_{\Delta t \to 0} \frac{\mathbf{M}_{III}(t + \Delta t) - \mathbf{M}_{I}(t + \Delta t)}{\Delta t} \tag{13·5}$$

The first limit above is, by definition, the rate of change of momentum within the control *volume*,

$$\frac{d\mathbf{M}_{CV}}{dt} \equiv \lim_{\Delta t \to 0} \left(\frac{\mathbf{M}_{CV}(t + \Delta t) - \mathbf{M}_{CV}(t)}{\Delta t} \right)$$

The second limit in Eq. (13·5) is related to the *flows* of momentum across the *control-volume boundaries*. For small Δt an elemental volume of III can be represented by

$$dV_{III} = \mathbf{V}_{\text{rel}} \, \Delta t \cdot d\mathbf{A}$$

Here $d\mathbf{A}$ is an element of the *surface area* bounding regions II and III, and $\mathbf{V}_{\text{rel}}$ is the *outflow* velocity of the fluid relative to the control-volume boundaries; $\mathbf{V}_{\text{rel}} \, \Delta t$ is the *distance* outward from the boundaries which the fluid travels in time Δt. Similarly,

$$dV_{I} = -\mathbf{V}_{\text{rel}} \, \Delta t \cdot d\mathbf{A}$$

where the minus sign is needed because we retain the convention that $\mathbf{V}_{\text{rel}}$ is taken positive for flow *out* of the control volume. Then, the second limit in Eq. (13·5) becomes

$$\lim_{\Delta t \to 0} \frac{\int_{A_3} \rho \mathbf{V}(\mathbf{V}_{rel} \, \Delta t \cdot d\mathbf{A}) + \int_{A_1} \rho \mathbf{V}(\mathbf{V}_{rel} \, \Delta t \cdot d\mathbf{A})}{\Delta t}$$

Since $A_1 + A_3 = A_{CV}$, the surface area of the control *volume*, this limit is simply

$$\int_{A_{CV}} \rho \mathbf{V}(\mathbf{V}_{rel} \cdot d\mathbf{A}) = \int_{CS} \mathbf{V}(\rho \mathbf{V}_{rel} \cdot d\mathbf{A})$$

where we use CS to denote the *control surface*, that is, the surface area of the control volume. Note that $\rho \mathbf{V}_{rel} \cdot d\mathbf{A}$ represents an elemental mass flow rate across the control-volume boundary, and $\mathbf{V}$ is the momentum per unit of mass at this point on the boundary. This term then represents the net *momentum outflow rate* from the *control volume*.

We now have

$$\frac{d\mathbf{M}_{CM}}{dt} = \frac{d\mathbf{M}_{CV}}{dt} + \int_{CS} \mathbf{V}(\rho \mathbf{V}_{rel} \cdot d\mathbf{A}) \tag{13·6}$$

Since the right-hand side involves only control-*volume* quantities, Eq. (13·1)

TABLE 13·1 SUMMARY OF EQUATIONS FOR A CONTROL VOLUME†

Conservation of mass: $\dot{\mathcal{P}}_M = 0$

$$\dot{\mathcal{P}}_M \equiv \frac{d}{dt} \int_{CV} \rho \, dV + \int_{CS} \rho \mathbf{V}_{rel} \cdot d\mathbf{A}$$

Conservation of energy: $\dot{\mathcal{P}}_E = 0$

$$\dot{\mathcal{P}}_E \equiv \frac{d}{dt} \int_{CV} e\rho \, dV + \int_{CS} (e + Pv)\rho \mathbf{V}_{rel} \cdot d\mathbf{A} - \dot{Q}_{in} + \dot{W}_{out}$$

Second law: $\dot{\mathcal{P}}_S \geq 0$

$$\dot{\mathcal{P}}_S \equiv \frac{d}{dt} \int_{CV} s\rho \, dV + \int_{CS} s\rho \mathbf{V}_{rel} \cdot d\mathbf{A} - \int_{CS} \frac{q''}{T} \, dA$$

Momentum principle: $\dot{\boldsymbol{\mathcal{P}}}_\mathbf{M} = g_c \mathbf{F}$

$$\dot{\boldsymbol{\mathcal{P}}}_\mathbf{M} \equiv \frac{d}{dt} \int_{CV} \mathbf{V}\rho \, dV + \int_{CS} \mathbf{V}(\rho \mathbf{V}_{rel} \cdot d\mathbf{A})$$

---

† $\mathbf{V}$ is the absolute velocity in an inertial frame, $\rho \mathbf{V}_{rel} \cdot d\mathbf{A}$ denotes *mass outflow* rate,

$$e \equiv u + \frac{V^2}{2g_c} + \cdots, \text{ and}$$

q'' denotes the *input heat flux* (heat-transfer rate per unit of surface area).

becomes

$$\blacktriangleright \qquad g_c \mathbf{F} = \frac{d\mathbf{M}_{CV}}{dt} + \int_{CS} \mathbf{V}(\rho \mathbf{V}_{\mathrm{rel}} \cdot d\mathbf{A}) \qquad\qquad (13 \cdot 7)$$

We could express $\mathbf{M}_{CV}$ as an integral over the control volume, and write (13·7) as

$$\blacktriangleright \qquad g_c \mathbf{F} = \frac{d}{dt}\int_{CV} \rho \mathbf{V} \, dV + \int_{CS} \mathbf{V}(\rho \mathbf{V}_{\mathrm{rel}} \cdot d\mathbf{A}) \qquad\qquad (13 \cdot 8)$$

The right-hand side of Eq. (13·8) can be interpreted as the *rate of production of momentum*, $\dot{\mathcal{P}}_\mathbf{M}$. The *momentum principle* then says

$$\dot{\mathcal{P}}_\mathbf{M} = g_c \mathbf{F} \qquad\qquad (13 \cdot 9)$$

Note that if there is no outflow, Eq. (13·8) reduces to the control-mass equation. Equation (13.8) as written is also correct for a *moving* control volume, with expanding boundaries, provided that $\mathbf{V}$ is measured in an inertial reference frame and $\mathbf{V}_{\mathrm{rel}}$ is measured relative to the local control-volume surface.

Table 13·1 summarizes the basic principles in their appropriate control-volume form.

The methodology for momentum-principle analysis follows that laid down for energy balances in Chap. Five.

1   Define the control volume. Since it is quantities at the boundary that will enter the equation, the boundaries should be placed either where you know something or where you want to know something.

2   Define on the sketch the sign for *positive* values for each force and velocity, just as we did for heat and work in Chap. Five. If a force is to be calculated, define it positive in what seems a reasonable direction. If the calculation yields a negative value it of course means that the force actually acts opposite to your arrow. Be careful to show *all* forces acting *on* this control volume (these are *opposite* to those forces that the control volume exerts on its environment).

3   Define the positive coordinate directions (on the system sketch). This is necessary because of the vector nature of forces and momentum.

4   Express the net forces in the positive directions in terms of the variables in the problem. The system sketch can often be used to define these terms.

5   Express the rates of momentum outflow and inflow, and the rate of momentum storage within the control volume (*zero in steady flow, steady state*), and then the total rate of production of momentum.

6   Apply the momentum principle.

7   Develop other equations from the other basic principles, bring in state information, and so on, as necessary to complete the problem.

Examples following illustrate this methodology.

13·2 SOME MOMENTUM-PRINCIPLE APPLICATIONS

Nozzle supporting force.   Consider the nozzle flow of Fig. 13·3. Suppose we wish to calculate the force in the pipe. We first choose an appropriate control volume, placing the control surface where we either know or want to know something. So, let's use the control volume shown in the figure. Next, we calculate the net force on the control volume. We only need to work with one component here.   Note the definition of F_p.   Then, choosing the positive x direction to the right, the net force in this direction is

$$F_x = P_1A_1 - P_2A_2 - P_a(A_1 - A_2) + F_p$$

Next we compute the rate of production of momentum. Assuming steady flow, steady state, there is no change in the momentum storage within the control volume (though the momentum of the fluid passing through the control volume changes significantly). Assuming one-dimensional flow at *1* and *2*, the rate of production of momentum is

$$\dot{\mathcal{P}}_M = \underset{\substack{\text{momentum} \\ \text{outflow} \\ \text{rate}}}{\dot{M}_2V_2} - \underset{\substack{\text{momentum} \\ \text{inflow} \\ \text{rate}}}{\dot{M}_1V_1} + \underset{\substack{\text{momentum} \\ \text{storage} \\ \text{rate}}}{0}$$

Then, the momentum principle says

$$g_c[P_1A_1 - P_2A_2 - P_a(A_1 - A_2) + F_p] = \dot{M}_2V_2 - \dot{M}_1V_1$$

Solving for F_p,

$$F_p = \frac{1}{g_c}(\dot{M}_2V_2 - \dot{M}_1V_1) + P_2A_2 - P_1A_1 + P_a(A_1 - A_2)$$

We must know everything on the right before we can calculate F_p. This will usually require additional analysis. For example, by conservation of mass,

$$\dot{M}_2 = \dot{M}_1$$

A thermodynamic analysis will usually be required to relate P_2 and V_2 to P_1 and V_1. The *continuity equation* ($\dot{M} = A\rho V$) would also be useful.

FIG. 13·3   *A force analysis on a nozzle*

FIG. 13·4 *A steam jet ejector*

Steam-air jet ejector. High-pressure steam is used to suck air out of a large tank for low-vacuum experiments. The analysis of such an ejector is based in part on the momentum principle.

The control volume is shown in Fig. 13·4. Note that we assume one-dimensional flow at *1*, *2*, and *3*, and neglect the friction force on the ejector wall. We also assume steady flow, steady state.

Choosing the positive x direction to the right, the net force on the control volume in this direction is

$$F_x = P_1A_1 + P_2A_2 - P_3A_3$$

The rate of production of momentum in the x direction is

$$\dot{\Phi}_M = \underset{\substack{\text{momentum} \\ \text{outflow} \\ \text{rate}}}{\dot{M}_3V_3} - \underset{\substack{\text{momentum} \\ \text{inflow} \\ \text{rate}}}{(\dot{M}_1V_1 + \dot{M}_2V_2)}$$

Hence, the momentum principle yields

$$g_c(P_1A_1 + P_2A_2 - P_3A_3) = \dot{M}_3V_3 - (\dot{M}_1V_1 + \dot{M}_2V_2)$$

If the mass flow rates and inlet states 1 and 2 were known, the unknowns would be P_3, V_3, and $\dot{M}_3$. The mass balance, the energy balance, and the continuity equation ($\dot{M} = A\rho V$), plus appropriate state information (here for air, steam, and air-water mixtures) would suffice to permit calculation of the discharge state.

13·3 STAGNATION PROPERTIES IN COMPRESSIBLE FLOW

In treating compressible fluid flow it is convenient to work with a hypothetical reference state and its associated properties. The *isentropic stagnation state* is the state a flowing fluid would reach if it were brought to rest isentropically in a steady flow, adiabatic, zero work output device. This reference state is commonly designated with the subscript zero. From an energy balance (Fig. 13·5) we find that the stagnation enthalpy, h_0, is related to the enthalpy

FIG. 13·5 *Definition of the isentropic stagnation state*

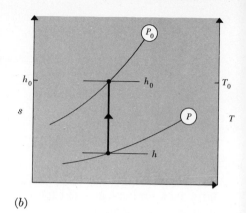

(a)   (b)

and velocity of the moving fluid by

$$h_0 = h + \frac{V^2}{2g_c} \tag{13·10}$$

The hypothetical isentropic stagnation process is shown in Fig. 13·5b.

For a perfect gas, since $h = h(T)$, the isentropic stagnation temperature T_0 can be related to the temperature and velocity of the flowing fluid. For a perfect gas with constant c_P,

$$h_0 - h = c_P(T_0 - T)$$

and hence,

$$\frac{T_0}{T} = 1 + \frac{V^2}{2g_c c_P T} \tag{13·11}$$

Using the perfect-gas equations relating entropy to temperature and pressure (Eq. 8·27), a relationship for the stagnation pressure may be derived,

$$\frac{P_0}{P} = \left(\frac{T_0}{T}\right)^{k/(k-1)} = \left(1 + \frac{V^2}{2g_c c_P T}\right)^{k/(k-1)} \tag{13·12}$$

As an example, let's calculate the isentropic stagnation conditions for air flowing at 1200 ft/sec, at 70°F, 50 psia

$$T_0 = 530 + \frac{(1200)^2}{2 \times 32.2 \times 0.24 \times 778} = 530 + 120 = 650°\text{R}$$
$$P_0 = 50(^{650}\!/_{530})^{3.5} = 102 \text{ psia}$$

13·4 MACH NUMBER, SPEED OF SOUND, REGIMES IN COMPRESSIBLE FLOW

The Mach number is defined as the ratio of the actual velocity, V, to the speed at which sound would propagate through the fluid. We shall denote the sound speed by c, and the Mach number by M. Then,

$$M \equiv \frac{V}{c}$$ (13·13)

Three flow regimes are defined:

For M < 1 the flow is subsonic
For M > 1 the flow is supersonic
For M = 1 the flow is exactly sonic

The speed of sound is an important parameter in compressible flow, both physically and as a reference speed. We can derive an equation for the speed of sound from an analysis of the motion of a small pressure wave through a compressible fluid since sound is in fact carried by weak pressure waves. In place of a source of sound let us set up a piston cylinder arrangement as shown in Fig. 13·6a. By putting the piston into motion to the right with a small velocity dV, we can set up a pressure wave that travels down the tube at the sonic velocity c. The wave divides the fluid that is at rest, and unaware of the piston motion, from the fluid that is moving with the piston velocity dV to the right. The fluid near the piston will have a slightly increased pressure, and will be slightly more dense.

It is easier to analyze this process if we follow the motion as an observer traveling with the wave front (Fig. 13·6b). In this case it appears to us that

FIG. 13·6   *An analysis to determine the speed of sound*

the fluid is moving toward us from the right with a velocity c, and moving away on the left at velocity $c - dV$. In this reference frame we can use a steady-state analysis. Applying the conservation of energy to the (adiabatic) control volume shown,

$$h + \frac{c^2}{2g_c} = (h + dh) + \frac{(c - dV)^2}{2g_c}$$

Neglecting higher-order differentials, we have

$$dh - \frac{c\,dV}{g_c} = 0 \qquad (13\cdot14)$$

Conservation of mass requires

$$\rho A c = (\rho + d\rho) A (c - dV)$$

Neglecting second-order differentials,

$$c\,d\rho - \rho\,dV = 0 \qquad (13\cdot15)$$

Since the wave is infinitesimal we can consider the process reversible, and it is, of course, adiabatic. Consequently, the process can be assumed isentropic. Utilizing the Gibbs equation with $ds = 0$,

$$dh = v\,dP = \frac{dP}{\rho} \qquad (13\cdot16)$$

Substituting in the energy equation,

$$\frac{c\,dV}{g_c} = \frac{dP}{\rho} \qquad (13\cdot17)$$

and combining with the continuity equation,

$$\frac{c^2\,d\rho}{\rho g_c} = \frac{dP}{\rho} \qquad (13\cdot18)$$

Since the process is isentropic, $dP/d\rho = (\partial P/\partial\rho)_s$, and thus

$$c^2 = g_c \left(\frac{\partial P}{\partial \rho}\right)_s$$

so,

$$\blacktriangleright \quad c = \sqrt{g_c \left(\frac{\partial P}{\partial \rho}\right)_s} \qquad (13\cdot19)$$

Note that the same relation can be derived using the momentum and continuity equations. Alternatively, the momentum equation may be used to show that the process is isentropic.

For a perfect gas with constant specific heats it may easily be shown that

$$\left(\frac{\partial P}{\partial \rho}\right)_s = kRT$$

and hence

$$c = \sqrt{g_c k R T} = \sqrt{g_c k \left(\frac{\mathfrak{R}}{\hat{M}}\right) T} \qquad (13 \cdot 20)$$

Thus, for a given gas, the speed of sound depends only upon the *local* temperature. Note that c is a *thermodynamic property* of the fluid.

Let's calculate the speed of sound in air at 70°F and at 1200°F, and at an altitude of 50,000 feet ($-70°F$). At 70°

$$c = \sqrt{g_c k R T} = \sqrt{1.4 \times 32.2 \frac{\text{lbm-ft}}{\text{lbf-sec}^2} \times 53.3 \frac{\text{ft-lbf}}{\text{lbm-°R}} \times 530°R}$$

$$= 1125 \text{ ft/sec}$$

At 1200°F one finds c = 1996 ft/sec, while at $-70°F$ c = 968 ft/sec. For hydrogen R = 767 ft-lbf/lbm-°R, and c is about 3.8 times that in air, while for a heavy gas such as the freons c is considerably less than that in air. Note that the speed of sound at the isentropic stagnation state is greater than that of the flowing fluid since $T_0 > T$.

Some further helpful ideas follow. Let us imagine a source of sound at a given point as shown in Fig. 13·7a. In time t the sound waves traverse a distance ct relative to the fluid. If the source of sound is stationary or moves slowly (M < 1), the disturbance is felt throughout the fluid (Fig. 13·7a, b). When the source moves at just the speed of sound, the disturbances created are not able to propagate ahead of the source and zones are created within which the disturbance is felt (*zone of action*) and not felt (*zone of silence*). If M > 1 the zone of action is a *cone* (the *Mach cone*). The passage of a supersonic aircraft overhead is announced to persons on the ground when the Mach cone passes their position. Note that the angle of the Mach cone is related to the Mach number.

The ratios T_0/T and P_0/P can be expressed in terms of the Mach number. Noting that

$$\frac{V^2}{2g_c c_P T} = \frac{Rk}{2c_P} \frac{V^2}{g_c k R T} = \frac{k-1}{2} M^2$$

Eq. (13·11) gives

$$\blacktriangleright \qquad \frac{T_0}{T} = 1 + \frac{k-1}{2} M^2 \qquad (13 \cdot 21)$$

and Eq. (13·12) gives

$$\blacktriangleright \qquad \frac{P_0}{P} = \left(1 + \frac{k-1}{2} M^2\right)^{k/(k-1)} \qquad (13 \cdot 22)$$

FIG. 13·7 *The effect of a moving sound source*

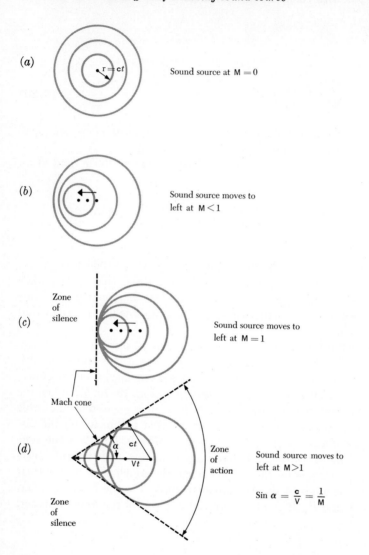

(a)   Sound source at M = 0

(b)   Sound source moves to
                                     left at M < 1

(c)   Zone
       of
       silence   Sound source moves to
                                     left at M = 1

Mach cone

(d)   Zone   Sound source moves to
                         of   left at M > 1
                         action
       Zone
       of $\text{Sin } \alpha = \dfrac{c}{V} = \dfrac{1}{M}$
       silence

13·5 A NOZZLE DESIGN PROBLEM

Let's now bring these ideas together in an example. Suppose we wish to design a nozzle to produce an air flow at a Mach number of 1.75. The air inlet state is to be 80 psia, 500°F. The mass flow rate will be 100 lbm/sec. We wish to calculate the flow area as a function of the local speed. We can then shape the nozzle to obtain a suitable distribution of acceleration along the flow.

Our flow model will be as follows:

1   one-dimensional flow in the nozzle core, negligible effects of wall boundary layers†
2   Isentropic flow in the core
3   Steady flow, steady state
4   Velocity negligible at the inlet state
5   Perfect gas with constant c_P

With these assumptions each point in the core flow will have the same isentropic stagnation state, with

$$T_0 = 960°\text{R} \qquad P_0 = 80 \text{ psia}$$

Hence, at any point, Eqs. (13·21) and (13·22) apply. Then, choosing values for M at some point in the nozzle, the local T and P can be calculated. This fixes the thermodynamic state, and hence the local density and speed of sound. Then, the local velocity can be calculated from $V = Mc$, and finally the flow area calculated from $A = \dot{M}/\rho V$. Table 13·2 summarizes this calculation. Note that the speed of sound decreases as the Mach number increases along the nozzle. It may be surprising that the flow area first decreases, but then must be *increased* to obtain further acceleration of the flow. Note that the point of least area (the *nozzle throat*) appears to be near the point where M = 1. We see striking differences between the flow in the subsonic and supersonic portions of the nozzle. The reasons for this are evident when the density is considered. Note that ρ falls off slowly as the flow expands in the subsonic region, and then decreases very rapidly as the flow expands to supersonic speeds. This expansion is so rapid that the flow area must be *enlarged* as we move downstream past the throat.

† Boundary layers on the nozzle walls, produced by viscous effects, are normally very thin in these circumstances.

TABLE 13·2

P, psia	T, °R	V, ft/sec	ρ, lbm/ft³	$c = \sqrt{g_c k R T}$, ft/sec	A, ft²	M
80	960	0	0.225	1520	∞	0.000
70	924	655	0.205	1490	0.745	0.440
60	885	950	0.183	1454	0.575	0.652
50	840	1200	0.161	1419	0.519	0.845
42	798	1392	0.142	1380	0.505	1.010
40	787	1440	0.137	1372	0.506	1.050
30	725	1680	0.112	1319	0.532	1.270
20	645	1940	0.084	1245	0.612	1.560
15	595	2100	0.068	1195	0.700	1.750

Here we carried out calculations for a specific case. Considerable insight and convenience are provided by the general treatment and nondimensional results developed in the next section.

Suppose we wanted to increase the discharge velocity. There is a *maximum velocity* that a flow can reach isentropically from its stagnation state. This occurs when $T \rightarrow 0$. From Eq. (13·21),

$$\mathsf{V}_{max} = \sqrt{2g_c c_P T_0} \tag{13·23}$$

This is important in rocket design. For our stagnation temperature of 960°R, $\mathsf{V}_{max} = 3360$ ft/sec, and this is the maximum speed that we could obtain by further increase in the nozzle exit area.

13·6 ONE-DIMENSIONAL STEADY ISENTROPIC FLOW

The flow discussed in the previous section was modeled as frictionless and adiabatic, or equivalently as *isentropic*. This section deals with a general treatment of one-dimensional steady isentropic flow, a model that is quite useful in engineering analysis.

The manner in which the different flow properties vary from one another can be shown most simply from differential equations relating the variables. We shall develop these now. The solutions to these equations may be obtained by manipulating them into separable forms and integrating, or alternatively one can work directly with algebraic equations like Eqs. (13·21) and (13·22). The latter method is easier, and hence we shall use the differential equations merely for insight.

The appropriate energy equation is

$$h_0 = h + \frac{\mathsf{V}^2}{2g_c} = \text{constant}$$

Differentiating,

$$\blacktriangleright \quad dh + \frac{\mathsf{V}\,d\mathsf{V}}{g_c} = 0 \tag{13·24}$$

This relates enthalpy and velocity changes along the flow. As the velocity goes up the enthalpy goes down, and vice versa. This represents the continual exchange of organized energy (bulk kinetic energy and flow work) and disorganized energy (the internal energy of the gas).

The continuity equation is

$$\rho A \mathsf{V} = \text{constant}$$

In differential form,

$$A\mathsf{V}\,d\rho + \rho A\,d\mathsf{V} + \rho\mathsf{V}\,dA = 0$$

or

$$\blacktriangleright \quad \frac{d\rho}{\rho} + \frac{d\mathsf{V}}{\mathsf{V}} + \frac{dA}{A} = 0 \tag{13·25}$$

This equation reveals the complex coupling between area, density, and velocity changes. *If the density did not change*, A would decrease as V increases. At very high speeds $V \rightarrow V_{max}$, and hence the velocity no longer changes as the area increases. Equation (13·25) then shows that as the density decreases the area increases, as observed in the last section.

Now, the Gibbs equation requires

$$T \, ds = du + P \, dv = dh - \frac{1}{\rho} \, dP$$

Since $ds = 0$,

$$\blacktriangleright \qquad dh = \frac{1}{\rho} \, dP \qquad\qquad\qquad (13\cdot26)$$

This equation tells us that the enthalpy and pressure will vary in the same manner, with the pressure decreasing as the enthalpy decreases (and the velocity increases). Combining the energy and Gibbs equations one has

$$\blacktriangleright \qquad \frac{V \, dV}{g_c} + \frac{1}{\rho} \, dP = 0 \qquad\qquad\qquad (13\cdot27)$$

This equation again tells us that as the velocity increases the pressure must decrease. Equation (13·27) is a differential form of *Bernoulli's equation*. Note that it cannot be integrated unless we know how ρ varies with P. For the *special case* of ρ = constant, as encountered in elementary fluid mechanics courses, integration gives the Bernoulli equation, *but only for incompressible flows.*†

Now, from the equation for the sound speed c (Eq. (13·19)),

$$\frac{dP}{d\rho} = \left(\frac{\partial P}{\partial \rho}\right)_s = \frac{c^2}{g_c}$$

so

$$dP = \frac{c^2}{g_c} \, d\rho \qquad\qquad\qquad (13\cdot28)$$

This equation tells us that as the pressure increases the density will also increase, and vice versa.

Finally, we combine Eqs. (13·25), (13·26), and (13·28) to obtain

$$\frac{dA}{A} = \frac{g_c \, dP}{\rho V^2} \left(1 - \frac{V^2}{c^2}\right) = \frac{g_c \, dP}{\rho V^2} (1 - M^2) \qquad\qquad\qquad (13\cdot29)$$

This equation tells us how A must vary with pressure. For *subsonic flow* ($M < 1$), dP and dA will be of the *same sign*, and hence a *reduction* in A is necessary to produce a reduction in P (flow acceleration). For *supersonic flow* ($M > 1$) dP and dA will be of *opposite signs*, and an *increase* in A is required

† However, gas flows in which the density varies only slightly are usually treated by the incompressible form of Bernoulli equation.

for further reduction in P (increase in V). This supports the suggestions made on the basis of the calculation example in the last section. We remark that the developments of this section have not yet required any equation-of-state assumptions, and therefore these conclusions hold for all gases and liquids. Figure 13·8 summarizes the variations in properties in subsonic and supersonic isentropic flow.

Now we turn to the generalized dimensionless equations representing the behavior for isentropic flow. To nondimensionalize we need suitable reference values for T, P, A, and so on. We have seen that the stagnation state provides useful reference values T_0, P_0, ρ_0, c_0. The area at stagnation is infinite, and we must look elsewhere for a suitable reference area. The *sonic* point, or throat, where M = 1 provides the reference area, which is smaller than the area at any other point in the flow. Conditions at M = 1 are customarily denoted by the superscript *. A^* is then the throat area.

Conditions at the sonic point follow immediately from Eqs. (13·21) and (13·22),

$$\frac{T_0}{T^*} = \left(1 + \frac{k-1}{2}\right) \tag{13·30}$$

$$\frac{P_0}{P^*} = \left(1 + \frac{k-1}{2}\right)^{k/(k-1)} \tag{13·31}$$

For a gas with $k = 1.4$,

$$\frac{T^*}{T_0} = 0.833 \qquad \frac{P^*}{P_0} = 0.528 \qquad \frac{\rho^*}{\rho_0} = 0.634$$

Expressions for A/A^*, ρ/ρ^*, T/T^*, and so on as functions of M and k may be developed very easily from the algebraic forms of the continuity and state equations. We leave this as an exercise for the student. Extensive tables of

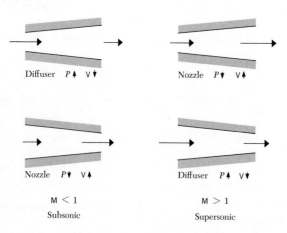

Diffuser P▲ V▼   Nozzle P▼ V▲

Nozzle P▼ V▲   Diffuser P▲ V▼

M < 1   M > 1   **FIG. 13·8** *Effect of area change*
Subsonic   Supersonic   *in subsonic and supersonic flow*

these results are available,† and a short table for $k = 1.4$ is included as Table B·18.

To illustrate the use of the Isentropic Flow Tables, let's redo the previous example for the design of a supersonic nozzle, but this time using the gas tables. Let's treat the exit pressure of 15 psia as specified, and the exit Mach number as a quantity to be determined.

State 1

$P_0 = 80$ psia   assume $V_1 = 0$
$T_0 = 960°R$

State 2

$P_2 = 15$ psia
$s_2 = s_1$

Let us first find the final Mach number. Now,

$$\frac{P_2}{P_0} = \frac{15}{80} = 0.1875$$

Using this value for P/P_0, we find from Table B·18

$M_2 = 1.75$ (interpolating)

We have thus immediately determined that the nozzle is supersonic since $M_2 > 1$. Since the ratio of P_2/P_0 is less than the *critical pressure ratio* $(P*/P_0 = 0.528$ for $k = 1.4)$, this had to be the case.

We must establish the throat conditions before we can calculate any flow areas. Using the ratios at $M = 1$,

$P* = 0.528 \times 80 = 42.3$ psia
$T* = 0.833 \times 960 = 800°R$

Now,

$$\rho_0 = \frac{P_0}{RT_0} = \frac{80 \times 144}{53.3 \times 960} = 0.225 \text{ lbm/ft}^3$$

thus

$\rho* = 0.634 \times 0.225 = 0.143 \text{ lbm/ft}^3$

Alternatively,

$$\rho* = \frac{P*}{RT*} = \frac{42.3 \times 144}{53.3 \times 800} = 0.143 \text{ lbm/ft}^3$$

† See Keenan and Kaye, *Gas Tables*, John Wiley and Sons, Inc., New York, 1948.

At the throat†

$$M = 1 = \frac{V}{c}$$

$$c^* = \sqrt{g_c k R T^*} = 1385 \text{ ft/sec}$$

$$V = 1385 \text{ ft/sec}$$

Thus

$$A^* = \frac{\dot{M}}{\rho^* V^*} = \frac{100}{0.143 \times 1385} = 0.50 \text{ ft}^2$$

in agreement with the previous result. Finally, at the exit, we read (for $M = 1.75$) the various ratios and then calculate as follows:

$$\frac{T}{T_0} = 0.620 \qquad\qquad T = 0.620 \times 960 = 595°\text{R}$$

$$M^* \equiv \frac{V}{V^*} = 1.509 \qquad V = 1.509 \times 1385 = 2090 \text{ ft/sec}$$

$$\frac{A}{A^*} = 1.386 \qquad\qquad A = 1.386 \times 0.50 = 0.70 \text{ ft}^2$$

$$\frac{\rho}{\rho_0} = 0.303 \qquad\qquad \rho = 0.303 \times 0.225 = 0.068 \text{ lbm/ft}^3$$

The answers are in good agreement with the previous example, although slide rule and interpolation errors show up in some values.

A relationship between the flow rate, throat area, and stagnation state is useful. We start with

$$\dot{M} = A^* \rho^* V^*$$

Manipulating and substituting for V^*

$$\dot{M} = A^* \frac{\rho^*}{\rho_0} \rho_0 \sqrt{g_c k R T^*} = \frac{\rho^*}{\rho_0} \sqrt{g_c k R \left(\frac{T^*}{T_0}\right)} A^* \rho_0 \sqrt{T_0}$$

$$= \frac{\rho^*}{\rho_0} \sqrt{g_c k R \left(\frac{T^*}{T_0}\right)} A^* \frac{P_0}{R T_0} \sqrt{T_0}$$

$$= \left(\frac{\rho^*}{\rho_0} \sqrt{\frac{g_c k}{R} \frac{T^*}{T_0}}\right) A^* \frac{P_0}{\sqrt{T_0}} \qquad (13 \cdot 32)$$

The term in parentheses is a constant, and a dimensional number for a given gas. For air, one has

$$\blacktriangleright \qquad \dot{M} = 0.532 A^* \frac{P_0}{\sqrt{T_0}} \qquad \textit{for air} \qquad (13 \cdot 33)$$

† Note that c^* is denoted by V^* in many tables. Also,

$$M^* \equiv \frac{V}{V^*} = \frac{V}{c^*}$$

where $\dot{M}$ is in lbm/sec

A^* is in ft^2
P_0 is in lbf/ft^2
T_0 is in °R

This is called Fliegner's formula.

We remark that the sonic state, like the stagnation state, is a *reference* state which may or may not occur in the flow. Hence, the concept of A^* is useful even in purely subsonic compressible flows.

13·7 CHOKING IN ISENTROPIC FLOW

Suppose we have a converging duct fed (Fig. 13·9) at P_0, T_0 and discharging into a box in which the back pressure on the nozzle P_B can be varied. Imagine starting with $P_B = P_0$ (curve *1*). Then, if we drop the back pressure a little (curve *2*) there will be a little flow through the nozzle. The nozzle exit pressure P_E will be equal to P_B as long as no shock waves form in the flow. As we shall see in the next section, shock waves form only in supersonic flows, so long as the flow is subsonic at the exit $P_B = P_E$. As we drop P_B the exit Mach number M_E will increase, but because of the duct geometry, $M_E = 1$ forms an upper limit. The sonic condition will be reached at E (curve *3*) when $P_B/P_0 = P^*/P_0$, which for $k = 1.4$ occurs when $P_B/P_0 = 0.528$. At this point the flow rate is given by Eq. (13·33). *This is the maximum flow that can be passed by this nozzle for the given stagnation condition.* The duct is said to be *choked* when $M_E = 1$, and the value of P_B at this point is called the *critical back pressure.* If we drop P_B further, the news that P_B has decreased cannot propagate upstream against the sonic flow, and hence the same maximum flow will

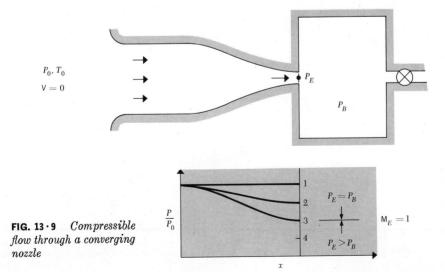

FIG. 13·9 *Compressible flow through a converging nozzle*

FIG. 13·10 *Choking in a converging nozzle*

be maintained for all $P_B < P^*$. For $P_B > P^*$ we can "yell" upstream, request-ing more flow, and our call will be heard. But for $P_B < P^*$ our shouts are swept downstream faster than they can propagate upstream, and our request goes unanswered. Figure 13·10 shows the behavior of $\dot{M}$ and P_E/P_0 with P_B/P_0.

Choked flow (or critical flow) nozzles are often used as flow-rate measuring devices. Since the flow rate is independent of back pressure in the choked con-ditions, measurement of P_0, T_0, and A^* suffice to fix $\dot{M}$. Choked nozzles also provide a means for maintaining a steady flow into a system, such as a chemical reactor, independent of fluctuations in the reaction chamber pressure.

13·8 ISENTROPIC FLOW IN CONVERGENT-DIVERGENT PASSAGES

To get to supersonic velocities it is necessary to have a *converging-diverging* nozzle. Figure 13·11 illustrates what happens in this case as the back pressure

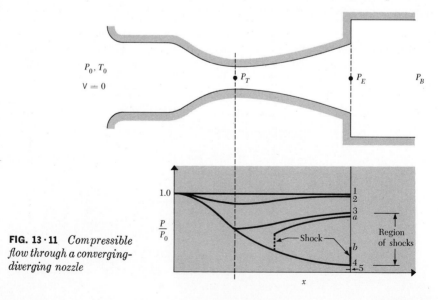

FIG. 13·11 *Compressible flow through a converging-diverging nozzle*

is lowered. Again, decreasing the back pressure from state 1 causes flow to start. The flow accelerates to the throat but since $(P_T/P_0) > (P^*/P_0)$ the velocity is subsonic at the throat so that the diverging portion of the duct acts as a simple subsonic diffuser, and the pressure rises again (curve 2). At some back pressure the velocity in the throat reaches the sonic value and M = 1. The velocity can then either decelerate with a pressure rise to 3 or continue to accelerate. Point 4 represents a back pressure for which acceleration occurs *isentropically* such that the flow is supersonic at the nozzle exit and $P_{E4} = P_{B4}$. This condition of supersonic flow past the throat with isentropic conditions and the exit pressure equal to the back pressure is called the "design" pressure ratio of the nozzle. If the pressure is lowered to state 5 no further decrease in *exit* pressure occurs and the adjustment in pressure occurs outside the nozzle.

The conditions between 3 and 4 represent an exit pressure ratio P_E/P_0 which requires a shock to occur in the diverging section of the duct. A shock is a highly irreversible phenomenon and consequently represents a nonisentropic flow condition. We shall study shocks in the next section.

Let's first do an example. Air with $k = 1.4$ flows through a convergent-divergent nozzle with a throat area of 1 in². The stagnation conditions are $T_0 = 960°R$, $P_0 = 200$ psia. Let's first find the maximum possible flow rate.

We know that the maximum flow occurs when M = 1 at the throat. Under these conditions Fliegner's formula (Eq. 13·33) for air gives

$$\dot{M} = \frac{0.532 \times 200 \times 144 \times \frac{1}{144}}{\sqrt{960}} = 3.44 \text{ lbm/sec}$$

The throat conditions are then

$P^* = 0.528(P_0) = 105.5$ psia
$T^* = 0.833(T_0) = 800°R$

Suppose now that the nozzle exit has an area of 2.2 in.²; let's determine the exit conditions assuming *isentropic* flow through the nozzle and M = 1 at the throat. The question immediately arises as to whether the diverging section acts as a supersonic nozzle or a subsonic diffuser. We shall work out both cases. In Table B·18 we see that there are two conditions for $A/A^* = 2.2/1 = 2.2$. One corresponds to $M_E = 2.305$ and one to $M_E = 0.275$.

For M = 2.305 we read values and then calculate the exit condition as follows:

$$\frac{P}{P_0} = 0.079 \qquad P_E = 15.8 \text{ psia}$$

$$\frac{T}{T_0} = 0.484 \qquad T_E = 464°R$$

$$\frac{\rho}{\rho_0} = 0.163 \qquad \rho_E = 0.163 \frac{P_0}{RT_0} = 0.092 \text{ lb/ft}^3$$

$$M^* \equiv \frac{V^*}{V} = 1.758$$

Now the exit velocity can be determined from either $V = 1.758\ V^*$ or from

$$V_E = M_E c_E = 2.305\ \sqrt{g_c k R T_E}$$

From the latter we find

$$V_E = 2430\ \text{ft/sec}$$

Let's check by determining $\dot{M}$ at the exit.

$$\dot{M} = \rho A V = 0.092 \times \left(\frac{2.2}{144}\right) \times 2430 = 3.44\ \text{lbm/sec}$$

in agreement with our value determined at the throat.

The subsonic exit condition is handled in a similar manner. For $M = 0.275$,

$$\frac{P}{P_0} = 0.948 \qquad\qquad P_E = 189\ \text{psia}$$

$$\frac{T}{T_0} = 0.985 \qquad\qquad T_E = 945°\text{R}$$

$$M^* = \frac{V^*}{V} = 0.299 \qquad V_E = 0.275\ \sqrt{g_c k R T_E} = 415\ \text{ft/sec}$$

Which of these two solutions is correct? The answer is that both are correct. For isentropic flow with $M = 1$ at the throat, the exit condition can be at either the calculated subsonic or supersonic condition. However, what would happen in an actual laboratory test would depend upon how the test was made. If the back pressure were gradually lowered from point *1* to point *3*, the flow would be subsonic at the exit. Continued lowering of the pressure would result in a shock wave occurring in the divergent sections of the nozzle until the pressure was reduced to state 4, at which point the flow would be supersonic in the divergent section *1* (see Fig. 13·11).

The student probably knows that modern rocket motors use convergent-divergent nozzles. He may be surprised to learn that steam turbines also use such nozzles to produce high-velocity flow. Supersonic airplane engines use convergent-divergent passages in the opposite manner, taking an initially supersonic inlet flow down to a low subsonic speed suitable for compression and combustion (see the example ending the chapter).

13·9 SHOCK WAVES

We have seen that under certain conditions the flow in the divergent section of a supersonic nozzle appears to lie in between two isentropic paths, and on Fig. 13·11 we designated this region as one where shock waves occur.

Experiments reveal that shock waves are highly localized irreversibilities in the flow. In a layer of the order of a few molecular mean-free paths thick the flow passes from a supersonic to a subsonic state, the velocity decreases

FIG. 13·12   *The control volume for analysis of shock waves*

markedly, and the pressure sharply rises. Enormous decelerations are imposed on a fluid particle passing through a shock, decelerations produced by very strong viscous effects within the shock layer.

Analysis of the details of the shock structure is a very complex problem in compressible viscous nonequilibrium flow. However, the overall changes that occur across the shock can be analyzed by control-volume methods if we place the boundaries just upstream and downstream of the shock. At the boundaries viscous effects can be neglected, and thermodynamic equilibrium assumed, which greatly simplifies the problem. We shall treat only *normal* shocks, that is, shock waves perpendicular to the flow.

Shocks provide an excellent example of an analysis that combines *all* of the thermodynamic principles with the momentum principle. The control volume that we use is shown in Fig. 13·12. Assuming steady flow, steady state, and neglecting energy transfer as heat from the control volume, application of these basic principles leads to the following equations. Note that the subscripts x and y denote the upstream and downstream states, respectively.

Continuity

$$\frac{\dot{M}}{A} = \rho_x \mathsf{V}_x = \rho_y \mathsf{V}_y \qquad (13\cdot34)$$

Momentum

$$A(P_x - P_y) = \frac{\dot{M}}{g_c}(\mathsf{V}_y - \mathsf{V}_x) \qquad (13\cdot35)$$

Energy

$$h_x + \frac{\mathsf{V}_x^2}{2g_c} = h_y + \frac{\mathsf{V}_y^2}{2g_c} = h_0 \qquad (13\cdot36)$$

Second Law

$$s_y - s_x \geq 0 \qquad (13\cdot37)$$

When combined with equations of state, Eqs. (13·34) to (13·36) will suffice to solve for the downstream conditions given the upstream conditions, and Eq. (13·37) will rule out those solutions that are not possible.

Some insight can be obtained by studying two partial solutions of these equations. We introduce the *mass velocity G*,

$$G \equiv \rho V \tag{13.38}$$

Note that G is the mass flow rate per unit of area. The continuity equation tells us that G is constant in the flow. Combining the continuity and energy equations, and dropping the x and y subscripts,

$$h_0 = h + \frac{G^2}{2g_c\rho^2} = \text{constant} \tag{13.39}$$

Given the values of G and h_0, this equation relates h and ρ, and hence will trace out a line on any thermodynamic plane. This line, the locus of points with the same mass velocity and stagnation enthalpy, is called a *Fanno line*. The end states of our shock wave must lie somewhere on this line.

The Fanno line is of some interest in another connection. Adiabatic flow in a constant-area duct with friction, when modeled in a one-dimensional manner, has both constant G and constant h_0, and hence must follow a Fanno line. We shall discuss this process later in this chapter.

The second partial solution is obtained from a combination of the continuity and momentum equations. Dropping the subscripts, the momentum equation (Eq. 13.35) may be written in terms of the *impulse pressure I* as

$$I \equiv P + \frac{\rho V^2}{g_c} = \text{constant}$$

Combining with continuity,

$$I = P + \frac{G^2}{\rho g_c} \tag{13.40}$$

Given the values for I and G, this equation relates P and ρ, and hence will trace out another line on any thermodynamic plane. This line is the locus of states with the same impulse pressure and mass velocity, and is called a *Rayleigh* line. The end states of our shock must lie somewhere on this line since $I_x = I_y$ and $G_x = G_y$.

The Rayleigh line is also a model for flow in a constant-area duct with heat transfer, but *without* friction. While this is not a very realistic situation, certain qualitative features of the model process are relevant to real compressible flow heat-transfer processes, and we shall discuss it later in this chapter.

Since the end state of the shock must lie on both the Fanno and Rayleigh lines, the end states must be fixed by their intersection, as shown in Fig. 13.13. Only the intersection state of lower entropy can be the upstream state x, and hence the shock process must pass from the lower to the upper intersection in Fig. 13.13. This graphical shock solution method is particularly useful for shocks in real gases, where the absence of simple algebraic equations of state precludes analytic solution of the shock equations.

If we use the perfect gas with constant c_P as a fluid model, closed-form

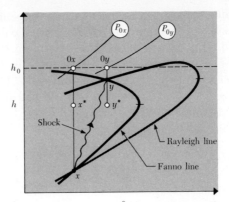

FIG. 13·13   *The shock process on the h-s plot*

algebraic solutions can be obtained for the shock equations. For such a gas the impulse pressure is

$$P + \frac{\rho V^2}{g_c} = P + \frac{\rho M^2 c^2}{g_c} = P + \frac{\rho(g_c k R T) M^2}{g_c}$$
$$= P(1 + k M^2) \tag{13·41}$$

Since the impulse pressure has the same value on both sides of the shock wave,

$$\blacktriangleright \qquad \frac{P_y}{P_x} = \frac{1 + k M_x^2}{1 + k M_y^2} \tag{13·42}$$

Since the stagnation enthalpy is constant, for the perfect gas the isentropic stagnation temperatures are identical on both sides of the shock,

$$T_{0x} = T_{0y} \tag{13·43}$$

and hence, from Eq. (13·21)

$$\blacktriangleright \qquad \frac{T_y}{T_x} = \frac{1 + (k-1) M_x^2 / 2}{1 + (k-1) M_y^2 / 2} \tag{13·44}$$

The continuity equation gives

$$\blacktriangleright \qquad \frac{\rho_y}{\rho_x} = \frac{M_x c_x}{M_y c_y} = \sqrt{\frac{T_x}{T_y}} \frac{M_x}{M_y} \tag{13·45}$$

The perfect-gas equation may be put in a similar form,

$$\frac{P_x}{P_y} = \frac{\rho_x}{\rho_y} \frac{T_x}{T_y} \tag{13·46}$$

Equations (13·42) to (13·46) may be combined to obtain one equation relating M_x and M_y. One finds

$$\blacktriangleright \qquad M_y^2 = \frac{M_x^2 + 2/(k-1)}{2k M_x^2 / (k-1) - 1} \tag{13·47}$$

Thus for a given M_x we can now solve directly for M_y. Table B·19 gives the results of this computation for several values of M_x. Once these are determined, Eq. (13·42) can be used to determine P_y/P_x as listed in the table. Equation (13·44) can then be used to determine T_y/T_x. Equation (13·45) is then used to fix the conditions on ρ_y/ρ_x and V_y/V_x. The last column listed in the table gives P_{0y}/P_{0x}, and the irreversibility of the shock shows up as a reduction in isentropic stagnation pressure (see Fig. 13·13). By suitable manipulations, one may show that

▶
$$\frac{P_{0y}}{P_{0x}} = \left[\frac{(k+1)M_x^2/2}{1+(k-1)M_x^2/2} \right]^{k/(k-1)} \bigg/ \left[\frac{2k}{k+1}M_x^2 - \frac{k-1}{k+1} \right]^{k/(k-1)}$$
(13·48)

Calculations show that if $M_x > 1$, $M_y < 1$, and the flow abruptly slows down as it passes through the shock. Much of the kinetic energy upstream is suddenly scrambled and converted to molecular (internal) energy by the shock, and hence the flow leaves the shock slower and hotter than it entered. The second-law equation says that the reverse process, that is, a sudden *unscrambling* of the internal energy into organized kinetic energy, is impossible.

A bullet or an airplane moving at supersonic speed carries a *bow shock* (Fig. 13·14) with it. The shock suddenly announces the coming of the object, and quickly moves the motionless air out of the way. The bow shock is curved, but at the nose of the object is perpendicular to the flow, and the theory of normal shocks developed here applies. The sudden increase in temperature as the flow passes through the shock makes it very hot near the nose, and reentry bodies must have adequate protection against this high-temperature gas. The bow shock is weak far from the body, and hence approaches a Mach cone. Some shock pressure rise remains even at great distances from the body, and it is this pressure jump that is known as *sonic boom*.

To illustrate the use of the normal shock tables and equations, suppose a stream of air with a Mach number of 3 passes through a normal shock. The upstream pressure and temperature are 20 psia and 40°F. Let's calculate the downstream conditions.

FIG. 13·14   *A bow shock*

From Table B·19, for $M_x = 3.0$,

$$M_y = 0.475$$

$$\frac{P_y}{P_x} = 10.333$$

$$\frac{T_y}{T_x} = 2.679$$

$$\frac{\rho_y}{\rho_x} = \frac{V_x}{V_y} = 3.857$$

$$\frac{P_{0y}}{P_{0x}} = 0.328$$

Thus

$$P_y = 10.333 \times 20 = 206.66 \text{ psia}$$
$$T_y = 2.679 \times 500 = 1340°\text{R}$$

The magnitude of the pressure and temperature jumps should be impressive. What about the velocity change?

$$M_x = \frac{V_x}{c_x} = 3.0 \qquad c_x = \sqrt{g_c k R T} = 1092 \text{ ft/sec}$$

$$V_x = 3276 \text{ ft/sec}$$

$$V_y = \frac{3276}{3.857} = 850 \text{ ft/sec}$$

To calculate the isentropic stagnation pressures we first use Table B·18, at $M = 3$,

$$\frac{P}{P_0} = 0.02722 = \frac{P_x}{P_{0x}}$$

so,

$$P_{0x} = \frac{20}{0.02722} = 743 \text{ psia}$$

and

$$P_{0y} = 743 \times 0.328 = 248 \text{ psia}$$

Let's verify that the entropy change across the shock is positive. Using Eq. (8·27),

$$s_y - s_x = c_P \ln \frac{T_y}{T_x} - R \ln \frac{P_y}{P_x}$$

$$= 0.24 \ln (2.679) - \frac{53.3}{778} \times \ln (10.33)$$

$$= 0.078 \text{ Btu/lbm-°R} > 0$$

A very useful result for normal shocks follows from Fliegner's formula (Eq. 13·33). Since both $\dot{M}$ and T_0 are the same on both sides of a normal shock, the product A^*P_0 is also preserved. Hence

$$\blacktriangleright \qquad \frac{A_y^*}{A_x^*} = \frac{P_{0x}}{P_{0y}} \qquad\qquad\qquad (13\cdot49)$$

13·10 COMPRESSIBILITY EFFECTS IN FLOWS WITH FRICTION AND HEAT TRANSFER

We mentioned in the last section that the Fanno line equation also holds for a one-dimensional model of adiabatic flow in a constant-area duct with friction. While the quantitative predictions of this simple model are not very accurate, the qualitative effects are correct, and we shall discuss these now.

For adiabatic flow the entropy must increase in the flow direction. Hence, a Fanno process must follow its Fanno line to the right (Fig. 13·15). We know from our normal shock calculation that the upper branch of the Fanno curve corresponds to *subsonic* flow. The nose corresponds to the sonic point. Hence, since friction will tend to move the fluid state to the right on the Fanno line, the Mach number of subsonic flows *increases* in the downstream direction, while in supersonic flows friction acts to decrease the Mach number. *Friction therefore tends to drive the flow toward the sonic point* (Fig. 13·15).

In the previous chapters we analyzed adiabatic friction flows by neglecting the flow kinetic energy, and found that the flow enthalpy remained unchanged. Now we see that this is only a valid model at low Mach numbers, where the Fanno line approaches a line of constant h (Fig. 13·15).

Suppose we have a short duct with a given h_0 and G, that is, a given Fanno line, with a given subsonic exit Mach number. If we add more length to the duct, the new exit Mach number will be increased, but the exit state will lie on the same Fanno line. If we lengthen the duct sufficiently to make the exit state sonic, there is nowhere else to go on the Fanno line, and a further increase in length is impossible without a reduction in the mass flow rate. Hence, subsonic flows can become *choked* by friction. There is a *maximum flow rate* that can be passed by a pipe with given stagnation conditions. This has important consequences in engineering practice. Choking also occurs in supersonic flow

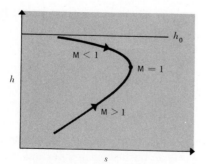

FIG. 13·15 *A Fanno line on the h-s plot*

FIG. 13·16 *A Rayleigh line on the h-s plot*

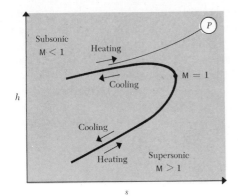

FIG. 13·16 *A Rayleigh line on the h-s plot*

with friction, usually in a very short length. It is this that makes it very difficult to use such flows in applications.

Flows with heating or cooling in a constant-area duct, *neglecting friction*, may be treated in a one-dimensional model by the *Rayleigh* process. This model is qualitatively correct but quantitatively accurate only at very low Mach numbers. The Rayleigh process diagram is shown in Fig. 13·16. Since this idealized process is reversible, the direction of entropy change is determined by the sign of the heat input, as shown in Fig. 13·16. We have also identified the subsonic and supersonic branches and the sonic point.

Heating a compressible flow has the same effect as friction, namely, the Mach number is driven toward unity. Hence, for a given flow rate, there is a *maximum heat input* for which the prescribed flow can be passed by the duct. Compressible flows therefore exhibit *choking due to heating*, which has very important applications, particularly in the design of very high-temperature gas heat exchangers or gas-cooled nuclear reactors.

In the earlier chapters we often modeled steady-flow heating or cooling by a constant-pressure process. As Fig. 13·16 suggests, this is valid in frictionless flow at low Mach numbers, where the changes in the kinetic energy of the flow are negligible.

It is not obvious from the curves, but *cooling* increases the flow stagnation pressure. Hence, in principle a nonmechanical pump can be made by *cooling* a compressible flow. This wonderful idea is defeated by friction, which rears its ugly head in all real devices and outweighs the pumping effects of cooling.

13·11 EXAMPLES OF COMPRESSIBLE FLOW CALCULATIONS

Convergent-divergent duct flow. We can now see what happens in the convergent-divergent nozzle analyzed earlier in Sec. 13·8 (see Fig. 13·11). When the back pressure lies in between states 3 and 4, then it is impossible for the fluid to follow an *isentropic path* down the nozzle and the fluid must undergo a shock in the divergent portion of the nozzle. As the back pressure is lowered, the shock moves down the nozzle until it just stands in the exit plane at condition b. As the pressure is lowered between b and 4, the pressure in the exit plane is lower than the back pressure. A compression outside of the nozzle must occur. If the back pressure is lowered below state 4, then there is an expansion outside of the nozzle. Note that a lowering of the pressure below 3 does not increase the flow rate, since the conditions at the throat are already sonic.

Let's determine the exit conditions for which M = 1 at the throat and the flow in the divergent section is subsonic throughout. Recall the design parameters (Sect. 13·5):

$$P_0 = 80 \text{ psia}$$
$$T_0 = 960°R$$
$$A_{\text{throat}} = 0.505 \text{ ft}^2$$
$$A_{\text{exit}} = 0.70 \text{ ft}^2$$

Thus,

$$\frac{A_E}{A^*} = \frac{0.70}{0.505} = 1.386$$

Corresponding to this value in Table B·18, we find a choice,

$$M = 0.47 \quad \text{or} \quad M = 1.75$$

We want the subsonic case, so for M = 0.47,

$$\frac{P}{P_0} = 0.856 \quad P_E = 0.856 \times 80 = 68.48 \text{ psia}$$
$$\frac{T}{T_0} = 0.956 \quad T_E = 0.956 \times 960 = 919°R$$

Now, let's determine the exit condition for which M = 1 at the throat and $P_E = 60$ psia. This condition has a P_E less than the all-subsonic case of 68.48 psia, but greater than the design condition for all-supersonic flow with $P_E = 15$ psia. We therefore expect a shock in the divergent section of the nozzle. The h-s process representation for this case is shown in Fig. 13·17.

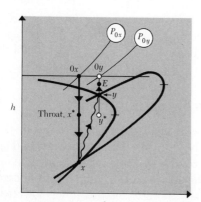

FIG. 13·17 *The process*

We have to find a solution technique which will lead to the given condition that $P_E = 60$ psia. We thus need to find a condition for M_x for which the rise in pressure across the shock to P_y plus the subsequent pressure rise in the subsonic diffuser section leads to $P_E = 60.0$ psia. Let us guess some M_x values and find the solution by trial and error. Assume

$$M_x = 1.50$$

Then, from Table B·19,

$$M_y = 0.701$$
$$\frac{P_{0y}}{P_{0x}} = \frac{A_x^*}{A_y^*} = 0.930 \qquad \frac{P_y}{P_x} = 2.458$$

At $M = 1.5$, from Table B·18,

$$\frac{P_x}{P_{0x}} = 0.272$$

So,

$$P_x = 0.272 \times 80 = 21.8 \text{ psia}$$
$$P_y = 2.458 \times 21.8 = 53.45 \text{ psia}$$

The reference area A_y^* does not occur in the flow, but is nonetheless useful. Its value is

$$A_y^* = \frac{0.505}{0.930} = 0.543 \text{ ft}^2$$

Also,

$$P_{0y} = 0.930 \, P_{0x} = 0.930 \times 80 = 74.5 \text{ psia}$$

Now, since the flow is isentropic from y to the exit,

$$A_y^* = A_E^* \qquad \text{and} \qquad P_{0y} = P_{0E}$$

Then,

$$\left(\frac{A}{A^*}\right)_E = \frac{0.70}{0.543} = 1.290$$

This will establish the exit state in the isentropic flow table. Table B·18 gives, for $A/A^* = 1.290$ (subsonic branch),

$$M = 0.527$$
$$\frac{P}{P_0} = 0.827$$

So,

$$P_E = 0.827 \times 74.5 = 62.2 \text{ psia}$$

But we wanted to come out with $P_E = 60$ psia. A repeat with $M_x = 1.54$ does the job.

Finally, let's determine the back pressure for which $M = 1$ at the throat and the shock wave stands just in the exit. From Table B·19, for

$$M_x = M_E = 1.75 \qquad \frac{P_y}{P_x} = 3.406$$

We know that $P_E = P_x = 15$ psia in this case, and hence

$$P_B = P_y = 3.406 \times 15 = 51 \text{ psia}$$

We have thus determined a complete range of operation for the nozzle. For $80 > P_b > 68.48$ the flow is subsonic in the nozzle; for $68.48 > P_b > 51$ psia a shock stands in the divergent section of the nozzle; for $51 > P_b > 15$ the adjustment from the exit pressure to the back pressure occurs as a compression outside the nozzle; for $P_b = 15$ psia the nozzle is at the design condition; for $P_b < 15$ psia the adjustment from the exit pressure to the back pressure occurs as an expansion outside the nozzle. The expansion and compression processes outside the nozzle are complicated, and involve a diamond pattern of shock waves and expansions. This sort of pattern is observed in the engine discharge during launch of a rocket, which passes through all these regimes during startup and passage up through the atmosphere.

Steam nozzle design. Suppose we want to accelerate a 4 lbm/sec steam flow from stagnation at 150 psia, 700°F to a Mach number of 1.0. We must first decide how to model the fluid, that is, how much of the perfect-gas model to employ. The value of k listed in Table B·6 for steam is 1.33 and this value is all right for low-pressure ($P < 200$ psia) steam. If we treat steam as a perfect gas,

$$\frac{P^*}{P_0} = \left(\frac{2}{k+1}\right)^{k/(k-1)} = 0.543$$

Note that this expression is not too sensitive to the k value used. So let's presume that we want to expand down to

$$P_E = 0.543 \times 150 = 81.5 \text{ psia}$$

However, Fig. B·2 shows that $h = h(T, P)$ in the exit region of this nozzle, and hence the real-gas effects on velocity and density are probably significant. We shall therefore use the real-gas enthalpy and density data in the calculation. The local velocity is calculated from the energy equation,

$$V = \sqrt{2g_c(h_0 - h)}$$

The calculation is made by following a line of constant s on the Mollier diagram. Continuity is used to calculate the local flow area. The calculation is summarized in Table 13·3. Note that the exit density ratio is

$$\frac{\rho_E}{\rho_0} = \frac{4.55}{7.35} = 0.618$$

TABLE 13·3

P, psia	h, Btu/lbm-°F	V, ft/sec	v, ft³/lbm	A, ft²
150	1375	0	4.55	—
125	1353	1048	5.20	0.0198
100	1327	1548	6.18	0.0160
81.5	1304	1880	7.35	0.0156

For a perfect gas with $k = 1.33$, the corresponding ratio is 0.635, which is somewhat off the real-gas value. However, this area is slowly varying near $M = 1$, and hence our design of 0.0156 ft² is probably quite adequate.

Nuclear ramjet design. Consider a nuclear ramjet engine as pictured in Fig. 13·18a. The engine is to be designed to fly at Mach 3 through air at $-60°F$ and 2 psia. The reactor will heat the air to 1600°F and the pressure drop through the reactor is 5 psia. The flow velocity in the reactor is low, so states 4 and 5 are approximated as stagnation states. The areas are:

$$A_1 = 10 \text{ ft}^2$$
$$A_2 = A_3 = 2.8 \text{ ft}^2$$
$$A_7 = 15 \text{ ft}^2$$

A_6 is adjustable. This problem will entail a preliminary design of the ramjet engine.

(a) *A nuclear ramjet engine*

(b) *The process representation*

FIG. 13·18

(c) *The control volume for the momentum analysis*

We shall make various other modeling assumptions as we do the analysis. Since the inlet flow is supersonic, and we want to slow the flow to a low subsonic speed where we can heat it without chances of choking, we must somehow make the flow subsonic. While it is theoretically possible to design a convergent-divergent diffuser passage for steady flow, such passages of fixed geometry cannot be *started* because the bow shock must be swallowed and moved through the entire engine. We can, however, design the engine to permit the shock to stand in the throat, where the shock stagnation pressure drop loss is least. The divergent portion then acts as a subsonic diffuser, but because of boundary-layer separation produced by the shock the subsonic diffusion process is far from isentropic. In order to account for separation effects in the subsonic diffuser, we can assume some typical value for the *diffuser pressure recovery factor*, defined by

$$C_P = \frac{\text{actual pressure rise}}{\text{isentropic pressure rise}}$$

A value of C_P of 0.6 might be typical, and we shall use this in our analysis. We shall treat the supersonic diffuser and nozzle as isentropic flows, which is reasonable for a first analysis. Figure 13·18b shows the h-s process representation drawn considering these assumptions.

The analysis consists of working our way through the engine in the usual manner.

State 1

M = 3 $A = 10$ ft² $P = 2$ psia $T = 400°$R specified

From Table B·16, at M = 3

$$\frac{P}{P_0} = 0.0272 \qquad \frac{T}{T_0} = 0.357 \qquad \frac{A}{A^*} = 4.234$$

So,

$$P_0 = \frac{2}{0.0272} = 73.4 \text{ psia}$$

$$T_0 = \frac{400}{0.357} = 1120°\text{R}$$

$$A^* = \frac{10}{4.234} = 2.36 \text{ ft}^2$$

The reference quantities above apply for the process 1-2. Also, at 1,

$c_1 = \sqrt{32.2 \times 1.4 \times 53.3 \times 400} = 982$ ft/sec
$V_1 = 3 \times 982 = 2946$ ft/sec

State 2

$A = 2.8 \text{ ft}^2$ specified

$$\frac{A}{A^*} = \frac{2.8}{2.36} = 1.186$$

From Table B·18, at $A/A^* = 1.186$, $M_2 = 1.51$

$$\frac{P}{P_0} = 0.269 \qquad P_2 = 0.269 \times 73.4 = 19.6 \text{ psia}$$

State 2 corresponds to the upstream (x) state for the normal shock.

State 3

Shock at $M_x = 1.51$. From Table B·19,

$$M_y = M_3 = 0.697$$

$$\frac{P_{0y}}{P_{0x}} = 0.926$$

$$\frac{P_y}{P_x} = 2.49$$

$$\frac{A_x^*}{A_y^*} = 0.926$$

So,

$$P_{03} = 0.926 \times 73.4 = 67.8 \text{ psia}$$
$$P_3 = 2.49 \times 19.6 = 48.6 \text{ psia}$$
$$A_3^* = \frac{2.36}{0.927} = 2.55 \text{ ft}^2$$

State 4

We assume that the velocity is sufficiently low that the local pressure and isentropic stagnation pressures will be identical. For example, for $M_4 = 0.2$, $P/P_0 = 0.493$ (Table B·18) and $A/A^* = 2.96$. Hence A_4 would have to be about $2.96 \times 2.55 = 7.5 \text{ ft}^2$, assuming isentropic diffusion. So, a sufficiently large area for nearly complete diffusion will be possible within the 10 ft² engine opening area. Then,

$$P_{4s} = P_{0y} = P_{03} = 67.8 \text{ psia}$$

If $C_P = 0.6$

$$P_4 = P_3 + C_P(P_{4s} - P_3) = 48.6 + 0.6 \times (67.8 - 48.6)$$
$$= 60.1 \text{ psia}$$

Since the flow is adiabatic from 1 to 4, h_0 and hence T_0 is constant from 1 to 4. Then,

$$T_{04} = T_4 = T_{01} = 1120°R$$

State 5

$P_4 - P_5 = 5$ psia specified, so
$P_5 = 60.1 - 5 = 55.1$ psia $= P_{05}$
$T_5 = 2060°R$ (specified) $= T_{05}$

States 6 and 7

The nozzle flow is modeled as isentropic. Any exit Mach number can be obtained by adjustment of A_6. Let's design to adjust A_6 so that P_7 matches the ambient pressure (2 psia) and the flow at 7 is supersonic.

$P_7 = 2$ psia $P_{07} = P_{05} = 55.1$ psia

So,

$$\left(\frac{P}{P_0}\right)_7 = \frac{2}{55.1} = 0.0363$$

In Table B·18, for $\frac{P}{P_0} = 0.0363$,

$M = 2.80$ $\frac{T}{T_0} = 0.389$ $\frac{A}{A*} = 3.50$

So, for *state 7*

$T_7 = 0.389 \times 2060 = 800°R$
$c_7 = \sqrt{32.2 \times 1.4 \times 53.3 \times 800} = 1380$ ft/sec
$V_7 = 2.80 \times 1380 = 3860$ ft/sec

The required throat area is then

$$A_6 = \frac{15}{3.50} = 4.29 \text{ ft}^2$$

Now, the flow rate can be calculated from the data at any point. Let's take point 1:

$$\rho_1 = \frac{P_1}{RT_1} = \frac{2 \times 144}{53.3 \times 400} = 0.0135 \text{ lbm/ft}^3$$
$$\dot{M} = A_1\rho_1V_1 = 10 \times 0.0135 \times 2946 = 400 \text{ lbm/sec}$$

The reactor power requirement is then

$$\dot{Q} = \dot{M}(h_5 - h_4) = \dot{M}c_P(T_5 - T_4)$$
$$= 400 \times 0.24(2060 - 1120) = 90,500 \text{ Btu/sec}$$
$$= 95.5 \text{ Mw}$$

Finally, let's calculate the force delivered to the air frame by the engine. Applying the momentum principle to the control volume of Fig. 13·18c, neglecting any skin friction drag on the engine and assuming that there is no net pressure force on the control volume (recall $P_1 = P_7$),

$$F = \frac{\dot{M}}{g_c} (V_7 - V_1) = \frac{400}{32.2} \times (3869 - 2946) = 11{,}360 \text{ lbf}$$

The specific impulse is

$$SI = \frac{F}{\dot{M}} = \frac{11{,}360}{400} = 28.4 \text{ lbf/(lbm/sec)}$$

Such propulsion systems have been suggested for use on airplanes such as the SST. The ramjet engines would be cut in after the plane has achieved supersonic speed and is at a high altitude and would run using conventional fuel sources, not nuclear energy.

This example deserves some discussion. Note that the exit Mach number was *less* than that at the inlet, and yet we derive thrust. This is because by heating the flow the stagnation temperature is increased, and thus the exit velocity is substantially bigger than the inlet. The specific impulse is *low* in comparison to subsonic jet engines (see Sec. 9·17). To achieve higher specific impulse we would have to increase the discharge velocity. If we wish to keep the exit pressure at 2 psia, the exit Mach number must be held at 2.80. The only hope is to increase the reactor outlet temperature, which is already pushing the metallurgical limit for an aircraft engine. If we could get to $T_5 = 2600°F$, then $V_7 = 4700$ ft/sec, the thrust would be 22,300 lbf, and the specific impulse would be a respectable 56 lbf/(lbm/sec), but the reactor power would be increased to about 190 Mw. A thrust of 22,000 lbf is comparable with modern jet engines; a power level of 190 Mw is comparable to the power requirements of a city of 200,000 people.

SELECTED READING

Obert, E. F., and R. L. Young, *Elements of Thermodynamics and Heat Transfer*, 2d ed., chap. 13, McGraw-Hill Book Company, New York, 1962.

Owczarek, J. A., *Fundamentals of Gas Dynamics*, chap. 1, sec. 6.2, International Textbook Company, Scranton, Pa., 1964.

Shapiro, A., *Dynamics and Thermodynamics of Compressible Fluid Flow*, vol. I, chaps. 1–7, The Ronald Press Company, New York, 1953.

QUESTIONS

13·1 Why is $F \neq Ma$ for a control volume?

13·2 What is the momentum principle?

13·3 Sketch the pressure distribution on the wall of a (convergent) rocket nozzle. This force is clearly down, so why does the rocket move up?

13·4 What is the isentropic stagnation state?

13·5 How is the speed of sound defined?

13·6 How would you determine the sound speed in a *real* gas from thermodynamic data?

13·7 What is one-dimensional gas dynamics?

13·8 When is the isentropic flow model reasonable?

13·9 What is choking?

13·10 What happens to the state of a gas as it passes through a shock wave?

13·11 How can a shock wave form?

13·12 What is the role of thermodynamics in gas dynamics theory?

PROBLEMS

13·1 A proposed electric jet car takes in atmospheric air (14.7 psia, 70°F) at a low speed through a vertical intake in its roof, and discharges hot gases to the rear at 1500 ft/sec. The air-flow rate is 5 lbm/sec and the pressure in the jet exhaust is 20 psia. The engine uses 500 kw of electrical power to compress and heat the air. Calculate the nozzle discharge area and the drag force on the body, neglecting the horizontal force between the wheels and the road.

13·2 The reaction control system for smaller space vehicles uses nitrogen, stored in a high-pressure bottle. When maneuvering is desired a valve is opened, allowing the gas to escape through a nozzle. The pressure upstream of the nozzle is typically about 250 psia, and the pressure in the jet at the nozzle exit plane is about 1 psia. Estimate the *specific impulse* (thrust force per unit of mass flow) of this system (the upstream temperature may be estimated as that of the vehicle, say 80°F). Typically one set of nozzles are sized to produce about 40 lbf thrust, and another set produces about 200 lbf. Estimate the flow rate through each of these nozzles during operation and the exit area of the nozzles.

13·3 In a hydrogen rocket, H_2 enters the nozzle at about 4000°R and 1000 psia; the pressure in the exit plane is about 1.5 psia. Estimate the specific impulse of this system, and calculate the required hydrogen flow rate for 2×10^6 lbf thrust. Calculate the nozzle exit area.

13·4 In an ion rocket engine cesium ions and electrons are accelerated by electric fields to about 0.0003 times the speed of light, mixed together to form a plasma, and emitted from the engine. Estimate the specific impulse of this system. Calculate the thrust force produced by expulsion of 100 lbm of cesium per day.

13·5 Discuss the differences between the applications of the three thrusting systems of Probs. 13·2, 13·3, and 13·4.

13·6 Consider steady frictionless, one-dimensional flow of a perfect gas in a constant area duct. Energy as heat is added to the flow from the walls of the duct. Under these conditions show that

(a) $\dfrac{d\rho}{\rho} + \dfrac{dV}{V} = 0$

(b) $\dfrac{dM}{M} = \dfrac{dV}{V} - \dfrac{1}{2}\dfrac{dT}{T}$

(c) $dP = \dfrac{1}{g_c} V^2 \, d\rho$

Which applies in other flow models?

13·7 Show that the model of Prob. 13·6 implies that the flow process is reversible.

13·8 When Newton first tried to compute the propagation velocity of a pressure pulse (speed of sound) he assumed that the wave process is isothermal (rather than isentropic). Calculate the error in the sonic velocity using this assumption for a perfect gas. What is the numerical value of this error for air at room conditions?

13·9 Consider one-dimensional flow of a perfect gas in a constant-area adiabatic duct without friction. Changes in state come about as a result of changes in elevation in the earth's gravitational force field, which acts in the negative z direction. Starting from first principles, derive the continuity, momentum, and energy equations in differential form. Then, discuss the direction of change (increase or decrease) of the Mach number, velocity, sound speed, density, pressure, stagnation pressure for a positive increase in altitude z.

13·10 Starting with the steady-state energy equation, show that the velocity of a perfect gas leaving a frictionless adiabatic nozzle is given by

$$V = \sqrt{2g_c P_o v_o \frac{k}{k-1}\left[1 - \left(\frac{P_e}{P_o}\right)^{(k-1)/k}\right]}$$

The subscripts o and e correspond to the stagnation (zero velocity) and exit states, respectively.

13·11 A plane flies at a low altitude at 700 ft/sec. Calculate the pressure rise that could be achieved if the air is brought nearly to rest by a diffuser in one of the engines. What is the pressure rise if the velocity is 2000 ft/sec? Can you see a way to take advantage of the pressure rise in a turbojet engine?

13·12 Calculate the speed of sound at 530°R in air, helium, sulfur dioxide, steam, and isobutane.

13·13 A diffuser is to be designed to reduce the Mach number of air from $M_1 = 0.75$ to $M_2 = 0.10$. Determine the diffuser area ratio A_1/A_2, assuming isentropic flow.

13·14 The standard atmosphere† is reproduced in short form in the table. Calculate the speed of sound at each of the given altitudes, and discuss the implications on the flight of a subsonic airplane (M = 0.9).

U.S. STANDARD ATMOSPHERE

Altitude, ft	Temperature, °R	°F	Pressure, in. Hg
0	518.67	59.0	29.92
10,000	483.67	23.3	20.57
20,000	447.41	−12.3	13.76
50,000	389.97	−69.7	3.44
100,000	408.57	−51.1	0.33
200,000	456.99	−2.67	0.58×10^{-2}

13·15 A vehicle moves at 2000 ft/sec through the atmosphere. Calculate the stagnation temperature on its nose as a function of altitude (see Prob. 13·14).

† U.S. Standard Atmosphere, 1962, U.S. Government Printing Office.

13·16 Consider a flying saucer moving at a Mach number of 7 at an altitude of 200,000 ft (see Prob. 13·14). What is the stagnation temperature at the nose of the saucer?

13·17 Steam flows at 1100 ft/sec, 80 psia, 450°F. Determine the stagnation pressure and temperature.

13·18 "Bernoulli's equation" may be written as $P_o = P + \dfrac{1}{2g_c} \rho V^2$. An equation that corrects for compressibility effects is

$$P_o = P + \frac{1}{2g_c} \rho V^2 \left(1 + \frac{M^2}{4} + \frac{2-k}{24} M^4 + \cdots \right)$$

Plot $C_P \equiv (P_o - P)2g_c/(\rho V^2)$. At what Mach number is the error in Bernoulli's equation 1 percent, 2 percent, and 10 percent? How would you calculate C_P at $M = 3$?

13·19 Derive the two equations given in Prob. 13·18. List all the assumptions for each equation.

13·20 A pitot-static tube records a static pressure of 4 psig and a difference between the impact and static pressures of 10 in. of mercury. The barometer reads 29.9 in. of mercury at 70°F. Compute the air velocity assuming the air is (a) incompressible, (b) compressible.

13·21 Derive the equation $(\partial P/\partial \rho)_s = c^2/g_c$ from the continuity and momentum equations rather than the energy and continuity equations as was done in the text.

13·22 Using the continuity, momentum, and energy equations for frictionless, one-dimensional adiabatic flow, show that the flow process is isentropic.

13·23 A large diffuser with an intake area of 2 ft² and an exit area of 6 ft² has air entering at 590°R at a pressure of 50 psia and a velocity of 750 ft/sec. Find the thrust on the diffuser if its outside surface is at atmospheric pressure.

13·24 A converging-diverging nozzle is designed such that the inlet area is 10 in.², the throat area is 2 in.², and the exit area is 4 in.² The inlet conditions are air at 100 psia, 540°R with a flow rate of 3.5 lbm/sec. Is the flow at the exit supersonic?

13·25 Air is accelerated by a nozzle in an isentropic process. The inlet velocity is 20 ft/sec and the exit velocity is 750 ft/sec. The inlet state is 68°F, 15 psia. Find the exit temperature, pressure, density, and the stagnation temperature and pressure.

13·26 It is desired to accelerate air through a converging nozzle whose exit area is 2 in.² If the upstream conditions are 50 psia, 200°F, what is the maximum flow that can pass through the nozzle? If the upstream pressure is doubled, how much is the maximum flow increased?

13·27 Determine the maximum flow for air, argon, carbon dioxide, and isobutane that can be passed through a converging nozzle if the upstream conditions are 100 psia at 500°R and the nozzle exit area is 1 in.²

13·28 A convergent nozzle has an exit diameter of 1 in. Air enters the nozzle at 50 psia and 240°F. Assuming isentropic flow, calculate the mass flow rates for an exit pressure of 40 psia, 26.4 psia, and 14.7 psia.

13·29 Low-velocity air enters the nozzles of a gas turbine at 2000°R and 60 psia. The nozzles are used to accelerate the air before it impinges upon the turbine blades.

Expansion in the nozzles is such that the air leaves at 15 psia. If 15 lbm/sec of air is flowing through each nozzle, find the exit velocity, the exit and throat areas, and the exit Mach number.

13·30 A converging nozzle has an efficiency of 0.94 and an exit pressure of 30 psia. If the entrance conditions are 40 psia, 140°F, compare the exit velocity and temperature to those that would occur if the nozzle were isentropic.

13·31 Dry steam flows through a converging nozzle such that the process is isentropic and follows the path $Pv^{1.3}$ = constant. If the inlet state is 200 psia, 750°F, determine the maximum flow rate possible for an exit area of 1 in.^{2} What is the flow rate if the exit pressure is 75 psia?

13·32 A nozzle is to be designed to provide 2.0 lbm/sec flow rate at an exit velocity of 2000 ft/sec. At the entry to the nozzle the stagnation pressure is 100 psia and stagnation temperature is 1500°R. Assume the flow is isentropic. Determine the area of the nozzle at the throat and at the exit if the gas is air. What is the exit Mach number?

13·33 Air enters a converging-diverging nozzle at 100 psia and 500°R and a low velocity. It is desired to accelerate this flow to M = 4. What are the exit pressure, temperature, and density? What are the throat temperature, pressure, and density? What is the ratio of exit area to throat area?

13·34 Air enters a converging-diverging nozzle at 200 psia with a temperature of 240°F. The exit throat area ratio is 1.55. If the exit velocity is subsonic but the throat velocity is sonic, determine the exit temperature and pressure assuming isentropic flow. If the exit velocity is supersonic, determine the exit temperature and pressure, again assuming that the flow is isentropic. If the back pressure is 100 psia, what is the nature of the flow in the diverging section of the nozzle?

13·35 Steam at 100 psia and 200°F of superheat expands isentropically in a nozzle to a pressure of 20 psia. Find the mass flow rate per square inch of throat area. How can you tell that this must be a converging-diverging nozzle ($k = 1.30$)?

13·36 A normal shock wave occurs such that the upstream conditions are Mach number 2.4, 540°R, 14.7 psia. Calculate the conditions behind the shock.

13·37 A simple ramjet engine is shown below. At operating conditions the following data have been obtained: $M_1 = 2.0$, altitude 20,000 ft ($T_1 = 447°R$, $P_1 = 6.7$ psia), $A_1 = 2.5$ ft^2, $M_2 = 0.2$, $T_3 = 3200°R$. It is known that at 4 the flow is choked, the fuel has a heating value of 20,000 Btu/lbm, and a normal shock takes place at point 1. Assume that $M_3 \approx M_2$. Find the flow rate, the area A_2, the exhaust velocity V_4, the fuel consumption, and the thrust. List all idealizations employed.

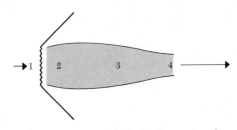

13·38 A blunt-shaped vehicle reenters the earth's atmosphere such that a Mach number of 10 is achieved. The shock wave stands slightly off of the body and is normal to the flow at the vehicle centerline. Estimate the conditions behind the normal shock ($T_x = -60°F$, $P_x = 2$ psia).

13·39 A blast wave caused by a nuclear explosion travels through still air (initially at 70°F and 14.7 psia) at a speed of 50,000 ft/sec. Estimate the changes in pressure and temperature observed as the wave passes over an observer. Will he enjoy this experience?

13·40 Air flows through a convergent-divergent nozzle with an upstream stagnation pressure of 50 psia and a throat area of 1 in.^{2} If a normal shock occurs where $A/A^* = 2.0$, what will be the Mach numbers on the upstream and downstream sides of the shock? If the Mach number in the exit plane is 0.5, what should be the back pressure to maintain the shock in the given location?

13·41 Consider a convergent-divergent nozzle operating with a shock wave in the divergent section of the nozzle. The upstream stagnation pressure is 200 psia at a temperature of 700°R. If the shock wave is located at the point where M = 1.8, find the exit pressure and Mach number, assuming that the exit area is three times the throat area.

13·42 Determine the exit velocity for water flowing through a nozzle if the upstream pressure is 100 psia at 70°F and the downstream pressure is 1 atm. Assume frictionless adiabatic flow.

13·43 A chemical processing plant requires 2 lbm/sec of O_2. This will be supplied from bottled O_2 at 70°F, 1000 psia, and must be delivered at 100 ft/sec at 190°F, 20 psia. The flow rate must be constant during back pressure variations of ± 5 psia. Design a system to provide this flow.

13·44 Discuss the phenomenon of choking. What difficulties can it cause and what advantages does it provide?

13·45 A gas dynamics experiment requires a gas with c = 2000 ft/sec at 60°F. Specify an appropriate gas mixture.

13·46 A small thrusting backpack system capable of delivering 50 lbf thrust for astronaut lunar mobility is required. Combustion systems cannot be used. Design a system. If the propellant storage volume is limited to 1 ft^3, what is the flying time of your system?

13·47 A small windtunnel for studies at M = 2 is desired. The test section area must be 6 in. by 6 in., and the stagnation conditions must be $T_0 = 1500°R$, $P_0 = 1$ atm. Design such a system, specifying all states, compressor and heater power requirements, nozzle parameters, and so on.

13·48 Do Prob. 13·47 for M = 5 with stagnation conditions appropriate for flight at 200,000 ft (see Prob. 13·14).

13·49 Reflecting on Chap. Twelve, criticize the idealizations in the normal shock theory presented in this chapter. Under what conditions is this theory worst? How could you formulate a better theory, assuming chemical equilibrium was maintained?

13·50 The states on either side of a shock wave are normally treated as equilibrium states. Consider a gas AB which dissociates by the reaction $AB \rightleftharpoons A + B$. Develop a theory for normal shocks in such a gas assuming (a) equilibrium downstream, (b) that the downstream composition is "frozen" at the upstream equilibrium composition. Compare your theories with single-component theory, quantitatively for typical gases at low and elevated temperatures.

CHAPTER FOURTEEN

AN INTRODUCTION TO HEAT TRANSFER

14·1 SOME BASIC CONCEPTS

By the time the student has reached this final chapter he will have developed considerable skill at applying the principles of thermodynamics in engineering analysis. There is one important aspect of such analysis on which we have yet to touch, and this is the evaluation of the *rate* at which energy is transferred as heat in a specified situation. The theory of heat-transfer rates rests on models and laws beyond the scope of thermodynamics, and heat transfer is usually treated as a separate and distinct subject. Heat transfer is of interest in many engineering disciplines. The thermal control of a space vehicle, the cooling of a component in an electronic system, the calculation of thermal expansion of a suspension bridge, and the problem of energy removal from a nuclear power reactor are all examples of engineering problems involving heat transfer. This wide range of important applications makes an elementary knowledge of heat-transfer theory of considerable importance to all engineers.

In this chapter we shall present a very limited introduction to heat transfer. The objectives of this chapter are (1) to make the student conversant with the terminology of heat transfer so he can work with thermal engineers, (2) to show how thermodynamic analysis can be further applied in a new area, and (3) to give the student some operational ability to solve simple heat-transfer problems.

Heat-transfer theory rests on certain fundamental equations called *rate equations*, which relate the rate of energy transfer as heat between two systems to the thermodynamic properties of those systems. These rate equations, when combined with energy balances and thermodynamic state equations, yield equations from which the temperature distribution and heat-transfer rates can be found. Heat-transfer theory is then essentially "thermodynamics with rate equations added."

Before we can write down any rate equations we must think carefully about the meaning of energy transfer as heat. We can often identify energy transfer as work between two systems; that is not heat. We can often identify energy convection from one system to another by mass which moves from one to the other; that also is not heat. Sometimes we can identify energy transfer due to organized charge flow; that is not heat either. Heat is the energy transfer which we can *not* identify with work, or convection, or electric current; it is all the energy transfer we can't see, all the "disorganized" transfer associated with the microscopic interchanges between the systems which is not included in macroscopic representations of the work, charge flow, and so on.

We set up the concept of temperature as a "pointer" for heat transfer *in the absence of mass or current flows*. We talked qualitatively of temperature as the driving potential for energy transfer as heat. Indeed, in the absence of mass and current flows, the equations of heat transfer do relate the heat-transfer rate to temperature differences or gradients. However, temperature is not the sole potential for energy transfer as heat. There can be heat transfer, in the sense described, in the absence of any temperature differences but in the presence of voltage differences. Such effects are very important in thermoelectricity. Correspondingly, if substantial concentration gradients are present there can be a heat flow driven by these gradients in an isothermal system. Hence, the classical idea of heat as being driven by temperature differences is not quite correct, although it is indeed quite adequate for most situations. The case of *coupled flows* will not be treated in this chapter, and we shall restrict ourselves to situations in which temperature differences or gradients are the *only* driving force for heat transfer.†‡

There are *two* basic mechanisms for energy transfer as heat. The first mechanism is *conduction*, the process of energy transfer as heat through a stationary medium, such as copper, water, or air. In solids the energy transfer arises because atoms at the higher temperature vibrate more excitedly, and hence they can transfer energy to more lackadaisical atoms nearby by "microscopic work," that is, heat. In metals the free electrons also contribute to the heat-conduction process. In a liquid or gas the molecules are also mobile, and energy is also conducted by molecular collisions.

The second heat-transfer mechanism is *radiation*, the transfer of energy by "disorganized photon propagation." Any body continually emits photons randomly in direction and time, and the net energy transferred by those

---

† See Reynolds, *Thermodynamics*, 2d ed., McGraw-Hill Book Company, New York, 1968, chap. 14, for a discussion of coupled irreversible flows.

‡ The statement that "heat is energy transfer by virtue of a temperature difference" is only true in the absence of coupled effects. This definition of heat is therefore appropriate for the material in this chapter.

photons gets counted as heat. In contrast, any *organized* photon energy, such as radio transmission, can be macroscopically identified and is not considered as heat.

Often engineers speak of a third mechanism of heat transfer, *convection*. This term is applied to energy transfer between solids and moving fluids. However, it is not *heat* that is being convected but *internal energy*. There may be some energy transfer as heat by conduction within the moving fluid, and a convection analysis often involves a consideration of the effects of this conduction on the state of the fluid as determined by energy balances.

Heat-transfer analysts work both with the heat-transfer rate, which we will denote by

$$\dot{Q} \quad \text{(Btu/hr or watts)}$$

and the *heat flux*, that is, the *heat-transfer rate per unit of area* normal to the direction of heat flow,

$$\blacktriangleright \qquad q'' \equiv \frac{\dot{Q}}{A} \qquad \text{(Btu/hr-ft}^2 \text{ or watts/cm}^2\text{)}$$

The double prime notation is useful to remind the analyst that it is the flow per unit area that is considered. The rate equations are generally written first in terms of the heat flux, and then a simple multiplication by area or integration over the area gives the *total* heat-transfer rate. The concept of heat flux is somewhat analogous to that of current flux, the electrical current flow per unit of conductor area. Since notation varies widely in the heat-transfer literature, the reader of a text or journal article must take care to identify the particular author's notations for heat-transfer rates and heat flux.

14·2 THE CONDUCTION RATE EQUATION

Consider two systems connected by a metal rod (Fig. 14·1). In the absence of coupled effects discussed in the last section, any energy transfer between the systems must be as heat. Our objective is to reason out a satisfactory equation for the rate of conduction heat transfer through the rod.

We expect that the rate of energy transfer as heat must depend upon the thermodynamic states of the two systems, and on the physical and geometrical properties of the metal rod. However, in view of our concept of temperatures,

FIG. 14·1 *Transfer of energy as heat by conduction between two systems*

we might expect that the only properties of A and B relevant to the heat-transfer rate are their temperatures. Hence we might express the conduction heat-transfer rate (cal/sec, Btu/hr, watts) as some function of T_A, T_B, and the bar,

$$\dot{Q} = f_1(T_A, T_B, \text{bar})$$

Alternatively, we could express $\dot{Q}$ as a function of one of the temperatures, the temperature difference, and the bar,

$$\dot{Q} = f_2(T_A - T_B, T_A, \text{bar})$$

If we can establish this function f_2 we shall have the needed rate equation.

One requirement on f_2 is that it must be zero when $T_A = T_B$. Then, for small $T_A - T_B$, a Taylor series expansion of f_2 about $T_A - T_B = 0$ would give†

$$\dot{Q} = \left[\frac{\partial f_2}{\partial(T_A - T_B)} \right]_{T_A - T_B = 0} (T_A - T_B) + \cdots \tag{14.1}$$

The derivative in Eq. (14.1) is evaluated when $T_A - T_B = 0$, that is, when there is equilibrium between A and B. It must therefore be a *property* of the bar, one that can be measured experimentally and tabulated as a function of the equilibrium state. Since $\dot{Q} > 0$ if $T_A > T_B$, this property must be positive. If the cross-sectional area of the bar is uniform, it seems likely that $\dot{Q}$ should be proportional to this area. However, the longer we make the bar, the less should be the energy flow for a given $T_A - T_B$. Hence, the coefficient of $(T_A - T_B)$ in Eq. (14.1) most probably is proportional to the cross-sectional area A and inversely proportional to the length L. These considerations suggest that

$$\left[\frac{\partial f_2}{\partial(T_A - T_B)} \right]_{T_A - T_B = 0} = \frac{kA}{L} \tag{14.2}$$

where A is the bar area, L its length, and k is a property of the bar material. Then,

$$\dot{Q} = \frac{kA}{L}(T_A - T_B) + \cdots$$

Now let us shrink the bar and at the same time bring T_A very close to T_B. In the limit, as $L \to 0$

$$\frac{T_A - T_B}{L} = -\frac{T_B - T_A}{L} \to -\frac{dT}{dx}$$

The higher-order terms are negligible in the limit, and Eq. (14.1) becomes a

---

† To expand $f(x)$ in a Taylor series about a,

$$f(a + \Delta x) = f(a) + \frac{df}{dx}\bigg|_{x=a} \Delta x + \frac{d^2f}{dx^2}\bigg|_{x=a} \frac{\Delta x^2}{2!} + \cdots$$

rate equation for the heat flux $q'' \equiv \dot{Q}/A$,

▶ $$q'' = -k\frac{dT}{dx} \qquad (14\cdot3)$$

This is the *Fourier law*,† the basic rate equation of conduction heat transfer. The property k is called the *thermal conductivity* of the bar material. Values of k vary widely from material to material. Appendix C gives some representative values. Note that k also depends on the state of the material, particularly upon its temperature. k can be determined from laboratory experiments based on Eq. (14·3), or in the case of gases and some solids, predicted from molecular kinetic theory.

For solids the conduction is due both to motions of free electrons within the solid and the action of the vibrations of the molecules within the solid. Since electrical conductors have a large supply of free electrons they are typically good heat conductors. The strength of these two mechanisms, and hence k, is strongly temperature-dependent. For gases the conduction is due to molecular translational motions. These motions, and hence k, increase with increasing temperature.

The thermal conductivity of a material is one of its *transport properties*. Others are the *viscosity*, μ, associated with the transport of momentum, and the *diffusion coefficient* associated with the transport of mass. As our Taylor series expansion (Eq. 14·1) suggests, we can tabulate the transport properties as functions of the thermodynamic equilibrium state.

14·3 SOME SIMPLE CONDUCTION PROBLEMS

Conduction theory centers on the problem of solution of the differential equation for the temperature field in the conducting medium. The differential equation is obtained by applying an energy balance on an elemental volume of the system under study, and bringing in the Fourier rate equation to relate the heat-transfer rates to and from the volume to the temperature field.

Let's illustrate the method by development of the equation for steady-state one-dimensional conduction in a bar of varying area (Fig. 14·2). Assum-

---

† For conduction in more than one direction in an isotropic media, Fourier's law relates the *heat-flux vector* $\mathbf{q}''$ to the temperature gradient,

$$\mathbf{q}'' = -k\ \mathbf{grad}\ T$$

FIG. 14·2 *Conduction through a variable-area rod*

ing steady state, the energy balance is

$$\dot{Q}_x = \dot{Q}_{x+dx}$$

Now, from the Fourier rate equation,

$$\dot{Q}_x = -k\left(A\frac{dT}{dx}\right)_x \qquad \dot{Q}_{x+dx} = -k\left(A\frac{dT}{dx}\right)_{x+dx}$$

Note we are treating k as constant here. Now, from a Taylor series expansion of $\dot{Q}_{x+dx}$ about $\dot{Q}_x$,

$$\dot{Q}_{x+dx} = -k\left[\left(A\frac{dT}{dx}\right)_x + \frac{d}{dx}\left(A\frac{dT}{dx}\right)_x dx + \cdots\right]$$

Substituting in the energy balance,

$$-k\left(A\frac{dT}{dx}\right)_x = -k\left(A\frac{dT}{dx}\right)_x + \frac{d}{dx}\left(-kA\frac{dT}{dx}\right)_x dx + \cdots$$

The leading terms cancel, and our differential equation is obtained from the next order terms,

$$\frac{d}{dx}\left(A\frac{dT}{dx}\right) = 0 \tag{14·4}$$

Now, given an area profile $A(x)$ and some boundary conditions on T, we could solve Eq. (14·4) to find $T(x)$.

For example, consider the problem of heat transfer through a plane slab (Fig. 14·3). Here $A(x)$ is constant, and the heat flux is

$$q'' = -k\frac{dT}{dx} \tag{14·5}$$

The energy equation (Eq. 14·4) tells us that the heat flux is *constant*, and that

$$\frac{d^2T}{dx^2} = 0 \tag{14·6}$$

FIG. 14·3

(a) *Conduction through a slab. The temperature distribution through the slab is linear*

(b) *The corresponding thermal circuit*

Now, if we impose temperatures T_1 and T_2 at the two faces of the slab, the boundary conditions on $T(x)$ are

$$T(0) = T_1 \qquad T(L) = T_2 \tag{14·7}$$

The solution to Eq. (14·6) is

$$T = C_1 x + C_2$$

where C_1 and C_2 are constants of integration fixed by the boundary conditions. Applying Eqs. (14·7), one finds

$$C_2 = T_1 \qquad C_1 = \frac{T_2 - T_1}{L}$$

and hence

$$T = T_1 + \frac{T_2 - T_1}{L}\,x \tag{14·8}$$

The temperature distribution is therefore linear across the slab. From Eq. (14·5), the heat flux is

$$q'' = k\left(\frac{T_1 - T_2}{L}\right)$$

so

$$\dot{Q} = Aq'' = \left(\frac{kA}{L}\right)(T_1 - T_2) \tag{14·9}$$

It is very often useful to think of heat flow in analogous electrical terms. Analogous to current is the heat flow $\dot{Q}$, and the temperature difference $T_1 - T_2$ is analogous to the voltage drop. The slab then is analogous to a *pure resistance*, and the factor analogous to the electrical resistance is the *thermal resistance*,

$$\blacktriangleright \qquad \mathsf{R} \equiv \frac{L}{kA} \tag{14·10}$$

Equation (14·9) can then be written as

$$\blacktriangleright \qquad \dot{Q} = \frac{T_1 - T_2}{\mathsf{R}}$$

which is fully analogous to Ohm's law for an electrical resistor. Figure 14·3 includes the heat flow circuit diagram for this slab.

This network approach to heat flow is especially helpful in considering composite structures. If the heat flows in series first through one slab, then another, the thermal circuit is as shown in Fig. 14·4a. Note that the overall resistance is the sum of the component resistances, just as in an electrical circuit. On the other hand, if the heat flow is carried in *parallel* by the heat conductors, then the overall *thermal conductance* $(1/\mathsf{R})$ is the sum of the thermal

FIG. 14·4

(a)   A composite wall and the corresponding series circuit

(b)   A composite wall and the corresponding parallel circuit

conductances, just as in a parallel electric circuit (Fig. 14·4b). The simplest types of heat-transfer analysis deal with series-parallel conduction circuits of this type, and once the network approach is understood such calculations are very simple.

For example, consider the composite slab of Fig. 14·5a. The solution (14·8) applies in each region, and the thermal circuit is shown in Fig. 14·5b. The total thermal resistance R is

$$\mathsf{R} = \mathsf{R}_1 + \mathsf{R}_2 + \mathsf{R}_3 = \frac{L_1}{k_1 A} + \frac{L_2}{k_2 A} + \frac{L_3}{k_3 A}$$

So, using thermal conductivity data from Table C·2,

$$\mathsf{R}A = \frac{\frac{1}{12}}{0.043} + \frac{\frac{3}{12}}{0.40} + \frac{\frac{1}{12}}{0.039}$$
$$= 1.94 + 0.62 + 2.15 = 4.71 \text{ hr-ft}^2\text{-}°\text{F/Btu}$$

FIG. 14·5

(a)   An insulated wall

(b)   The corresponding thermal circuit

Note that we treat the conductivity as constant through each slab, but use two different k values for the two magnesia slabs, using estimates of their individual temperatures. The heat flux is then

$$q'' = \frac{T_1 - T_4}{RA} = \frac{300 - 60}{4.71} = 51.0 \text{ Btu/hr-ft}^2$$

Then, since the same heat flux passes through each slab,

$$T_1 - T_2 = q''R_1A = 51.0 \times 1.94 = 98°F$$

$$T_2 - T_3 = q''R_2A = 51.0 \times 0.62 = 32°F$$

$$T_3 - T_4 = q''R_3A = 51.0 \times 2.15 = 110°F$$

Hence,

$$T_2 = 202°F \qquad T_3 = 170°F$$

According to Eq. (14·8), the temperature distribution is linear in each slab, as shown in Fig. 14·5a.

Suppose that the composite wall of the previous example has one ½-in. diameter steel bolt passing through for every square foot of area (Fig. 14·6a). The bolt will transfer energy as heat in *parallel* with the other materials, and hence the thermal circuit is as shown in Fig. 14·6b. Now, the bolt cross-sectional area per square foot of wall is

$$\frac{A_b}{A} = \frac{\pi d^2}{4} = \frac{\pi}{4}\left(\frac{0.5}{12}\right)^2 = 0.00137 \text{ ft}^2/\text{ft}^2 \text{ of wall}$$

The change in the brick resistance caused by the bolt hole is negligible. However, the steel bolt has a relatively high thermal conductivity ($k = 25$ Btu/hr-ft-°F) and hence the effect of its parallel resistance is significant. Its resistance,

FIG. 14·6

(a) *An insulated wall with a bolt. The bolt may increase the heat transfer rate significantly*

(b) *The corresponding thermal circuit*

per square foot of wall area, is

$$\mathsf{R}A = \left(\frac{L}{k}\right)\frac{A}{A_b} = \frac{5\!/\!12}{25}\frac{1}{0.00137} = 12.2 \text{ hr-ft}^2\text{-}°\text{F}/\text{Btu}$$

Then, the total overall resistance of the parallel circuit is given by the sum of the *thermal conductances* (reciprocal resistances). For $A = 1$ ft^2,

$$\frac{1}{\mathsf{R}} = \frac{1}{\mathsf{R}_1 + \mathsf{R}_2 + \mathsf{R}_3} + \frac{1}{\mathsf{R}_4} = \frac{1}{4.71} + \frac{1}{12.2} = 0.296 \text{ Btu}/\text{hr-}°\text{F}$$

So

$$\mathsf{R}A = \frac{1}{0.296} = 3.38 \text{ hr-ft}^2\text{-}°\text{F}/\text{Btu}$$

Note that the bolts cause a substantial reduction in the thermal resistance of the wall. The total heat transfer rate per unit of surface area is then

$$q'' = \frac{T_1 - T_4}{\mathsf{R}} = \frac{240}{3.38} = 71.0 \text{ Btu}/\text{hr-ft}^2$$

The bolts increase the "heat leak" through the wall by almost 40 percent.

In the model above we assumed that the ends of the bolt were at the same temperatures as the faces of the slab. However, the bolt would act to depress the temperature on the hot face and increase the temperature on the cold face, and this will tend to reduce the heat flow through the bolt. Hence our analysis overpredicts the total heat-transfer rate. Refinement of the analysis would require a very complicated solution of the *three*-dimensional conduction problem in the composite slab; fortunately our simple analysis would normally be quite adequate for engineering purposes.

Let's now turn to a second geometry. Consider the pipeline insulation of Fig. 14·7. We shall idealize the temperature distribution as *one-dimensional*, meaning that $T = T(r)$. Then, for a unit length of pipe, the conduction area at any point r is $2\pi r$. Hence, the energy balance for steady heat flow gives

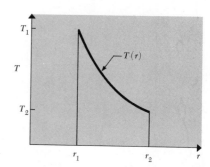

FIG. 14·7   *Conduction through a hollow cylinder.*
$T = T_1$ at $r = r_1$; $T = T_2$ at $r = r_2$

(see Eq. 14·4)

$$\frac{d}{dr}\left(2\pi r \frac{dT}{dr}\right) = 0 \qquad (14 \cdot 11)$$

Now, if the temperatures are prescribed at two radii r_1 and r_2, the temperature distribution is obtained by solving Eq. (14·11). One finds

$$T = T_1 + \frac{T_2 - T_1}{\ln (r_2/r_1)} \ln \frac{r}{r_1} \qquad (14 \cdot 12)$$

Note that in this cylindrical geometry the temperature distribution is logarithmic, not linear as for the slab. Moreover, the heat flux is not constant with r, but decreases as the area increases (q'' is proportional to $1/r$). The total heat-transfer rate may be calculated from the heat flux at any point. In particular, we may set

$$\dot{Q} = -kA \left.\frac{dT}{dr}\right|_{r=r_1} = -k2\pi r_1 L \frac{T_2 - T_1}{\ln (r_2/r_1)} \frac{1}{r_1}$$

So, for a cylinder of length L,

$$\dot{Q} = \frac{2\pi k L}{\ln (r_2/r_1)} (T_1 - T_2) \qquad (14 \cdot 13)$$

If we define the thermal resistance R of the annular insulation as

$$\blacktriangleright \qquad \mathsf{R} = \frac{\ln (r_2/r_1)}{2\pi k L} \qquad (14 \cdot 14)$$

we again have a rate equation analogous to Ohm's law,

$$\blacktriangleright \qquad \dot{Q} = \frac{T_2 - T_1}{\mathsf{R}}$$

Composite annular insulations, and insulations with parallel metallic penetrations, may be treated in the manner of the previous examples, using this definition of thermal resistance.

In nuclear reactors and electrical resistance heaters there is a conversion of energy from some form to internal energy, and conduction is the mechanism by which this energy is removed from the material. We can extend our previous analyses to cover the case of such "heat sources." Let's denote by s the local volumetric rate of conversion of energy into internal energy; s will have dimensions of Btu/hr-ft³ or perhaps watts/cm³. The governing differential equations for plane and cylindrical geometries (see Eq. 14·4) then become

Plane

$$\blacktriangleright \qquad \frac{d}{dx}\left(k \frac{dT}{dx}\right) + \mathsf{s} = 0 \qquad (14 \cdot 15)$$

Cylindrical

$$\blacktriangleright \qquad \frac{d}{dr}\left(kr\,\frac{dT}{dr}\right) + r\mathsf{s} = 0 \qquad\qquad (14\cdot16)$$

The development of these equations from first principles is left to the student. Note that we permit k to vary in Eqs. (14·15) and (14·16). We shall illustrate the method of development by consideration of a spherical geometry (Fig. 14·8). An energy balance on an elemental shell within the sphere gives, for steady state,

$$(4\pi r^2\,dr)\mathsf{s} + \dot{Q}_r = \dot{Q}_{r+dr}$$

As in the development of Eq. (14·4), the heat-transfer rates are related to the temperature gradients by the Fourier rate equation

$$\dot{Q}_r = \left(-k4\pi r^2\,\frac{dT}{dr}\right)_r \qquad \dot{Q}_{r+dr} = \left(-k4\pi r^2\,\frac{dT}{dr}\right)_r$$

$$+ \frac{d}{dr}\left(-k4\pi r^2\,\frac{dT}{dr}\right)_r dr + \cdots$$

Hence, the governing equation for the temperature field for radial heat flow in the sphere is

Spherical

$$\blacktriangleright \qquad \frac{d}{dr}\left(kr^2\,\frac{dT}{dr}\right) + r^2\mathsf{s} = 0 \qquad\qquad (14\cdot17)$$

One important application of Eq. (14·17) is the calculation of the temperature at the center of a uranium fuel pellet (Fig. 14·8). Integrating Eq.

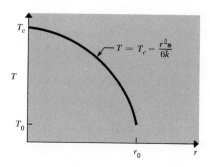

FIG. 14·8 *A sphere with a uniform heat source* s *and the resulting temperature distribution*

(14·17) from $r = 0$, one has

$$kr^2 \frac{dT}{dr} + \frac{r^3 \mathsf{s}}{3} = C_1$$

So,

$$k \frac{dT}{dr} = \frac{C_1}{r^2} - \frac{r\mathsf{s}}{3}$$

Since the temperature gradient must be finite at $r = 0$, $C_1 = 0$. Then, we integrate again and obtain

$$T = \frac{-r^2 \mathsf{s}}{6k} + C_2$$

The second integration constant C_2 is seen to represent the center temperature T_c. If the surface temperature at $r = r_0$ is T_0, we have

$$T_0 = T_c - \frac{r_0{}^2 \mathsf{s}}{6k} \tag{14·18}$$

For example, suppose that the fuel pellet is a uranium alloy with $k = 8$ Btu/hr-ft-°F, the pellet diameter is 0.5 in., and the source strength s is 2×10^7 Btu/hr-ft³. Then

$$T_c - T_0 = \left(\frac{0.25}{12}\right)^2 \times \frac{2 \times 10^7}{6 \times 8} = 181°\mathrm{F}$$

Such a high temperature difference over such a small distance could cause serious thermal stresses that might lead to failure of the fuel element.

So far we have only discussed *steady, one-dimensional conduction* heat-transfer analysis. This simplified model breaks down when the temperature field becomes strongly two- or three-dimensional or time-dependent. The theory then involves solution of partial differential equations, and is beyond the scope of this introductory treatment. However, a simplified model of transient heat conduction is often very useful, particularly if the main energy storage occurs in a good conductor and the main thermal resistance is caused by material with little energy storage capability. This model is known as the *lumped parameter* model, and is a simple extension of the electrical analogy already discussed.

Consider a piece of material receiving energy as heat at a rate $\dot{Q}$ (Fig. 14·9). An energy balance on the material gives

$$\dot{Q} = \frac{dU}{dt} \tag{14·19}$$

Control volume

$\dot{Q}$

$\dfrac{dU}{dt}$

$\dot{Q} = \dfrac{dU}{dt}$

FIG. 14·9 *How can we compute the temperature-time history?*

where U is the total internal energy of the material. If we can justifiably calculate U by the assumption that the temperature is uniform throughout the material at any instant, and if we can treat the material as a simple incompressible solid (Sec. 8·5), then

$$dU \approx M\, du = Mc\, dT$$

and the energy balance gives

$$\blacktriangleright \quad \dot{Q}_{in} = Mc\frac{dT}{dt} \qquad\qquad (14 \cdot 20)$$

If we again regard heat flow as analogous to current flow, and temperature as analogous to voltage, then if we define the *thermal capacitance* of the material by

$$\mathsf{C} \equiv Mc$$

Eq. (14·20) becomes fully analogous to the equation describing a simple electrical capacitance,

$$\dot{Q} = \mathsf{C}\frac{dT}{dt} \qquad\qquad (14 \cdot 21)$$

To illustrate the use of this model consider the system of Fig. 14·10. Suppose at time $t = 0$ the system is at a uniform temperature T_0, and then

FIG. 14·10

(a) *A transient heat flow system*

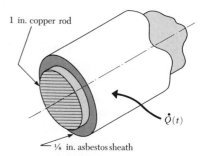

1 in. copper rod

$\dot{Q}(t)$

⅛ in. asbestos sheath

(b) *The corresponding thermal circuit. It is assumed that the thermal capacitance is in the copper rod and the thermal resistance is in the asbestos insulation*

$R_{asbestos}$

T_1 $T(t)$

$\dot{Q}(t)$

C_{rod}

(c) *Temperature as a function of time for the system*

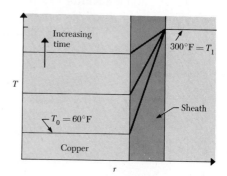

Increasing time

$300°F = T_1$

T

$T_0 = 60°F$

Sheath

Copper

r

the outside face of the asbestos insulation is suddenly heated to temperature T_1. We want to calculate the temperature-time history $T(t)$ for the copper rod. The thermal circuit is shown in Fig. 14·10b. Note that we model the copper rod as a lump of thermal capacitance, and treat the insulation as purely resistive. The lumped-parameter equations are

Energy balance on rod

$$\dot{Q} = \mathsf{C}\frac{dT}{dt} \qquad\qquad (14\cdot22a)$$

Rate equation for insulation

$$\dot{Q} = \frac{1}{\mathsf{R}}(T_1 - T) \qquad\qquad (14\cdot22b)$$

Combining, we obtain the differential equation for $T(t)$

$$\frac{dT}{dt} = \frac{1}{\mathsf{RC}}(T_1 - T) \qquad\qquad (14\cdot23)$$

This is to be solved, subject to the *initial condition*

$$T(0) = T_0$$

The solution is

$$T = T_1 - (T_1 - T_0)e^{-t/\mathsf{RC}} \qquad\qquad (14\cdot24)$$

which is identical with the analogous expression for the voltage rise in a suddenly energized RC electrical circuit.

Let's complete the calculation for a 1-ft length of rod, taking $T_0 = 60°F$ and $T_1 = 300°F$. From Eq. (14·14),

$$\mathsf{R} = \frac{\ln(0.625/0.5)}{2\pi \times 0.096 \times 1} = 0.37 \text{ hr-°F/Btu}$$

The rod thermal capacitance is

$$\mathsf{C} = Mc = \left(\frac{\pi D^2 L}{4}\right)\rho c = \frac{\pi(\frac{1}{2})^2}{4} \times 1 \times 559 \times 0.09$$
$$= 0.273 \text{ Btu/°F}$$

The RC product is called the *thermal time constant* of the circuit,

$$\mathsf{RC} = 0.37 \times 0.273 = 0.10 \text{ hr} = 6 \text{ min}$$

Six minutes after the start of heating the rod temperature will be [Eq. (14·24)]

$$T = 300 - (300 - 60)\,e^{-\frac{6}{6}} = 212°F$$

Note that the temperature rise is about 67 percent completed in one time con-

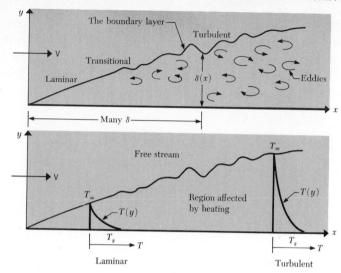

FIG. 14·11   (a)   The thermal boundary layer (thickness greatly
enlarged) for flow over a surface at high Reynolds
number. In turbulent flow the action of the eddies
flattens the temperature profile. The boundary layer
thickness $\delta(x) \ll x$

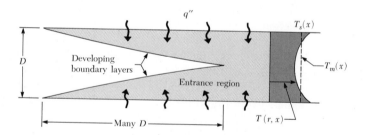

(b)   Flow in the entrance region of a pipe. For laminar
flow, $\mathrm{Re} = \mathsf{V}_m D \rho / \mu < 2000$

(c)   Natural convection from a horizontal circular
cylinder. The warm fluid rises because of buoyant
effects

stant. After three time constants the response is 95 percent complete. Hence, knowledge of the *thermal time constant* provides considerable insight into the transient thermal response.

The lumped-parameter technique provides a simple approach for transient heat conduction but is limited in application by the lumping assumptions. Numerical techniques are often used now to provide computer solutions to more difficult transient problems, and such general purpose programs are available at modern computing centers.

14·4   CONVECTION

When a fluid passes over a hot solid surface, energy is transferred to the fluid from the wall by the process of conduction. This energy is then carried, or *convected*, downstream by the fluid, and diffused throughout the fluid by conduction within the fluid. This type of energy-transfer process is called *convection heat transfer.*

If the fluid flow process is induced by a pump or other circulating system the term *forced convection* is used. In contrast, if the fluid flow arises because of fluid buoyancy caused by the heating the process is called *free* or *natural* convection. Figure 14·11 qualitatively depicts several convection situations.

In order to understand convection it is helpful to have some idea about the temperature distribution in the fluid. If the surface is hotter than the fluid, the temperature distribution will be as in Fig. 14·11a. The convection of energy reduces the outward conduction in the fluid, and consequently the temperature gradient decreases away from the surface. If the fluid flows rapidly past the solid body the region of fluid heated by the wall will be confined to a thin *boundary layer* near the surface. In contrast, in pipe flow (Fig. 14·11b) the boundary layer eventually fills the pipe, and thereafter all of the flow feels the heating from the wall.

Until the early 1950s the subject of convection heat transfer was largely empirical. Experimenters found that the heat-transfer behavior of fluids in pipes, over wings, and so forth, could be correlated with the flow velocity, fluid properties, and the geometry (but not the material properties) of the solid surfaces. Since that time significant theoretical advances have been made, and it is now often possible to predict the heat-transfer performance in a new configuration with sufficient accuracy for engineering purposes. The theory of course substantiates the correlations, and in fact it is the correlations themselves (whether experimentally or theoretically determined) that the engineer uses in his design calculations.

The first theoretical advances came in *laminar* flow, where the fluid moves in smooth layers sheared slowly by the action of fluid viscosity. More recent work has dealt with *turbulent* flow, which is much more complicated because of the stochastic nature of the turbulent motion and energy convection. Theories of convection are beyond the scope of this limited treatment, and the interested student is referred to the excellent heat-transfer texts listed at the chapter end.

In order to do simple engineering calculations involving convection, one needs a general understanding of the physical processes, and an understanding of (and the willingness to use) the correlations. There are many parameters affecting the convection heat transfer in a particular geometry. These include the system length scale L, the *fluid* thermal conductivity k, usually the fluid velocity V, density ρ, viscosity μ, specific heat c_P, and sometimes other factors relating to the manner of heating (uniform wall temperature or varying wall temperature). The heat flux from the solid surface will also depend on the surface temperature, T_s, and fluid temperature, T_f, but it is usually assumed that only the *difference* in these temperatures, $\Delta T = T_s - T_f$, is significant. However, if the fluid properties vary markedly over the convecting region, then the absolute temperatures T_s and T_f may also be important factors in the correlation. It is obvious that with so many important variables any specific correlations will be unwieldy, and consequently the correlations are usually represented in terms of *dimensionless groupings* that permit much simpler representations. Also, the factors with less important influence, such as fluid property variation and wall temperature distribution, are often ignored to simplify the correlations, and adequate estimations (± 20 percent) of the heat-transfer rate can often be obtained from the simplified nondimensional correlations.

The heat-transfer rate is usually expressed through the *heat flux*, which may vary along the solid surface. The correlation for pipes and other heat exchanger surfaces is generally expressed in terms of the *average* heat flux, while for external boundary layer flows, such as that over a wing or compressor blade, the *local* heat flux is usually used. The heat flux (local or average) is in turn related to the imposed temperature difference through the *convection heat transfer coefficient* (*convective conductance*) h, defined by

$$\blacktriangleright \qquad q'' = h\,\Delta T \qquad\qquad\qquad (14\cdot25)$$

This may be interpreted as the *convection rate equation*. Knowing h and ΔT, q'' can be calculated and it is the correlations which give the engineer values for h. Note that h has the dimensions of *heat flux per unit of temperature difference*, for example, Btu/hr-ft²-°F, or watts/cm²-°C.

With boundary layer flow it is customary to use the free-stream temperature (the fluid temperature outside of the boundary layer) in defining ΔT. In pipe flow it is more convenient and sensible to use a suitable *average* temperature. The same idea is used in hydrodynamic analysis, where for example the mass flow in the tube is written as

$$\dot{M} = A\rho V_m$$

and V_m is the *average* velocity, defined by this equation. Similarly, we write the energy flow rate in a pipe as

$$\dot{E} = \dot{M}h_m$$

where h_m is the *mixed-mean* enthalpy. Note that if the heated flow were mixed adiabatically h_m would be the resulting enthalpy. The *mixed mean temperature* is that associated with h_m, that is, it is the temperature at which the fluid would emerge from an adiabatic zero pressure drop mixer. The concept of mixed-mean properties permits us to treat the energy flows in boundary layers and pipes on a one-dimensional basis. The mixed-mean temperature is especially important in internal flow, where it is used as the fluid temperature in the calculation of ΔT.

Two dimensionless groupings involving h are commonly used. These are the *Nusselt* number,

$$\blacktriangleright \qquad \mathrm{Nu} \equiv \frac{hL}{k} \qquad\qquad (14 \cdot 26a)$$

and the *Stanton* number

$$\blacktriangleright \qquad \mathrm{St} \equiv \frac{h}{V \rho c_P} \qquad\qquad (14 \cdot 26b)$$

Once either of these numbers has been determined (by correlation, theory, or a good engineering guess), h, and then q'', and then finally $\dot{Q}$, can be calculated.

The Nusselt or Stanton numbers are usually correlated in terms of the *Prandtl* number,

$$\blacktriangleright \qquad \mathrm{Pr} \equiv \frac{\mu c_P}{k} \qquad\qquad (14 \cdot 27)$$

and the *Reynolds* number,

$$\blacktriangleright \qquad \mathrm{Re} \equiv \frac{VL\rho}{\mu} \qquad\qquad (14 \cdot 28)$$

The Prandtl number is indicative of the relative ability of the fluid to diffuse momentum and internal energy by molecular mechanisms. For oils, which are highly viscous, Pr is typically large (100 to 10,000) indicating rapid diffusion of momentum (by viscous action) compared to the slow diffusion of internal energy. In contrast, liquid metals typically have Pr = 0.003 to 0.01, indicating more rapid diffusion of internal energy. For almost all gases Pr $\approx$ 0.7, and for water Pr $\approx$ 2 to 8, depending upon the temperature.

The Reynolds number is indicative of the relative importance of inertial and viscous effects in the fluid motion. At low Re the viscous effects dominate, and the motion is laminar. At high Re the inertial effects lead to turbulence, and dominate the momentum and energy-transfer processes in turbulent flow. Hence the nature of the correlation is usually quite different at low and high Re. It is also often difficult to predict the Nusselt number accurately in the *transition region* between laminar and turbulent flow.

In natural convection the Nusselt number is usually related to the Prandtl and *Grashof* numbers. The Grashof number is defined by

$$\blacktriangleright \quad \text{Gr} = \frac{g\beta(\Delta T)L^3\rho^2}{\mu^2} \tag{14·29}$$

where β is the isobaric compressibility (Sec. 4·7). The Grashof number can be viewed as a measure of the relative strength of buoyancy and viscous forces. Natural convection is usually suppressed at sufficiently small Gr, begins at some *critical* value of Gr, depending upon the system, and then becomes more and more effective as Gr increases.

To summarize, convection transfer correlations are usually expressed in the form

$$\text{Nu} = f(\text{Pr}, \text{Re}) \qquad \text{or} \qquad \text{St} = f(\text{Pr}, \text{Re})$$

or, for natural convection,

$$\text{Nu} = f(\text{Gr}, \text{Pr})$$

and as such apply to a particular flow geometry. The surface temperature distribution and fluid property variations usually have minor influence on these correlations, and often can be ignored for engineering calculations. For accurate prediction (± 10 percent) these secondary effects should be considered, and the beginning heat-transfer practitioner should at least be aware of their existence. The correlations in laminar flow are usually developed analytically, and confirmed by experiment. Those for turbulent flow are usually determined experimentally, but can sometimes be generated by an experienced heat-transfer analyst if needed for a new situation. Appendix C includes several graphs and tables giving representative correlations for convection heat transfer.

We remark that this discussion is limited to *single phase* flow. Convection heat transfer in two-phase flow is more complicated, and beyond the scope of our brief introduction.

The computing procedure for convection analysis is as follows:

1   Establish the values of Re (or Gr) and Pr, and determine Nu or St from the appropriate correlation.
2   Calculate h from the Nu or St value.
3a   If Δt is specified, calculate q'' or $\dot{Q}$ from $q'' = \text{h}\,\Delta T$ or $\dot{Q} = \text{h}A\,\Delta T$.
3b   Or, if $\dot{Q}$ or q'' is specified, calculate ΔT.

Examples of such calculations constitute the next section. The physical aspects of convection are discussed further in these examples, and they should be studied for this content.

14·5   CONVECTION CALCULATION EXAMPLES

Electrically heated pipe. Air flows at 10 lb/hr through an electrically heated 0.2 in. diameter tube, 2 ft long, entering at 200°F. The electrical power dis-

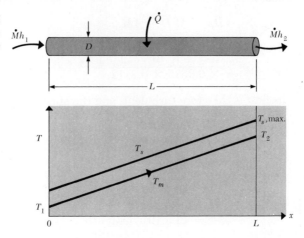

FIG. 14·12 *The wall and mixed-mean temperatures along an electrically heated tube*

sipation is 180 watts. Calculate the outlet temperature and the maximum tube wall temperature (Fig. 14·12).

We shall first use thermodynamics (an energy balance) on the air inside the tube to determine the mixed-mean exit temperature T_2. From an energy balance,

$$\dot{M}(h_2 - h_1) = \dot{Q}$$

Treating the air as a perfect gas, $h_2 - h_1 = c_P(T_2 - T_1)$. Then

$$T_2 = T_1 + \frac{\dot{Q}}{\dot{M}c_P} = 200 + \frac{3.413 \times 180}{(10)(0.24)} = 456°\text{F}$$

We next use the heat-transfer data to calculate the wall temperature. Now, at any location along the tube the heat flux is

$$q'' = h(T_s - T_m)$$

where T_s and T_m are the local wall and mixed-mean fluid temperatures, respectively. If we assume h is constant along the tube, the maximum T_s will occur at the exit. To choose the proper correlation from Table C·8, we need to know the Reynolds and Prandtl numbers. These contain the fluid properties, which vary somewhat with temperature. Let's base the Re and Pr on an average temperature of 325°F. Then, from Table C·5,

$\mu = 0.0585$ lbm/hr-ft
$k = 0.0208$ Btu/hr-ft-°F
Pr = 0.69

Then,

$$\text{Re} = \frac{VD\rho}{\mu} = \frac{\dot{M}}{A}\frac{D}{\mu} = \frac{4\dot{M}}{\pi\mu D}$$

$$= \frac{4 \times 10}{\pi \times 0.0585 \times 0.2/12} = 13,100$$

The flow is therefore turbulent, and the appropriate correlation is (Table C·8)

$$\text{Nu} = 0.022 \text{ Re}^{0.8} \text{ Pr}^{0.6}$$
$$= 0.022 \times (13,100)^{0.8} \times (0.69)^{0.6} = 35$$

Then, since $\text{Nu} = \text{h}D/k$,

$$\text{h} = \text{Nu}\frac{k}{D} = \frac{35 \times 0.0208}{0.2/12}$$
$$= 43.5 \text{ Btu/hr-ft}^2\text{-°F}$$

Now, the heat flux is

$$q'' = \frac{\dot{Q}}{L\pi D} = \frac{3.413 \times 180}{2 \times \pi \times 0.2/12}$$
$$= 5870 \text{ Btu/hr-ft}^2$$

Then, the local wall-to-fluid temperature difference is

$$T_s - T_m = \frac{q''}{\text{h}} = \frac{5870}{43.5} = 135°\text{F}$$

The maximum tube wall temperature is therefore

$$456 + 135 = 591°\text{F}$$

To assess the accuracy of this prediction, we note that the fluid at the exit will have a temperature distribution ranging from about 591°F down to less than 456°F. Table B·5 reveals that k varies by about 15 percent over this range. We actually used a k appropriate for 365°F, which is about 20 percent below k at 591°F. These considerations suggest that our predictions for h and hence $T_s - T_m$ might be off by as much as 20 percent, which is about 25°F. Since the conductivity we used was probably low, the tube temperature we predict is probably high by 0 to 25°F. We would probably accept this accuracy in an engineering situation. The choice is to use a more elaborate correlation which corrects for fluid property variations; such a correlation could be found in a heat-transfer textbook or reference manual.

Turbulent flow in a pipe consists of randomly moving globs of fluid, or "eddies," that serve as carriers of momentum and energy within the flow (Fig. 14·13). Since the eddies are very effective at energy transport, the heat-transfer coefficients in turbulent flow are typically much greater than for laminar flow. For example, we calculated Nu = 35 in this turbulent flow, and would have

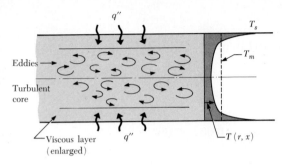

found Nu = 4.36 in laminar flow. Much smaller temperature differences are therefore required to sustain a given heat flux in turbulent flow, and hence high-performance heat-transfer devices are usually designed for turbulent flow. In contrast, where thermal protection from hot gases is required, such as on the nose of a reentry body, laminar flow gives lower heat input and hence the designers (and the astronauts!) strive to maintain laminar flow.

Window convection. A large building has glass walls 10 ft high and 20 ft wide. Calculate the convection heat transfer from the glass when the glass surface temperature is 60°F and the outdoor temperature is 20°F.

This is a problem in natural convection (Fig. 14·14). We can model the window as a *vertical plate*, for which correlations are given in Table C·8. First we must calculate the Grashof number; using data in Table C·5, at an average temperature of 40°F

$$\mu = 0.042 \text{ lbm/hr-ft} \qquad k = 0.014 \text{ Btu/hr-ft-°F} \qquad \text{Pr} = 0.71$$

For ideal gases the isobaric compressibility β is simply $1/T$, so

$$\beta = \frac{1}{500°\text{R}} = \frac{0.002}{°\text{R}}$$

The air density is also needed. It can be calculated from the perfect-gas equa-

FIG. 14·14 *Velocity and temperature profiles for natural convection from a vertical wall*

(a) *Velocity boundary layer*

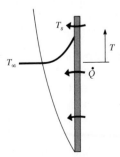

(b) *Temperature boundary layer*

tion of state,

$$\rho = \frac{P}{RT} = \frac{14.7 \times 144}{53.3 \times 500} = 0.0792 \text{ lbm/ft}^3$$

Then,

$$\begin{aligned}
\text{Gr} &= \frac{\rho^2 g \beta (T_s - T_f) L^3}{\mu^2} \\
&= \frac{(0.0792)^2 \times 32.2 \times (3600)^2 \times 0.002 \times (60 - 20) \times 10^3}{0.042^2} \\
&= 1.2 \times 10^{11}
\end{aligned}$$

So,

$$\text{GrPr} = 1.2 \times 10^{11} \times 0.71 = 8.5 \times 10^{10}$$

According to Table C·8, in this range the natural convection will be turbulent, and the appropriate correlation is

$$\text{Nu}_{av} = 0.021 \,(\text{GrPr})^{0.4}$$

Note that this gives the *average* Nusselt number over the height of the plate. This is just what we need to calculate the total heat-transfer rate.

$$\text{Nu}_{av} = 0.021 \times (8.5 \times 10^{10})^{0.4} = 500$$

Then,

$$h_{av} = \text{Nu}_{av} \frac{k}{L} = \frac{500 \times 0.014}{10} = 0.7 \text{ Btu/hr-ft}^2\text{-°F}$$

So,

$$\begin{aligned}
\dot{Q} &= h_{av} A \cdot (T_s - T_f) = 0.7 \times (10 \times 20) \times (60 - 20) \\
&= 5600 \text{ Btu/hr}
\end{aligned}$$

This corresponds to an average heat flux of

$$q''_{av} = \frac{\dot{Q}}{A} = \frac{5600}{10 \times 20} = 28 \text{ Btu/hr-ft}^2$$

The window "heat loss" $\dot{Q}$ is equivalent to 1650 watts, and at 3¢/kw-hr the luxury of the glass could cost the user about 5¢/hr, or a few hundred dollars per year on his heating bill, per window this size!

Boundary layer flow. Air at 60°F, 2 atm flows at 25 ft/sec between the two metal sheets shown in Fig. 14·15. Calculate the heat-transfer rate from each sheet when the sheet temperature is 100°F.

At first thought it might seem reasonable to model the space between the sheets by an "equivalent pipe," and the approach would be quite reasonable if the plates were much longer in comparison to their spacing. However, the boundary layers that form on the plate are relatively thin in this situation, and do not fill the flow passage. Hence a boundary layer treatment is appro-

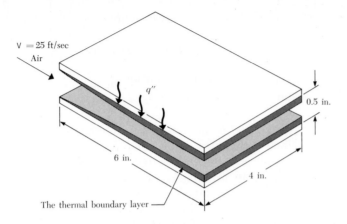

priate, and we shall use this example to illustrate several aspects of boundary layer convection.

The *flat plate* (Table C·8) forms a satisfactory model for this problem. Let's first calculate the Reynolds number at the end of the 6-in. plates. The air density is

$$\rho = \frac{P}{RT} = \frac{2 \times 14.7 \times 144}{53.3 \times 540} = 0.146 \text{ lbm/ft}^3$$

From Table C·5, at an average temperature

$$\mu = 0.044 \text{ lbm/hr-ft} = 1.22 \times 10^{-5} \text{ lbm/sec-ft}$$
$$k = 0.015 \text{ Btu/hr-ft-}°F$$
$$Pr = 0.7$$

So,

$$\text{Re}_L = \frac{V\rho L}{\mu} = \frac{25 \times 0.146 \times 0.5}{1.22 \times 10^{-5}}$$
$$= 148,000$$

Hence, the entire boundary layer is laminar, and the *average* Nusselt number is given by (Table C·8)

$$\text{Nu}_{av} = 0.664 \text{ Re}_L^{0.5} \text{ Pr}^{0.33}$$
$$= 0.664 \times 148,000^{0.5} \, 0.7^{0.33} = 224$$

Then,

$$h_{av} = \text{Nu}\frac{k}{L} = \frac{224 \times 0.015}{0.5} = 6.7 \text{ Btu/hr-ft}^2\text{-}°F$$

So,

$$\dot{Q} = hA(T_s - T_f) = 6.7 \times (0.5 \times 0.33) \times (100 - 60)$$
$$= 44 \text{ Btu/hr (per plate)}$$

To check on the boundary layer nature of the flow, let's determine the thermal boundary layer thickness at the end of the plate. The hydrodynamic laminar boundary layer thickness δ can be estimated from†

$$\delta = 5 \sqrt{\frac{x\mu}{V\rho}} = 5 \sqrt{\frac{0.5 \times 1.22 \times 10^{-5}}{25 \times 0.146}} = 6.4 \times 10^{-3} \text{ ft} = 0.078 \text{ in.}$$

So, the hydrodynamic boundary layers clearly do not fill the gap between the plates. Note that the boundary layer is extremely thin in comparison to its length.

The thermal boundary layer (the region affected by the heating) will in general be of different thickness than the hydrodynamic boundary layer. Since the Prandtl number is a measure of the relative ability of the fluid to diffuse momentum in comparison to internal energy, low Prandtl number fluids have thin hydrodynamic boundary layers and thick thermal boundary layers. In contrast, high Prandtl number fluids have thick hydrodynamic boundary layers and thin thermal layers. For gases, with $\text{Pr} \approx 1$, the two layers will be about the same thickness, and hence we can take 0.078 in. as an estimate of the thermal boundary layer thickness for this example.

14·6 FINS

Fins are often used in heat exchange devices to increase the convection heat-transfer area, thereby improving the heat-transfer performance. Figure 14·16 shows some typical examples of finned surfaces. Automobile radiators,

† See your Fluid Mechanics text for a derivation.

FIG. 14·16 *Types of fins*

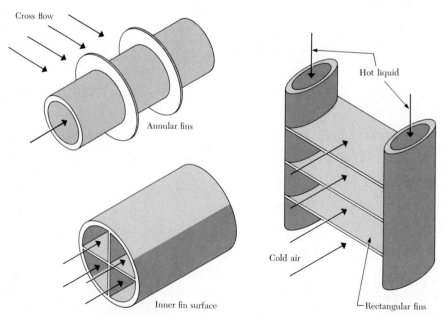

Cross flow

Annular fins

Hot liquid

Cold air

Inner fin surface

Rectangular fins

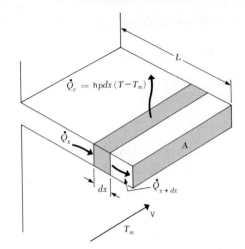

FIG. 14·17   *The control volume for*
a fin analysis

household refrigerator condensers, and transistor "heat sinks" are familiar examples.

The theory of fin heat transfer is based on a combination of an energy balance and rate equations. These provide one with the differential equation for the temperature distribution in the fin. We shall illustrate the essential ideas by a special case. Figure 14·17 shows a simple fin of uniform rectangular cross section. In setting up the governing equation we must include the effects of convective heat transfer between the fin and the surrounding fluid and the conduction heat transfer within the fin. If the fin is thin relative to its length we can treat the conduction as being one-dimensional, and assume that $T = T(x)$. Further simplifications are obtained if we assume steady state, treat the fin conductivity as constant, neglect radiation, and assume that the convection coefficient h and fluid temperature T_∞ are independent of x. Satisfactory solutions to engineering problems are usually obtained with this simple model.

With these simplifying assumptions the energy balance on the elemental control volume of Fig. 14·17 gives

$$\dot{Q}_x = \dot{Q}_{x+dx} + \dot{Q}_c$$

The conduction rate equation gives

$$\dot{Q}_{x+dx} - \dot{Q}_x = -kA \frac{d^2T}{dx^2} dx$$

where A is the conduction *cross-sectional area* (not surface area) of the fin. The convection rate equation gives

$$\dot{Q}_c = hp \, dx(T - T_\infty)$$

where p is the convection perimeter of the fin ($2b$ for a wide flat fin). Combining, the differential equation for $T(x)$ is found as

$$\blacktriangleright \quad \frac{d^2T}{dx^2} - \frac{hp}{kA}(T - T_\infty) = 0 \qquad (14\cdot30)$$

This equation must be solved, subject to appropriate boundary conditions on $T(x)$. Three commonly used sets are

(a) *Infinite fin*

$$T(0) = T_0, \; T(\infty) \to T_\infty \qquad (14\cdot31a)$$

(b) *End temperatures specified*

$$T(0) = T_0, \; T(L) = T_e \qquad (14\cdot31b)$$

(c) *End leak negligible*

$$T(0) = T_0, \left(\frac{dT}{dx}\right)_{x=L} = 0 \qquad (14\cdot31c)$$

Case (a) is useful for long fins, (b) is useful when the fin is stretched between two surfaces of known temperatures, and (c) is useful for thin fins of finite length or in configurations where $x = L$ is a point of symmetry in $T(x)$. For the infinite fin model the solution may be written as

$$\frac{T - T_\infty}{T_0 - T_\infty} = e^{-mx} \qquad (14\cdot32)$$

where

$$m^2 \equiv \frac{hp}{kA}$$

The solutions for the other two cases are left as problems for the student. The local convective heat flux $q''(x)$ for the infinite length fin is

$$q''(x) = h(T - T_\infty) = h(T_0 - T_\infty)e^{-mx}$$

Note that the heat flux becomes less and less as x increases. The total heat-transfer rate can be found either by integrating the heat flux over the fin surface, or by considering the conduction into the fin at its root. The latter is more convenient and gives

$$\dot{Q}_0 = -kA \frac{dT}{dx}\Big|_{x=0}$$

which for our model is

$$\dot{Q}_0 = kA \cdot m(T_0 - T_\infty) = \sqrt{hpkA} \, (T_0 - T_\infty) \qquad (14\cdot33)$$

The form of this expression clearly shows that it is a combination of convection and conduction that acts to remove the energy conducted in at the fin root.

For a fin of finite length L the end-leakage-negligible model gives

$$\dot{Q}_0 = \sqrt{hpkA}\ (T_0 - T_\infty)\tanh{(mL)} \tag{14·34}$$

If all of this fin were at the root temperature T_0, more heat would be removed from the surface; let's call this maximum possible heat-transfer rate $\dot{Q}_{max}$. Then,

$$\dot{Q}_{max} = hpL(T_0 - T_\infty)$$

The *fin effectiveness* ϵ is defined by

$$\blacktriangleright \qquad \epsilon = \frac{\dot{Q}_0}{\dot{Q}_{max}} \tag{14·35}$$

and is the ratio of the actual fin heat transfer to that which could be convected with all the surface at the fin root temperature. For the end-leakage-negligible model Eqs. (14·34) and (14·35) yield

$$\blacktriangleright \qquad \epsilon = \frac{1}{mL}\tanh{(mL)} \tag{14·36}$$

Figure 14·18 shows $\epsilon(mL)$ as given by Eq. (14·36). Note that increasing the length of a fin provides diminishing returns, and seldom does one find heat exchanger equipment with effectiveness below 35 percent ($mL > 3$).

FIG. 14·18 *Effectiveness of rectangular fins*

To illustrate a fin calculation, suppose we wish to transfer 50,000 Btu/hr from a high-temperature surface at 800°F by blowing ambient air at 100°F between aluminum fins attached to the surface. The fins will be 6 in. long, $\frac{1}{16}$ in. thick, and 1 ft. wide. Suppose a convection calculation reveals that $h = 20$ Btu/hr-ft²-°F in this situation, and we wish to determine how many fins must be used. The parameters are

$$h = 20 \text{ Btu/hr-ft}^2\text{-°F} \qquad p = 2 \times 1 = 2 \text{ ft}$$

$$k = 120 \text{ Btu/hr-ft-°F} \qquad A = \frac{(\frac{1}{16}) \times 12}{144} = 0.0052 \text{ ft}^2$$

So,

$$m = \sqrt{\frac{hp}{kA}} = \sqrt{\frac{20 \times 2}{120 \times 0.0052}} = 8.0/\text{ft}$$

Using the infinite fin model,

$$\dot{Q}_0 = 120 \times 0.0052 \times 8.0 \times (800 - 100) = 3500 \text{ Btu/hr}$$

Let's check to see if the finite fin model is needed. Since

$$mL = 8.0 \times 0.5 = 4.0$$

Eq. (14·34) gives

$$\dot{Q} = 3500 \times \tanh (4.0) \approx 3500$$

The fins are clearly long enough to be considered infinite (they are probably too long for good design). Then, to obtain 50,000 Btu/hr, a total of 50,000/3500 or about 14 fins are required. A good engineer would recommend that the fins be shortened. For 3 in. fins $mL = 2.0$ and the heat transfer rate per fin is

$$\dot{Q} = 3500 \times \tanh (2.0) = 3380 \text{ Btu/hr}$$

and 14 or 15 fins will still remove the required 50,000 Btu/hr.

14·7 HEAT EXCHANGERS

A heat exchanger is typically a device in which energy is transferred from one fluid to another across a solid surface. Exchanger analysis and design therefore involve both convection and conduction. The *thermal circuit* concept can be used to simplify the analysis, and Fig. 14·19 shows the circuit at some point in the exchanger. Note that resistances have been assigned to the fluid. The *convection resistances* (unit area basis) are defined by

$$R_C \equiv \frac{1}{h}$$

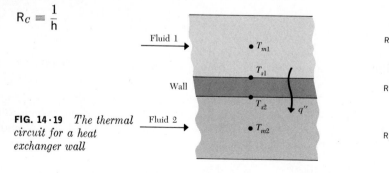

FIG. 14·19 *The thermal circuit for a heat exchanger wall*

The convection rate equation then becomes

$$q'' = \frac{\Delta T}{R_C}$$

analogous again to Ohm's law. Treating the wall as a plane slab of thickness δ, the wall resistance is (unit area basis; see Eq. 14·10)

$$R_w = \frac{\delta}{k_w}$$

and we then have

$$q'' = \frac{(T_{s1} - T_{s2})}{R_w}$$

The *overall* resistance is then (per unit area)

$$R = \frac{1}{h_1} + \frac{\delta}{k_w} + \frac{1}{h_2}$$

It is customary to work with the *overall* conductance, U, defined by

$$U \equiv \frac{1}{R} = \frac{1}{\dfrac{1}{h_1} + \dfrac{\delta}{k_w} + \dfrac{1}{h_2}}$$

The heat-transfer rate equation relating the local heat flux from fluid 1 to fluid 2 to their local mixed-mean temperatures is then

$$q'' = U(T_{m1} - T_{m2}) \tag{14·37}$$

Equation (14·37), together with differential equations for the local fluid mixed-mean temperatures, forms the basis for heat exchanger analysis.

For example, let's consider an exchanger in which the temperature of the hot fluid is uniform along the exchanger. This could be realized by condensing the hot fluid at a fixed pressure, or approximated by having a high hot fluid flow in comparison to the cold fluid flow. The exchanger and the general shape of the cold fluid temperature distribution are shown in Fig. 14·20.

We could calculate the rate of heat transfer between the two fluids if we just knew the temperature rise of the cold fluid. But in order to find this temperature rise we need to calculate the distribution $T_{m2}(x)$ throughout the exchanger. To do this we need the differential equation for $T_{m2}(x)$ which is obtained from an *energy balance* on an elemental length of the exchanger (Fig. 14·20c). If we neglect axial heat conduction in the exchanger and flow kinetic energy, the energy balance is

$$\dot{M}\left(h_{m2} + \frac{dh_{m2}}{dx}\,dx + \cdots\right) - \dot{M}h_{m2} = q''A'\,dx$$

Here h_{m2} is the mixed-mean fluid enthalpy, and A' is the exchanger surface

FIG. 14·20

(a)   *A parallel-flow heat exchanger*

(c)   *The control volume to analyze the heat exchanger*

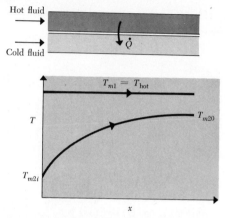

$$\dot{Q} = A'\mathsf{U}(T_{m1} - T_{m2})\,dx$$

(b)   *The mean temperature distributions in a parallel-flow heat exchanger with an isothermal hot side*

area per unit of length. Neglecting the effect of pressure drop on the fluid enthalpy, we may write

$$\frac{dh_{m2}}{dx} = c_P \frac{dT_{m2}}{dx}$$

Combining and simplifying, we have

$$\frac{dT_{m2}}{dx} = \frac{q''A'}{\dot{M}c_P} \tag{14·38}$$

The product of $\dot{M}c_P$ is sometimes called the *capacity rate* of the flow, and denoted by C

$$C \equiv \dot{M}c_P$$

Now, we bring in the *overall rate equation* for the heat flux, Eq. (14·37). Then, Eq. (14·38) becomes

▶ $$\frac{dT_{m2}}{dx} = \frac{A'\mathsf{U}}{C}(T_{m1} - T_{m2}) \tag{14·39}$$

This equation must be solved subject to the initial *condition*

$$T_{m2} = T_{m2i} \qquad \text{at} \qquad x = 0$$

The solution is

$$T_{m2} = T_{m2i} + (T_{m1} - T_{m2i})(1 - e^{-A'\mathsf{U}x/C}) \tag{14·40}$$

Of particular interest is the mixed-mean outlet temperature T_{m20}, obtained from Eq. (14·40) by setting $x = L$. The result may be expressed as

$$\blacktriangleright \qquad \frac{T_{m20} - T_{m2i}}{T_{m1} - T_{m2i}} = 1 - e^{-\text{NTU}} \qquad\qquad (14\cdot41)$$

where the *single parameter* NTU (*number of transfer units*) is defined as

$$\blacktriangleright \qquad \text{NTU} \equiv \frac{A\mathsf{U}}{C} \qquad\qquad (14\cdot42)$$

and A is $A'L$, the *total* heat transfer area. Note that the exchanger NTU depends both upon the exchanger geometry and the flow rate and properties of the two fluids. Given these quantities one can calculate the NTU, and then calculate the outlet temperature from Eq. (14·41). Or, given the required outlet temperature, the exchanger NTU can be calculated, and the information used to design an exchanger of appropriate size. The NTU concept is therefore central to heat exchanger analysis.

We note that the left-hand side of Eq. (14·41) is the ratio of the actual temperature rise of fluid 2 to the *maximum possible* temperature rise. This is a special definition of the *heat exchanger effectiveness* ϵ, the general definition of which is

$$\blacktriangleright \qquad \epsilon = \frac{\text{actual heat-transfer rate}}{\text{maximum possible heat-transfer rate}} \qquad\qquad (14\cdot43)$$

The maximum possible heat-transfer rate is

$$\dot{Q}_{\text{max}} = C_{\text{min}}(T_{\text{hot in}} - T_{\text{cold in}}) \qquad\qquad (14\cdot44)$$

We see that for this particular heat exchanger the effectiveness is a function only of the NTU. In general, theory reveals that the effectiveness also depends upon the *capacity rate ratio* of the two fluids and upon the exchanger flow configuration,

$$\epsilon = f(\text{NTU}, \frac{C_{\text{min}}}{C_{\text{max}}}, \text{flow arrangement})$$

$$\text{NTU} \equiv \frac{A\mathsf{U}}{C_{\text{min}}}$$

The functional dependence can be determined by solution of the appropriate differential equations, and some tables summarizing the solutions are included in Appendix C.

As an example, suppose we have a counterflow heat exchanger with 150 ft² of heat-transfer surface. Suppose that the hot and cold side convection coefficients, capacity ratios, and inlet temperatures are as given below and we wish to determine the outlet temperatures.

Cold side

C_c = 3000 Btu/hr
h_c = 40 Btu/hr-ft²-°F
$T_{c_{in}}$ = 60°F

Hot side

C_h = 6000 Btu/hr
h_h = 75 Btu/hr
$T_{h_{in}}$ = 250°F

To calculate the outlet temperatures we need the effectiveness. Since $C_c < C_h$, $C_{min} = C_c$ = 3000 Btu/hr and

$$\dot{Q}_{max} = C_{min}(T_{h_{in}} - T_{c_{in}}) = 3000(250 - 60)$$
$$= 570,000 \text{ Btu/hr}$$
$$\frac{C_{min}}{C_{max}} = \frac{3000}{6000} = 0.5$$

Neglecting the wall resistance, which is usually small compared to the convection resistances, the overall conductance is

$$U = \frac{1}{(1/h_h) + (1/h_c)} = \frac{1}{(1/45) + (1/70)} = 28 \text{ Btu/hr-ft}^2\text{-°F}$$

So,

$$NTU = \frac{AU}{C_{min}} = \frac{150 \times 28}{3000} = 1.4$$

For a counterflow exchanger with NTU = 1.4 and $C_{min}/C_{max} = 0.5$, Table C·9A gives ϵ = 0.67. Hence, the actual heat-transfer rate is

$$\dot{Q} = \epsilon \dot{Q}_{max} = 0.67 \times 570,000 = 380,000 \text{ Btu/hr}$$

Finally, the cold and hot fluid exit temperatures can be calculated from energy balances,

$$\dot{Q} = C_h(T_{h_{in}} - T_{h_{out}}) \qquad \dot{Q} = C_c(T_{c_{out}} - T_{c_{in}})$$

So,

$$T_{h_{out}} = 250 - \frac{380,000}{6,000} = 186°F$$

$$T_{c_{out}} = 60 + \frac{380,000}{3,000} = 188°F$$

Note that the hot fluid emerges cooler than the cold fluid emerges. This is possible with the counterflow arrangement, but is not possible with parallel flow exchangers.

14·8 RADIATION

We have already mentioned that all bodies radiate energy and that this energy consists of photons moving with random direction, phase, and frequency. When these photons are in the wavelength range of 0.38 to 0.76 microns (1 micron = 10^{-6} m) they affect our eyes as visible light. At wavelengths just longer than the visible limit the radiation is called *infrared* radiation, and at wavelengths just shorter than the visible limit the radiation is said to be in the *ultraviolet* region. These regions are a part of the electromagnetic-wave spectrum that ranges continuously from long wavelength radiowaves to the very short wavelength cosmic rays.

When radiated photons reach another surface they are either absorbed, reflected, or transmitted through the surface. Three surface properties which measure these quantities are

α absorptivity, the fraction of incident radiation absorbed
ρ reflectivity, the fraction of incident radiation reflected
τ transmissivity, the fraction of incident radiation transmitted

From energy considerations

$$\alpha + \rho + \tau = 1 \tag{14·45}$$

The reflected energy may be either *diffuse*, where the reflections are independent of the incident radiation angle, or *specular*, where the angle of reflection equals the angle of incidence. Most engineering surfaces exhibit a combination of the two types of reflection.

The energy radiation flux (Btu/hr-ft²) from a surface is defined as the *emissive power*, E. Thermodynamic reasoning shows that E is proportional to the fourth power of the absolute temperature.†

For a body with $\alpha = 1$, $\rho = \tau = 0$ (a *black body*)

$$E_b = \sigma T^4 \tag{14·46}$$

where σ is the *Stefan-Boltzmann constant*,

$$\sigma = 0.1714 \times 10^{-8} \text{ Btu/hr-ft}^2\text{-}^\circ\text{R}$$

Real bodies are not "black" and radiate less energy than the black body. To account for this one can define an *emissivity*, ϵ, in terms of the emissive powers of the real body and the black body, both evaluated at the same temperature,

$$\blacktriangleright \qquad \epsilon \equiv \frac{E}{E_b} \tag{14·47}$$

---

† See for example Reynolds, *Thermodynamics*, 2d ed., McGraw-Hill Book Company, New York, 1968.

The absorptivity is related to the emissivity through *Kirchoff's law* which states that at *thermal equilibrium*

$$\epsilon = \alpha \tag{14·48}$$

Note that the absorptivity only equals the emissivity under conditions of thermal equilibrium, that is, when the incoming radiation to be absorbed comes from a body at the same temperature as the emitting body.

Radiation of all frequencies is emitted from a hot surface. The emissive power E therefore has contributions at all frequencies, and we write

$$E = \int_0^\infty E_\lambda \, d\lambda$$

where $E_\lambda \, d\lambda$ is the energy emitted in the frequency band between λ and $\lambda + d\lambda$. E_λ is a function of the surface and its temperature. For a black body, that is, a surface which absorbs all incident radiation, E_λ takes the form shown in Fig. 14·21. Figure 14·21 also shows E_λ for a typical real surface. Simplified approximate radiation calculations can often be made by the *gray body approximation*, in which E_λ is taken as $\epsilon E_{\lambda b}$ at all wavelengths (see Fig. 14·21). More accurate calculations require consideration of variation in the emission with wavelength, variations in absorptivity and transmissivity with wavelength, and wavelength-dependent combinations of specular and diffuse radiation. One must usually rely extensively on computer analysis to solve a radiation problem including all of these effects, and this area of heat transfer is currently the center of much research activity. Such calculations are beyond the scope of this brief introduction, and we shall restrict ourselves henceforth to the simple gray body models.

All surfaces radiate energy, but there will be a net energy exchange only if the bodies are at different temperatures. Two facing parallel plates will radiate to each other, but if their temperatures are equal there is no net energy transfer. To evaluate radiation between bodies when their temperatures

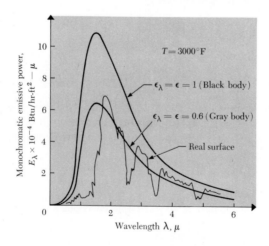

FIG. 14·21 *Black body and real surface emissive power as functions of wavelength and temperature*

are different the geometry must be considered. Two facing parallel plates radiating only from their facing sides see only each other, but two rectangular plates meeting at right angles do not radiate solely to each other and their *shape factor* must be determined. The shape factor F_{12} represents the fraction of the radiation emitted from surface 1 that is intercepted by surface 2. A case of particular interest is that of a surface 1 that sees only a surface 2, such as one of two closely spaced plates or the inner of two concentric spheres. In this case

$$F_{12} = 1$$
$$F_{21} = \frac{A_1}{A_2} \tag{14·49}$$

For black body radiation between surfaces 1 and 2 the rate equations for the *net* energy transfer are

$$\dot{Q} = A_1 F_{12}(E_{b1} - E_{b2})$$
$$\dot{Q} = \sigma A_1 F_{12}(T_1{}^4 - T_2{}^4) \tag{14·50}$$

Since all of the incident radiation is absorbed by a black body there are no reflections to consider and thus the rate equation is relatively simple.

As an example, let's use the black body model to determine the radiation heat flux between two closely spaced parallel plates radiating only to each other if their temperatures are 1000°F and 500°F. For parallel plates, $F_{12} = 1$. Then,

$$q'' = \sigma(T_1{}^4 - T_2{}^4) = (0.1714 \times 10^{-8})(1460^4 - 960^4)$$
$$= 6340 \text{ Btu/hr-ft}^2$$

For gray bodies a factor is required in the rate equation to account for the reflections. The rate equation for radiation between two gray bodies *which see each other and nothing else* is given by

$$\blacktriangleright \qquad \dot{Q} = A_1 \mathfrak{F}_{12}(E_{b1} - E_{b2}) \tag{14·51}$$

where

$$A_1 \mathfrak{F}_{12} = \cfrac{1}{\cfrac{1 - \epsilon_1}{\epsilon_1 A_1} + \cfrac{1}{A_1 F_{12}} + \cfrac{1 - \epsilon_2}{\epsilon_2 A_2}} \tag{14·52}$$

Let's assume that the two parallel plates of the previous example each have emissivities of 0.5, and recalculate the heat flux using the gray body model.

$$q'' = \frac{1}{A} \cfrac{E_{b_1} - E_{b_2}}{\cfrac{1 - \epsilon_1}{\epsilon_1 A_1} + \cfrac{1}{A_1 F_{12}} + \cfrac{1 - \epsilon_2}{\epsilon_2 A_2}}$$

Here

$$A = A_1 = A_2 \qquad \text{and} \qquad F_{12} = 1$$

so

$$q'' = \frac{\sigma(T_1{}^4 - T_2{}^4)}{\dfrac{1 - \epsilon_1}{\epsilon_1} + 1 + \dfrac{1 - \epsilon_2}{\epsilon_2}} = 2113 \text{ Btu/hr}$$

Note that if the emissivity of each plate is only one half that of a black body, heat flux is reduced by a factor of 3.

As a further example, consider a deep space probe constructed as a 2 ft diameter polished aluminum sphere. Let's estimate the equilibrium temperature that the probe reaches if the solar energy received† is $q_s'' = 100$ Btu/hr-ft^2. Our energy balance gives

$$\underset{\substack{\text{from sun}}}{\dot{Q}_{\text{input}}} = \underset{\substack{\text{output}}}{\dot{Q}_{\text{radiation}}}$$

For solar radiation the absorptivity of aluminum is about 0.3. The heat input is determined by the projected area of the sphere, and so

$$\dot{Q}_{\text{in}} = \alpha q_s'' A = 0.3 \times 100 \times \frac{\pi(2)^2}{4} = 94 \text{ Btu/hr}$$

The outgoing radiation goes to space where the temperature is low enough to be neglected. Therefore

$$\dot{Q}_{\text{out}} = \epsilon \sigma A T^4$$

Equating these, using $\epsilon = 0.04$ (Table C·7), and using the total surface area of the sphere, we find

$$94 = \epsilon \sigma A T^4$$
$$T = \left[\frac{94}{0.04 \times 0.1714 \times 10^{-8} \times 4\pi} \right]^{\frac{1}{4}}$$
$$T = (1080 \times 10^8)^{\frac{1}{4}} = 570°\text{R}$$

Note that $\alpha \neq \epsilon$ in our calculation. We evaluated α at solar frequencies, and use an average ϵ appropriate for aluminum at lower temperatures. The low emissivity of aluminum at these temperatures compared to its relatively high absorptivity for solar radiation explains this surprisingly high equilibrium temperature.

14·9   SUMMARY

This brief chapter has only introduced the ideas of heat transfer. The important point is that heat transfer is founded on the concepts of thermo-

---

† The *solar constant* at the *outside* of the earth's atmosphere is about 440 Btu/hr-ft^2. Because of absorption, scattering, and so on, less radiation reaches the earth's surface, and, as a rule of thumb, about 300 Btu/hr-ft^2 reaches the surface at the latitudes of the United States.

dynamics, but because it is an irreversible process, more information than thermodynamics can provide is required. The rate equations provide this additional information. The combination of the energy balance and the rate equations is sufficient to derive the differential equations that govern the energy transfer. Their solution provides knowledge of the temperature as a function of position and time. The theory of irreversible thermodynamics, of which heat transfer forms only a small part, provides us with a general framework within which heat transfer, diffusive mass transfer, electrical conduction, and many other phenomena can be analyzed.

SELECTED READING

Holman, J. P., *Heat Transfer*, 2d ed., chaps. 1, 2, sec. 4.2, chaps. 5–8, 10, McGraw-Hill Book Company, New York, 1963.

Kays, W. M., *Convective Heat and Mass Transfer*, pp. ix–xi, chaps. 6, 8, 10, McGraw-Hill Book Company, New York, 1966.

Kreith, F., *Principles of Heat Transfer*, 2d ed., chaps. 1, 2, secs. 4.1–4.3, chaps. 5, 8, 9, 11, International Textbook Company, Scranton, Pa., 1965.

Obert, E. F., and R. L. Young, *Elements of Thermodynamics and Heat Transfer*, 2d ed., chaps. 19, 20, McGraw-Hill Book Company, New York, 1962.

QUESTIONS

14·1 How does heat-transfer theory differ from thermodynamics?

14·2 What is the objective of a heat-transfer analysis?

14·3 What are the two mechanisms for heat transfer?

14·4 What is convection?

14·5 What is the difference between heat, heat flux, and heat-transfer rate, and heat-transfer coefficient?

14·6 What are the fundamental conduction and convection rate equations?

14·7 How would you describe a thermal circuit to an electrical engineer?

14·8 When do thermal resistances act in parallel, when in series?

14·9 Why are convection correlations expressed nondimensionally?

14·10 What is a Nusselt number?

14·11 What is a Reynolds number?

14·12 What is the Grashof number?

14·13 What is the Prandtl number?

14·14 What is a zip code?

14·15 Why do fins increase the rate of heat transfer from a surface?

14·16 Would fins work in space?

14·17 What is the NTU of a heat exchanger?

14·18 What happens to the NTU of a parallel-flow exchanger when its length is cut in half? What happens to its effectiveness?

14·19 What is the black body model?

14·20 Can you sketch the emission spectrum of a black body?

14·21 How do real surfaces differ from black bodies?

14·22 What heat-transfer processes are involved in atmospheric reentry?

PROBLEMS

14·1 A brick wall 8 in. thick is finished on the inside with 1 in. of plaster. Calculate the total thermal resistance of the wall, and the heat-transfer rate per ft² when the overall temperature difference is 80°F. Is the sign of the temperature difference important?

14·2 A steam turbine casing of $\frac{1}{4}$-in. thick steel has an inside surface temperature of 212°F. The resistances for radiation and free convection on the outside are each about 0.67 hr-ft²-°F/Btu. The outside ambient air temperature is 70°F. What is the outer surface temperature? Suppose the outer surface is covered with a 1-in. layer of insulation ($k = 0.05$ Btu/hr-ft-°F); will the insulation be safe to touch?

14·3 The $\frac{1}{8}$-in. thick wall of a gas turbine casing is made from a nickel alloy ($k = 10$ Btu/hr-ft-°F). If the convective heat-transfer resistances on the inside and outside are $\frac{1}{35}$ and $\frac{1}{6}$ hr-ft²-°F/Btu, respectively, find the heat-transfer rate per ft² if the overall temperature difference is 1200°F.

14·4 Prescribe sufficient insulation for the turbine casing of Prob. 14·3 to reduce the heat flux to 300 Btu/hr-ft².

14·5 The wall for a cold storage is constructed of standard 2 by 4 fir studs ($1\frac{3}{4}$ in. × $3\frac{3}{4}$ in.) on 16-in. centers. The walls are sheathed on both sides with $\frac{1}{2}$-in. fir plywood and both external surfaces lined with $\frac{1}{16}$-in. galvanized steel. The space between the studs is filled with ground cork. The inner surface of the inner liner is to be maintained at 15°F. The outside ambient air temperature is 80°F. The thermal conductivities of the various materials are:

Ground cork, 0.025 Btu/hr-ft-°F

Fir, 0.087 Btu/hr-ft-°F

Steel, 26 Btu/hr-ft-°F

The outside radiation resistance will be about 1 hr-ft²-°F/Btu, and the outside resistance for convection will be about the same.

What is the heat leak into the room per *average* square foot of wall? Plot the temperature through the wall at a point through a stud, and through the insulation. What percentage goes through the studs? How critical is the assumption of convection and radiation resistances in a problem of this type? Draw the complete thermal circuit showing clearly each of the various resistances involved. What idealizations did you have to make to construct this circuit?

14·6 Calculate the conduction heat-transfer rate per foot of pipe through a single hollow cylinder made from 1.5 percent C steel 4 in. thick on a 3-in. inner radius. The inside temperature is 750°F and the outside is 400°F.

14·7 Add 2 in. of 85 percent magnesia to the outside of the cylinder in Prob. 14·6 and recalculate the heat-transfer rate for the same overall temperature difference. Calculate the temperature at the steel-insulation interface.

14·8 Derive an expression for the temperature distribution and heat transfer through a hollow sphere of inner radius r_i, outer radius r_0, and conductivity k. The inner and outer temperatures T_i and T_0 are known.

14·9 Design an experiment to measure k for plastics.

14·10 Derive Eq. (14·15). Give an expression for the difference between the centerline and surface temperature in a slab with a uniform heat source (analogous to Eq. 14·18).

14·11 A nuclear reactor has fuel elements that are slabs of uranium ($k = 18$ Btu/hr-ft°F) covered with a thin coating of aluminum. The uranium is $\frac{1}{4}$ in. thick and the fission process in the reactor generates 96×10^5 Btu/hr-ft³. Estimate the difference between the uranium centerline and surface temperature. (See Prob. 14·10.)

14·12 A thin slab of thickness L has a high temperature T_1 imposed on one face and a lower temperature T_2 imposed on the other face. In addition, a uniform heat source s Btu/hr-ft³ exists within the slab. To analyze the thermal stress distribution it is required to determine the temperature distribution through the slab. Derive an expression for this temperature difference, and an expression for the point of maximum temperature.

14·13 A particular nuclear reactor operates with a source strength of 10^7 Btu/hr-ft³. The fuel element is made up of 1-in. thick plates made from a uranium alloy ($k = 18$ Btu/hr-ft-°F). At one point in the reactor a temperature of 1000°F is expected on the left side of the plate and 800°F on the right side. Determine the location of maximum temperature and specify whether the element will fail. (Failure occurs if any temperature is greater than 1350°F.) (See Prob. 14·12.)

14·14 In a particular nuclear reactor the uranium fuel is in the form of solid circular rods, 1 in. in diameter. The thermal conductivity of uranium is about 18 Btu/hr-ft²-°F/ft. High-pressure water at 2000 psia flows normal to the rods at a temperature of 575°F. The convection conductance (reciprocal resistance) at the rod surface is about 2000 Btu/hr-ft²-°F and it is specified that the uranium rod centerline temperature should not exceed 800°F. At this condition, what will be the reactor power level, expressed in Btu/ft³ of uranium and in Btu/ft² of cooling surface? If the surface temperature exceeds the water saturation temperature, local boiling (which happens to be undesirable here) will occur. Is this a problem here?

14·15 A farmer produces hay for market. His hay baler forms *long* cylindrical hay bales some 12 in. in diameter. As the hay cures, heat is uniformly generated at a measured rate of 800 Btu/hr-ft³. If the outside surface temperature of the bale is 90°F and $k = 0.25$ Btu/hr-ft-°F, what is the maximum temperature within the bale?

14·16 Show that Laplace's equation, $(\partial^2 T/\partial x^2) + (\partial^2 T/\partial y^2) = 0$ in two dimensions, is the governing differential equation for the temperature field in a steady-state system with constant k and no sources.

14·17 Suppose the thermal conductivity of a material can be approximated by $k = k_0(1 + aT)$ where a is a constant. Derive an expression for the temperature distribution through a slab of this material if the inner and outer temperatures are T_i and T_0 respectively.

14·18 One brand of cooking ware has stainless steel pots with copper bases. Discuss the engineering reasons for this design.

14·19 A copper wire 0.1 in. in diameter initially at 200°F is cooled by 60°F air blowing over its surface. The convection conductance (reciprocal resistance) is 6 Btu/hr-ft²-°F. Calculate the time constant of the system and the time required to cool to 80°F.

14·20 The wire of Prob. 14·19 carries 100 amp. Derive a general expression for the temperature-time history of the wire, and plot for this specific case.

14·21 Consider the thermal circuit of Fig. 14·10b. Derive an expression for the capacitance temperature $T(t)$ for the case where the driving temperature is oscillated such that $T_1 = T_0 + A \cos \omega t$, where ω and A are constants. Plot the amplitude of the rod temperature oscillation (normalized on A) versus RC. For the specific rod of Fig. 14·10, calculate the frequency for which the rod temperature oscillation is $\frac{1}{2}A$.

14·22 Using the correlations given in the Appendix, determine values of h for
(a) Air flow at 30 ft/sec, 1 atm, $T = 100°F$ in a 1-in. diameter pipe
(b) Air flow as above except at 10 atm
(c) Water flow inside a 1-in. diameter pipe at 5 ft/sec, 100°F
Discuss the physical reasons for the differences in these values.

14·23 Estimate the rate of heat transfer per ft² on a thin, nearly flat airfoil 6 in. downstream from the leading edge. The fluid velocity is 50 ft/sec, the airfoil is maintained at 100°F, and the fluid temperature is 70°F.

14·24 In the "Sea Lab" experiments it was necessary to maintain the atmosphere at a temperature of 88°F because of the large heat loss from the skin of the participants. The atmosphere was largely helium. Verify the need to maintain a high temperature.

14·25 Air at 60°F, 1 atm, is blown across an electrically heated copper wire 0.460 in. in diameter. The wire carries 325 amp and has a resistance of 0.26 ohm/mile. Calculate the air velocity required to keep the wire surface at 125°F.

14·26 A semiconductor device has to dissipate 1 watt. The device is a $\frac{1}{2}$-in. diameter cylinder, $1\frac{1}{4}$ in. high. If the ambient air is at 70°F, find the equilibrium temperature of the device.

14·27 Steam at 250°F, 0.1 atm, flows through an uninsulated 6-in. diameter pipe between two buildings 100 ft apart. If the air is at 40°F and there is no wind, find the heat loss from the pipe.

14·28 Steam flows through a 4-in. diameter pipe at 8 ft/sec, 500°F, 100 psia. The pipe is $\frac{1}{2}$-in. thick iron and has a 1-in. thick covering of glass wool. If the ambient temperature is 60°F, estimate the heat loss per foot of pipe.

14·29 A 1-in. diameter copper pipe running under the house carries hot water at 120°F from the utility room to the kitchen, a distance of 10 ft. The flow rate is 1 gpm and the outside air temperature is 30°F. If the outside h is 3 Btu/hr-ft²-°F, is insulation warranted?

14·30 Air is to be heated at 1 atm from 60°F to 300°F. The flow rate is 10 lb/min. A thin electrically heated tube (or tubes) will be used, and the tube temperature cannot exceed 550°F. Design a system to meet these specifications. Give the tube diameter and length, the total power input, and the maximum tube temperature.

14·31 Repeat Prob. 14·30 for helium, and discuss the physical reasons for the differences in the designs.

14·32 Optimize the design of Prob. 14·30, minimizing the *volume* of the heater system.

14·33 A 4-in. diameter copper sphere is heated to 500°F during a chemical reaction. Estimate the time required for the sphere to cool down to 150°F if air at a velocity of 30 ft/sec and a temperature of 60°F, 1 atm, is available as the cooling medium.

14·34 A long thin nickel-chrome fin has a temperature of 400°F at its base. If the ambient temperature is 70°F and the fin is of rectangular shape having a 2-in. perimeter and 0.10-in.² area, calculate the rate of heat transfer from the fin assuming that $h = 7$ Btu/hr-ft²-°F.

14·35 A recent heat-exchanger design called for a plastic piece (failure point 220°F) at the end of a rectangular metal fin. The fin is stainless steel, ⅛ in. thick and 4 in. long. The convective conductance is 3 Btu/hr-ft²-°F, the base temperature is 400°F, and the gas temperature is 70°F. Will the plastic fail?

14·36 An aluminum cooking pot has an aluminum handle that is roughly shaped as a 1 in. × ⅛ in. rectangle. If the pot contains boiling water, how long should the handle be before you would use it to pick up the pot?

14·37 A stainless steel clad thermometer is placed 1 in. into a superheated steam duct at right angle to the flow direction. The thermometer reads 247°F when the steam velocity is 15 ft/sec, the pressure 14.7 psia, and the base of the thermometer is at the wall temperature of 150°F. Assuming the thermometer is a ¼-in. diameter stainless rod, find the true steam temperature. What is the steam temperature if the thermometer reads the same but is inserted 3 in. into the steam?

14·38 The barrel of an engine cylinder consists of a ⅜-in. thick steel liner on the outside of which is bonded a ¼-in. aluminum muff. Circumferential cooling fins are then bonded to the outside of the muff. The fins are 1.5 in. long, 0.030 in. thick, with a space between fins of 0.085 in., and the muff diameter is 7 in. During a complete engine cycle, the average effective temperature of the gases in the cylinder is 1500°F. The cooling air temperature averages 70°F.

Making suitable simplifying assumptions and educated guesses, calculate the temperatures at the inner cylinder wall, the inner surface of the aluminum muff, the base of the fins, and the tip of the fins. Calculate the heat-transfer rate per ft² of muff area.

14·39 Equation (14·30) assumes that A is constant. For the case of circular fins on a rod this is not true since the cross-sectional area is a function of the radius. Derive the analogous "fin equation" including the effect of changing area; give the fin equation for circular fins of uniform thickness.

14·40 Consider a thin plate with a uniform heat source s (Btu/hr-ft³). The plate is exposed to a flow for which the average convective conductance over each side of the plate is h. The plate is suspended in the flow between two side plates, as shown in the figure. The side-plate temperature is T_0, and the flow temperature is T_∞. Derive an expression for the temperature distribution $T(x)$ along the plate using the coordinate system shown. Discuss engineering situations in which this theory would be useful.

14·41 Air at the rate of 15,000 lbm/hr enters a heat exchanger at 200°F and 50 psia. The air is cooled in a single pass counterflow arrangement. If the water coolant enters at 60°F at 20,000 lbm/hr, find the air and water outlet temperatures. The overall heat transfer coefficient is 30 Btu/hr-ft²-°F and is based on a tube area of 200 ft².

14·42 Repeat Prob. 14·41 for parallel-flow and cross-flow configurations. Discuss the advantages of the various flow arrangements.

14·43 A simple tube-within-a-tube heat exchanger is to heat an organic fluid ($c_P =$ 0.6 Btu/lbm-°F) from 50 to 150°F. The fluid flow rate is 100 lbm/hr. The heating fluid is water which cools from 200 to 100°F as it passes through the exchanger. The overall heat-transfer coefficient based on the area of the organic side is 50 Btu/hr-ft^2-°F. Sketch to scale the hot and cold fluid temperature distributions along the exchanger, indicating flow directions. What water flow rate and what surface area are required to meet this design? If the direction of the water flow were reversed, what would be the outlet temperature of the organic fluid assuming the same flow rates, *inlet* temperature, and heat exchanger?

14·44 It is required to specify the size of a heat exchanger to meet the following conditions: water inlet temperature 100°F, water exit temperature 185°F, oil inlet temperature 300°F. The water flow rate is 4500 lbm/hr, the oil flow rate is 8000 lbm/hr, and the oil specific heat is 0.45 Btu/lbm-°F. How many transfer units are required to meet these conditions and what is the oil outlet temperature? Assume that because of piping problems a parallel flow arrangement must be used.

14·45 Hot water at 180°F passes through 50 ft of copper tubing underneath a house. The tube is completely exposed to still air at a temperature of 50°F. The flow rate is to be 1 gpm. The tube O.D. is 1 in., I.D. is 0.83 in. Determine an overall U Btu/hr-ft^2-°F based on the outside area. Treating the system as a heat exchanger, find the exchanger effectiveness. Calculate the exit water temperature and then make a recommendation as to whether insulation is warranted.

14·46 A counterflow heat exchanger operates using river water as the coolant. During the winter water is available at 45°F. The exchanger is to be designed to cool 4000 lbm/hr of oil ($c_P = 0.50$ Btu/lbm-°F) entering at 400°F to 210°F. Specify a water flow rate in lbm/hr and the NTU required to achieve the design. Will your design work in the summer when the river inlet is at 65°F?

14·47 Air is to be cooled by passing it through a tube immersed in still water at 60°F. The air enters at 180°F and must be cooled to 65°F. The air velocity should not exceed 100 ft/sec in the tube, and the flow rate is 5 lbm/min. The nominal air density is 0.4 lbm/ft^3. Specify a suitable tube diameter and length for this operation.

14·48 Design a concentric tube heat exchanger to cool 10 gpm of water from 180°F to 80°F. Water entering at 60°F will be used as the coolant. Neither stream should exceed 15 ft/sec. Specify the tube geometry and the required coolant flow rate.

14·49 Optimize the design of Prob. 14·48, minimizing the exchanger volume.

14·50 Calculate the radiant energy emission flux, Btu/hr-ft^2, from a black body at 100°F, 1000°F, and 2000°F.

14·51 A pan of water is set outside on a clear, cloudless still night. The water is at 60°F initially. The sky radiating temperature is about 20°F. Sketch the water temperature versus time, and explain qualitatively the shape that you draw. What is the mechanism by which smudge pots protect fruit from freezing on cold nights?

14·52 Estimate the heat loss through a 1.5-in. diameter "peephole" in a scrap metal furnace. The inside temperature is 2540°F and the outside temperature seen by the hole is 140°F.

14·53 A flat piece of oxidized steel receives radiant energy from the sun at the rate of 300 Btu/hr-ft². If the ambient temperature is 70°F and a convective heat-transfer coefficient of 1.8 Btu/hr-ft²-°F is appropriate, determine the equilibrium temperature of the steel, assuming no heat loss from the back side of the plate.

14·54 A cylindrical container 20 cm long, 5 cm in diameter contains liquid helium (7°R). There is an evacuated space between it and an outer annular container, which in turn contains liquid nitrogen at 140°R. Both containers are of a polished nickel alloy. Estimate the rate of heat leak into the helium (cal/hr) and the percent evaporative loss per hour.

14·55 A black asphalt street ($\epsilon = 1$) absorbs radiant energy at the rate of 350 Btu/hr-ft² during the summer. If a mild breeze is blowing such that the ambient temperature is 90°F and the heat-transfer coefficient between the air and street is 2.8 Btu/hr-ft²-°F, estimate the street temperature.

14·56 Liquid oxygen is to be stored in a spherical container 1 ft in diameter at 1 atm. The system is insulated by an evacuated space between the inner sphere and a surrounding 1.5-ft inner diameter concentric sphere. Both spheres are made of aluminum ($\epsilon = 0.03$) and the temperature of the outer sphere is 40°F. Estimate the rate of heat flow by radiation to the oxygen in the container, and the rate of evaporation of the O_2, assuming it is vented to keep the pressure constant.

14·57 In a steelmaking apparatus two parallel plates, large compared to the distance between them, are at 1000°R and 500°R.

(*a*) Calculate the radiation exchange per square foot of area if $\alpha_1 = \alpha_2 = 1$.

(*b*) A third parallel black plate is located between the two plates. What is its steady-state temperature? How is the heat-transfer rate altered?

(*c*) Suppose the hotter of the two plates is oxidized steel while the cooler is oxidized aluminum. What is the heat rate of transfer and what is the temperature of the black plate between?

(*d*) Discuss briefly the significance of this exercise.

14·58 A large duct conveys a high-temperature stream of air at 15 ft/sec. The duct Neglecting conduction up the wire, what is the gas temperature when the thermocouple reads 1000°F? Treat the thermocouple well as a ¼-in. diameter cylinder in cross-flow.

14·59 A thermocouple is to be designed to measure accurately the temperature of hot atmospheric air (1000°F) in a cool duct (200°F). The thermocouple wire is 20 gage and is strung across the flow. Design suitable radiation shielding to permit a gas temperature measurement to within 1°F. The air velocity is 50 ft/sec.

UNIT SYSTEMS AND DIMENSIONAL EQUIVALENTS

The conceptual basis of unit systems was discussed in Chap. One. Table A·1 shows the dimensions of mechanical quantities in four commonly used unit systems. Note that the constant in Newton's second law, g_c, is arbitrarily taken as unity, except in the engineering system where its value of 32.17 ft-lbm/lbf-sec² is conceptually experimental. Three common electromagnetic unit systems are shown in Table A·2. Note that the differences are in the manner that charge is handled; some differences in the definitions are also involved. Table A·3 contains a selected list of dimensional equivalents, and Table A·4 gives values for several important physical constants.

Dimensional equivalents are most easily obtained by considering a given magnitude of the quantity in the two unit systems. Two examples of this procedure follow.

1 Find the equivalent of 1 newton of force in the engineering unit system. To determine this dimensional equivalent, consider a body having a mass of 1 kg being accelerated by a force at the rate of 1 m/sec². The force acting on the body is, in the mks system,

$$F = ma = 1 \text{ kg-m/sec}^2$$

The mass of the body in the engineering system is (Table A·3) 2.2046 lbm. Its acceleration is

$$1 \text{ m} \times 3.280 \text{ (ft/m)/sec}^2 = 3.280 \text{ ft/sec}^2$$

In the engineering system the force is

$$F = \frac{1}{g_c} ma = \frac{2.2046 \text{ lbm} \times 3.280 \text{ ft/sec}^2}{32.17 \text{ ft-lbm/lbf-sec}^2} = 0.2248 \text{ lbf}$$

495

Therefore,

$$1 \text{ newton} \equiv 1 \text{ kg-m/sec}^2 = 0.2248 \text{ lbf}$$

2 Determine the dimensional equivalents of the magnetic induction B and the magnetization M in the rationalized practical mksc and absolute magnetostatic cgs unit systems. This calculation is complicated by the difference in definition. We have

$$B = H + 4\pi M \qquad \text{magnetostatic cgs system} \qquad (A \cdot 1a)$$
$$B = \mu_0(H + M) \qquad \text{mksc system} \qquad (A \cdot 1b)$$

Consider two charges, each of 1 coul, separated by a distance of 1 m, moving in opposite directions perpendicular to the line between them at 1 m/sec.

From the Biot-Savart law the force in the mksc system is

$$F = \frac{1.256 \times 10^{-6}}{4\pi} \text{ kg-m/coul}^2 \times 1 \text{ coul}^2 \times 1 \text{ m}^2/\text{sec}^2 \times \frac{1 \text{ m}}{1 \text{ m}^3}$$

$$= \frac{1.256 \times 10^{-6}}{4\pi} \text{ kg-m/sec}^2 = 10^{-7} \text{ kg-m/sec}^2$$

In the absolute magnetostatic unit system the charge, distance, and speed have the magnitudes

$$Q = 0.1 \text{ g}^{\frac{1}{2}}\text{-cm}^{\frac{1}{2}}$$
$$R = 100 \text{ cm}$$
$$V = 100 \text{ cm/sec}$$

The force in the magnetostatic cgs system is therefore

$$F = 0.1^2 \text{ g-cm} \times 100^2 \text{ cm}^2/\text{sec}^2 \frac{100 \text{ cm}}{100^3 \text{ cm}^3} = 0.01 \text{ g-cm/sec}^2$$

The magnetic induction B, in either system, is

$$B = \frac{F}{VQ} \qquad (A \cdot 2)$$

In the rationalized practical mksc system

$$B = \frac{10^{-7} \text{ kg-m/sec}^2}{1 \text{ coul} \times 1 \text{ m/sec}}$$

$$= 10^{-7} \text{ kg/coul-sec}$$

In the absolute magnetostatic cgs system

$$\mathsf{B} = \frac{0.01 \ \text{g-cm/sec}^2}{0.1 \ \text{g}^{1/2}\text{-cm}^{1/2} \times 100 \ \text{cm/sec}}$$
$$= 0.001 \ \text{g}^{1/2}/\text{cm}^{1/2}\text{-sec}$$

In terms of the aliases

$$1 \ \text{tesla} \equiv 1 \ \text{kg/coul-sec}$$
$$1 \ \text{gauss} \equiv 1 \ \text{g}^{1/2}/\text{cm}^{1/2}\text{-sec}$$

we have

$$10^{-7} \ \text{tesla} = 0.001 \ \text{gauss}$$

So for B

$$1 \ \text{tesla} = 10^4 \ \text{gauss}$$

We hasten to point out that the correspondence between tesla and gauss does not apply to H and M. To find the dimensional equivalents for H we consider a field with $\mathsf{B} = 1$ tesla and $\mathsf{M} = 0$. Then, in the rationalized practical mksc system,

$$\mathsf{H} = \frac{\mathsf{B}}{\mu_0}$$
$$= \frac{1 \ \text{kg/coul-sec}}{1.256 \times 10^{-6} \ \text{kg-m/coul}^2} = \frac{1}{1.256 \times 10^{-6}} \ \text{coul/m-sec}$$

In the absolute magnetostatic cgs system $\mathsf{B} = \mathsf{H} = 10^4$ gauss. Equating the two values for H, we find

$$1 \ \text{gauss of } \mathsf{H} = \frac{1}{1.256 \times 10^{-2}} \ \text{coul/m-sec}$$

To obtain the equivalents for M we imagine a field of 1 tesla with $\mathsf{H} = 0$. Then, in the rationalized practical mksc unit system,

$$\mathsf{M} = \frac{\mathsf{B}}{\mu_0} = \frac{1}{1.256 \times 10^{-6}} \ \text{coul/m-sec}$$

In the absolute magnetostatic cgs system

$$\mathsf{M} = \frac{\mathsf{B}}{4\pi} = \frac{10^4}{4\pi} \ \text{gauss}$$

Equating the two magnetizations, we find

$$1 \ \text{gauss of } \mathsf{M} = 10^3 \ \text{coul/m-sec}$$

The dimensional equivalence for B might be put in the form

1 gauss of B $= 10^{-4}$ kg/coul-sec

This example illustrates the importance of keeping straight just what the dimensional equivalent is for. One gauss is not always equivalent to the same number of coul/m-sec; sometimes it is equivalent to a number of kg/coul-sec!

Converting units from one system to another is a confusing task which can be made simple by noting that multiplication of anything by unity leaves it unchanged. The number 1 can be written in many useful ways, two of which are

$$1 = \frac{12 \text{ in.}}{1 \text{ ft}}$$

$$1 = \frac{778.16 \text{ ft-lbf}}{1 \text{ Btu}}$$

Then, to express an energy density of 50 Btu/in.^{3} in terms of ft-lbf/ft^3,

$$\frac{E}{V} = 50 \text{ Btu/in.}^3 \times 778.16 \text{ ft-lbf/Btu} \times (12 \text{ in./ft})^3$$

$$= 6.72 \times 10^6 \text{ ft-lbf/ft}^3$$

You are encouraged to acquire the habit of always writing down units in a numerical problem. Dimensions provide an easy check on equations and are an essential part of the answer to any engineering problem.

TABLE A·1 MECHANICAL UNIT SYSTEMS

	Mks	Cgs	Absolute engineering	Engineering†
Primary quantities and their units				
Length	Meter, m	Centimeter, cm	Foot, ft	Foot, ft
Mass	Kilogram, kg	Gram, g	...	Pound mass, lbm
Time	Second, sec	Second, sec	Second, sec	Second, sec
Force	...	...	Pound force, lbf	Pound force, lbf
Newton's second law, $\mathbf{F} = \dfrac{m\,dV}{g_c\,dt}$	$g_c = 1$ (selected)	$g_c = 1$ (selected)	$g_c = 1$ (selected)	$g_c = 32.17$ ft-lbm/lbf-sec² (experimental)
Secondary quantities and their units				
Force	kg-m/sec²	g-cm/sec²	...	...
Mass	...	...	lbf-sec²/ft	...
Energy, $dW = \mathbf{F}\,dX$	kg-m²/sec²	g-cm²/sec²	ft-lbf	ft-lbf
Power, $\dot{W}$	kg-m²/sec³	g-cm²/sec³	ft-lbf/sec	ft-lbf/sec
Aliases				
Force	1 newton = 1 kg-m/sec²	1 dyne = 1 g-cm/sec²	...	...
Mass	...	...	1 slug = 1 lbf-sec²/ft	...
Energy	1 joule = 1 kg-m²/sec² = 1 newton-m	1 erg = 1 g-cm²/sec² = 1 dyne-cm	...	...
Power	1 watt = 1 kg-m²/sec³ = 1 joule/sec	...	...	...

† A body having a weight of 1 lbf on the surface of the earth will have a mass of approximately 1 lbm.

TABLE A·2 ELECTROMAGNETIC UNIT SYSTEMS

	Mksc	Absolute cgs electrostatic (esu)	Absolute cgs magnetostatic (emu)
Primary quantities and their units			
Length	Meter, m	Centimeter, cm	Centimeter, cm
Mass	Kilogram, kg	Gram, g	Gram, g
Time	Second, sec	Second, sec	Second, sec
Charge	Coulomb, coul	…	…
Coulomb's law,	$k_C = \dfrac{1}{4\pi\epsilon_0}$	$k_C \equiv 1$ (selected)	$k_C = 0.8992 \times 10^{17}$ cm²-sec⁻² (experimental)
$F_{12} = k_C \dfrac{Q_1 Q_2}{R_{12}{}^2}$	$\epsilon_0 = 8.854 \times 10^{-12}$ coul²-sec²- kg⁻¹-m⁻³ (experimental)		
Biot-Savart law,	$k_B = \dfrac{\mu_0}{4\pi}$	$k_B = 1.112 \times 10^{-17}$ sec²-cm⁻² (experimental)	$k_B \equiv 1$ (selected)
$F_{12} = k_B \dfrac{Q_1 Q_2 \mathbf{V}_1 \times (\mathbf{V}_2 \times \mathbf{R})}{|\mathbf{R}|^3}$	$\mu_0 = 1.256 \times 10^{-6}$ kg-m-coul⁻² (experimental)		
Secondary quantities and their units			
Charge	…	$g^{1/2}\text{-}cm^{3/2}\text{-}sec^{-1}$	$g^{1/2}\text{-}cm^{1/2}$
Current density, $J = \dot{Q}/A$	coul-m⁻² sec⁻¹	$g^{1/2}\text{-}cm^{-1/2}\text{-}sec^{-2}$	$g^{1/2}\text{-}cm^{-3/2}\text{-}sec^{-1}$
Current, $I = \int J \cdot d\mathbf{A}$	coul-sec⁻¹	$g^{1/2}\text{-}cm^{3/2}\text{-}sec^{-2}$	$g^{1/2}\text{-}cm^{1/2}\text{-}sec^{-1}$
Electric and magnetic fields,			
$\mathbf{F} = Q(\mathbf{E} + \mathbf{V} \times \mathbf{B})$			
Electric field strength $\mathbf{E}$	kg-m-coul⁻¹-sec⁻²	$g^{1/2}\text{-}cm^{-1/2}\text{-}sec^{-1}$	$g^{1/2}\text{-}cm^{-1/2}\text{-}sec^{-2}$
Magnetic induction $\mathbf{B}$	kg-sec⁻¹-coul⁻¹	$g^{1/2}\text{-}cm^{-3/2}$	$g^{1/2}\text{-}cm^{-1/2}\text{-}sec^{-1}$

Quantity	MKS	Gaussian
Electrical potential $\mathcal{E}$ $d\mathcal{E} = \mathbf{E} \cdot d\mathbf{L}$	$\text{kg-m}^2\text{-coul}^{-1}\text{-sec}^{-2}$	$g^{1/2}\text{-cm}^{3/2}\text{-sec}^{-2}$
Electric displacement, polarization:	$\mathbf{D} = \epsilon_0\mathbf{E} + \mathbf{P}$	$\mathbf{D} = \mathbf{E} + 4\pi\mathbf{P}$
Displacement $\mathbf{D}$	coul-m^{-2}	$g^{1/2}\text{-cm}^{-1/2}\text{-sec}^{-1}$
Polarization $\mathbf{P}$	coul-m^{-2}	$g^{1/2}\text{-cm}^{-1/2}\text{-sec}^{-1}$
Magnetic field strength, magnetization:	$\mathbf{B} = \mu_0(\mathbf{H} + \mathbf{M})$	$\mathbf{B} = \mathbf{H} + 4\pi\mathbf{M}$
Magnetic field strength $\mathbf{H}$	$\text{coul-m}^{-1}\text{-sec}^{-1}$	$g^{1/2}\text{-cm}^{-1/2}\text{-sec}^{-1}$
Magnetization $\mathbf{M}$	$\text{coul-m}^{-1}\text{-sec}^{-1}$	$g^{1/2}\text{-cm}^{-1/2}\text{-sec}^{-1}$
Electric flux, $\Phi_E = \int \mathbf{E} \cdot d\mathbf{A}$	$\text{kg-m}^3\text{-coul}^{-1}\text{-sec}^{-2}$	$g^{1/2}\text{-cm}^{3/2}\text{-sec}^{-1}$
Magnetic flux, $\Phi_B = \int \mathbf{B} \cdot d\mathbf{A}$	$\text{kg-m}^2\text{-coul}^{-1}\text{-sec}^{-1}$	$g^{1/2}\text{-cm}^{3/2}\text{-sec}^{-1}$
Electrical conductivity, J/E	$\text{coul}^2\text{-sec-kg}^{-1}\text{-m}^{-3}$	sec^{-1}
Resistance, $R = \Delta\mathcal{E}/I$	$\text{kg-m}^2\text{-coul}^{-2}\text{-sec}^{-1}$	sec-cm^{-1}
Capacitance, $C = I/(d\mathcal{E}/dt)$	$\text{coul}^2\text{-sec}^2\text{-kg}^{-1}\text{-m}^{-2}$	cm
Inductance, $L = \Delta\mathcal{E}/(dI/dt)$	$\text{kg-m}^2\text{-coul}^{-2}$	$\text{sec}^2\text{-cm}^{-1}$

Aliases

Quantity	MKS	esu	emu
Charge	. . .	$1\ \text{statcoul} = 1\ g^{1/2}\text{-cm}^{3/2}\text{-sec}^{-1}$	$1\ \text{abcoul} = 1\ g^{1/2}\text{-cm}^{1/2}$
Current	$1\ \text{amp} = 1\ \text{coul-sec}^{-1}$	$1\ \text{statamp} = 1\ g^{1/2}\text{-cm}^{3/2}\text{-sec}^{-2}$	$1\ \text{abamp} = 1\ g^{1/2}\text{-cm}^{1/2}\text{-sec}^{-1}$
Magnetic induction	$1\ \text{tesla} = 1\ \text{kg-sec}^{-1}\text{-coul}^{-1}$		$1\ \text{gauss} = 1\ g^{1/2}\text{-cm}^{-1/2}\text{-sec}^{-1}$
Electric potential	$1\ \text{volt} = 1\ \text{kg-m}^2\text{-coul}^{-1}\text{-sec}^{-2}$	$1\ \text{statvolt} = 1\ g^{1/2}\text{-cm}^{1/2}\text{-sec}^{-1}$	$1\ \text{abvolt} = 1\ g^{1/2}\text{-cm}^{3/2}\text{-sec}^{-2}$
Magnetic flux	$1\ \text{weber} = 1\ \text{kg-m}^2\text{-coul}^{-1}\text{-sec}^{-1}$		
Resistance	$1\ \text{ohm} = 1\ \text{kg-m}^2\text{-coul}^{-2}\text{-sec}^{-1}$	$1\ \text{statohm} = 1\ \text{sec-cm}^{-1}$	$1\ \text{abohm} = 1\ \text{cm-sec}^{-1}$
Capacitance	$1\ \text{farad} = 1\ \text{coul}^2\text{-sec}^2\text{-kg}^{-1}\text{-m}^{-2}$	$1\ \text{statfarad} = 1\ \text{cm}$	$1\ \text{abfarad} = 1\ \text{sec}^2\text{-cm}^{-1}$
Inductance	$1\ \text{henry} = 1\ \text{kg-m}^2\text{-coul}^{-2}$	$1\ \text{stathenry} = 1\ \text{sec}^2\text{-cm}^{-1}$	$1\ \text{abhenry} = 1\ \text{cm}$

TABLE A · 3 SELECTED DIMENSIONAL EQUIVALENTS

Length	1 m = 3.280 ft = 39.37 in.
	1 cm ≡ 10^{-2} m ≐ 0.394 in. = 0.0328 ft
	1 mm ≡ 10^{-3} m
	1 micron (μ) ≡ 10^{-6} m
	1 angstrom (Å) ≡ 10^{-10} m
Time	1 hr ≡ 3600 sec = 60 min
	1 millisec ≡ 10^{-3} sec
	1 microsec (μsec) ≡ 10^{-6} sec
	1 nanosec (nsec) = 10^{-9} sec
Mass	1 kg ≡ 1000 g = 2.2046 lbm = 6.8521×10^{-2} slugs
	1 slug ≡ 1 lbf-sec²/ft = 32.174 lbm
Force	1 newton ≡ 1 kg-m/sec²
	1 dyne ≡ 1 g-cm/sec²
	1 lbf = 4.448×10^5 dynes = 4.448 newtons
Energy	1 joule ≡ 1 kg-m²/sec²
	1 Btu ≡ 778.16 ft-lbf = 1.055×10^{10} ergs = 252 cal
	1 cal ≡ 4.186 joules
	1 kcal ≡ 4186 joules = 1000 cal
	1 erg ≡ 1 g-cm²/sec²
	1 ev ≡ 1.602×10^{-19} joules
Power	1 watt ≡ 1 kg-m²/sec³ = 1 joule/sec
	1 hp ≡ 550 ft-lbf/sec
	1 hp = 2545 Btu/hr = 746 watts
	1 kw ≡ 1000 watts = 3413 Btu/hr
Pressure	1 atm ≡ 14.696 lbf/in.² = 760 torr
	1 mmHg = 0.01934 lbf/in.² ≡ 1 torr
	1 dyne/cm² = 145.04×10^{-7} lbf/in.²
	1 bar = 14.504 lbf/in.² ≡ 10^6 dynes/cm²
	1 micron (μ) ≡ 10^{-6} mHg = 10^{-3} mmHg
Volume	1 gal ≡ 0.13368 ft³
	1 liter ≡ 1000.028 cm³
Temperature	1 K° = 1 C° = 1.8 F° = 1.8 R°
	0°C corresponds to 32°F, 273.16°K, and 491.69°R
Magnetic quantities	1 gauss ≡ 1 $g^{1/2}$/$cm^{1/2}$-sec
	1 gauss = 10^3 coul/m-sec for M
	1 gauss = $(1/4\pi) \times 10^3$ coul/m-sec for H
	1 gauss = 10^{-4} tesla for B
	1 tesla ≡ 1 kg/coul-sec

TABLE A · 4 PHYSICAL CONSTANTS

Avogadro's number	$N_0 = 6.025 \times 10^{23}/\text{gmole}$
Boltzmann's constant	$k = 1.380 \times 10^{-23} \text{ joule}/°K$
Gas constant	$\mathcal{R} = 1545.33 \text{ ft-lbf/lbmole-}°R$
	$= 8.317 \text{ joule/gmole-}°K$
	$= 1.986 \text{ Btu/lbmole-}°R$
	$= 1.986 \text{ cal/gmole-}°K$
Planck's constant	$h = 6.625 \times 10^{-34} \text{ joule-sec}$
Coulomb constant	$1/4\pi\epsilon_0 = 8.987 \times 10^9 \text{ kg-m}^3/\text{coul}^2\text{-sec}^2$
Biot-Savart constant	$\mu_0/4\pi = 1.0000 \times 10^{-7} \text{ kg-m/coul}^2$
Electronic charge	$e = -1.6021 \times 10^{-19} \text{ coul}$
Speed of light	$c = 2.998 \times 10^8 \text{ m/sec}$
Newton constant	$g_c = 32.174 \text{ ft-lbm/lbf-sec}^2$
Gravitational constant	$k_G = 6.67 \times 10^{-11} \text{ m}^3/\text{kg-sec}^2$

THERMODYNAMIC
PROPERTIES
OF SUBSTANCES

FIG. B·1 *Thermodynamic properties of steam* (H_2O). *Redrawn from Joseph H. Keenan and Joseph Keyes*, Thermodynamic Properties of Steam, *John Wiley & Sons, Inc., New York, 1952, by permission*

Specific volume, ft³/lbm

Specific internal energy, Btu/lbm

Critical point
3206.2 psia 705.40°F

Saturated liquid

Triple point, 32.02°F

Saturated vapor

1 psia (101.74°F)
2 psia (126.08°F)
5 psia (162.24°F)
10 psia (193.21°F)
14.696 psia (212.00°F)
50 psia (281.01°F)
100 psia (381.79°F)
200 psia (467.01°F)
500 psia (544.61°F)
1000 psia
2000 psia

1 psia
2 psia
5 psia
10 psia
14.696 psia
50 psia
100 psia
200 psia
500 psia
1000 psia
2000 psia
3000 psia
4000 psia
5500 psia

x = .10
x = .20
x = .30
x = .40
x = .50
x = .60
x = .70
x = .80
x = .90

200°F 300°F 400°F 500°F 600°F 700°F 800°F 900°F 1000°F 1100°F 1200°F 1400°F 1600°F

900°F 1000°F 1100°F 1200°F 1400°F 1600°F

Mollier diagram for steam (H_2O). *From Joseph H. Keenan and Joseph Keyes*, Thermodynamic Properties of Steam, *John Wiley & Sons, Inc., New York, 1936, by permission*

Temperature-entropy diagram for steam (H₂O). From Joseph H. Keenan and Joseph Keyes, Thermodynamic Properties of Steam, *John Wiley & Sons, Inc., New York, as adapted by Lay,* Thermodynamics, *Charles E. Merrill, Inc., Englewood Cliffs, N.J., 1963, by permission*

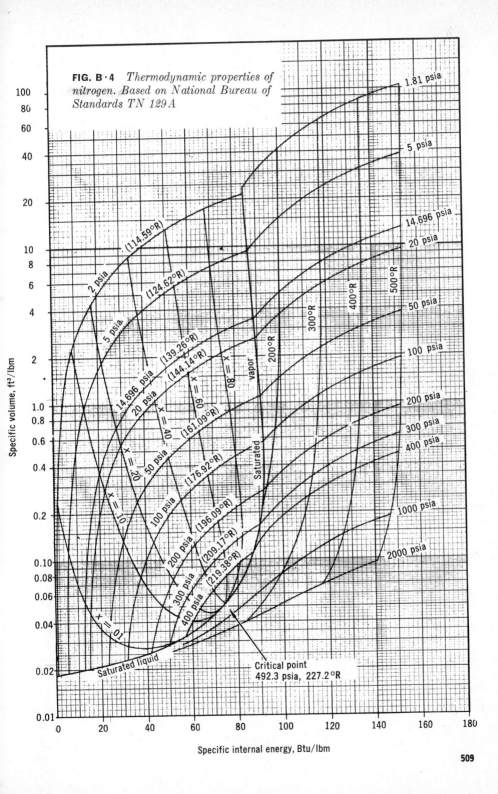

FIG. B·4 *Thermodynamic properties of nitrogen. Based on National Bureau of Standards TN 129A*

Specific volume, ft³/lbm

1.81 psia
5 psia
14.696 psia
20 psia
50 psia
100 psia
200 psia
300 psia
400 psia
1000 psia
2000 psia

2 psia
5 psia
14.696 psia
20 psia
50 psia
100 psia
200 psia
300 psia
400 psia

(114.59°R)
(124.62°R)
(139.26°R)
(144.14°R)
(161.09°R)
(176.92°R)
(196.09°R)
(209.17°R)
(219.38°R)

200°R
300°R
400°R
500°R

x = 80
vapor
Saturated
x = .90
x = .60
x = .40
x = .20
x = .10
x = .01

Saturated liquid

Critical point
492.3 psia, 227.2°R

Specific internal energy, Btu/lbm

FIG. B·5 *Thermody-
namic properties of oxy-
gen. From NBS D-2573.
1 cal = 4.184 joules, v in
ml/gmole, T in °K, s in
cal/gmole-°K*

Enthalpy, cal/gmole

Pressure, atm

Constant temperature

Constant volume

Constant entropy

Saturated vapor

Saturated liquid

Constant entropy

Constant quality

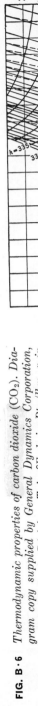

FIG. B·6 *Thermodynamic properties of carbon dioxide (CO₂). Diagram copy supplied by General Dynamics Corporation, Liquid Carbonic Division. T in °F, h in Btu/lbm, v in ft³/lbm, s in Btu/lbm-°F; at critical point P = 1066.3 psia, T = 87.8°F*

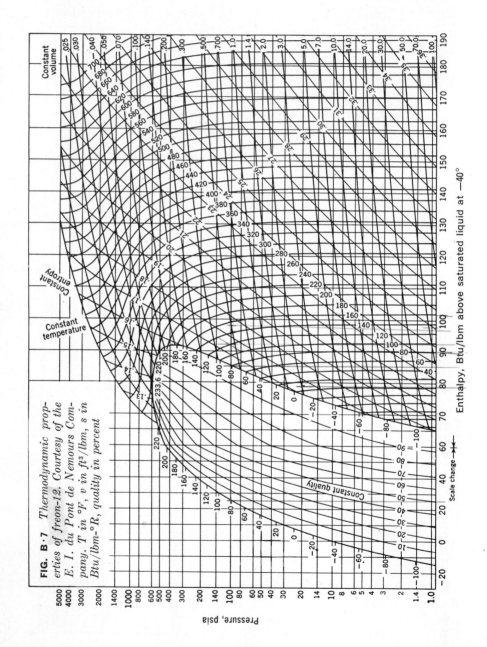

FIG. B·7 *Thermodynamic properties of freon-12. Courtesy of the E. I. du Pont de Nemours Company. T in °F, v in ft³/lbm, s in Btu/lbm-°R, quality in percent*

Constant volume

Constant entropy

Constant temperature

Constant quality

Scale change

Pressure, psia

Enthalpy, Btu/lbm above saturated liquid at −40°

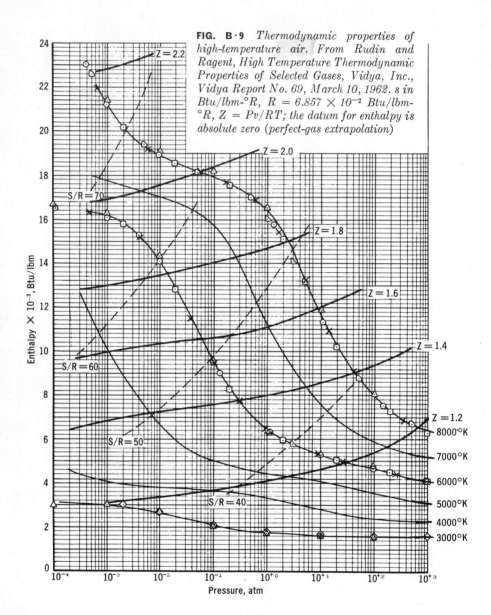

FIG. B·9 *Thermodynamic properties of high-temperature air. From Rudin and Ragent, High Temperature Thermodynamic Properties of Selected Gases, Vidya, Inc., Vidya Report No. 69, March 10, 1962. s in Btu/lbm-°R, $R = 6.857 \times 10^{-2}$ Btu/lbm-°R, $Z = Pv/RT$; the datum for enthalpy is absolute zero (perfect-gas extrapolation)*

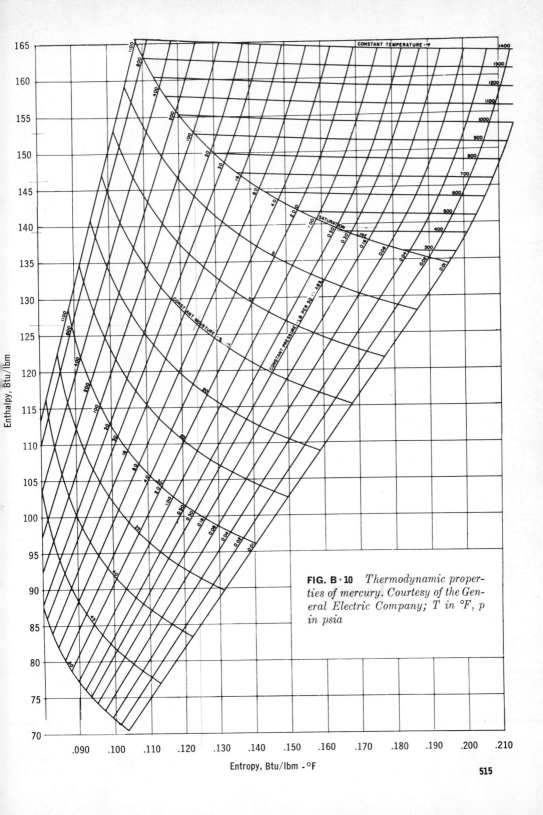

FIG. B·10 *Thermodynamic properties of mercury. Courtesy of the General Electric Company; T in °F, p in psia*

Enthalpy, Btu/lbm

Entropy, Btu/lbm - °F

515

Thermodynamic properties of cesium.
Redrawn from WADD Report 61-96

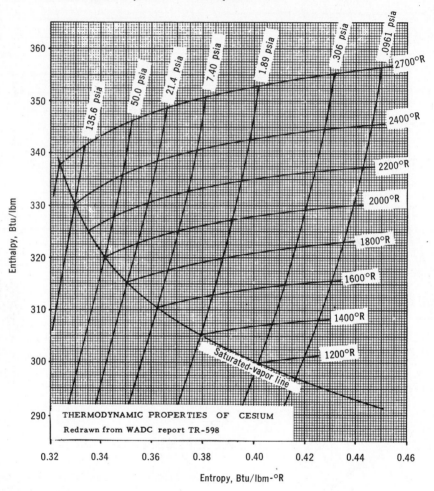

THERMODYNAMIC PROPERTIES OF CESIUM
Redrawn from WADC report TR-598

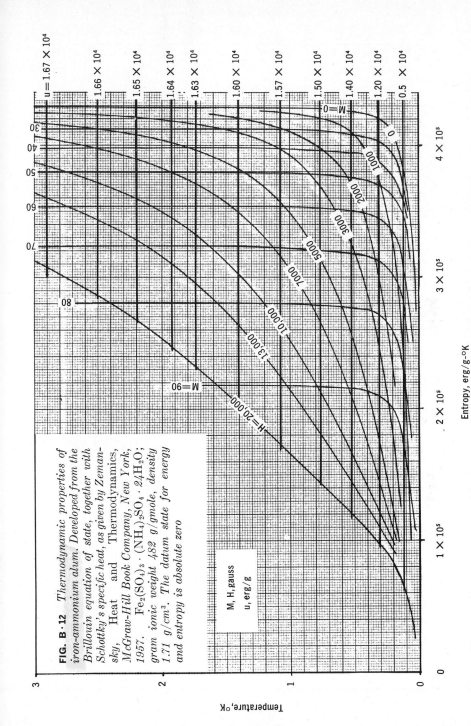

FIG. B·12 *Thermodynamic properties of iron-ammonium alum. Developed from the Brillouin equation of state, together with Schottky's specific heat, as given by Zemansky, Heat and Thermodynamics, McGraw-Hill Book Company, New York, 1957.* $Fe_2(SO_4)_3 \cdot (NH_4)_2SO_4 \cdot 24H_2O$; *gram ionic weight 482 g/gmole, density 1.71 g/cm³. The datum state for energy and entropy is absolute zero*

M, H, gauss
u, erg/g

$u = 1.67 \times 10^4$
1.66×10^4
1.65×10^4
1.64×10^4
1.63×10^4
1.60×10^4
1.57×10^4
1.50×10^4
1.40×10^4
1.20×10^4
0.5×10^4

M=0
0
1000
2000
3000
5000
7000
10,000
13,000
M=90
H=20,000

30
40
50
60
70
80

Temperature, °K

Entropy, erg/g-°K

1×10^5
2×10^5
3×10^5
4×10^5

FIG. B·13 *Psychrometric chart (for 1 atm pressure). Courtesy of the General Electric Company.*
Barometric pressure, 14.696 lbf/in.² (1 lbm = 7000 grains)

Water vapor in 1 lbm of "dry air", grains

Dry-bulb temperature, °F

Pressure of water vapor, lbf/in.²

Barometric pressure, 14.696 lb/sq in.
(1 lb = 7000 grains)

Enthalpy, Btu/lbm = dry air (unsaturated air)

Wet-bulb and dew-point temperatures, °F

Ft³/lbm of dry air

Relative humidity

Wet-bulb lines

ref: fig 10.3 pg 340 : "Dry air does not mean that it
contains zero water vapour. Rather, it is defined as the air
at STATE ① FIG 10.3

Note: reference, or zero
①

518

FIG. B·14a *Generalized compressibility chart—low-pressure range. Data from L. C. Nelson and E. F. Obert, Generalized Compressibility Charts, Chem. En., vol. 61, p. 203, 1954. Note:* $v/v_c \equiv P_c v/RT_c$

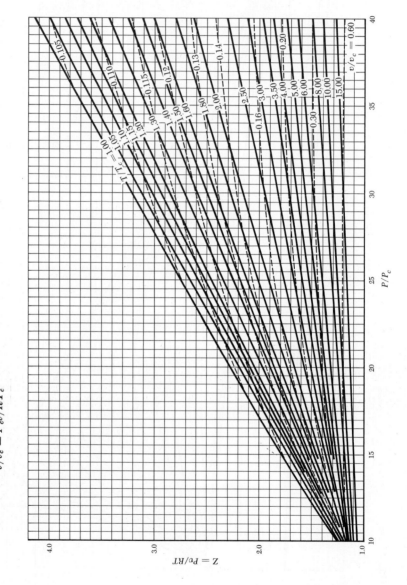

FIG. B · 14b *Generalized compressibility chart—high-pressure range. Adapted from E. F. Obert, Concepts of Thermodynamics, McGraw-Hill Book Company, New York, 1960. Note:* $v/v_c \equiv P_c v/RT_c$

FIG. B·15 *Generalized enthalpy chart. Adapted from K. Wark, Thermodynamics, McGraw-Hill Book Company, New York, 1966*

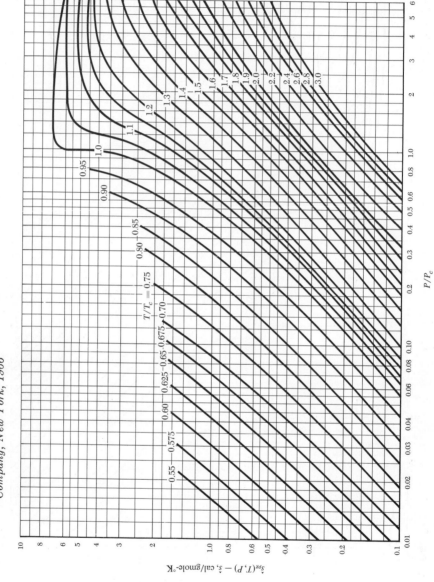

FIG. B·16 Generalized entropy chart. Adapted from K. Wark, Thermodynamics, McGraw-Hill Book Company, New York, 1966

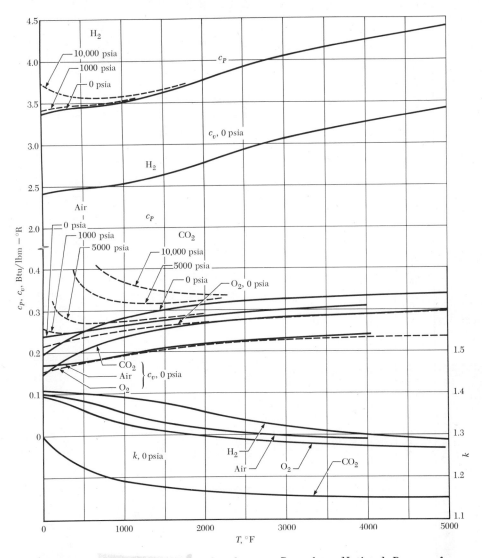

FIG. B·17 *Specific heats of selected gases. Data from National Bureau of Standards*

TABLE B·1A SATURATED H₂O: TEMPERATURE TABLE

Temp., °F	Abs. press., psia	Specific vol., ft³/lbm			Enthalpy, Btu/lbm			Entropy, Btu/lbm-°R		
		Sat. liq.	Evap.	Sat. vap.	Sat. liq.	Evap.	Sat. vap.	Sat. liq.	Evap.	Sat. vap.
T	P	v_f	v_{fg}	v_g	h_f	h_{fg}	h_g	s_f	s_{fg}	s_g
32	0.08854	0.01602	3306	3306	0.00	1075.8	1075.8	0.0000	2.1877	2.1877
35	0.09995	0.01602	2947	2947	3.02	1074.1	1077.1	0.0061	2.1709	2.1770
40	0.12170	0.01602	2444	2444	8.05	1071.3	1079.3	0.0162	2.1435	2.1597
45	0.14752	0.01602	2036.4	2036.4	13.06	1068.4	1081.5	0.0262	2.1167	2.1429
50	0.17811	0.01603	1703.2	1703.2	18.07	1065.6	1083.7	0.0361	2.0903	2.1264
60	0.2563	0.01604	1206.6	1206.7	28.06	1059.9	1088.0	0.0555	2.0393	2.0948
70	0.3631	0.01606	867.8	867.9	38.04	1054.3	1092.3	0.0745	1.9902	2.0647
80	0.5069	0.01608	633.1	633.1	48.02	1048.6	1096.6	0.0932	1.9428	2.0360
90	0.6982	0.01610	468.0	468.0	57.99	1042.9	1100.9	0.1115	1.8972	2.0087
100	0.9492	0.01613	350.3	350.4	67.97	1037.2	1105.2	0.1295	1.8531	1.9826
110	1.2748	0.01617	265.3	265.4	77.94	1031.6	1109.5	0.1471	1.8106	1.9577
120	1.6924	0.01620	203.25	203.27	87.92	1025.8	1113.7	0.1645	1.7694	1.9339
130	2.2225	0.01625	157.32	157.34	97.90	1020.0	1117.9	0.1816	1.7296	1.9112
140	2.8886	0.01629	122.99	123.01	107.89	1014.1	1122.0	0.1984	1.6910	1.8894
150	3.718	0.01634	97.06	97.07	117.89	1008.2	1126.1	0.2149	1.6537	1.8685
160	4.741	0.01639	77.27	77.29	127.89	1002.3	1130.2	0.2311	1.6174	1.8485
170	5.992	0.01645	62.04	62.06	137.90	996.3	1134.2	0.2472	1.5822	1.8293
180	7.510	0.01651	50.21	50.23	147.92	990.2	1138.1	0.2630	1.5480	1.8109
190	9.339	0.01657	40.94	40.96	157.95	984.1	1142.0	0.2785	1.5147	1.7932
200	11.526	0.01663	33.62	33.64	167.99	977.9	1145.9	0.2938	1.4824	1.7762

210	14.123	0.01670	27.80	27.82	178.05	971.6	1149.7	0.3090	1.4508	1.7598
212	14.696	0.01672	26.78	26.80	180.07	970.3	1150.4	0.3120	1.4446	1.7566
220	17.186	0.01677	23.13	23.15	188.13	965.2	1153.4	0.3239	1.4201	1.7440
230	20.780	0.01684	19.365	19.382	198.23	958.8	1157.0	0.3387	1.3901	1.7288
240	24.969	0.01692	16.306	16.323	208.34	952.2	1160.5	0.3531	1.3609	1.7140
250	29.825	0.01700	13.804	13.821	216.48	945.5	1164.0	0.3675	1.3323	1.6998
260	35.429	0.01709	11.746	11.763	228.64	938.7	1167.3	0.3817	1.3043	1.6860
270	41.858	0.01717	10.044	10.061	238.84	931.8	1170.6	0.3958	1.2769	1.6727
280	49.203	0.01726	8.628	8.645	249.06	924.7	1173.8	0.4096	1.2501	1.6597
290	57.556	0.01735	7.444	7.461	259.31	917.5	1176.8	0.4234	1.2238	1.6472
300	67.013	0.01745	6.449	6.466	269.59	910.1	1179.7	0.4369	1.1980	1.6350
310	77.68	0.01755	5.609	5.626	279.92	902.6	1182.5	0.4504	1.1727	1.6231
320	89.66	0.01765	4.896	4.914	290.28	894.9	1185.2	0.4637	1.1478	1.6115
330	103.06	0.01776	4.289	4.307	300.68	887.0	1187.7	0.4769	1.1233	1.6002
340	118.01	0.01787	3.770	3.788	311.13	879.0	1190.1	0.4900	1.0992	1.5891
350	134.63	0.01799	3.324	3.342	321.63	870.7	1192.3	0.5029	1.0754	1.5783
360	153.04	0.01811	2.939	2.957	332.18	862.2	1194.4	0.5158	1.0519	1.5677
370	173.37	0.01823	2.606	2.625	342.79	853.5	1196.3	0.5286	1.0287	1.5573
380	195.77	0.01836	2.317	2.335	353.45	844.6	1198.1	0.5413	1.0059	1.5471
390	220.37	0.01850	2.0651	2.0836	364.17	835.4	1199.6	0.5539	0.9832	1.5371
400	247.31	0.01864	1.8447	1.8633	374.97	826.0	1201.0	0.5664	0.9608	1.5272
410	276.75	0.01878	1.6512	1.6700	385.83	816.3	1202.1	0.5788	0.9386	1.5174
420	308.83	0.01894	1.4811	1.5000	396.77	806.3	1203.1	0.5912	0.9166	1.5078
430	343.72	0.01910	1.3308	1.3499	407.79	796.0	1203.8	0.6035	0.8947	1.4982
440	381.59	0.01926	1.1979	1.2171	418.90	785.4	1204.3	0.6158	0.8730	1.4887

TABLE B·1A SATURATED H_2O: TEMPERATURE TABLE (CONTINUED)

Temp., °F	Abs. press., psia	Specific vol., ft³/lbm			Enthalpy, Btu/lbm			Entropy, Btu/lbm-°R		
		Sat. liq.	Evap.	Sat. vap.	Sat. liq.	Evap.	Sat. vap.	Sat. liq.	Evap.	Sat. vap.
T	P	v_f	v_{fg}	v_g	h_f	h_{fg}	h_g	s_f	s_{fg}	s_g
450	422.6	0.0194	1.0799	1.0993	430.1	774.5	1204.6	0.6280	0.8513	1.4793
460	466.9	0.0196	0.9748	0.9944	441.4	763.2	1204.6	0.6402	0.8298	1.4700
470	514.7	0.0198	0.8811	0.9009	452.8	751.5	1204.3	0.6523	0.8083	1.4606
480	566.1	0.0200	0.7972	0.8172	464.4	739.4	1203.7	0.6645	0.7868	1.4513
490	621.4	0.0202	0.7221	0.7423	476.0	726.8	1202.8	0.6766	0.7653	1.4419
500	680.8	0.0204	0.6545	0.6749	487.8	713.9	1201.7	0.6887	0.7438	1.4325
520	812.4	0.0209	0.5385	0.5594	511.9	686.4	1198.2	0.7130	0.7006	1.4136
540	962.5	0.0215	0.4434	0.4649	536.6	656.6	1193.2	0.7374	0.6568	1.3942
560	1133.1	0.0221	0.3647	0.3868	562.2	624.2	1186.4	0.7621	0.6121	1.3742
580	1325.8	0.0228	0.2989	0.3217	588.9	588.4	1177.3	0.7872	0.5659	1.3532
600	1542.9	0.0236	0.2432	0.2668	617.0	548.5	1165.5	0.8131	0.5176	1.3307
620	1786.6	0.0247	0.1955	0.2201	646.7	503.6	1150.3	0.8398	0.4664	1.3062
640	2059.7	0.0260	0.1538	0.1798	678.6	452.0	1130.5	0.8679	0.4110	1.2789
660	2365.4	0.0278	0.1165	0.1442	714.2	390.2	1104.4	0.8987	0.3485	1.2472
680	2708.1	0.0305	0.0810	0.1115	757.3	309.9	1067.2	0.9351	0.2719	1.2071
700	3093.7	0.0369	0.0392	0.0761	823.3	172.1	995.4	0.9905	0.1484	1.1389
705.4	3206.2	0.0503	0	0.0503	902.7	0	902.7	1.0580	0	1.0580

Abridged from Joseph H. Keenan and Frederick G. Keyes, *Thermodynamic Properties of Steam*, John Wiley & Sons, Inc., New York, 1937. By permission of the authors.

TABLE B · 1B SATURATED H₂O: PRESSURE TABLE

Abs. press., psia	Temp., °F	Specific vol., ft³/lbm		Enthalpy, Btu/lbm			Entropy, Btu/lbm-°R			Internal energy, Btu/lbm	
		Sat. liq.	Sat. vap.	Sat. liq.	Evap.	Sat. vap.	Sat. liq.	Evap.	Sat. vap.	Sat. liq.	Sat. vap.
P	T	v_f	v_g	h_f	h_{fg}	h_g	s_f	s_{fg}	s_g	u_f	u_g
1.0	101.74	0.01614	333.6	69.70	1036.3	1106.0	0.1326	1.8456	1.9782	69.70	1044.3
2.0	126.08	0.01623	173.73	93.99	1022.2	1116.2	0.1749	1.7451	1.9200	93.98	1051.9
3.0	141.48	0.01630	118.71	109.37	1013.2	1122.6	0.2008	1.6855	1.8863	109.36	1056.7
4.0	152.97	0.01636	90.63	120.86	1006.4	1127.3	0.2198	1.6427	1.8625	120.85	1060.2
5.0	162.24	0.01640	73.52	130.13	1001.0	1131.1	0.2347	1.6094	1.8441	130.12	1063.1
6.0	170.06	0.01645	61.98	137.96	996.2	1134.2	0.2472	1.5820	1.8292	137.94	1065.4
7.0	176.85	0.01649	53.64	144.76	992.1	1136.9	0.2581	1.5586	1.8167	144.74	1067.4
8.0	182.86	0.01653	47.34	150.79	988.5	1139.3	0.2674	1.5383	1.8057	150.77	1069.2
9.0	188.28	0.01656	42.40	156.22	985.2	1141.4	0.2759	1.5203	1.7962	156.19	1070.8
10	193.21	0.01659	38.42	161.17	982.1	1143.3	0.2835	1.5041	1.7876	161.14	1072.2
14.696	212.00	0.01672	26.80	180.07	970.3	1150.4	0.3120	1.4446	1.7566	180.02	1077.5
15	213.03	0.01672	26.29	181.11	969.7	1150.8	0.3135	1.4415	1.7549	181.06	1077.8
20	227.96	0.01683	20.089	196.16	960.1	1156.3	0.3356	1.3962	1.7319	196.10	1081.9
25	240.07	0.01692	16.303	208.42	952.1	1160.6	0.3533	1.3606	1.7139	208.34	1085.1
30	250.33	0.01701	13.746	218.82	945.3	1164.1	0.3680	1.3313	1.6993	218.73	1087.8
35	259.28	0.01708	11.898	227.91	939.2	1167.1	0.3807	1.3063	1.6870	227.80	1090.1
40	267.25	0.01715	10.498	236.03	933.7	1169.7	0.3919	1.2844	1.6763	235.90	1092.0
45	274.44	0.01721	9.401	243.36	928.6	1172.0	0.4019	1.2650	1.6669	243.22	1093.7
50	281.01	0.01727	8.515	250.09	924.0	1174.1	0.4110	1.2474	1.6585	249.93	1095.3
55	287.07	0.01732	7.787	256.30	919.6	1175.9	0.4193	1.2316	1.6509	256.12	1096.7
60	292.71	0.01738	7.175	262.09	915.5	1177.6	0.4270	1.2168	1.6438	261.90	1097.9
65	297.97	0.01743	6.655	267.50	911.6	1179.1	0.4342	1.2032	1.6374	267.29	1099.1

TABLE B·1B SATURATED H₂O: PRESSURE TABLE (CONTINUED)

Abs. press., psia	Temp., °F	Specific vol., ft³/lbm		Enthalpy, Btu/lbm			Entropy, Btu/lbm-°R			Internal energy, Btu/lbm	
		Sat. liq.	Sat. vap.	Sat. liq.	Evap.	Sat. vap.	Sat. liq.	Evap.	Sat. vap.	Sat. liq.	Sat. vap.
P	T	v_f	v_g	h_f	h_{fg}	h_g	s_f	s_{fg}	s_g	u_f	u_g
70	302.92	0.01748	6.206	272.61	907.9	1180.6	0.4409	1.1906	1.6315	272.38	1100.2
75	307.60	0.01753	5.816	277.43	904.5	1181.9	0.4472	1.1787	1.6259	277.19	1101.2
80	312.03	0.01757	5.472	282.02	901.1	1183.1	0.4531	1.1676	1.6207	281.76	1102.1
85	316.25	0.01761	5.168	286.39	897.8	1184.2	0.4587	1.1571	1.6158	286.11	1102.9
90	320.27	0.01766	4.896	290.56	894.7	1185.3	0.4641	1.1471	1.6112	290.27	1103.7
95	324.12	0.01770	4.652	294.56	891.7	1186.2	0.4692	1.1376	1.6068	294.25	1104.5
100	327.81	0.01774	4.432	298.40	888.8	1187.2	0.4740	1.1286	1.6026	298.08	1105.2
110	334.77	0.01782	4.049	305.66	883.2	1188.9	0.4832	1.1117	1.5948	305.30	1106.5
120	341.25	0.01789	3.728	312.44	877.9	1190.4	0.4916	1.0962	1.5878	312.05	1107.6
130	347.32	0.01796	3.455	318.81	872.9	1191.7	0.4995	1.0817	1.5812	318.38	1108.6
140	353.02	0.01802	3.220	324.82	868.2	1193.0	0.5069	1.0682	1.5751	324.35	1109.6
150	358.42	0.01809	3.015	330.51	863.6	1194.1	0.5138	1.0556	1.5694	330.01	1110.5
160	363.53	0.01815	2.834	335.93	859.2	1195.1	0.5204	1.0436	1.5640	335.39	1111.2
170	368.41	0.01822	2.675	341.09	854.9	1196.0	0.5266	1.0324	1.5590	340.52	1111.9
180	373.06	0.01827	2.532	346.03	850.8	1196.9	0.5325	1.0217	1.5542	345.42	1112.5
190	377.51	0.01833	2.404	350.79	846.8	1197.6	0.5381	1.0116	1.5497	350.15	1113.1
200	381.79	0.01839	2.288	355.36	843.0	1198.4	0.5435	1.0018	1.5453	354.68	1113.7
250	400.95	0.01865	1.8438	376.00	825.1	1201.1	0.5675	0.9588	1.5263	375.14	1115.8
300	417.33	0.01890	1.5433	393.84	809.0	1202.8	0.5879	0.9225	1.5104	392.79	1117.1
350	431.72	0.01913	1.3260	409.69	794.2	1203.9	0.6056	0.8910	1.4966	408.45	1118.0
400	444.59	0.0193	1.1613	424.0	780.5	1204.5	0.6214	0.8630	1.4844	422.6	1118.5
450	456.28	0.0195	1.0320	437.2	767.4	1204.6	0.6356	0.8378	1.4734	435.5	1118.7
500	467.01	0.0197	0.9278	449.4	755.0	1204.4	0.6487	0.8147	1.4634	447.6	1118.6

550	476.94	0.0199	0.8424	460.8	743.1	1203.9	0.6608	0.7934	1.4542	458.8	1118.2
600	486.21	0.0201	0.7698	471.6	731.6	1203.2	0.6720	0.7734	1.4454	469.4	1117.7
650	494.90	0.0203	0.7083	481.8	720.5	1202.3	0.6826	0.7548	1.4374	479.4	1117.1
700	503.10	0.0205	0.6554	491.5	709.7	1201.2	0.6925	0.7371	1.4296	488.8	1116.3
750	510.86	0.0207	0.6092	500.8	699.2	1200.0	0.7019	0.7204	1.4223	498.0	1115.4
800	518.23	0.0209	0.5687	509.7	688.9	1198.6	0.7108	0.7045	1.4153	506.6	1114.4
850	525.26	0.0210	0.5327	518.3	678.8	1197.1	0.7194	0.6891	1.4085	515.0	1113.3
900	531.98	0.0212	0.5006	526.6	668.8	1195.4	0.7275	0.6744	1.4020	523.1	1112.1
950	538.43	0.0214	0.4717	534.6	659.1	1193.7	0.7355	0.6602	1.3957	530.9	1110.8
1000	544.61	0.0216	0.4456	542.4	649.4	1191.8	0.7430	0.6467	1.3897	538.4	1109.4
1100	556.31	0.0220	0.4001	557.4	630.4	1187.8	0.7575	0.6205	1.3780	552.9	1106.4
1200	567.22	0.0223	0.3619	571.7	611.7	1183.4	0.7711	0.5956	1.3667	566.7	1103.0
1300	577.46	0.0227	0.3293	585.4	593.2	1178.6	0.7840	0.5719	1.3559	580.0	1099.4
1400	587.10	0.0231	0.3012	598.7	574.7	1173.4	0.7963	0.5491	1.3454	592.7	1095.4
1500	596.23	0.0235	0.2765	611.6	556.3	1167.9	0.8082	0.5269	1.3351	605.1	1091.2
2000	635.82	0.0257	0.1878	671.7	463.4	1135.1	0.8619	0.4230	1.2849	662.2	1065.5
2500	668.13	0.0287	0.1307	730.6	360.5	1091.1	0.9126	0.3197	1.2322	717.3	1030.6
3000	695.36	0.0346	0.0858	802.5	217.8	1020.3	0.9731	0.1885	1.1615	783.4	972.7
3206.2	705.40	0.0503	0.0503	902.7	0	902.7	1.0580	0	1.0580	872.9	872.9

Abridged from Joseph H. Keenan and Frederick G. Keyes, *Thermodynamic Properties of Steam*, John Wiley & Sons, Inc., New York, 1937. By permission of the authors.

TABLE B · 2   PROPERTIES OF SUPERHEATED STEAM

Abs. press., psia (sat. temp.)		Temperature, °F												
		200	300	400	500	600	700	800	900	1000	1100	1200	1400	1600
1 (101.74)	v, ft³/lbm	392.6	452.3	512.0	571.6	631.2	690.8	750.4	809.9	869.5	929.1	988.7	1107.8	1227.0
	h, Btu/lbm	1150.4	1195.8	1241.7	1288.3	1335.7	1383.8	1432.8	1482.7	1533.5	1585.2	1637.7	1745.7	1857.5
	s, Btu/lbm-°R	2.0512	2.1153	2.1720	2.2233	2.2702	2.3137	2.3542	2.3923	2.4283	2.4625	2.4952	2.5566	2.6137
5 (162.24)	v, ft³/lbm	78.16	90.25	102.26	114.22	126.16	138.10	150.03	161.95	173.87	185.79	197.71	221.6	245.4
	h, Btu/lbm	1148.8	1195.0	1241.2	1288.0	1335.3	1383.6	1432.7	1482.6	1533.4	1585.1	1637.7	1745.7	1857.4
	s, Btu/lbm-°R	1.8718	1.9370	1.9942	2.0456	2.0927	2.1361	2.1767	2.2148	2.2509	2.2851	2.3178	2.3792	2.4363
10 (193.21)	v, ft³/lbm	38.85	45.00	51.04	57.05	63.03	69.01	74.98	80.95	86.92	92.88	98.84	110.77	122.69
	h, Btu/lbm	1146.6	1193.9	1240.6	1287.5	1335.1	1383.4	1432.5	1482.4	1533.2	1585.0	1637.6	1745.6	1857.3
	s, Btu/lbm-°R	1.7927	1.8595	1.9172	1.9689	2.0160	2.0596	2.1002	2.1383	2.1744	2.2086	2.2413	2.3028	2.3598
14.696 (212.00)	v, ft³/lbm	...	30.53	34.68	38.78	42.86	46.94	51.00	55.07	59.13	63.19	67.25	75.37	83.48
	h, Btu/lbm	...	1192.8	1239.9	1287.1	1334.8	1383.2	1432.3	1482.3	1533.1	1584.8	1637.5	1745.5	1857.3
	s, Btu/lbm-°R	...	1.8160	1.8743	1.9261	1.9734	2.0170	2.0576	2.0958	2.1319	2.1662	2.1989	2.2603	2.3174
20 (227.96)	v, ft³/lbm	...	22.36	25.43	28.46	31.47	34.47	37.46	40.45	43.44	46.42	49.41	55.37	61.34
	h, Btu/lbm	...	1191.6	1239.2	1286.6	1334.4	1382.9	1432.1	1482.1	1533.0	1584.7	1637.4	1745.4	1857.2
	s, Btu/lbm-°R	...	1.7808	1.8396	1.8918	1.9392	1.9829	2.0235	2.0618	2.0978	2.1321	2.1648	2.2263	2.2834
40 (267.25)	v, ft³/lbm	...	11.040	12.628	14.168	15.688	17.198	18.702	20.20	21.70	23.20	24.69	27.68	30.66
	h, Btu/lbm	...	1186.8	1236.5	1284.8	1333.1	1381.9	1431.3	1481.4	1532.4	1584.3	1637.0	1745.1	1857.0
	s, Btu/lbm-°R	...	1.6994	1.7608	1.8140	1.8619	1.9058	1.9467	1.9850	2.0212	2.0555	2.0883	2.1498	2.2069
60 (292.71)	v, ft³/lbm	...	7.259	8.357	9.403	10.427	11.441	12.449	13.452	14.454	15.453	16.451	18.446	20.44
	h, Btu/lbm	...	1181.6	1233.6	1283.0	1331.8	1380.9	1430.5	1480.8	1531.9	1583.8	1636.6	1744.8	1856.7
	s, Btu/lbm-°R	...	1.6492	1.7135	1.7678	1.8162	1.8605	1.9015	1.9400	1.9762	2.0106	2.0434	2.1049	2.1621

Pressure (sat. temp)	Property												
80 (312.03)	v, ft³/lbm	6.220	7.020	7.797	8.562	9.322	10.077	10.830	11.582	12.332	13.830	15.325
	h, Btu/lbm	1230.7	1281.1	1330.5	1379.9	1429.7	1480.1	1531.3	1583.4	1636.2	1744.5	1856.5
	s, Btu/lbm-°R	1.6791	1.7346	1.7836	1.8281	1.8694	1.9079	1.9442	1.9787	2.0115	2.0731	2.1303
100 (327.81)	v, ft³/lbm	4.937	5.589	6.218	6.835	7.446	8.052	8.656	9.259	9.860	11.060	12.258
	h, Btu/lbm	1227.6	1279.1	1329.1	1378.9	1428.9	1479.5	1530.8	1582.9	1635.7	1744.2	1856.2
	s, Btu/lbm-°R	1.6518	1.7085	1.7581	1.8029	1.8443	1.8829	1.9193	1.9538	1.9867	2.0484	2.1056
120 (341.25)	v, ft³/lbm	4.081	4.636	5.165	5.683	6.195	6.702	7.207	7.710	8.212	9.214	10.213
	h, Btu/lbm	1224.4	1277.2	1327.7	1377.8	1428.1	1478.8	1530.2	1582.4	1635.3	1743.9	1856.0
	s, Btu/lbm-°R	1.6287	1.6869	1.7370	1.7822	1.8237	1.8625	1.8990	1.9335	1.9664	2.0281	2.0854
140 (353.02)	v, ft³/lbm	3.468	3.954	4.413	4.861	5.301	5.738	6.172	6.604	7.035	7.895	8.752
	h, Btu/lbm	1221.5	1275.2	1326.4	1376.8	1427.3	1478.2	1529.7	1581.9	1634.9	1743.5	1855.7
	s, Btu/lbm-°R	1.6087	1.6683	1.7190	1.7645	1.8063	1.8451	1.8817	1.9163	1.9493	2.0110	2.0683
160 (363.53)	v, ft³/lbm	3.008	3.443	3.849	4.244	4.631	5.015	5.396	5.775	6.152	6.906	7.656
	h, Btu/lbm	1217.6	1273.1	1325.0	1375.7	1426.4	1477.5	1529.1	1581.4	1634.5	1743.2	1855.5
	s, Btu/lbm-°R	1.5908	1.6519	1.7033	1.7491	1.7911	1.8301	1.8667	1.9014	1.9344	1.9962	2.0535
180 (373.06)	v, ft³/lbm	2.649	3.044	3.411	3.764	4.110	4.452	4.792	5.129	5.466	6.136	6.804
	h, Btu/lbm	1214.0	1271.0	1323.5	1374.7	1425.6	1476.8	1528.6	1581.0	1634.1	1742.9	1855.2
	s, Btu/lbm-°R	1.5745	1.6373	1.6894	1.7355	1.7776	1.8167	1.8534	1.8882	1.9212	1.9831	2.0404
200 (381.79)	v, ft³/lbm	2.361	2.726	3.060	3.380	3.693	4.002	4.309	4.613	4.917	5.521	6.123
	h, Btu/lbm	1210.3	1268.9	1322.1	1373.6	1424.8	1476.2	1528.0	1580.5	1633.7	1742.6	1855.0
	s, Btu/lbm-°R	1.5594	1.6240	1.6767	1.7232	1.7655	1.8048	1.8415	1.8763	1.9094	1.9713	2.0287
220 (389.86)	v, ft³/lbm	2.125	2.465	2.772	3.066	3.352	3.634	3.913	4.191	4.467	5.017	5.565
	h, Btu/lbm	1206.5	1266.7	1320.7	1372.6	1424.0	1475.5	1527.5	1580.0	1633.3	1742.3	1854.7
	s, Btu/lbm-°R	1.5453	1.6117	1.6652	1.7120	1.7545	1.7939	1.8308	1.8656	1.8987	1.9607	2.0181

TABLE B·2 PROPERTIES OF SUPERHEATED STEAM (CONTINUED)

Abs. press., psia (sat. temp.)		Temperature, °F												
		200	300	400	500	600	700	800	900	1000	1100	1200	1400	1600
240 (397.37)	v, ft³/lbm	...	...	1.9276	2.247	2.533	2.804	3.068	3.327	3.584	3.839	4.093	4.597	5.100
	h, Btu/lbm	...	...	1202.5	1264.5	1319.2	1371.5	1423.2	1474.8	1526.9	1579.6	1632.9	1742.0	1854.5
	s, Btu/lbm-°R	...	...	1.5319	1.6003	1.6546	1.7017	1.7444	1.7839	1.8209	1.8558	1.8889	1.9510	2.0084
260 (404.42)	v, ft³/lbm	...	...	...	2.063	2.330	2.582	2.827	3.067	3.305	3.541	3.776	4.242	4.707
	h, Btu/lbm	...	...	...	1262.3	1317.7	1370.4	1422.3	1474.2	1526.3	1579.1	1632.5	1741.7	1854.2
	s, Btu/lbm-°R	...	...	...	1.5897	1.6447	1.6922	1.7352	1.7748	1.8118	1.8467	1.8799	1.9420	1.9995
280 (411.05)	v, ft³/lbm	...	...	...	1.9047	2.156	2.392	2.621	2.845	3.066	3.286	3.504	3.938	4.370
	h, Btu/lbm	...	...	...	1260.0	1316.2	1369.4	1421.5	1473.5	1525.8	1578.6	1632.1	1741.4	1854.0
	s, Btu/lbm-°R	...	...	...	1.5796	1.6354	1.6834	1.7265	1.7662	1.8033	1.8383	1.8716	1.9337	1.9912
300 (417.33)	v, ft³/lbm	...	...	...	1.7675	2.005	2.227	2.442	2.652	2.859	3.065	3.269	3.674	4.078
	h, Btu/lbm	...	...	...	1257.6	1314.7	1368.3	1420.6	1472.8	1525.2	1578.1	1631.7	1741.0	1853.7
	s, Btu/lbm-°R	...	...	...	1.5701	1.6268	1.6751	1.7184	1.7582	1.7954	1.8305	1.8638	1.9260	1.9835
350 (431.72)	v, ft³/lbm	...	...	...	1.4923	1.7036	1.8980	2.084	2.266	2.445	2.622	2.798	3.147	3.493
	h, Btu/lbm	...	...	...	1251.5	1310.9	1365.5	1418.5	1471.1	1523.8	1577.0	1630.7	1740.3	1853.1
	s, Btu/lbm-°R	...	...	...	1.5481	1.6070	1.6563	1.7002	1.7403	1.7777	1.8130	1.8463	1.9086	1.9663
400 (444.59)	v, ft³/lbm	...	...	...	1.2851	1.4770	1.6508	1.8161	1.9767	2.134	2.290	2.445	2.751	3.055
	h, Btu/lbm	...	...	...	1245.1	1306.9	1362.7	1416.4	1469.4	1522.4	1575.8	1629.6	1739.5	1852.5
	s, Btu/lbm-°R	...	...	...	1.5281	1.5894	1.6398	1.6842	1.7247	1.7623	1.7977	1.8311	1.8936	1.9513

Temperature, °F

Abs. press., psia (sat. temp.)		500	550	600	620	640	660	680	700	800	900	1000	1200	1400	1600
450 (456.28)	v, ft³/lbm	1.1231	1.2155	1.3005	1.3332	1.3652	1.3967	1.4278	1.4584	1.6074	1.7516	1.8929	2.170	2.443	2.714
	h, Btu/lbm	1238.4	1272.0	1302.8	1314.6	1326.2	1337.5	1348.8	1359.9	1414.3	1467.7	1521.0	1628.6	1738.7	1851.9
	s, Btu/lbm-°R	1.5095	1.5437	1.5735	1.5845	1.5951	1.6054	1.6153	1.6250	1.6699	1.7108	1.7486	1.8177	1.8803	1.9381
500 (467.01)	v, ft³/lbm	0.9927	1.0800	1.1591	1.1893	1.2188	1.2478	1.2763	1.3044	1.4405	1.5715	1.6996	1.9504	2.197	2.442
	h, Btu/lbm	1231.3	1266.8	1298.6	1310.7	1322.6	1334.2	1345.7	1357.0	1412.1	1466.0	1519.6	1627.6	1737.9	1851.3
	s, Btu/lbm-°R	1.4919	1.5280	1.5588	1.5701	1.5810	1.5915	1.6016	1.6115	1.6571	1.6982	1.7363	1.8056	1.8683	1.9262
550 (476.94)	v, ft³/lbm	0.8852	0.9686	1.0431	1.0714	1.0989	1.1259	1.1523	1.1783	1.3038	1.4241	1.5414	1.7706	1.9957	2.219
	h, Btu/lbm	1223.7	1261.2	1294.3	1306.8	1318.9	1330.8	1342.5	1354.0	1409.9	1464.3	1518.2	1626.6	1737.1	1850.6
	s, Btu/lbm-°R	1.4751	1.5131	1.5451	1.5568	1.5680	1.5787	1.5890	1.5991	1.6452	1.6868	1.7250	1.7946	1.8575	1.9155
600 (486.21)	v, ft³/lbm	0.7947	0.8753	0.9463	0.9729	0.9988	1.0241	1.0489	1.0732	1.1899	1.3013	1.4096	1.6208	1.8279	2.033
	h, Btu/lbm	1215.7	1255.5	1289.9	1302.7	1315.2	1327.4	1339.3	1351.1	1407.7	1462.5	1516.7	1625.5	1736.3	1850.0
	s, Btu/lbm-°R	1.4586	1.4990	1.5323	1.5443	1.5558	1.5667	1.5773	1.5875	1.6343	1.6762	1.7147	1.7846	1.8476	1.9056
700 (503.10)	v, ft³/lbm	…	0.7277	0.7934	0.8177	0.8411	0.8639	0.8860	0.9077	1.0108	1.1082	1.2024	1.3853	1.5641	1.7405
	h, Btu/lbm	…	1243.2	1280.6	1294.3	1307.5	1320.3	1332.8	1345.0	1403.2	1459.0	1513.9	1623.5	1734.8	1848.8
	s, Btu/lbm-°R	…	1.4722	1.5084	1.5212	1.5333	1.5449	1.5559	1.5665	1.6147	1.6573	1.6963	1.7666	1.8299	1.8881
800 (518.23)	v, ft³/lbm	…	0.6154	0.6779	0.7006	0.7223	0.7433	0.7635	0.7833	0.8763	0.9633	1.0470	1.2088	1.3662	1.5214
	h, Btu/lbm	…	1229.8	1270.7	1285.4	1299.4	1312.9	1325.9	1338.6	1398.6	1455.4	1511.0	1621.4	1733.2	1847.5
	s, Btu/lbm-°R	…	1.4467	1.4863	1.5000	1.5129	1.5250	1.5366	1.5476	1.5972	1.6407	1.6801	1.7510	1.8146	1.8729
900 (531.98)	v, ft³/lbm	…	0.5264	0.5873	0.6089	0.6294	0.6491	0.6680	0.6863	0.7716	0.8506	0.9262	1.0714	1.2124	1.3509
	h, Btu/lbm	…	1215.0	1260.1	1275.9	1290.9	1305.1	1318.8	1332.1	1393.9	1451.8	1508.1	1619.3	1731.6	1846.3
	s, Btu/lbm-°R	…	1.4216	1.4653	1.4800	1.4938	1.5066	1.5187	1.5303	1.5814	1.6257	1.6656	1.7371	1.8009	1.8595

TABLE B·2 PROPERTIES OF SUPERHEATED STEAM (CONTINUED)

Abs. press., psia (sat. temp.)		Temperature, °F 500	550	600	620	640	660	680	700	800	900	1000	1200	1400	1600
1000 (544.61)	v, ft³/lbm		0.4533	0.5140	0.5350	0.5546	0.5733	0.5912	0.6084	0.6878	0.7604	0.8294	0.9615	1.0893	1.2146
	h, Btu/lbm		1198.3	1248.8	1265.9	1281.9	1297.0	1311.4	1325.3	1389.2	1448.2	1505.1	1617.3	1730.0	1845.0
	s, Btu/lbm-°R		1.3961	1.4450	1.4610	1.4757	1.4893	1.5021	1.5141	1.5670	1.6121	1.6525	1.7245	1.7886	1.8474
1100 (556.31)	v, ft³/lbm			0.4532	0.4738	0.4929	0.5110	0.5281	0.5445	0.6191	0.6866	0.7503	0.8716	0.9885	1.1031
	h, Btu/lbm			1236.7	1255.3	1272.4	1288.5	1303.7	1318.3	1384.3	1444.5	1502.2	1615.2	1728.4	1843.8
	s, Btu/lbm-°R			1.4251	1.4425	1.4583	1.4728	1.4862	1.4989	1.5535	1.5995	1.6405	1.7130	1.7775	1.8363
1200 (567.22)	v, ft³/lbm			0.4016	0.4222	0.4410	0.4586	0.4752	0.4909	0.5617	0.6250	0.6843	0.7967	0.9046	1.0101
	h, Btu/lbm			1223.5	1243.9	1262.4	1279.6	1295.7	1311.0	1379.3	1440.7	1499.2	1613.1	1726.9	1842.5
	s, Btu/lbm-°R			1.4052	1.4243	1.4413	1.4568	1.4710	1.4843	1.5409	1.5879	1.6293	1.7025	1.7672	1.8263
1400 (587.10)	v, ft³/lbm			0.3174	0.3390	0.3580	0.3753	0.3912	0.4062	0.4714	0.5281	0.5805	0.6789	0.7727	0.8640
	h, Btu/lbm			1193.0	1218.4	1240.4	1260.3	1278.5	1295.5	1369.1	1433.1	1493.2	1608.9	1723.7	1840.0
	s, Btu/lbm-°R			1.3639	1.3877	1.4079	1.4258	1.4419	1.4567	1.5177	1.5666	1.6093	1.6836	1.7489	1.8083
1600 (604.90)	v, ft³/lbm				0.2733	0.2936	0.3112	0.3271	0.3417	0.4034	0.4553	0.5027	0.5906	0.6738	0.7545
	h, Btu/lbm				1187.8	1215.2	1238.7	1259.6	1278.7	1358.4	1425.3	1487.0	1604.6	1720.5	1837.5
	s, Btu/lbm-°R				1.3489	1.3741	1.3952	1.4137	1.4303	1.4964	1.5476	1.5914	1.6669	1.7328	1.7926
1800 (621.03)	v, ft³/lbm					0.2407	0.2597	0.2760	0.2907	0.3502	0.3986	0.4421	0.5218	0.5968	0.6693
	h, Btu/lbm					1185.1	1214.0	1238.5	1260.3	1347.2	1417.4	1480.8	1600.4	1717.3	1835.0
	s, Btu/lbm-°R					1.3377	1.3638	1.3855	1.4044	1.4765	1.5301	1.5752	1.6520	1.7185	1.7786
2000 (635.82)	v, ft³/lbm					0.1936	0.2161	0.2337	0.2489	0.3074	0.3532	0.3935	0.4668	0.5352	0.6011
	h, Btu/lbm					1145.6	1184.9	1214.8	1240.0	1335.5	1409.2	1474.5	1596.1	1714.1	1832.5
	s, Btu/lbm-°R					1.2945	1.3300	1.3564	1.3783	1.4576	1.5139	1.5603	1.6384	1.7055	1.7660

Press. (Temp.)	Property								
2500 (668.13)	v, ft³/lbm	0.1484	0.1686	0.2294	0.2710	0.3061	0.3678	0.4244	0.4784
	h, Btu/lbm	1132.3	1176.8	1303.6	1387.8	1458.4	1585.3	1706.1	1826.2
	s, Btu/lbm-°R	1.2687	1.3073	1.4127	1.4772	1.5273	1.6088	1.6775	1.7389
3000 (695.36)	v, ft³/lbm	...	0.0984	0.1760	0.2159	0.2476	0.3018	0.3505	0.3966
	h, Btu/lbm	...	1060.7	1267.2	1365.0	1441.8	1574.3	1698.0	1819.9
	s, Btu/lbm-°R	...	1.1966	1.3690	1.4439	1.4984	1.5837	1.6540	1.7163
3206.2 (705.40)	v, ft³/lbm	...	...	0.1583	0.1981	0.2288	0.2806	0.3267	0.3703
	h, Btu/lbm	...	...	1250.5	1355.2	1434.7	1569.8	1694.6	1817.2
	s, Btu/lbm-°R	...	...	1.3508	1.4309	1.4874	1.5742	1.6452	1.7080
3500	v, ft³/lbm	...	0.0306	0.1364	0.1762	0.2058	0.2546	0.2977	0.3381
	h, Btu/lbm	...	780.5	1224.9	1340.7	1424.5	1563.3	1689.8	1813.6
	s, Btu/lbm-°R	...	0.9515	1.3241	1.4127	1.4723	1.5615	1.6336	1.6968
4000	v, ft³/lbm	...	0.0287	0.1052	0.1462	0.1743	0.2192	0.2581	0.2943
	h, Btu/lbm	...	763.8	1174.8	1314.4	1406.8	1552.1	1681.7	1807.2
	s, Btu/lbm-°R	...	0.9347	1.2757	1.3827	1.4482	1.5417	1.6154	1.6795
4500	v, ft³/lbm	...	0.0276	0.0798	0.1226	0.1500	0.1917	0.2273	0.2602
	h, Btu/lbm	...	753.5	1113.9	1286.5	1388.4	1540.8	1673.5	1800.9
	s, Btu/lbm-°R	...	0.9235	1.2204	1.3529	1.4253	1.5235	1.5990	1.6640
5000	v, ft³/lbm	...	0.0268	0.0593	0.1036	0.1303	0.1696	0.2027	0.2329
	h, Btu/lbm	...	746.4	1047.1	1256.5	1369.5	1529.5	1665.3	1794.5
	s, Btu/lbm-°R	...	0.9152	1.1622	1.3231	1.4034	1.5066	1.5839	1.6499
5500	v, ft³/lbm	...	0.0262	0.0463	0.0880	0.1143	0.1516	0.1825	0.2106
	h, Btu/lbm	...	741.3	985.0	1224.1	1349.3	1518.2	1657.0	1788.1
	s, Btu/lbm-°R	...	0.9090	1.1093	1.2930	1.3821	1.4908	1.5699	1.6369

Abridged from Joseph H. Keenan and Frederick G. Keyes, *Thermodynamic Properties of Steam*, John Wiley & Sons, Inc., New York, 1937. By permission of the authors.

TABLE B·3 THERMODYNAMIC PROPERTIES OF SATURATED MERCURY

P, psia	T, °F	Enthalpy, Btu/lbm			Entropy, Btu/lbm-°R			Volume, ft³/lbm	
		Sat. liq.	Evap.	Sat. vap.	Liquid	Evap.	Sat. vap.	Sat. liq.	Sat. vap.
0.010	233.57	6.668	127.732	134.400	0.01137	0.18428	0.19565	1.21×10^{-3}	3637
0.020	259.88	7.532	127.614	135.146	0.01259	0.17735	0.18994	1.21	1893
0.030	276.22	8.068	127.540	135.608	0.01332	0.17332	0.18664	1.21	1292
0.050	297.97	8.778	127.442	136.220	0.01427	0.16821	0.18248	1.21	799
0.100	329.73	9.814	127.300	137.114	0.01561	0.16126	0.17687	1.22	416
0.200	364.25	10.936	127.144	138.080	0.01699	0.15432	0.17131	1.22×10^{-3}	217.3
0.300	385.92	11.639	127.047	138.686	0.01783	0.15024	0.16807	1.22	148.6
0.400	401.98	12.159	126.975	139.134	0.01844	0.14736	0.16580	1.22	113.7
0.500	415.00	12.568	126.916	139.484	0.01892	0.14511	0.16403	1.22	92.18
0.600	425.82	12.929	126.868	139.797	0.01932	0.14328	0.16260	1.23	77.84
0.800	443.50	13.500	126.788	140.288	0.01994	0.14038	0.16032	1.23×10^{-3}	59.58
1.00	457.72	13.959	126.724	140.683	0.02045	0.13814	0.15859	1.24	48.42
2.00	504.93	15.476	126.512	141.988	0.02205	0.13116	0.15321	1.24	25.39
3.00	535.25	16.439	126.377	142.816	0.02302	0.12706	0.15008	1.24	17.50
5.00	575.7	17.741	126.193	143.934	0.02430	0.12188	0.14618	1.24	10.90
7.00	604.7	18.657	126.065	144.722	0.02516	0.11846	0.14362	1.25×10^{-3}	8.04
10.00	637.0	19.685	125.919	145.604	0.02610	0.11483	0.14093	1.25	5.81
20.00	706.0	21.864	125.609	147.473	0.02800	0.10779	0.13579	1.26	3.09
40.00	784.4	24.345	125.255	149.600	0.03004	0.10068	0.13072	1.27	1.648
60.00	835.7	25.940	125.024	150.964	0.03127	0.09652	0.12779	1.28	1.144

80	874.8	27.149	124.849	152.008	0.03218	0.09356	0.12574	1.29×10^{-3}	0.885
100	906.8	28.152	124.706	152.858	0.03290	0.09127	0.12417	1.29	0.725
150	969.4	30.367	124.424	154.791	0.03425	0.08707	0.12132	1.30	0.507
200	1017.2	31.560	124.209	155.769	0.03523	0.08411	0.11934	1.31	0.392
250	1057.2	32.784	124.029	156.813	0.03603	0.08178	0.11781	1.31	0.322
300	1091.2	33.824	123.876	157.700	0.03669	0.07989	0.11658	1.32×10^{-3}	0.276
400	1148.4	35.565	123.620	159.185	0.03775	0.07688	0.11463	1.32	0.215
450	1173.2	36.315	123.509	159.824	0.03820	0.07566	0.11386	1.32	0.194
500	1196.0	37.006	123.406	160.412	0.03861	0.07455	0.11316	1.33	0.177
600	1236.8	38.245	123.221	161.466	0.03932	0.07264	0.11196	1.34	0.151
700	1273.3	39.339	123.058	162.397	0.03993	0.07102	0.11095	1.34×10^{-3}	0.132
800	1306.1	40.324	122.910	163.234	0.04047	0.06961	0.11008	1.34	0.118
900	1336.2	41.226	122.775	164.001	0.04095	0.06837	0.10932	1.35	0.106
1000	1364.0	42.056	122.649	164.705	0.04139	0.06726	0.10865	1.35	0.098
1100	1390.0	42.828	122.533	165.361	0.04179	0.06625	0.10804	1.36	0.090

From Lucian A. Sheldon, *Thermodynamic Properties of Mercury Vapor*, General Electric Company. Liquid densities from WADC TR-59-598.

TABLE B·4 THERMODYNAMIC PROPERTIES OF SATURATED CESIUM

T, °R	P, psia	Equilibrium molal mass, lbm/lbmole	Enthalpy, Btu/lbm h_f	Enthalpy, Btu/lbm h_g	Entropy, Btu/lbm-°R s_f	Entropy, Btu/lbm-°R s_g	Volume, ft³/lbm v_f	Volume, ft³/lbm v_g
700	3.41×10^{-5}	133.0	4.14×10^{1}	2.84×10^{2}	1.796×10^{-1}	5.262×10^{-1}	8.765×10^{-3}	1.654×10^{6}
800	5.24×10^{-4}	133.2	4.71×10^{1}	2.87×10^{2}	1.873×10^{-1}	4.878×10^{-1}	8.841×10^{-3}	1.231×10^{5}
900	4.38×10^{-3}	133.5	5.29×10^{1}	2.90×10^{2}	1.940×10^{-1}	4.585×10^{-1}	8.918×10^{-3}	1.653×10^{4}
1000	2.39×10^{-2}	133.9	5.86×10^{1}	2.94×10^{2}	2.000×10^{-1}	4.356×10^{-1}	8.994×10^{-3}	3.347×10^{3}
1100	9.61×10^{-2}	134.6	6.43×10^{1}	2.97×10^{2}	2.055×10^{-1}	4.172×10^{-1}	9.070×10^{-3}	9.128×10^{2}
1200	3.06×10^{-1}	135.3	7.00×10^{1}	3.00×10^{2}	2.105×10^{-1}	4.022×10^{-1}	9.147×10^{-3}	3.109×10^{2}
1300	8.15×10^{-1}	136.3	7.57×10^{1}	3.02×10^{2}	2.150×10^{-1}	3.897×10^{-1}	9.223×10^{-3}	1.255×10^{2}
1400	1.89×10^{0}	137.3	8.15×10^{1}	3.054×10^{2}	2.193×10^{-1}	3.793×10^{-1}	9.300×10^{-3}	5.791×10^{1}
1500	3.91×10^{0}	138.5	8.72×10^{1}	3.080×10^{2}	2.232×10^{-1}	3.704×10^{-1}	9.376×10^{-3}	2.971×10^{1}
1600	7.40×10^{0}	139.7	9.29×10^{1}	3.104×10^{2}	2.269×10^{-1}	3.629×10^{-1}	9.452×10^{-3}	1.661×10^{1}
1700	1.29×10^{1}	141.0	9.86×10^{1}	3.128×10^{2}	2.304×10^{-1}	3.564×10^{-1}	9.529×10^{-3}	9.970×10^{0}
1800	2.14×10^{1}	142.3	1.04×10^{2}	3.152×10^{2}	2.337×10^{-1}	3.508×10^{-1}	9.605×10^{-3}	6.346×10^{0}
1900	3.34×10^{1}	143.6	1.10×10^{2}	3.177×10^{2}	2.367×10^{-1}	3.460×10^{-1}	9.682×10^{-3}	4.245×10^{0}
2000	5.00×10^{1}	144.9	1.15×10^{2}	3.201×10^{2}	2.397×10^{-1}	3.418×10^{-1}	9.758×10^{-3}	2.961×10^{0}
2100	7.20×10^{1}	146.2	1.21×10^{2}	3.226×10^{2}	2.425×10^{-1}	3.382×10^{-1}	9.834×10^{-3}	2.141×10^{0}
2200	1.00×10^{2}	147.5	1.27×10^{2}	3.251×10^{2}	2.451×10^{-1}	3.351×10^{-1}	9.911×10^{-3}	1.597×10^{0}
2300	1.35×10^{2}	148.8	1.32×10^{2}	3.276×10^{2}	2.477×10^{-1}	3.323×10^{-1}	9.987×10^{-3}	1.224×10^{0}
2400	1.78×10^{2}	150.0	1.38×10^{2}	3.302×10^{2}	2.501×10^{-1}	3.299×10^{-1}	1.006×10^{-2}	9.604×10^{-1}
2500	2.30×10^{2}	151.1	1.44×10^{2}	3.328×10^{2}	2.524×10^{-1}	3.278×10^{-1}	1.014×10^{-2}	7.694×10^{-1}
2600	2.92×10^{2}	152.3	1.50×10^{2}	3.355×10^{2}	2.547×10^{-1}	3.260×10^{-1}	1.022×10^{-2}	6.277×10^{-1}
2700	3.63×10^{2}	153.4	1.55×10^{2}	3.382×10^{2}	2.568×10^{-1}	3.244×10^{-1}	1.029×10^{-2}	5.206×10^{-1}

W. D. Weatherford et al., *Properties of Inorganic Energy-conversion and Heat-transfer Fluids for Space Applications*, WADD Report 61-96, November, 1961.

TABLE B·5 PROPERTIES OF SATURATED FREON-12

T,°F	P, psia	Enthalpy, Btu/lbm		Entropy, Btu/lbm-°F		Density, lbm/ft³	
		Sat. liq.	Sat. vap.	Sat. liq.	Sat. vap.	Sat. liq.	Sat. vap.
−40	9.32	0	73.50	0	0.17517	94.58	0.2557
−30	12.02	2.03	74.70	0.00471	0.17387	93.59	0.3238
−20	15.28	4.07	75.87	0.00940	0.17275	92.58	0.4042
−10	19.20	6.14	77.05	0.01403	0.17175	91.57	0.4993
0	23.87	8.25	78.21	0.01869	0.17091	90.52	0.6109
+10	29.35	10.39	79.36	0.02328	0.17015	89.45	0.7402
20	35.75	12.55	80.49	0.02783	0.16949	88.37	0.8921
30	43.16	14.76	81.61	0.03233	0.16887	87.24	1.065
40	51.68	17.00	82.71	0.03680	0.16833	86.10	1.263
50	61.39	19.27	83.78	0.04126	0.16785	84.94	1.485
60	72.41	21.57	84.82	0.04568	0.16741	83.78	1.740
70	84.82	23.90	85.82	0.05009	0.16701	82.60	2.028
80	98.76	26.28	86.80	0.05446	0.16662	81.39	2.353
90	114.3	28.70	87.74	0.05882	0.16624	80.11	2.721
100	131.6	31.16	88.62	0.06316	0.16584	78.80	3.135
110	150.7	33.65	89.43	0.06749	0.16542	77.46	3.610
120	171.8	36.16	90.15	0.07180	0.16495	76.02	4.167

Abridged from the *Handbook of Chemistry and Physics,* American Rubber Company.

TABLE B·6 NOMINAL THERMODYNAMIC PROPERTIES OF GASES AT LOW PRESSURES

Substance	$\hat{M}$, lbm/lbmole, g/gmole	c_P, Btu/lbm-°R	$\hat{c}_P$, Btu/lbmole-°R	c_v, Btu/lbm-°R	$\hat{c}_v$, Btu/lbmole-°R	R, ft-lbf/lbm-°R	R, Btu/lbm-°R	$k = c_P/c_v$
Argon, A	39.94	0.123	4.91	0.074	2.96	38.65	0.0496	1.67
Helium, He	4.003	1.25	5.00	0.75	3.000	386.3	0.4963	1.66
Hydrogen, H_2	2.016	3.42	6.89	2.43	4.90	767.0	0.9856	1.41
Nitrogen, N_2	28.02	0.248	6.95	0.177	4.96	55.13	0.0708	1.40
Oxygen, O_2	32.00	0.219	7.01	0.156	4.99	48.24	0.0620	1.40
Carbon monoxide, CO	28.01	0.249	6.97	0.178	4.98	55.13	0.0708	1.40
Air	28.97	0.240	6.95	0.171	4.95	53.34	0.0686	1.40
Water vapor, H_2O	18.016	0.446	8.07	0.336	6.03	85.58	0.1099	1.33
Methane, CH_4	16.04	0.532	8.53	0.403	6.46	96.4	0.1236	1.32
Carbon dioxide, CO_2	44.01	0.202	8.91	0.156	6.87	35.1	0.0451	1.30
Sulfur dioxide, SO_2	64.07	0.154	9.87	0.122	7.82	24.1	0.0310	1.26
Acetylene, C_2H_2	26.04	0.409	10.65	0.333	8.67	59.4	0.0761	1.23
Ethylene, C_2H_4	28.05	0.374	10.49	0.304	8.53	55.1	0.0707	1.23
Ethane, C_2H_6	30.07	0.422	12.69	0.357	10.73	51.3	0.0658	1.18
Propane, C_3H_8	44.09	0.404	17.81	0.360	15.87	35.0	0.0450	1.12
Isobutane, C_4H_{10}	58.12	0.420	24.41	0.387	22.49	26.6	0.0342	1.09

Based on a compilation by J. Lay, *Thermodynamics*, Charles E. Merrill Books, Inc., Columbus, Ohio, 1963.

TABLE B·7 PROPERTIES OF COPPER AT 1 ATM

T, °K	$\hat{v}$, cm³/gmole	β, 1/°K	κ, cm²/dyne	$\hat{c}_P$, cal/gmole-°K	$\hat{c}_v$, cal/gmole-°K	$k = \hat{c}_P/\hat{c}_v$
0	(7.0)†	(0)	(0.710) × 10⁻¹²	(0)	(0)	1.00
50	(7.002)	(11.5) × 10⁻⁶	(0.712)	1.38	1.38	1.00
100	(7.008)	31.5	0.721	3.88	3.86	1.00
150	(7.018)	41.0	0.733	5.01	4.95	1.01
200	(7.029)	45.6	0.748	5.41	5.32	1.02
250	7.043	48.0	0.762	5.65	5.52	1.02
300	7.062	49.2	0.776	5.87	5.71	1.03
500	7.115	54.2	0.837	6.25	5.95	1.05
800	7.256	60.7	0.922	6.70	6.14	1.09
1200	7.452	69.7	1.030	7.34	6.34	1.16

From M. Zemansky, *Thermodynamics*, McGraw-Hill Book Company, New York, 1957.
† Values in parentheses are extrapolated.

TABLE B·8 THERMODYNAMIC PROPERTIES AT THE CRITICAL POINT

Substance	T, °K	P, atm	$\hat{v}$, cm³/gmole	$Z = Pv/RT$
Air	132.41	37.25	92.35	
Argon, A	150.72	47.99	75	0.291
Helium, He	5.19	2.26	58	0.308
Carbon monoxide, CO	132.91	34.529	93	0.294
Hydrogen, H_2	33.24	12.797	65	0.304
Nitrogen, N_2	126.2	33.54	90	0.291
Oxygen, O_2	154.78	50.14	74	0.292
Carbon dioxide, CO_2	304.20	72.90	94	0.275
Sulfur dioxide, SO_2	430.7	77.8	122	0.269
Water, H_2O	647.27	218.167	56	0.230
Acetylene, C_2H_2	309.5	61.6	113	0.274
Ethane, C_2H_6	305.48	48.20	148	0.285
Ethylene, C_2H_4	283.06	50.50	124	0.270
n-Butane, C_4H_{10}	425.17	37.47	255	0.274
Methane, CH_4	190.7	45.8	99	0.290
Propane, C_3H_8	370.01	42.1	200	0.277

Based on a compilation by J. Lay, *Thermodynamics*, Charles E. Merrill Books, Inc., Columbus, Ohio, 1963.

TABLE B · 9 THERMODYNAMIC PROPERTIES OF AIR AT LOW PRESSURES

T, °R	T, °F	h, Btu/lbm	p_r	u, Btu/lbm	v_r	φ, Btu/lbm-°R	T, °R	T, °F	h, Btu/lbm	p_r	u, Btu/lbm	v_r	φ, Btu/lbm-°R
100	−360	23.7	0.00384	16.9	9640	0.1971	1100	640	266.0	17.41	190.6	23.4	0.7743
120	−340	28.5	0.00726	20.3	6120	0.2408	1120	660	271.0	18.60	194.2	22.3	0.7788
140	−320	33.3	0.01244	23.7	4170	0.2777	1140	680	276.1	19.86	197.9	21.3	0.7833
160	−300	38.1	0.01982	27.1	2990	0.3096	1160	700	281.1	21.2	201.6	20.29	0.7877
180	−280	42.9	0.0299	30.6	2230	0.3378	1180	720	286.2	22.6	205.3	19.38	0.7920
200	−260	47.7	0.0432	34.0	1715	0.3630	1200	740	291.3	24.0	209.0	18.51	0.7963
220	−240	52.5	0.0603	37.4	1352	0.3858	1220	760	296.4	25.2	212.8	17.70	0.8005
240	−220	57.2	0.0816	40.8	1089	0.4067	1240	780	301.5	27.1	216.5	16.93	0.8047
260	−200	62.0	0.1080	44.2	892	0.4258	1260	800	306.6	28.8	220.3	16.20	0.8088
280	−180	66.8	0.1399	47.6	742	0.4436	1280	820	311.8	30.6	224.0	15.52	0.8128
300	−160	71.6	0.1780	51.0	624	0.4601	1300	840	316.9	32.4	227.8	14.87	0.8168
320	−140	76.4	0.2229	54.5	532	0.4755	1320	860	322.1	34.3	231.6	14.25	0.8208
340	−120	81.2	0.2754	57.9	457	0.4900	1340	880	327.3	36.3	235.4	13.67	0.8246
360	−100	86.0	0.336	61.3	397	0.5037	1360	900	332.5	38.4	239.2	13.12	0.8265
380	−80	90.8	0.406	64.7	347	0.5166	1380	920	337.7	40.6	243.1	12.59	0.8323
400	−60	95.5	0.486	68.1	305	0.5289	1400	940	342.9	42.9	246.9	12.10	0.8360
420	−40	100.3	0.576	71.5	270	0.5406	1420	960	348.1	45.3	250.8	11.62	0.8398
440	−20	105.1	0.678	74.9	241	0.5517	1440	980	353.4	47.8	254.7	11.17	0.8434
460	0	109.9	0.791	78.4	215.3	0.5624	1460	1000	358.6	50.3	258.5	10.74	0.8470
480	+20	114.7	0.918	81.8	193.6	0.5726	1480	1020	363.9	53.0	262.4	10.34	0.8506
500	40	119.5	1.059	85.2	174.9	0.5823	1500	1040	369.2	55.9	266.3	9.95	0.8542
520	60	124.3	1.215	88.6	158.6	0.5917	1520	1060	374.5	58.8	270.3	9.58	0.8568
540	80	129.1	1.386	92.0	144.3	0.6008	1540	1080	379.8	61.8	274.2	9.23	0.8611

560	100	133.9	1.574	95.5	131.8	0.6095	1560	1100	385.1	65.0	278.1	8.89	0.8646
580	120	138.7	1.780	98.9	120.7	0.6179	1580	1120	390.4	68.3	282.1	8.57	0.8679
600	140	143.5	2.00	102.3	110.9	0.6261	1600	1140	395.7	71.7	286.1	8.26	0.8713
620	160	148.3	2.25	105.8	102.1	0.6340	1620	1160	401.1	75.3	290.0	7.97	0.8746
640	180	153.1	2.51	109.2	94.3	0.6416	1640	1180	406.4	79.0	294.0	6.69	0.8779
660	200	157.9	2.80	112.7	87.3	0.6490	1660	1200	411.8	82.8	298.0	7.42	0.8812
680	220	162.7	3.11	116.1	81.0	0.6562	1680	1220	417.2	86.8	302.0	7.17	0.8844
700	240	167.6	3.45	119.6	75.2	0.6632	1700	1240	422.6	91.0	306.1	6.92	0.8876
720	260	172.4	3.81	123.0	70.1	0.6700	1720	1260	428.0	95.2	310.1	6.69	0.8907
740	280	177.2	4.19	126.5	65.4	0.6766	1740	1280	433.4	99.7	314.1	6.46	0.8939
760	300	182.1	4.61	130.0	61.1	0.6831	1760	1300	438.8	104.3	318.2	6.25	0.8970
780	320	186.9	5.05	133.5	57.2	0.6894	1780	1320	444.3	109.1	322.2	6.04	0.9000
800	340	191.8	5.53	137.0	53.6	0.6956	1800	1340	449.7	114.0	326.3	5.85	0.9031
820	360	196.7	6.03	140.5	50.4	0.7016	1820	1360	455.2	119.2	330.4	5.66	0.9061
840	380	201.6	6.67	144.0	47.3	0.7075	1840	1380	460.6	124.5	334.5	5.48	0.9091
860	400	206.5	7.15	147.5	44.6	0.7132	1860	1400	466.1	130.0	338.6	5.30	0.9120
880	420	211.4	7.76	151.0	42.0	0.7189	1880	1420	471.6	135.6	342.7	5.13	0.9150
900	440	216.3	8.41	154.6	39.6	0.7244	1900	1440	477.1	141.5	346.8	4.97	0.9179
920	460	221.2	9.10	158.1	37.4	0.7298	1920	1460	482.6	147.6	351.0	4.82	0.9208
940	480	226.1	9.83	161.7	35.4	0.7351	1940	1480	488.1	153.9	355.1	4.67	0.9236
960	500	231.1	10.61	165.3	33.5	0.7403	1960	1500	493.6	160.4	359.3	4.53	0.9264
980	520	236.0	11.43	168.8	31.8	0.7454	1980	1520	499.1	167.1	363.4	4.39	0.9293
1000	540	241.0	12.30	172.4	30.1	0.7504	2000	1540	504.7	174.0	367.6	4.26	0.9320
1020	560	246.0	13.22	176.0	28.6	0.7554	2020	1560	510.3	181.2	371.8	4.13	0.9348
1040	580	251.0	14.18	179.7	27.2	0.7602	2040	1580	515.8	188.5	376.0	4.01	0.9376
1060	600	256.0	15.20	183.3	25.8	0.7650	2060	1600	521.4	196.2	380.2	3.89	0.9403
1080	620	261.0	16.28	186.9	24.6	0.7696	2080	1620	527.0	204.0	384.4	3.78	0.9430

TABLE B·9 THERMODYNAMIC PROPERTIES OF AIR AT LOW PRESSURES (CONTINUED)

T, °R	T, °F	h, Btu/lbm	p_r	u, Btu/lbm	v_r	ϕ, Btu/lbm-°R	T, °R	T, °F	h, Btu/lbm	p_r	u, Btu/lbm	v_r	ϕ, Btu/lbm-°R
2100	1640	532.6	212	388.6	3.67	0.9456	2900	2440	761.4	815	562.7	1.318	1.0379
2120	1660	538.2	220	392.8	3.56	0.9483	2920	2460	767.3	839	567.1	1.289	1.0399
2140	1680	543.7	229	397.0	3.46	0.9509	2940	2480	773.1	864	571.6	1.261	1.0419
2160	1700	549.4	238	401.3	3.36	0.9535	2960	2500	779.0	889	576.1	1.233	1.0439
2180	1720	555.0	247	405.5	3.27	0.9561	2980	2520	784.8	915	580.6	1.206	1.0458
2200	1740	560.6	257	409.8	3.18	0.9587	3000	2540	790.7	941	585.0	1.180	1.0478
2220	1760	566.2	266	414.0	3.09	0.9612	3020	2560	796.5	969	589.5	1.155	1.0497
2240	1780	571.9	276	418.3	3.00	0.9638	3040	2580	802.4	996	594.0	1.130	1.0517
2260	1800	577.5	287	422.6	2.92	0.9663	3060	2600	808.3	1025	598.5	1.106	1.0536
2280	1820	583.2	297	426.9	2.84	0.9688	3080	2620	814.2	1054	603.0	1.083	1.0555
2300	1840	588.8	308	431.2	2.76	0.9712	3100	2640	820.0	1083	607.5	1.060	1.0574
2320	1860	594.5	319	435.5	2.69	0.9737	3120	2660	825.9	1114	612.0	1.038	1.0593
2340	1880	600.2	331	439.8	2.62	0.9761	3140	2680	831.8	1145	616.6	1.016	1.0612
2360	1900	605.8	343	444.1	2.55	0.9785	3160	2700	837.7	1176	621.1	0.995	1.0630
2380	1920	611.5	355	448.4	2.48	0.9809	3180	2720	843.6	1209	625.6	0.975	1.0649
2400	1940	617.2	368	452.7	2.42	0.9833	3200	2740	849.5	1242	630.1	0.955	1.0668
2420	1960	622.9	380	457.0	2.36	0.9857	3220	2760	855.4	1276	634.6	0.935	1.0686
2440	1980	628.6	394	461.4	2.30	0.9880	3240	2780	861.3	1310	639.2	0.916	1.0704
2460	2000	634.3	407	465.7	2.24	0.9904	3260	2800	867.2	1345	643.7	0.898	1.0722
2480	2020	640.0	421	470.0	2.18	0.9927	3280	2820	873.1	1381	648.3	0.880	1.0740
2500	2040	645.8	436	474.4	2.12	0.9950	3300	2840	879.0	1418	652.8	0.862	1.0758
2520	2060	651.5	450	478.8	2.07	0.9972	3320	2860	884.9	1455	657.4	0.845	1.0776
2540	2080	657.2	466	483.1	2.02	0.9995	3340	2880	890.9	1494	661.9	0.828	1.0794

2560	2100	663.0	481	487.5	1.971	1.0018	3360	2900	896.8	1533	666.5	0.812	1.0812
2580	2120	668.7	497	491.9	1.922	1.0040	3380	2920	902.7	1573	671.0	0.796	1.0830
2600	2140	674.5	514	496.3	1.876	1.0062	3400	2940	908.7	1613	675.6	0.781	1.0847
2620	2160	680.2	530	500.6	1.830	1.0084	3420	2960	914.6	1655	680.2	0.766	1.0864
2640	2180	686.0	548	505.0	1.786	1.0106	3440	2980	920.6	1697	684.8	0.751	1.0882
2660	2200	691.8	565	509.4	1.743	1.0128	3460	3000	926.5	1740	689.3	0.736	1.0899
2680	2220	697.6	583	513.8	1.702	1.0150	3480	3020	932.4	1784	693.9	0.722	1.0916
2700	2240	703.4	602	518.3	1.662	1.0171	3500	3040	938.4	1829	698.5	0.709	1.0933
2720	2260	709.1	621	522.7	1.623	1.0193	3520	3060	944.4	1875	703.1	0.695	1.0950
2740	2280	714.9	640	527.1	1.585	1.0214	3540	3080	950.3	1922	707.6	0.682	1.0967
2760	2300	720.7	660	531.5	1.548	1.0235	3560	3100	956.3	1970	712.2	0.670	1.0984
2780	2320	726.5	681	536.0	1.512	1.0256	3580	3120	962.2	2018	716.8	0.637	1.1000
2800	2340	733.3	702	540.4	1.478	1.0277	3600	3140	968.2	2068	721.4	0.645	1.1017
2820	2360	738.2	724	544.8	1.444	1.0297	3620	3160	974.2	2118	726.0	0.633	1.1034
2840	2380	744.0	746	549.3	1.411	1.0318	3640	3180	980.2	2170	730.6	0.621	1.1050
2860	2400	749.8	768	553.7	1.379	1.0338	3660	3200	986.1	2222	735.3	0.610	1.1066
2880	2420	755.6	791	558.2	1.348	1.0359	3680	3220	992.1	2276	739.9	0.599	1.1083

Abridged from Joseph H. Keenan and Joseph Kaye, *Gas Tables*, John Wiley & Sons, Inc., New York, 1948. By permission of the authors.

TABLE B·10 SPECIFIC HEATS OF SELECTED LIQUIDS

Substance	State	c_P, Btu/lbm-°R	Substance	State	c_P, Btu/lbm-°R
Water	1 atm, 32°F	1.007	Glycerin	1 atm, 50°F	0.554
	1 atm, 77°F	0.998		1 atm, 120°F	0.617
	1 atm, 212°F	1.007	Bismuth	1 atm, 800°F	0.0345
Ammonia	sat., 0°F	1.08		1 atm, 1000°F	0.0369
	sat., 120°F	1.22		1 atm, 1400°F	0.0393
Freon-12	sat., −40°F	0.211	Mercury	1 atm, 50°F	0.033
	sat., 0°F	0.217		1 atm, 600°F	0.032
	sat., 120°F	0.244	Sodium	1 atm, 200°F	0.33
Benzene	1 atm, 60°F	0.43		1 atm, 1000°F	0.30
	1 atm, 150°F	0.46	n-Butane	1 atm, 32°F	0.550
Light oil	1 atm, 60°F	0.43			
	1 atm, 300°F	0.54	Propane	1 atm, 32°F	0.576

Based on values from *Handbook of Chemistry and Physics*, American Rubber Company.

TABLE B·11 SPECIFIC HEATS OF SELECTED SOLIDS

$P = 1$ atm

Substance	T, °C	c_P, cal/g-°K	Substance	T, °C	c_P, cal/g-°K
Ice	−200	0.168	Lead	−270	0.00001
	−140	0.262		−259	0.0073
	−60	0.392		−100	0.0283
	−11	0.468		0	0.0297
	−2.6	0.500		+100	0.0320
Aluminum	−250	0.0039		300	0.0356
	−200	0.076	Iron	20	0.107
	−100	0.167	Silver	20	0.0558
	0	0.208			
	+100	0.225	Sodium	20	0.295
	300	0.248	Tungsten	20	0.034
	600	0.277	Graphite	20	0.17
Platinum	−256	0.00123	Wood	20	0.42
	−152	0.0261			
	0	0.0316	Rubber	20	0.44
	+500	0.0349	Mica	20	0.21
	1000	0.0381			

Based on values from the *Handbook of Chemistry and Physics*, American Rubber Company.

TABLE B·12 STANDARDIZED ENTHALPIES AND ABSOLUTE ENTROPIES OF SUBSTANCES IN EQUILIBRIUM STATES AT 77°F (25°C) AND 1 ATM

Substance	$\hat{h}°$, Btu/lbmole	$\hat{s}°$, Btu/lbmole-°R
Hydrogen, H_2	0	31.194
Carbon, C	0	1.360
Oxygen, O_2	0	48.986
Nitrogen, N_2	0	45.755
Water (liquid), H_2O	$-122,976$	16.72
Carbon dioxide, CO_2	$-169,183$	51.032
Carbon monoxide, CO	$-47,517$	47.272
Methane, CH_4	$-32,179$	44.47
Ethane, C_2H_6	$-36,401$	54.81
Propane, C_3H_8	$-44,647$	64.47
n-Butane, C_4H_{10}	$-53,627$	74.05
Acetylene, C_2H_2	97,495	47.966
Benzene, C_6H_6	35,653	64.30

Based on tabulations of the National Bureau of Standards.

TABLE B·13 STANDARDIZED ENTHALPIES AND ABSOLUTE ENTROPIES FOR GASES AT LOW PRESSURE

$\hat{s} = \hat{\phi}(T) - \Re \ln (P/P_0)$; $P_0 = 1$ atm; $\hat{h}$ in Btu/lbmole; $\hat{s}$ in Btu/lbmole-°R

T, °R	Oxygen $\hat{h}$	Oxygen $\hat{\phi}$	Nitrogen $\hat{h}$	Nitrogen $\hat{\phi}$	Hydrogen $\hat{h}$	Hydrogen $\hat{\phi}$	Air† $\hat{h}$	Air† $\hat{\phi}$
537	0	48.986	0	45.755	0	31.194	0	46.336
600	443.2	49.762	438.4	46.514	435.3	31.959	438.3	47.107
700	1154.2	50.858	1135.4	47.588	1129.9	33.031	1136.2	48.183
800	1876.9	51.821	1834.9	48.522	1826.8	33.961	2041.5	49.121
900	2612.8	52.688	2538.6	49.352	2525.0	34.784	2547.0	49.955
1000	3362.4	53.477	3248.4	50.099	3224.2	35.520	3263.2	50.710
1100	4125.3	54.204	3965.5	50.783	4014.3	36.188	3987.7	51.400
1200	4900.7	54.879	4690.5	51.413	4625.5	36.798	4721.0	52.038
1300	5687.8	55.508	5424.4	52.001	5328.4	37.360	5463.7	52.633
1400	6485.3	56.099	6167.4	52.551	6033.5	37.883	6215.8	53.190
1500	7292.0	56.656	6919.4	53.071	6741.2	38.372	6976.8	53.715
1600	8107.4	57.182	7680.2	53.561	7452.2	38.830	7746.6	54.212
1700	8930.5	57.680	8449.4	54.028	8167.1	39.264	9103.8	54.683
1800	9760.7	58.155	9226.8	54.472	8886.5	39.675	9310.1	55.425
1900	10597.0	58.607	10012.1	54.896	9610.6	40.067	9234.2	55.561
2000	11438.9	59.039	10804.9	55.303	10339.8	40.441	10903.4	55.971
2100	12285.8	59.451	11604.5	55.694	11074.2	40.799	11701.0	56.365
2200	13137.5	59.848	12410.3	56.068	11814.1	41.143	12522.3	56.743
2300	13993.7	60.228	13221.7	56.429	12559.5	41.475	13340.1	57.106
2400	14854.1	60.594	14038.4	56.777	13310.3	41.794	14162.9	57.456
2500	15718.3	60.946	14860.0	57.112	14067.0	42.104	14998.9	57.794
2600	16586.3	61.287	15686.3	57.436	14829.4	42.403	15822.0	58.120
2700	17457.8	61.616	16516.9	57.750	15597.5	42.692	16658.0	58.436
2800	18332.7	61.934	17351.6	58.053	16371.5	42.973	17497.6	58.742
2900	19211.0	62.242	18190.0	58.348	17151.2	43.247	18341.2	59.037
3000	20092.6	62.540	19032.0	58.632	17936.6	43.514	19188.0	59.324
3100	20977.4	62.831	19877.3	58.910	18727.4	43.773	20038.3	59.603
3200	21865.4	63.113	20725.5	59.179	19523.8	44.026	20891.4	59.874
3300	22756.5	63.386	21576.5	59.442	20325.2	44.273	21747.2	60.137
3400	23650.8	63.654	22430.2	59.697	21131.6	44.513	22605.9	60.394
3500	24548.2	63.914	23286.4	59.944	21942.6	44.748	23467.4	60.643
3600	25448.8	64.168	24144.9	60.186	22758.2	44.978	24331.0	60.887
3700	26352.4	64.415	25005.6	60.422	23578.2	45.203	25197.2	61.124
3800	27259.0	64.657	25868.4	60.652	24402.5	45.423	26065.8	61.356
3900	28168.5	64.893	26733.3	60.877	25230.8	45.638	26936.3	61.582
4000	29081.0	65.123	27599.9	61.097	26063.2	45.849	27808.9	61.803
4100	29996.5	65.350	28468.5	61.310	26899.5	46.056	28683.8	62.019
4200	30914.8	65.571	29338.6	61.520	27739.5	46.257	29560.4	62.230
4300	31836.0	65.788	30210.4	61.726	28583.2	46.456	30438.8	62.437
4400	32759.9	66.000	31083.6	61.927	29430.6	46.651	31318.9	62.639
4500	33686.7	66.208	31958.3	62.123	30281.3	46.842	32200.7	62.837
4600	34616.3	66.413	32834.3	62.316	31135.4	47.030	33084.3	63.031
4700	35548.5	66.613	33711.6	62.504	32022.7	47.215	33969.6	63.223
4800	36483.5	66.809	34590.0	62.689	32853.1	47.396	34276.4	63.408
4900	37421.0	67.003	35469.6	62.870	33716.6	47.574	35744.1	63.591
5000	38361.2	67.193	36350.3	63.049	34583.0	47.749	36633.4	63.771

† 78.03% N_2, 20.99% O_2, 0.98% A.

TABLE B·13 STANDARDIZED ENTHALPIES AND ABSOLUTE ENTROPIES FOR GASES AT LOW PRESSURE (CONTINUED)

Water vapor		Carbon monoxide		Carbon dioxide		Monatomic gases	
$\hat{h}$	$\hat{\phi}$	$\hat{h}$	$\hat{\phi}$	$\hat{h}$	$\hat{\phi}$	$\hat{h}$	$\hat{\phi}$
−103968.0	45.079	−47517.0	47.272	−169183.0	51.032	0	36.942
−103471.6	45.970	−47078.5	48.044	−168612.3	52.038	212.7	37.512
−102660.9	47.219	−46380.5	49.120	−167661.2	53.503	809.2	38.278
−101839.4	48.316	−45678.3	50.058	−166660.3	54.839	1305.7	38.941
−101005.4	49.298	−44970.1	50.892	−165615.6	56.070	1802.1	39.525
−100157.4	50.191	−44254.3	51.646	−164531.1	57.212	2298.6	40.048
−99294.3	51.013	−43529.7	52.337	−163410.6	58.281	2795.1	40.522
−98415.9	51.777	−42795.7	52.976	−162257.9	59.283	3291.5	40.954
−97521.8	52.494	−42051.9	53.571	−161076.3	60.229	3788.0	41.351
−96611.5	53.168	−41298.5	54.129	−159868.5	61.124	4284.5	41.719
−95684.9	53.808	−40535.4	54.655	−158636.5	61.974	4781.0	42.061
−94741.4	54.418	−39763.1	55.154	−157383.5	62.783	5277.4	42.382
−93780.9	54.999	−38982.2	55.628	−156111.8	63.555	5773.9	42.683
−92803.3	55.559	−38193.3	56.078	−154821.0	64.292	6270.4	42.967
−91808.8	56.097	−37396.7	56.509	−153514.7	64.999	6766.8	43.235
−90797.3	56.617	−36593.3	56.922	−152193.8	65.676	7263.3	43.490
−89769.4	57.119	−35783.2	57.317	−150859.8	66.327	7759.8	43.732
−88725.5	57.605	−34967.1	57.696	−149513.5	66.953	8256.2	43.963
−87665.7	58.077	−34145.5	58.062	−148156.2	67.557	8752.7	44.183
−86590.6	58.535	−33319.1	58.414	−146788.5	68.139	9249.2	44.395
−85500.9	58.980	−32487.7	58.754	−145411.3	68.702	9745.7	44.597
−84396.8	59.414	−31652.2	59.081	−144025.4	69.245	10242.1	44.792
−83279.1	59.837	−30812.5	59.398	−142631.3	69.771	10738.6	44.980
−82148.3	60.248	−29969.3	59.705	−141229.7	70.282	11235.1	45.160
−81005.1	60.650	−29122.7	60.002	−139821.0	70.776	11731.5	45.334
−79850.0	61.043	−28273.1	60.290	−138405.9	71.255	12228.0	45.503
−78683.5	61.426	−27420.5	60.569	−136984.6	71.722	12724.5	45.663
−77506.1	61.801	−26565.3	60.841	−135557.8	72.175	13220.9	45.823
−76318.1	62.167	−25707.5	61.105	−134125.8	72.616	13717.4	45.973
−75120.3	62.526	−24847.2	61.362	−132688.9	73.045	14213.9	46.124
−73912.8	62.876	−23984.7	61.612	−131247.3	73.462	14710.5	46.266
−72696.2	63.221	−23119.9	61.855	−129801.5	73.870	15206.8	46.408
−71470.9	63.557	−22253.0	62.093	−128351.9	74.267	15703.3	46.542
−70237.4	63.887	−21384.2	62.325	−126898.4	74.655	16199.8	46.676
−68996.1	64.210	−20513.6	62.551	−125441.5	75.033	16696.3	46.803
−67747.2	64.528	−19641.3	62.772	−123981.1	75.404	17192.7	46.931
−66490.9	64.839	−18767.4	62.988	−122517.4	75.765	17689.2	47.052
−65227.9	65.144	−17892.1	63.198	−121050.5	76.119	18185.6	47.173
−63958.3	65.444	−17015.3	63.405	−119580.4	76.464	18682.1	47.289
−62682.4	65.738	−16137.3	63.607	−118107.4	76.803	19178.6	47.404
−61400.4	66.028	−15257.9	63.805	−116631.5	77.135	19675.0	47.515
−60112.7	66.312	−14377.2	63.998	−115152.8	77.460	20171.4	47.625
−58819.4	66.591	−13495.5	64.188	−113671.4	77.779	20668.0	47.731
−57520.8	66.866	−12612.6	64.374	−112187.6	78.091	21164.5	47.836
−56217.3	67.135	−11728.7	64.556	−110701.2	78.398	21661.0	47.938
−54908.9	67.401	−10843.8	64.735	−109212.5	78.698	22157.4	48.039

Derived from Joseph H. Keenan and Joseph Kaye, *Gas Tables*, John Wiley & Sons, Inc., 1948, using standardized enthalpies based on NBS Circulars 467 and 500.

TABLE B·14 LOGARITHMS TO THE BASE 10 OF THE EQUILIBRIUM CONSTANT K FOR THE REACTION

$$\nu_1 C_1 + \nu_2 C_2 \rightleftharpoons \nu_3 C_3 + \nu_4 C_4 \qquad K(T) = \frac{X_3^{\nu_3} X_4^{\nu_4}}{X_1^{\nu_1} X_2^{\nu_2}} \left(\frac{P}{P_0}\right)^{\nu_3 + \nu_4 - \nu_1 - \nu_2} \qquad P_0 = 1 \text{ atm}$$

T, °K	$H_2 \rightleftharpoons 2H$	$O_2 \rightleftharpoons 2O$	$H_2O \rightleftharpoons$ $H_2 + \frac{1}{2}O_2$	$H_2O \rightleftharpoons$ $OH + \frac{1}{2}H_2$	$CO_2 \rightleftharpoons$ $CO + \frac{1}{2}O_2$	$N_2 \rightleftharpoons 2N$	$\frac{1}{2}O_2 + \frac{1}{2}N_2$ $\rightleftharpoons NO$	$Na \rightleftharpoons$ $Na^+ + e^-$	$Cs \rightleftharpoons$ $Cs^+ + e^-$
298	−71.210	−80.620	−40.047	−46.593	−45.043	−119.434	−15.187	−32.3	−25.1
400	−51.742	−58.513	−29.241	−33.910	−32.41	−87.473	−11.156	−24.3	−17.5
600	−32.667	−36.859	−18.663	−21.470	−20.07	−56.206	−7.219	−14.6	−10.0
800	−23.074	−25.985	−13.288	−15.214	−13.90	−40.521	−5.250	−9.58	−6.15
1000	−17.288	−19.440	−10.060	−11.444	−10.199	−31.084	−4.068	−6.54	−3.79
1200	−13.410	−15.062	−7.896	−8.922	−7.742	−24.619	−3.279	−4.47	−2.18
1400	−10.627	−11.932	−6.334	−7.116	−5.992	−20.262	−2.717	−2.97	−1.010
1600	−8.530	−9.575	−5.175	−5.758	−4.684	−16.869	−2.294	−1.819	−0.108
1800	−6.893	−7.740	−4.263	−4.700	−3.672	−14.225	−1.966	−0.913	+0.609
2000	−5.579	−6.269	−3.531	−3.852	−2.863	−12.016	−1.703	−0.175	+1.194
2200	−4.500	−5.064	−2.931	−3.158	−2.206	−10.370	−1.488	+0.438	+1.682
2400	−3.598	−4.055	−2.429	−2.578	−1.662	−8.992	−1.309	+0.956	+2.098
2600	−2.833	−3.206	−2.003	−2.087	−1.203	−7.694	−1.157	+1.404	+2.46
2800	−2.176	−2.475	−1.638	−1.670	−0.807	−6.640	−1.028	+1.792	+2.77
3000	−1.604	−1.840	−1.322	−1.302	−0.469	−5.726	−0.915	+2.13	+3.05
3200	−1.104	−1.285	−1.046	−0.983	−0.175	−4.925	−0.817	+2.44	+3.29
3500	−0.458	−0.571	−0.693	−0.557	+0.201	−3.893	−0.692	+2.84	+3.62
4000	+0.406	+0.382	−0.221	−0.035	+0.699	−2.514	−0.526	+3.38	+4.07
4500	+1.078	+1.125	+0.153	+0.392	+1.081	−1.437	−0.345	+3.82	+4.43
5000	+1.619	+1.719	+0.450	+0.799	+1.387	−0.570	−0.298	+4.18	+4.73

Based on information provided by the National Bureau of Standards; ionization of Cs and Na from Saha equation.

TABLE B·15   THE NATURAL ELEMENTS

Substance	Symbol	Atomic number	$\hat{M}$†	Substance	Symbol	Atomic number	$\hat{M}$
Aluminum	Al	13	26.97	Molybdenum	Mo	42	95.95
Antimony	Sb	51	121.76	Neodymium	Nd	60	144.27
Argon	A	18	39.944	Neon	Ne	10	20.183
Arsenic	As	33	74.91	Nickel	Ni	28	58.69
Barium	Ba	56	137.36	Nitrogen	N	7	14.008
Beryllium	Be	4	9.02	Osmium	Os	76	190.2
Bismuth	Bi	83	209.00	Oxygen	O	8	16.0000
Boron	B	5	10.82	Palladium	Pd	46	106.7
Bromine	Br	35	79.916	Phosphorus	P	15	30.98
Cadmium	Cd	48	112.41	Platinum	Pt	78	195.23
Calcium	Ca	20	40.08	Potassium	K	19	39.096
Carbon	C	6	12.010	Praseodymium	Pr	59	140.92
Cerium	Ce	58	140.13	Proctactinium	Pa	91	231
Cesium	Cs	55	132.91	Radium	Ra	88	226.05
Chlorine	Cl	17	35.457	Radon	Rn	86	222
Chromium	Cr	24	52.01	Rhenium	Re	75	186.31
Cobalt	Co	27	58.94	Rhodium	Rh	45	102.91
Columbium	Cb	41	92.91	Rubidium	Rb	37	85.48
Copper	Cu	29	63.54	Ruthenium	Ru	44	101.7
Dysprosium	Dy	66	162.46	Samarium	Sm	62	150.43
Erbium	Er	68	167.2	Scandium	Sc	21	45.10
Europium	Eu	63	152.0	Selenium	Se	34	78.96
Fluorine	F	9	19.00	Silicon	Si	14	28.06
Gadolinium	Gd	64	156.9	Silver	Ag	47	107.880
Gallium	Ga	31	69.72	Sodium	Na	11	22.997
Germanium	Ge	32	72.60	Strontium	Sr	38	87.63
Gold	Au	79	197.2	Sulfur	S	16	32.066
Hafnium	Hf	72	178.6	Tantalum	Ta	73	180.88
Helium	He	2	4.003	Tellurium	Te	52	127.61
Holmium	Ho	67	164.94	Terbium	Tb	65	159.2
Hydrogen	H	1	1.0080	Thallium	Tl	81	204.39
Indium	In	49	114.76	Thorium	Th	90	232.12
Iodine	I	53	126.92	Thulium	Tm	69	169.4
Iridium	Ir	77	193.1	Tin	Sn	50	118.70
Iron	Fe	26	55.85	Titanium	Ti	22	47.90
Krypton	Kr	36	83.7	Tungsten	W	74	183.92
Lanthanum	La	57	138.92	Uranium	U	92	238.07
Lead	Pb	82	207.21	Vanadium	V	23	50.95
Lithium	Li	3	6.940	Xenon	Xe	54	131.3
Lutecium	Lu	71	174.99	Ytterbium	Yb	70	173.04
Magnesium	Mg	12	24.32	Yttrium	Y	39	88.92
Manganese	Mn	25	54.93	Zinc	Zn	30	65.38
Mercury	Hg	80	200.61	Zirconium	Zr	40	91.22

Based on a tabulation published by the *Journal of the American Chemical Society*.
† $\hat{M}$ in g/gmole, kg/kg-mole, or lbm/lbmole.

TABLE B·16 MOLAR SPECIFIC HEATS AT CONSTANT PRESSURE FOR THE IDEAL-GAS STATE—300 TO 1500°K

$$c_P = a + bT + cT^2$$

Gas	Formula	$a,$ cal/gmole-°K	$b \times 10^3,$ cal/gmole-°K^2	$c \times 10^6,$ cal/gmole-°K^3
Acetylene	C_2H_2	7.331	12.622	-3.889
Ammonia	NH_3	6.086	8.812	-1.506
Benzene	C_6H_6	-0.409	77.621	-26.429
Carbon dioxide	CO_2	6.214	10.396	-3.545
Carbon monoxide	CO	6.420	1.665	-0.196
Chlorine	Cl_2	7.576	2.424	-0.965
Ethyl alcohol	C_2H_6O	6.990	39.741	-11.926
Hydrogen	H_2	6.947	-0.200	0.481
Hydrogen chloride	HCl	6.732	0.433	0.370
Methane	CH_4	3.381	18.044	-4.300
Nitrogen	N_2	6.524	1.250	-0.001
Oxygen	O_2	6.148	3.102	-0.923
Sulfur dioxide	SO_2	7.116	9.512	3.511
Water	H_2O	7.256	2.298	0.283

From M. W. Zemansky and H. C. Van Ness, *Basic Engineering Thermodynamics*, McGraw-Hill Book Company, New York, 1966. By permission.

TABLE B·17 CONSTANTS FOR EQUATIONS OF STATE

Substance	Van der Waals Gas		Beattie-Bridgeman Gas				
	$a,$ $\dfrac{atm\text{-}ft^6}{lb\ mole^2}$	$b,$ $\dfrac{ft^3}{lb\ mole}$	$A_0,$ $\dfrac{atm\text{-}ft^6}{lb\ mole^2}$	$a,$ $\dfrac{ft^3}{lb\ mole}$	$B_0,$ $\dfrac{ft^3}{lb\ mole}$	$b,$ $\dfrac{ft^3}{lb\ mole}$	$c,$ $\dfrac{ft^3\text{-}°R^3}{lb\ mole}$
Air	343.8	0.585	334.1	0.309	0.739	-0.0176	4.05×10^6
Hydrogen, H_2	63.02	0.427	50.57	-0.0811	0.336	-0.698	0.0471×10^6
Nitrogen, N_2	346.0	0.618	344.92	0.419	0.808	-0.111	3.92×10^6
Oxygen, O_2	349.5	0.510	382.53	0.410	0.741	0.0674	4.48×10^6
Carbon monoxide, CO	374.7	0.630	344.9	0.419	0.808	-0.111	3.92×10^6
Carbon dioxide, CO_2	924.2	0.685	1284.9	1.143	1.678	1.159	61.65×10^6
Methane, CH_4	578.9	0.684	584.6	0.297	0.895	-0.254	11.98×10^6
Propane, C_3H_8	2374.0	1.446	305.8	1.173	2.90	0.688	112.2×10^6
n-Butane, C_4H_{10}	3675.0	1.944	456.5	1.948	3.944	1.51	327.02×10^6

From J. E. Lay, *Thermodynamics*, Charles E. Merrill Books, Inc., Columbus, Ohio, 1963. By permission. Evaluated from critical data and from Beattie and Bridgeman, *Proc. Am. Acad. Arts, Sci.*, vol. 63, pp. 229–308 (1928); *J. Am. Chem. Soc.*, vol. 50, p. 3133 (1928).

TABLE B·18 ONE-DIMENSIONAL ISENTROPIC COMPRESSIBLE-FLOW FUNCTIONS FOR AN IDEAL GAS WITH CONSTANT SPECIFIC HEAT AND $k = 1.4$

M	$M^* = V/c^*$	$\dfrac{A}{A^*}$	$\dfrac{P}{P_o}$	$\dfrac{\rho}{\rho_o}$	$\dfrac{T}{T_o}$
0	0	∞	1.00000	1.00000	1.00000
0.10	0.10943	5.8218	0.99303	0.99502	0.99800
0.20	0.21822	2.9635	0.97250	0.98027	0.99206
0.30	0.32572	2.0351	0.93947	0.95638	0.98232
0.40	0.43133	1.5901	0.89562	0.92428	0.96899
0.50	0.53452	1.3398	0.84302	0.88517	0.95238
0.60	0.63480	1.1882	0.78400	0.84045	0.93284
0.70	0.73179	1.09437	0.72092	0.79158	0.91075
0.80	0.82514	1.03823	0.65602	0.74000	0.88652
0.90	0.91460	1.00886	0.59126	0.68704	0.86058
1.00	1.00000	1.00000	0.52828	0.63394	0.83333
1.10	1.08124	1.00793	0.46835	0.58169	0.80515
1.20	1.1583	1.03044	0.41238	0.53114	0.77640
1.30	1.2311	1.06631	0.36092	0.48291	0.74738
1.40	1.2999	1.1149	0.31424	0.43742	0.71839
1.50	1.3646	1.1762	0.27240	0.39498	0.68965
1.60	1.4254	1.2502	0.23527	0.35573	0.66138
1.70	1.4825	1.3376	0.20259	0.31969	0.63372
1.80	1.5360	1.4390	0.17404	0.28682	0.60680
1.90	1.5861	1.5552	0.14924	0.25699	0.58072
2.00	1.6330	1.6875	0.12780	0.23005	0.55556
2.10	1.6769	1.8369	0.10935	0.20580	0.53135
2.20	1.7179	2.0050	0.09352	0.18405	0.50813
2.30	1.7563	2.1931	0.07997	0.16458	0.48591
2.40	1.7922	2.4031	0.06840	0.14720	0.46468
2.50	1.8258	2.6367	0.05853	0.13169	0.44444
2.60	1.8572	2.8960	0.05012	0.11787	0.42517
2.70	1.8865	3.1830	0.04295	0.10557	0.40684
2.80	1.9140	3.5001	0.03685	0.09462	0.38941
2.90	1.9398	3.8498	0.03165	0.08489	0.37286
3.00	1.9640	4.2346	0.02722	0.07623	0.35714
3.50	2.0642	6.7896	0.01311	0.04523	0.28986
4.00	2.1381	10.719	0.00658	0.02766	0.23810
4.50	2.1936	16.562	0.00346	0.01745	0.19802
5.00	2.2361	25.000	$189(10)^{-5}$	0.01134	0.16667
6.00	2.2953	53.180	$633(10)^{-6}$	0.00519	0.12195
7.00	2.3333	104.143	$242(10)^{-6}$	0.00261	0.09259
8.00	2.3591	190.109	$102(10)^{-6}$	0.00141	0.07246
9.00	2.3772	327.189	$474(10)^{-7}$	0.000815	0.05814
10.00	2.3904	535.938	$236(10)^{-7}$	0.000495	0.04762
∞	2.4495	∞	0	0	0

Abridged from Joseph H. Keenan and Joseph Kaye, *Gas Tables*, John Wiley & Sons, Inc., New York, 1948. By permission of the authors.

TABLE B·19 ONE-DIMENSIONAL NORMAL-SHOCK FUNCTIONS FOR AN IDEAL GAS WITH CONSTANT SPECIFIC HEAT AND $k = 1.4$

M_x	M_y	$\dfrac{P_y}{P_x}$	$\dfrac{\rho_y}{\rho_x}$	$\dfrac{T_y}{T_x}$	$\dfrac{P_{oy}}{P_{ox}} = \dfrac{A_x^*}{A_y^*}$	$\dfrac{P_{oy}}{P_x}$
1.00	1.00000	1.00000	1.00000	1.00000	1.00000	1.8929
1.10	0.91177	1.2450	1.1691	1.06494	0.99892	2.1328
1.20	0.84217	1.5133	1.3416	1.1280	0.99280	2.4075
1.30	0.78596	1.8050	1.5157	1.1909	0.97935	2.7135
1.40	0.73971	2.1200	1.6896	1.2547	0.95819	3.0493
1.50	0.70109	2.4583	1.8621	1.3202	0.92978	3.4133
1.60	0.66844	2.8201	2.0317	1.3880	0.89520	3.8049
1.70	0.64055	3.2050	2.1977	1.4583	0.85573	4.2238
1.80	0.61650	3.6133	2.3592	1.5316	0.81268	4.6695
1.90	0.59562	4.0450	2.5157	1.6079	0.76735	5.1417
2.00	0.57735	4.5000	2.6666	1.6875	0.72088	5.6405
2.10	0.56128	4.9784	2.8119	1.7704	0.67422	6.1655
2.20	0.54706	5.4800	2.9512	1.8569	0.62812	6.7163
2.30	0.53441	6.0050	3.0846	1.9468	0.58331	7.2937
2.40	0.52312	6.5533	3.2119	2.0403	0.54015	7.8969
2.50	0.51299	7.1250	3.3333	2.1375	0.49902	8.5262
2.60	0.50387	7.7200	3.4489	2.2383	0.46012	9.1813
2.70	0.49563	8.3383	3.5590	2.3429	0.42359	9.8625
2.80	0.48817	8.9800	3.6635	2.4512	0.38946	10.569
2.90	0.48138	9.6450	3.7629	2.5632	0.35773	11.302
3.00	0.47519	10.333	3.8571	2.6790	0.32834	12.061
4.00	0.43496	18.500	4.5714	4.0469	0.13876	21.068
5.00	0.41523	29.000	5.0000	5.8000	0.06172	32.654
10.00	0.38757	116.50	5.7143	20.388	0.00304	129.217
∞	0.37796	∞	6.000	∞	0	∞

Abridged from Joseph H. Keenan and Joseph Kaye, *Gas Tables*, John Wiley & Sons, Inc., New York, 1948. By permission of the authors.

INFORMATION
FOR HEAT TRANSFER
ANALYSIS

TABLE C·1 PROPERTIES OF METALS

Metal	T, °F	ρ, lbm/ft^3	c_P, Btu/lbm-°F	k, Btu/hr-ft-°F
Aluminum, pure	68	169	0.214	118
	392	. . .	. . .	124
	752	. . .	. . .	144
Lead	68	710	0.031	20
	300	. . .	. . .	17.2
Iron:				
Pure	68	493	0.108	42
	572	. . .	. . .	32
	1832	. . .	. . .	20
Wrought	68	490	0.11	34
Steel, (max 0.5% C)	68	489	0.111	31
Carbon steel, 1.5% C	68	484	0.116	21
	752	. . .	. . .	19
	2192	. . .	. . .	17
Stainless steel	68	. . .	. . .	7–26
Copper:				
Pure	68	559	0.0915	223
	572	. . .	. . .	213
	1112	. . .	. . .	204
Bronze, 75% Cu, 25% Sn	68	541	0.082	15
Brass, 70% Cu, 30% Sn	68	532	0.092	64
Silver, pure	68	657	0.0559	235
Tungsten	68	1208	0.0321	94

Adapted from E. R. G. Eckert and R. M. Drake, *Heat and Mass Transfer*, 2d ed., McGraw-Hill Book Company, 1959. By permission.

TABLE C·2 THERMAL CONDUCTIVITY OF NONMETALS

Substance	T, °F	k, Btu/hr-ft-°F
Structural and heat-resistant materials:		
Asphalt	68–132	0.43–0.44
Brick:		
Building brick, common	68	0.40
Building brick, face	. . .	0.76
Diatomaceous earth, molded and fired	400	0.14
	1600	0.18
Fireclay brick (burnt 2426°F)	932	0.60
	1472	0.62
	2012	0.63
Cement, portland	. . .	0.17
Concrete, stone 1-2-4 mix	69	0.79
Glass, window	68	0.45 (av)
Glass, borosilicate	86–167	0.63
Plaster, gypsum	70	0.28
Plaster, metal lath	70	0.27
Plaster, wood lath	70	0.16
Stone:		
Granite	. . .	1.0–2.3
Limestone	210–570	0.73–0.77
Wood (across the grain):		
Balsa, 8.8 lb/cu-ft	86	0.032
Yellow pine	75	0.085
White pine	86	0.065
Insulating material:		
Asbestos:		
Asbestos-cement boards	68	0.43
Asbestos sheets	124	0.096
Asbestos cement	. . .	1.2
Asbestos, loosely packed	−50	0.086
	32	0.089
	210	0.093
Corkboard, 10 lb/cu-ft	86	0.025
Cork, regranulated	90	0.026
Cork, ground	90	0.025
Diatomaceous earth (Sil-o-cel)	32	0.035
Fiber insulating board	70	0.028
Glass wool, 1.5 lb/cu-ft	75	0.022
Kapok	86	0.020
Magnesia, 85%	100	0.039
	200	0.041
	300	0.043
	400	0.046
Sawdust	75	0.034

Adapted from A. I. Brown and S. M. Marco, *Introduction to Heat Transfer*, 3d ed., McGraw-Hill Book Company, 1958. By permission.

TABLE C·3 PROPERTIES OF SATURATED LIQUIDS

$T,$ °F	$\rho,$ lbm/ft³	$c_P,$ Btu/lbm-°F	$\nu = \mu/\rho,$ ft²/sec	$k,$ Btu/hr-ft-°F	Pr	$\beta,$ 1/°R
Carbon dioxide (CO_2)						
−58	72.19	0.44	0.128×10^{-5}	0.0494	2.96	
−40	69.78	0.45	0.127	0.0584	2.46	
−22	67.22	0.47	0.126	0.0645	2.22	
−4	64.45	0.49	0.124	0.0665	2.12	
14	61.39	0.52	0.122	0.0635	2.20	
32	57.87	0.59	0.117	0.0604	2.38	
50	53.69	0.75	0.109	0.0561	2.80	
68	48.23	1.2	0.098	0.0504	4.10	3.67×10^{-3}
86	37.32	8.7	0.086	0.0406	28.7	
Dichlorodifluoromethane (freon)(CCl_2F_2)						
−58	96.56	0.2090	0.334×10^{-5}	0.039	6.2	1.4×10^{-4}
−22	92.99	0.2139	0.272	0.040	4.8	
14	89.24	0.2198	0.238	0.042	4.0	
32	87.24	0.2232	0.230	0.042	3.8	
68	83.04	0.2307	0.213	0.042	3.5	
104	78.48	0.2393	0.206	0.040	3.5	
122	75.91	9.2440	0.204	0.039	3.5	
Ethylene glycol [$C_2H_4(OH_2)$]						
32	70.59	0.548	61.92×10^{-5}	0.140	615	
68	69.71	0.569	20.64	0.144	204	0.36×10^{-3}
104	68.76	0.591	9.35	0.148	93	
140	67.90	0.612	5.11	0.150	51	
176	67.27	0.633	3.21	0.151	32.4	
212	66.08	0.655	2.18	0.152	22.4	
Mercury (Hg)						
32	850.78	0.0335	0.133×10^{-5}	4.74	0.0288	
68	847.71	0.0333	0.123	5.02	0.0249	1.01×10^{-4}
122	843.14	0.0331	0.112	5.43	0.0207	
212	835.57	0.0328	0.0999	6.07	0.0162	
392	820.61	0.0325	0.0863	7.13	0.0116	
482	813.16	0.0324	0.0823	7.55	0.0103	
600	802	0.032	0.0724	8.10	0.0083	

Adapted from E. R. G. Eckert and R. M. Drake, *Heat and Mass Transfer*, 2d ed., McGraw-Hill Book Company, 1959. By permission.

TABLE C·4 PROPERTIES OF WATER (SATURATED LIQUID)

°F	$c_P, \dfrac{Btu}{lbm\text{-}°F}$	$\rho, \dfrac{lbm}{ft^3}$	$\mu, \dfrac{lbm}{ft\text{-}hr}$	$k, \dfrac{Btu}{hr\text{-}ft\text{-}°F}$	$Pr, \dfrac{c_P\mu}{k}$	$\dfrac{g\beta\rho^2}{\mu^2}, \dfrac{1}{ft^3\text{-}°F}$
32	1.009	62.42	4.33	0.327	13.35	
40	1.005	62.42	3.75	0.332	11.35	
50	1.002	62.38	3.17	0.338	9.40	0.3×10^8
60	1.000	62.34	2.71	0.344	7.88	1.0×10^8
70	0.998	62.27	2.37	0.349	6.78	1.7×10^8
						2.3×10^8
80	0.998	62.17	2.08	0.355	5.85	3.0×10^8
90	0.997	62.11	1.85	0.360	5.12	3.9×10^8
100	0.997	61.99	1.65	0.364	4.53	5.2×10^8
110	0.997	61.84	1.49	0.368	4.04	6.6×10^8
120	0.997	61.73	1.36	0.372	3.64	7.7×10^8
130	0.998	61.54	1.24	0.375	3.30	8.9×10^8
140	0.998	61.39	1.14	0.378	3.01	10.2×10^8
150	0.999	61.20	1.04	0.381	2.73	12.0×10^8
160	1.000	61.01	0.97	0.384	2.53	13.9×10^8
170	1.001	60.79	0.90	0.386	2.33	15.5×10^8
180	1.002	60.57	0.84	0.389	2.16	17.1×10^8
190	1.003	60.35	0.79	0.390	2.03	
200	1.004	60.13	0.74	0.392	1.90	
220	1.007	59.63	0.65	0.395	1.66	
240	1.010	59.10	0.59	0.396	1.51	
260	1.015	58.51	0.53	0.396	1.36	
280	1.020	57.94	0.48	0.396	1.24	
300	1.026	57.31	0.45	0.395	1.17	
350	1.044	55.59	0.38	0.391	1.02	
400	1.067	53.65	0.33	0.384	1.00	
450	1.095	51.55	0.29	0.373	0.85	
500	1.130	49.02	0.26	0.356	0.83	
550	1.200	45.92	0.23			
600	1.362	42.37	0.21			

A. I. Brown and S. M. Marco, *Indroduction to Heat Transfer*, 3d ed., McGraw-Hill Book Company, New York, 1958. By permission.

TABLE C·5 PROPERTIES OF AIR AT MODERATE PRESSURE

T, °F	μ, lbm/hr-ft	k, Btu/hr-ft-°F	c_P, Btu/lbm-°F	Pr
−100	0.0319	0.0104	0.239	0.739
0	0.0394	0.0131	0.240	0.718
100	0.0459	0.0157	0.240	0.706
200	0.0519	0.0181	0.241	0.693
300	0.0574	0.0203	0.243	0.686
400	0.0626	0.0225	0.245	0.681
500	0.0675	0.0246	0.248	0.680
600	0.0721	0.0265	0.250	0.680
700	0.0765	0.0284	0.254	0.682
800	0.0806	0.0303	0.257	0.684
900	0.0846	0.0320	0.260	0.687
1000	0.0884	0.0337	0.263	0.690

From *Natl. Bur. Std. Circ.* 564, 1955.

TABLE C·6 PROPERTIES OF GASES AT MODERATE PRESSURES

T, °F	c_P, Btu/lbm-°F	μ, lbm/sec ft	k, Btu/hr-ft-°F	Pr
Helium				
−200	1.242	84.3×10^{-7}	0.0536	0.70
−100	1.242	105.2	0.0680	0.694
0	1.242	122.1	0.0784	0.70
200	1.242	154.9	0.0977	0.71
400	1.242	184.8	0.114	0.72
600	1.242	209.2	0.130	0.72
1000	1.242	256.5	0.159	0.72
Hydrogen				
−190	3.010	3.760×10^{-6}	0.0567	0.718
−100	3.234	4.578	0.741	0.719
−10	3.358	5.321	0.0902	0.713
80	3.419	6.023	0.105	0.706
170	3.448	6.689	0.119	0.697
260	3.461	7.300	0.132	0.690
440	3.465	8.491	0.157	0.675
620	3.472	9.599	0.182	0.664
800	3.481	10.68	0.203	0.659
980	3.505	11.69	0.222	0.664
1160	3.540	12.62	0.238	0.676
Oxygen				
−190	0.2192	7.721×10^{-6}	0.00790	0.773
−100	0.2181	9.979	0.01054	0.745
−10	0.2187	12.01	0.01305	0.725
80	0.2198	13.86	0.01546	0.709
170	0.2219	15.56	0.01774	0.702
260	0.2250	17.16	0.02000	0.695
440	0.2322	20.10	0.02411	0.697
620	0.2399	22.79	0.02792	0.704
Nitrogen				
−100	0.2491	8.700×10^{-6}	0.01054	0.747
80	0.2486	11.99	0.01514	0.713
260	0.2498	14.77	0.01927	0.691
440	0.2521	17.27	0.02302	0.684
800	0.2620	21.59	0.02960	0.691
1160	0.2738	25.19	0.03507	0.711
1340	0.2789	26.88	0.03741	0.724
1700	0.2875	29.90	0.04151	0.748
Carbon dioxide				
−64	0.187	7.462×10^{-6}	0.006243	0.818
−10	0.192	8.460	0.007444	0.793
80	0.208	10.051	0.009575	0.770
170	0.215	11.561	0.01183	0.755
260	0.225	12.98	0.01422	0.738
350	0.234	14.34	0.01674	0.721
440	0.242	15.63	0.01937	0.702
530	0.250	16.85	0.02208	0.685
620	0.257	18.03	0.02491	0.608

Adapted from E. R. G. Eckert and R. M. Drake, *Heat and Mass Transfer*, 2d ed., McGraw-Hill Book Company, 1959. By permission.

TABLE C·7 NORMAL TOTAL EMISSIVITY OF VARIOUS SURFACES

Surface	T, °F	Emissivity, ϵ
A. Metals and their oxides		
Aluminum:		
Highly polished plate, 98.3% pure	440–1070	0.039–0.057
Commercial sheet	212	0.09
Heavily oxidized	299–940	0.20–0.31
Al-surfaced roofing	100	0.216
Chromium (see nickel alloys for Ni-Cr steels),		
polished	100–2000	0.08–0.36
Copper:		
Polished	242	0.023
Polished	212	0.052
Plate, heated long time, covered with thick		
oxide layer	77	0.78
Gold, pure, highly polished	440–1160	0.018–0.035
Iron and steel (not including stainless).		
Steel, polished	212	0.066
Iron, polished	800–1880	0.14–0.38
Cast iron, newly turned	72	0.44
Cast iron, turned and heated	1620–1810	0.60–0.70
Mild steel	450–1950	0.20–0.32
Oxidized surfaces:		
Iron plate, pickled, then rusted red	68	0.61
Iron, dark-gray surface	212	0.31
Rough ingot iron	1700–2040	0.87–0.95
Sheet steel with strong, rough oxide layer	75	0.80
Nickel:		
Polished	212	0.072
Nickel oxide	1200–2290	0.59–0.86
Nickel alloys:		
Copper nickel, polished	212	0.059
Nichrome wire, bright	120–1830	0.65–0.79
Nichrome wire, oxidized	120–930	0.95–0.98
Platinum, polished plate, pure	440–1160	0.054–0.104
Silver:		
Polished, pure	440–1160	0.020–0.032
Polished	100–700	0.022–0.031
Stainless steels:		
Polished	212	0.074
Type 301	450–1725	0.54–0.63
Tin, bright tinned iron	76	0.043 and 0.064
Tungsten, filament	6000	0.39

TABLE C·7 NORMAL TOTAL EMISSIVITY OF VARIOUS SURFACES (CONTINUED)

Surface	T, °F	Emissivity, ϵ
B. *Refractories, building materials, paints, and miscellaneous*		
Alumina (85–99.5% Al_2O_3, 0–12% SiO_2, 0–1% Fe_2O_3); effect of mean grain size, microns (μ):		
10 μ	. . .	0.30–0.18
50 μ	. . .	0.39–0.28
100 μ	. . .	0.50–0.40
Asbestos, board	74	0.96
Brick:		
Red, rough, but no gross irregularities	70	0.93
Fireclay	1832	0.75
Carbon:		
T-carbon (Gebruder Siemens) 0.9% ash, started with emissivity at 260°F of 0.72, but on heating changed to values given	260–1160	0.81–0.79
Filament	1900–2560	0.526
Rough plate	212–608	0.77
Lampblack, rough deposit	212–932	0.84–0.78
Concrete tiles	1832	0.63
Enamel, white fused, on iron	66	0.90
Glass:		
Smooth	72	0.94
Pyrex, lead, and soda	500–1000	0.95–0.85
Paints, lacquers, varnishes:		
Snow-white enamel varnish on rough iron plate	73	0.906
Black shiny lacquer, sprayed on iron	76	0.875
Black shiny shellac on tinned iron sheet	70	0.821
Black matte shellac	170–295	0.91
Black or white lacquer	100–200	0.80–0.95
Flat black lacquer	100–200	0.96–0.98
Aluminum paints and lacquers:		
10% Al, 22% lacquer body, on rough or smooth surface	212	0.52
Other Al paints, varying age and Al content	212	0.27–0.67
Porcelain, glazed	72	0.92
Quartz, rough, fused	70	0.93
Roofing paper	69	0.91
Rubber, hard, glossy plate	74	0.94
Water	32–212	0.95–0.963

Adapted from W. H. McAdams, *Heat Transmission*, 3d ed., McGraw-Hill Book Company, New York, 1954. By permission.

TABLE C·8 CONVECTION HEAT TRANSFER CORRELATIONS

A. *Flow in circular tubes*

$$\mathrm{Re} \equiv \frac{VD\rho}{\mu}$$

$$\mathrm{Nu} \equiv \frac{hD}{k}$$

$$h \equiv \frac{q''}{\Delta T}$$

$$\Delta T = T_{\mathrm{wall}} - T_{\mathrm{mean}}$$

1. *Laminar flow*, $\mathrm{Re} < 2000$

   Fully developed flow $\quad \dfrac{L/D}{\mathrm{RePr}} > 0.05$

   $\mathrm{Nu} = 4.364 \quad$ (uniform wall heat flux)
   $\mathrm{Nu} = 3.66 \quad$ (uniform wall temperature)

2. *Turbulent flow*, $\mathrm{Re} > 2000$
   $\mathrm{Pr} < 0.1 \quad$ *(liquid metals)* $\quad 10^2 < (\mathrm{RePr}) < 10^4$
   $\quad \mathrm{Nu} = 4.82 + 0.0185\,(\mathrm{RePr})^{0.827} \quad$ (uniform wall heat flux)
   $0.5 < \mathrm{Pr} < 1.0 \quad$ *(gases)*
   $\quad \mathrm{Nu} = 0.022\,\mathrm{Pr}^{0.6}\mathrm{Re}^{0.8}$
   $1.0 < \mathrm{Pr} < 20 \quad$ *(water and light oils)*
   $\quad \mathrm{Nu} = 0.0155\,\mathrm{Pr}^{0.5}\mathrm{Re}^{0.83}$
   $\mathrm{Pr} > 20$
   $\quad \mathrm{Nu} = 0.0118\,\mathrm{Pr}^{0.3}\mathrm{Re}^{0.9}$

B. *Boundary layer on a flat plate*

$$q''_{\mathrm{av}} \equiv \frac{1}{L}\int_0^L q''(x)\,dX \qquad \Delta T \equiv T_{\mathrm{wall}} - T_{\mathrm{flow}}$$

$$h_x \equiv \frac{q''}{\Delta T} \qquad\qquad h_L \equiv \frac{q''_{\mathrm{av}}}{\Delta T}$$

$$\mathrm{Nu}_x \equiv \frac{h_x x}{k} \qquad \mathrm{Nu}_L \equiv \frac{h_L L}{k} \qquad \mathrm{Re}_L = \frac{V\rho L}{\mu} \qquad \mathrm{Re}_x = \frac{V\rho x}{\mu}$$

1. *Laminar flow*, $\mathrm{Re}_L < 300{,}000$
   $0.5 < \mathrm{Pr} < 15$
   $\left.\begin{array}{l} \mathrm{Nu}_x = 0.332\,\mathrm{Re}_x^{1/2}\mathrm{Pr}^{1/3} \\ \mathrm{Nu}_L = 0.664\,\mathrm{Re}_L^{1/2}\mathrm{Pr}^{1/3} \end{array}\right\} \quad$ (uniform wall temperature)

   $\left.\begin{array}{l} \mathrm{Nu}_x = 0.453\,\mathrm{Re}_x^{1/2}\mathrm{Pr}^{1/3} \\ \mathrm{Nu}_L = 0.906\,\mathrm{Re}_L^{1/2}\mathrm{Pr}^{1/3} \end{array}\right\} \quad$ (uniform wall heat flux)

2. *Turbulent flow*, $\mathrm{Re}_L > 300{,}000$
   $0.5 < \mathrm{Pr} < 10$
   $\mathrm{Nu}_x = 0.0295\,\mathrm{Pr}^{0.6}\mathrm{Re}^{0.8}$

TABLE C·8 CONVECTION HEAT TRANSFER CORRELATIONS (CONTINUED)

C. *Single circular cylinder or sphere in cross flow*

$$\text{Re} \equiv \frac{VD\rho}{\mu} \qquad \text{Nu} \equiv \frac{hD}{k}$$

$$h \equiv \frac{q''_{av}}{\Delta T} \qquad \Delta T = T_{wall} - T_{fluid}$$

1. *Cylinder*
    $\text{Nu} = C(\text{Re})^n$

Re	C, gases	C, liquids	n
4–40	0.821	0.911 $\text{Pr}^{1/3}$	0.385
40–4000	0.615	0.683 $\text{Pr}^{1/3}$	0.466
4000–40,000	0.174	0.193 $\text{Pr}^{1/3}$	0.618
40,000–400,000	0.0239	0.0266 $\text{Pr}^{1/3}$	0.805

2. *Sphere*
    $\text{Nu} = 0.37 \ \text{Re}^{0.6}$
    $17 < \text{Re} < 70,000$, gases
    $\text{Nu} = (1.2 + 0.53 \ \text{Re}_D{}^{0.54}) \ \text{Pr}^{0.3}$
    $1 < \text{Re} < 200,000, \ \text{Pr} > 3$

D. *Natural Convection from a Horizontal Cylinder (Nu, Gr based on diameter D)*
    $\text{Nu} = C(\text{GrPr})^n$

GrPr	C	n
10^3–10^9	0.53	$\frac{1}{4}$
10^9–10^{12}	0.13	$\frac{1}{3}$

E. *Natural Convection from Vertical Surfaces (Nu, Gr based on height L)*
    $\text{Nu} = C(\text{GrPr})^n$

GrPr	C	n
10^5–10^9	0.555	0.25
$> 10^9$	0.021	0.4

Compiled from W. M. Kays, *Convective Heat and Mass Transfer*, McGraw-Hill Book Company, New York, 1966; and W. H. McAdams, *Heat Transmission*, 3d ed., McGraw-Hill Book Company, New York, 1954.

TABLE C·9A COUNTERFLOW HEAT EXCHANGER PERFORMANCE

NTU	ϵ for indicated capacity rate ratios, C_{min}/C_{max}				
	0	0.25	0.50	0.75	1.00
0	0	0	0	0	0
0.25	0.221	0.216	0.209	0.205	0.200
0.50	0.393	0.378	0.362	0.347	0.333
0.75	0.528	0.502	0.476	0.452	0.429
1.00	0.632	0.598	0.565	0.532	0.500
1.25	0.713	0.674	0.635	0.598	0.556
1.50	0.777	0.735	0.691	0.645	0.600
1.75	0.826	0.784	0.737	0.687	0.636
2.00	0.865	0.823	0.774	0.722	0.667
2.50	0.918	0.880	0.832	0.776	0.714
3.00	0.950	0.919	0.874	0.817	0.750
3.50	0.970	0.945	0.905	0.848	0.778
4.00	0.982	0.962	0.927	0.873	0.800
4.50	0.989	0.974	0.944	0.893	0.818
5.00	0.993	0.982	0.957	0.909	0.833
∞	1	1	1	1	1

From W. M. Kays and A. L. London, *Compact Heat Exchangers*, 2d ed., McGraw-Hill Book Company, New York, 1964. By permission.

TABLE C·9B   PARALLEL-FLOW HEAT EXCHANGER PERFORMANCE

	ϵ for indicated capacity rate ratios, C_{min}/C_{max}				
NTU	0	0.25	0.50	0.75	1.00
0	0	0	0	0	0
0.25	0.221	0.215	0.208	0.202	0.197
0.50	0.393	0.372	0.352	0.333	0.316
0.75	0.528	0.487	0.450	0.418	0.388
1.00	0.632	0.571	0.518	0.472	0.432
1.25	0.713	0.632	0.564	0.507	0.459
1.50	0.777	0.677	0.596	0.530	0.475
1.75	0.826	0.710	0.618	0.544	0.489
2.00	0.865	0.734	0.633	0.554	0.491
2.50	0.918	0.765	0.651	0.564	0.497
3.00	0.950	0.781	0.659	0.568	0.498
3.50	0.970	0.790	0.663	0.570	0.499
4.00	0.982	0.795	0.665	0.571	0.500
4.50	0.989	0.797	0.666	0.571	0.500
5.00	0.993	0.799	0.666	0.571	0.500
∞	1	0.800	0.6667	0.5714	0.500

From W. M. Kays and A. L. London, *Compact Heat Exchangers*, 2d ed., McGraw-Hill Book Company, New York, 1964. By permission.

TABLE C·9C CROSSFLOW HEAT EXCHANGER WITH BOTH FLUIDS UNMIXED

| NTU | ϵ for the indicated capacity rate ratios, C_{min}/C_{max} | | | | |
	0	0.25	0.50	0.75	1.00
0	0	0	0	0	0
0.25	0.221	0.215	0.208	0.204	0.199
0.50	0.393	0.376	0.357	0.341	0.327
0.75	0.528	0.495	0.467	0.437	0.412
1.00	0.632	0.587	0.546	0.511	0.477
1.25	0.713	0.659	0.610	0.565	0.522
1.50	0.777	0.715	0.657	0.606	0.560
1.75	0.826	0.760	0.700	0.643	0.590
2.00	0.865	0.797	0.732	0.671	0.613
2.50	0.918	0.851	0.782	0.715	0.652
3.00	0.950	0.888	0.819	0.750	0.680
3.50	0.970	0.920	0.848	0.775	0.703
4.00	0.982	0.930	0.870	0.800	0.722
4.50	0.989	0.946	0.888	0.815	0.737
5.00	0.993	0.959	0.900	0.830	0.750
∞	1	1	1	1	1

From W. M. Kays and A. L. London, *Compact Heat Exchangers*, 2d ed., McGraw-Hill Book Company, New York, 1964. By permission.

NOMENCLATURE

A	Area
	Helmholtz function, $U - TS$
a	Acceleration
	Helmholtz function per unit of mass, $u - Ts$
$\hat{a}$	Helmholtz function per mole, $\hat{u} - T\hat{s}$
B, **B**	Magnetic induction
C	Constant, defined where used
	Curie constant of a substance
	Thermal capacitance
CM	Control mass
CV	Control volume
cop	Coefficient of performance
c	Speed of light
	Speed of sound
c_P	Specific heat at constant pressure
$\hat{c}_P$	Molal specific heat at constant pressure
c_v	Specific heat at constant volume
$\hat{c}_v$	Molal specific heat at constant volume
c	$c = c_P = c_v$ for an incompressible substance
c_H	Specific heat in a constant applied magnetic field
c_M	Specific heat at constant magnetization
D, **D**	Electric displacement
$\mathcal{E}$	Electrostatic potential
e	Charge of an electron
E	Energy
	Emissive power
e	Energy per unit of mass
E, **E**	Electric field strength
F	Shape factor
$\mathcal{F}$	Gray body radiation factor
F, **F**	Force

$f(x)$	Function of x
f	Fraction
g_c	Constant in Newton's law, $F = (1/g_c)Ma$
g_a	Local acceleration of gravity
g	Gibbs function per unit of mass, $h - Ts$
$\hat{g}$	Gibbs function per mole, $\hat{h} - T\hat{s}$
G	Gibbs function, $U + PV - TS$
	Mass velocity, ρV
ΔG_r	Gibbs-function change for a complete unit reaction
$G,\ \mathbf{G}$	Gravitational field strength
g	Magnetic Gibbs function per unit of mass, $h - Ts$
h	Enthalpy per unit of mass, $u + Pv$
$\hat{h}$	Enthalpy per mole, $u + Pv$
h	Magnetic enthalpy, $u - \mu_0 v \mathbf{H} \cdot \mathbf{M}$
h	Planck's constant
	Heat transfer coefficient
$H,\ \mathbf{H}$	Magnetic field strength
Δh_f°	Enthalpy of formation of a mole of compound from its elements at the standard reference state
ΔH_r	Enthalpy change for a complete unit reaction
i	Electric current
I	Moment of inertia
	Impulse function
k	Ratio of specific heats, c_P/c_v
	Thermal conductivity
k	Boltzmann constant
k_N	Constant in Newton's law, $k_N = 1/g_c$
k_C	Constant in Coulomb's law, $k_C = 1/(4\pi\epsilon_0)$
k_B	Constant in Biot-Savart's law, $k_B = \mu_0/(4\pi)$
k_G	Constant in the gravitational law
K	Equilibrium constant for ideal-gas reactions
KE	Kinetic energy
$\mathcal{K}$	An amount of entropy transfer with heat
$\dot{\mathcal{K}}$	Rate of entropy transfer with heat
L	Length
M	Mass
m	Molecular weight (dimensionless)
	Fin parameter, $m^2 = hp/kA$
$\hat{M}$	Molal mass
m	Mass of a particle
$\dot{M}$	Mass flow rate
$M,\ \mathbf{M}$	Magnetic dipole moment per unit of volume
	Momentum

M	Mach number
n, N	Number of particles
$\mathfrak{N}$	Number of moles
N_0	Avogadro's number
NTU	Number of transfer units
Nu	Nusselt number, $\mathsf{h}L/k$
Pr	Prandtl number, $\mu c_P/k$
PE	Potential energy
P	Pressure
P, **P**	Electric-dipole moment per unit of volume
$\mathcal{P}_E, \mathcal{P}_S, \mathcal{P}_\mathbf{M}$	Amounts of energy, entropy, momentum production
$\dot{\mathcal{P}}_E, \dot{\mathcal{P}}_S, \dot{\mathcal{P}}_\mathbf{M}$	Rates of energy, entropy, momentum production
p	Probability
	Perimeter of fin
p	Momentum of a particle
p_r	Reduced pressure
P^*	Pressure ratio
	Pressure in a pure phase
Q	An amount of energy transfer as heat
$\dot{Q}$	Rate of energy transfer as heat
$\mathcal{Q}$	Charge
q''	Heat flux
$\mathbf{q}''$	Heat-flux vector
R	Thermal resistance
Re	Reynolds number, $\mathsf{V}L\rho/\mu$
R	Gas constant for a particular gas, $R \doteq \mathfrak{R}/\hat{M}$
$\mathfrak{R}$	Universal gas constant
r	Radius
S	Entropy
s	Entropy per unit of mass
$\hat{s}$	Entropy per mole
$\hat{s}°$	Absolute entropy of a substance, per mole, at the standard reference state
ΔS_r	Entropy change for a complete unit reaction
s	Heat source strength
St	Stanton number, $\mathsf{h}/(\mathsf{V}\rho c_P)$
T	Absolute temperature
T^*	Temperature ratio
t	Time
U	Internal energy
u	Internal energy per unit of volume
u	Internal energy per unit of mass
$\hat{u}$	Internal energy per mole

U	Overall heat transfer conductance
V	Volume
V, **V**	Velocity
V_m	Mean velocity
v	Volume per unit of mass
$\hat{v}$	Volume per mole
W	An amount of energy transfer as work
$\dot{W}$	Rate of energy transfer as work
x	Quality of a two-phase mixture
X	Directional coordinate
x_i	Generalized intensified property (specific volume, magnetzation, etc.)
X_i	Gradient of a natural intensified property
Z	Compressibility, $Z = Pv/RT$
x, y, z	Coordinates
α	Isentropic compressibility
	Absorptivity
β	Isobaric compressibility
δ	Boundary layer thickness
ϵ	Emissivity
	Fin effectiveness
ϵ_i	Energy of a system in quantum state i
ε	Energy of a particle
ϵ_0	Permittivity of a vacuum
ϕ	Function of temperature for an ideal gas
	Relative humidity
	Scalar potential
γ	Specific humidity
κ	Isothermal compressibility
λ	Wavelength
μ	Electrochemical potential per unit of mass
	Viscosity
$\hat{\mu}$	Electrochemical potential per mole
μ_0	Permeability of a vacuum
Ω	Number of quantum states
ω	Angular frequency
Ψ	Volume fraction
Φ	Mass fraction
η	Cycle energy-conversion efficiency
η_s	Isentropic efficiency
σ	Stefan-Boltzmann constant
	Entropy production per unit of volume
	Interfacial tension
θ	Angle

ν	Frequency
ν_i	Stoichiometric coefficients in a chemical equation
τ	Torque
	Transmissivity
ρ	Density
	Reflectivity
χ	Mole fraction

Special notations

d	An infinitesimal increase in a property of matter
$đ$	An infinitesimal amount of transfer by some mechanism
Δ	A finite increase in a property of matter
	$\Delta \equiv$ final $-$ initial
$(\partial y / \partial x)_z$	The partial derivative of y with respect to x, obtained from the function $y(x,z)$
$f(x)$, $f(x,y)$	Functional relations
$f \cdot (x)$	f times x, used to avoid misreading as the function $f(x)$
x	The time-average value of a quantity of x
$\mathbf{B}$	The vector $\mathbf{B}$
B	The magnitude of vector $\mathbf{B}$
$\hat{u}$	A molal quantity
$\equiv$	Identity symbol, used when the equation defines the quantity on the left
$\sum_i x_i$	The sum $x_1 + x_2 + \cdots + x_n$
$\prod_i x_i$	The product $x_1 x_2 x_3 \cdots x_n$
$\dot{W}, \dot{Q}, \dot{M}$	Rates of transfer or flow; *not* to be interpreted as time derivatives

Frequently used subscripts

W_{12}, Q_{12}	Amounts of energy transfer as work and heat corresponding to a charge from state 1 to state 2
W_1, Q_1	Amounts of energy transfer as work and heat for process 1; *not* to be interpreted as the "work and heat at state 1"
h_f, h_g, h_s	Saturated-liquid, saturated-vapor, and saturated-solid states
h_{fg}, s_{fg}	$h_g - h_f$, $s_g - s_f$, etc.
h_{crit}	The critical state
χ_i	"Dummy indices" which could take on any of the possible integer values
T_0	Stagnation conditions
T_x	Upstream of a shock wave
T_y	Downstream of a shock wave

ANSWERS TO SELECTED PROBLEMS

1·5 $k_G M/r^2$

1·12 1 kg = 6.67×10^{-11} m³/sec²; 1 coul = 0.774 m³/sec²

2·11 150 ft-lbf; 15,150 ft-lbf; 30,150 ft-lbf

2·12 28,800 ft-lbf; 19,950 ft-lbf; 43,200 ft-lbf; 67,200 ft-lbf

2·18 72.5 Btu input

3·4 43.5 Btu/lbm

3·7 11.67 Btu/lbm

3·9 50.7 Btu/lbm

4·1 0.173 ft³/lbm; 73.4 Btu/lbm; 0.0045; 0.9955

4·14 0.292 Btu/lbm-°R

4·21 408°F

4·24 $c_v \approx 4$ Btu/lbm-°R; $c_P = \infty$

4·27 M/C; C/T; C/M; $-CH/M^2$

5·2 $h_{fg} = 78$ Btu/lbm

5·5 81 Btu

5·9 19 Btu

5·13 1–2: $Q_{in} = c_P(T_2 - T_1)$; $W_{out} = R(T_2 - T_1)$
2–3: $Q_{out} = c_v(T_2 - T_3)$; $W = 0$
3–1: $Q_{out} = W_{in} = RT_1 \ln (P_1/P_3)$
$(W_{out} - W_{in})/Q_{in} = 0.0884$

5·20 2740 Btu/min

5·23 3.7 hp; 2.9 hp

5·31 960°F

5·37 385°F; 0.184

5·46 294,000 lbm/hr; 284×10^6 Btu/hr

6·2 $1/N$ if molecules are indistinguishable from one another.
$\frac{1}{2}^N$ if they are distinguishable from one another.

6·10 $\frac{1}{6}$; $\frac{1}{6}$; $\frac{10}{36}$;
H: 1, $\frac{5}{6}$, $\frac{26}{36}$, . . . , $\frac{1}{2}$
T: 0, $\frac{1}{6}$, $\frac{10}{36}$, . . . , $\frac{1}{2}$
S: 0, 0.455, 0.591, . . . , 0.692

6·15 $e^{10^{25.8}}$; $10^{(0.432 \times 10^{25.8} - 22.2)}$

6·19 $S_2 - S_1 = (0.41 - 0.37)$ Btu/°R > 0

 7·4 $(\partial T/\partial u)_M > 0$

7·17 797 Btu/hr-°R

7·20 1740 kw

7·22 0.06°K

7·27 0.1

 8·2 418 ft/sec

 8·5 384°F, 61.5 Btu/lbm, 7.9 Btu/lbm

8·13 $u_2 - u_1 = a(T_2 - T_1) + (b/2)(T_2{}^2 - T_1{}^2)$
$s_2 - s_1 = a \ln (T_2/T_1) + b(T_2 - T_1)$

8·19 68 atm, 47.2 atm, 47.4 atm

8·29 2160 psia

8·37 $u_2 - u_1 = c_P(T_2 - T_1)$
$s_2 - s_1 = c_P \ln (T_2/T_1) - (vA/2)(\mathbf{P}_2{}^2 - \mathbf{P}_1{}^2)$

 9·1 0.73

 9·6 3120 ft/sec

 9·8 0.21

9·11 0.39, 8.6×10^8 Btu/hr, 6.6×10^5 lbm/hr

9·28 2.56 hp

9·35 isentropic, 172 Btu/lbm; isothermal 107 Btu/lbm

9·47 no bypass case, compressor 48 Btu/lbm; turbine 66 Btu/lbm, reactor
91.4 Btu/lbm

9·54 $T_{max} = 4080°R$; 50%

9·57 212 lbf/(lbm/sec); 1030 lbf/(lbm/sec); 3×10^5 lbf/(lbm/sec)

10·4 $\chi_{He} = 0.343$; $\chi_{o_2} = 0.657$; $\hat{M} = 22.4$ lbm/lbmole;
$c_P = 0.282$ Btu/lbm-°R

10·11 0.08 lbm/sec; 575°R

10·13 65°F, 43%, 0.013 lbm-H_2O/lbm-dry-air

10·19 66°F, 66%, 0.0092 lbm-H_2O/lbm-dry-air

10·23 0.44

10·31 $\chi_{CO_2} = \chi_{He} = 0.5$

11·4 15.15 lbm/lb-fuel

11·10 104°F, 13.7 lbm-air/lbm-fuel
71°F, 41.1 lbm-air/lbm-fuel

11·16 $-22,400$ Btu/lbm-fuel; $-21,400$ Btu/lbm-fuel

11·20 4330°R

11·26 1.12×10^6 Btu/hr

11·28 155,000 Btu/lbmole-C_2H_2

12·5 $\Delta P \simeq 0.05$ psia

12·6 $K = 0.0208$; $\log_{10} K = -1.68$

12·14 $\log_{10} K = -4.98$

12·18 0.65 CO_2 + 0.35 CO + 0.675 O_2 (3000°K)

12·22 4.7×10^{15} elec/cm^3
 13·2 S.I. $= 70.5$ lbf-sec/lbm, (40 lbf) 1×10^{-2} ft^2
 13·8 Error $\simeq 15$ percent
13·12 1125, 3300, 720, 1393, 704 ft/sec
13·20 (a) 780 ft/sec; (b) 664 ft/sec
13·28 0.68 lbm/sec, 0.789 lbm/sec, 0.789 lbm/sec
13·33 Exit; 119°R, 0.658 psia, $A = 10.7A^*$
13·41 155 psia, M $= 0.25$
 14·3 6100 Btu/hr-ft^2
14·14 29°F
14·22 7, 44, 1050 Btu/hr-ft^2-°F
14·26 $T \simeq 220°$F
14·35 Plastic OK
14·54 Approx. 140°F
14·59 1472°F

INDEX

Absorptivity, 483
Adiabatic demagnetization, 188
Adiabatic flame temperature, 367
Adiabatic process, 44, 185
Adiabatic-saturation temperature, 340
Adiabatic saturator, 340
Adiabatic wall, 44
Afterburner, 304
Air, properties of, 513, 514, 542, 559
Air-cycle refrigeration, 297
Air-fuel ratio, 356
Air-water-vapor mixtures, 337
Aliases, 18, 488, 501
Allowed quantum state, 139, 151
Amagat's rule, 334
Atmosphere, U.S. standard, 445
Atomic weight, 10
Availability, 202
Avogadro's number, 10

Back-work ratio, 258, 279, 282
Beattie-Bridgeman equation, 224
  constants for, 552
Bernoulli's equation, 421
Binary mixture, 387
Binary vapor cycle, 272, 316, 317
Biot-Savart law, 12, 500
Black body radiation, 483
Blowdown thruster, 300
Body force, 33
Boltzmann constant, 147, 212
Boundary layer, 419, 464, 472
Bow shock, 432
Brayton cycle, 285

Btu, 43, 51
Bypass fan, 304

Caloric theory of heat, 3, 42
Calorie, 51
Capacity rate, 480
Carbon dioxide, properties of, 511, 560
Carnot cycle, 192, 249
Carnot heat pump, 193, 251
Carnot refrigerator, 250
Cesium, properties of, 516, 538
Charge, concept of, 11
Charging process, 122
Chemical equation, 355
Chemical kinetics, 355
Chemical-rocket engines, 305
Choked flow, 425
  by friction, 434
  by heating, 435
Clapeyron equation, 191, 235, 242, 244
Clausius:
  inequality of, 207
  statement of, 207
Coefficient of expansion, 83
Coefficient of performance (cop), 127,
    250, 251, 276
Components of mixtures, 328
Compressibility:
  isentropic, 229
  isobaric, 83, 229
  isothermal, 83, 229
Compressibility chart, 223, 519, 520
Compressibility factor, 222

Compressible fluid flow, 407
  area changes in, 421
  tables for, 553, 554
Compression ignition engine, 293
Compression ratio, 292, 294
Compressors:
  adiabatic, 254
  isothermal, 254
Concepts, 3
Condensate, 260
Conductance:
  convective, 466
  overall, 479
  thermal, 455
Conduction, 450
Conductivity:
  thermal, 453
  values for, 555, 556
Conservation of mass, 9, 105
Constituent, 328
Constituent reservoir, 381
Continuum, 13
Control mass, 23, 94, 408
Control surface, 410
Control volume, 23, 94, 108, 197, 408
Convection, 451, 465
  forced, 465
  free, 465
  natural, 465, 471
Copper, properties of, 541
Corresponding states, principle of, 222
Coulomb's law, 12
Critical point, 77, 221
  data for, 541
Curie substance, 41, 241
Cut-off ratio, 294
Cycle, 247
  Brayton, 285
  Ericsson, 291
  Otto, 291
  Rankine, 255, 260
  Stirling, 296

Dalton's rule, 331
Datum state, 74
Degrees of reaction freedom, 393
Dehumidification, 347

Demagnetization, adiabatic, 188
Desalting, 353
Detonation, 293
Dew point, 338
Dielectric, 48, 245
Diesel cycle, 293
Diffusion coefficient, 453
Dimensions, systems of, 16, 495
Direct energy conversion, 307
Distillation, fractional, 351
Distribution, quantum-state, 142

Effectiveness, regenerator, 322
Efficiency:
  Carnot, 195
  energy conversion, 50, 192
  isentropic, 201, 252, 253
  isothermal, 320
Einstein-Planck equation, 140
Electrochemical potential, 330, 379, 381, 383
Electron gas, 119
Electron volt, 51
Electronic noise, 120
Electrostatic potential energy, 110
Elemental substance, 360
Elements, 551
Emissive power, 483
Emissivity, 483
  values for, 561, 562
Endothermic reaction, 357
Energy:
  conservation of, 28
  free, 396
  internal, 27, 65
  kinetic, 12, 27, 110
  potential, 13, 21, 110
  rotational, 26
  translational, 26
  vibrational, 26
Energy modes, 24
Energy transfer:
  as heat, 42, 57, 449
  as work, 30, 57
Engine, $2T$, 195
Ensemble, 141
Ensemble averages, 143

Enthalpy, 85, 98, 110, 123
  of combustion, 362
  of evaporation, 98
  of formation, 361
  generalized, 237
  magnetic, 240
  standardized, 361, 547, 548
  of sublimation, 99
Entropy, 137, 144, 156, 163
  absolute, 174
  dimensions of, 163
  evaluation of, 173
  generalized, 237
  specific, 163
Entropy production, 104, 186, 198, 199, 205
Entropy transfer with heat, 186, 205
Environment, 24
Equations of reaction equilibrium, 394
Equations of state, 69, 73
Equilibrium, 60, 168, 379
  chemical, 390
Equilibrium constant, 396, 550
Equilibrium distribution, 142
Ericsson cycle, 291
Ethylene glycol, properties of, 557
Eutectic solution, 388
Evaporative cooling, 349
Exact differential, 231
Excess air, 356
Excited states, 26
Exhaust turbine, 295
Exothermic reaction, 357
Expectation values, 143
Extensive properties, 65
Extraction fraction, 269
Extraction turbine, 267, 270

Fanno line, 430
Feedwater heating, 267
  closed heater, 268
  open heater, 268
Fins:
  effectiveness of, 477
  heat transfer with, 475
  infinite length for, 476
First law of thermodynamics, 45, 205

Fleigner's formula, 425
Fluid, work of compression, 36
Force, 4, 12
  body, 33
  surface, 33
Fourier's law, 453
Frame, reference, 6
Free energy, 396
Free-piston gas generator, 296
Freon-12, properties of, 512, 539, 557
Fuel cell, 310, 401

Gas:
  perfect, 86, 212
  real, 220
Gas constant:
  universal, 212
  values for, 503
Gas thermometer, 63
Generalized forces and displacements, 40
Generalized properties charts, 223, 521, 522
Geothermal power, 317
Gibbs equation, 171, 211, 230
  magnetic substance, 239
Gibbs function, 229, 392
  magnetic, 240
Gibbs phase rule, 377, 385
Gibbs rule, 330
Grashof number, 468
Gravitation, 11
Gravitational field, 12

Heat:
  energy transfer as, 42, 57, 450
  of formation, 361
  of reaction, 362
  reversible, 183
  specific, 85, 523, 546, 552, 557–559
Heat capacity, $85n$
  values for, 523, 546, 552, 557–559
Heat content, $85n$
Heat engine, 192, 249
Heat exchangers, 117, 478
  capacity rate of, 481
  number of transfer units for, 481
  performance tables for, 565–567

Heat flux, 451
Heat pump, 125, 196, 251
Heat sources, 459
Heat transfer coefficient, 466
Heating value, 362
    higher heating value, 362
    lower heating value, 362
Helium, properties of, 560
Helmholtz function, 229, 391
Horsepower, 51
Humidity:
    relative, 338
    specific, 338
Humidity ratio, 338
Hydroelectric power, 123
Hydrogen, properties of, 560
Hydrogen rocket, 305

Ideal (perfect) gas, 86, 212
Idealizations, 95
Impulse pressure, 430
Incompressible liquid, 224
Inequality of Clausius, 207
Inertial frame, 23
Injector, steam jet, 413
Intensive properties, 65, 229
Intensive state, 66
Intercooling, 289
Internal energy, 27, 65
    specific, 65
Ion engine, 305
Iron-ammonium alum, properties of, 517
Irreversible processes, 175, 178
Isentropic compressibility, 229
Isentropic efficiency, 201, 252, 253
Isentropic process, 185, 252
Isobaric compressibility, 229
Isobaric process, 41
Isolated system, 24
Isothermal compressibility, 229
Isothermal efficiency, 285, 320
Isothermal process, 41

Jet pumps and ejectors, 260, 261, 413
Joule-Kelvin coefficient, 244

Kelvin-Planck statement, 196
Kinetic energy, 12, 27, 110
Kinetic theory, 2
Kirchoff's law, 484

Laminar boundary layer, 464
    flow, 465
Latent heats, $42n$, $98n$, $99n$
Law of the lever, 7
Lift, refrigeration, 277
Liquefaction of a gas, 116, 278
Liquid:
    incompressible, 224
    work of surface extension, 38
Liquidus curve, 388

Mach cone, 417
Mach number, 324, 414
Macroscopic properties, 2, 58
Magnetic refrigeration, 313
Magnetic substance, 72, 100, 239
    Maxwell's equations for, 240
Magnetization:
    thermal, 99
    work of, 38
Magnetohydrodynamic energy conversion, 312
Mass:
    conservation of, 9, 106
    molal, 10
Mass action, law of, 397
Mass-flow rate, 14, 106
Mass flux, 14
Mass fractions, 328–329
Mass velocity, 430
Maxwell relations, 231
Mechanical energy reservoir, 181
Mercury, properties of, 515, 536–537, 557
Metastable states, 80
Microscopic properties, 2
Mixture, 328
    of independent substances, 330
    of perfect gas, 333
    simple compressible, 329
    simple reactive, 393
    stoichiometric, 356
Models, 3

Moisture, 103
Molal mass, 10
Molal properties, 332
Mole, 10
Mole fraction, 329
Molecular weight, 10
Mollier diagram, 255, 507
Momentum principle, 300, 410

Nernst theorem, 370
Newton's second law, 11
Nitrogen, properties of, 509
Noise, electronic, 120
Nozzle, 112, 254
    converging-diverging, 426
    supersonic, 407, 419
    throat, 419
Nusselt number, 467

Ohm's law, 455
One-dimensional flow, 105, 420
Orsat apparatus, 357
Otto cycle, 291
Oxygen, properties of, 510, 560

Partial pressure, 331
Partial volume, 334
Particle, 10
Pattern processes, 252
Peltier effect, 308
Perfect gas, 86, 212
Phase, 73, 328
Phase equilibrium, 378
Phase rule, 377, 385
Photovoltaic device, 310
Plasma, 77
Polarization, work of, 38
Polytropic exponent, 219, 283
Polytropic process, 219, 283
Potential energy, 13, 21, 110
Prandtl number, 467
Precooler, 322
Pressure, 15, 60, 189
    partial, 331
    reduced, 216
    thermodynamic definition, 168
Pressure fraction, 334

Pressure recovery factor, 298
Primary quantities, 16
Probability:
    average, 144
    distribution, 142
    quantum-state, 141
    transition, 152
Process, 40
    irreversible, 175, 178
    isothermal, 41
    reversible, 66, 175, 178, 185, 249
Process representation, 81, 95
Products of reaction, 355
Property, 57, 65, 229
Psychrometer, sling, 343
Psychrometric chart, 343, 518
Pure substance, 328

Quality, 79
Quantum states, 139
    probabilities, 141

Radiation, 450, 483
    black body, 483
    gray body, 484
    shape factor, 485
Ramjet, 305, 439
Rankine cycle, 255, 260
    with regeneration, 267
    with reheat, 266
    with superheat, 262
Rate equations, 449
    conduction, 453
    convection, 466
    radiation, 485
Rayleigh line, 430
Reactants, 355
Reaction equilibrium, equation of, 394
Reaction freedom, degrees of, 393
Reactions:
    chemical, 356
    rate of, 355
Reduced pressure, 216
Reduced volume, 216
Reference frame, 6, 23
    inertial, 23
Reflectivity, 483

Refrigeration, 196
  absorption, 279
  magnetic, 313
  thermoelectric, 309
  vacuum, 277
Regeneration, 267, 270, 287
Regenerator, rotary, 289
Regenerator effectiveness, 322
Reheat, 266
Resistance, thermal, 455, 459
Reversible process, 66, 175, 178, 185, 249
Reversible work modes, 66
Reynolds number, 467
Rocket:
  chemical, 291
  hydrogen, 291

Saturation states, 77
Schrödinger equation, 141
Second law of thermodynamics, 157, 205
Secondary quantities, 16
Seebeck effect, 307
Sensible heat, $42n$
Shape factor, 485
Shock waves, 428
  normal, 429
  tables for, 554
Simple dielectric, 72, 245
Simple substance, 72
  compressible, 72, 210–211
  dielectric, 72, 245
  elastic, 246
  magnetic, 72, 100, 239
Simple reactive mixture, 393
Simple surface, 245
Simple system, 72
Smog, 280, 356
Solar constant, 486
Solid, work of extension, 37
Solidus curves, 388
Solutions, ideal, 330
Sonic boom, 432
Sound, speed of, 324, 415, 417
  in air, 417
Spark-ignition engines, 291
Species, 328

Specific heat, 85, 215, 523, 546, 552, 557–559
Specific humidity, 338
Specific impulse, 302
Specific volume, 40, 65
Spray dehumidification, 346
Stagnation pressure, 414
Stagnation state, isentropic, 413
Stagnation temperature, 414
Standard reference state, 360
Stanton number, 467
State, 57, 59
  thermodynamic, 59, 66
State postulate, 67
Statistical thermodynamics, 2
Steady-flow system, 105
Steady-state system, 105
Steam, properties of, 506, 507, 508, 524–535
Stefan-Boltzmann constant, 483
Stirling cycle, 296
Stoichiometric coefficients, 355
Stoichiometric combustion, 356
Stoichiometric mixture, 356
Subcooled liquid, 77, 80
Substance:
  pure, 328
  simple, 72
  simple compressible, 72
  simple dielectric, 72, 245
  simple elastic, 246
  simple magnetic, 72, 100, 239
Supercharger, 295
Superconductor, 240
Supercritical cycle, 273, 317
Superheat tables, 78
Superheated liquid, 80
Superheated vapor, 77
Superheater, 262
Surface forces, 33
Swamp cooler, 349
System, 23
  closed, 94
  isolated, 24
  open, 94
  simple, 72

Temperature, 60, 61
  absolute, 64
  dry-bulb, 312
  mixed mean, 467
  negative absolute, 172
  scales for, 64
  thermodynamic, 164, 172, 190, 197
Theoretical air, 356
Thermal capacitance, 462
Thermal circuit, 455, 478
Thermal conductivity, 453
Thermal energy reservoir, 181
Thermal pollution, 318
Thermal resistance, 455, 458
Thermal time constant, 463
Thermionic converter, 309
Thermocouple, 308
Thermodynamic properties and state, 61
Thermoelectric converter, 307
Thermoelectric power, 119
Thermoelectric refrigerator, 309
Third law of thermodynamics, 355, 370
Ton, of refrigeration, 127, 276
Topping cycle, 273, 316
Transient heat conduction, 461
  lumped parameter, 461
Transmissivity, 483
Triple point, 63, 77, 385
Turbine, 114
Turbo-compound engine, 295
Turbofan engine, 304
Turbojet engine, 303
Turboprop engine, 248, 303
Turbulent boundary layer, 464
  flow, 465, 470

Unit systems, 16, 495

Valve, 126
Van der Waal's equation, 220, 221
  constants for, 552
van't Hoff equation, 400
Vapor, 77
Vapor-compression refrigeration, 274
Vapor dome, 77
Viscosity, 453
Volume, reduced, 216
Volume fraction, 334

Water, properties of, 506–508, 524–535
Weight, 9
  molecular, 10
Wet-bulb temperature, 343
Wet-bulb thermometer, 343
Work, 12, 30, 57
  of compression, 36
  energy transfer as, 30, 57
  evaluation of, 35
  of magnetization, 38
  of polarization, 38
  reversible, 66, 185
Work mode, 67
Working fluid, 247, 271

Young's modulus, 83, 246

Zeroth law of thermodynamics, 62
Zip code, 487
Zone of action, 417
Zone of silence, 417

Adiabatic Flame Temperature

- examine the upper limit to the flame temp.

fuel → products

air →

$T_{products} = ?$

W=0
Q=0

1) assume combustion is compl
2) products only CO_2 ; H_2O
   from fuel

eq   Methane burns with 100% excess air.
      (CH_4)
theoretical air

$$CH_4 + 2(O_2 + 3.76 N_2) \longrightarrow CO_2 + 2H_2O + 2(3.76) N_2$$

∴ for 100% excess air

$$CH_4 + 4(O_2 + 3.76 N_2) \longrightarrow CO_2 + 2H_2O + +2O_2 + 15.04 N$$